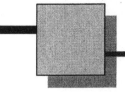

Instructor's Solutions Manual
for Stewart, Redlin, and Watson's
ALGEBRA AND
TRIGONOMETRY

John A. Banks

Evergreen Valley College
San Jose City College

BROOKS/COLE

™

THOMSON LEARNING

Australia • Canada • Mexico • Singapore • Spain • United Kingdom • United States

BROOKS/COLE

THOMSON LEARNING

Cover Design: *Roy R. Neuhaus*
Cover Art: *Bill Ralph*

For more information about this or any other Brooks/Cole product, contact:
BROOKS/COLE
511 Forest Lodge Road
Pacific Grove, CA 93950 USA
www.brookscole.com
1-800-423-0563 (Thomson Learning Academic Resource Center)

Printed in Canada

5   4   3   2

ISBN 0-534-38270-3

Table of Contents

Chapter One
Exercises 1.1

2. $(a + b) + c = a + (b + c)$

4. $a(b + c) = ab + ac$

6. $(a + b)^2 = a^2 + 2ab + b^2$

8. $(a - b) = -(b - a)$

10. The average of four numbers, a, b, c, and d, is $A = \dfrac{a + b + c + d}{4}$.

12. The length is $4 + w$, so the area is $(4 + w)w = 4w + w^2$.

14. The number of cents in n quarters is $25n$.

16. The sum of three consecutive integers is $S = n + (n + 1) + (n + 2) = 3n + 3$, where n is the smallest integer.

18. *Distance = rate · time* or $d = rt$.

20. The speed of a boat traveling d miles in t hours is $r = \dfrac{d}{t}$.

22. The volume of a cube of side x is $V = x^3$.

24. The surface area of a cube of side x is the sum of the areas of the 6 sides, each with area x^2; so $S = 6 \cdot x^2 = 6x^2$.

26. The length of one side of the square is $2r$, so its area is $(2r)^2 = 4r^2$. Since the area of the circle is πr^2, the area of what remains is $A = 4r^2 - \pi r^2$.

28. The race track consists of a rectangle of length x and width $2r$ and two semicircles of radius r. The area of the rectangle is $2rx$ and the area of a circle of radius r is πr^2. So the area enclosed is $A = 2rx + \pi r^2$.

30. This is the volume of the large ball minus the volume of the inside ball. The volume of a ball (sphere) is $\frac{4}{3}\pi (\text{radius})^3$. Thus the volume is $V = \frac{4}{3}\pi R^3 - \frac{4}{3}\pi r^3 = \frac{4}{3}\pi (R^3 - r^3)$.

32. (a) $4\dfrac{\text{ft}}{\text{sec}} \cdot 20 \text{ sec} = 80 \text{ ft}$

    (b) $d = 4\dfrac{\text{ft}}{\text{sec}} \cdot t \text{ sec} = 4t \text{ ft}$

    (c) Since 1 mile = 5280 ft, solve $d = 4t = 5280$ for t. We have $4t = 5280 \quad \Leftrightarrow$ $t = \frac{5280}{4} = 1320$ sec (22 minutes).

34. (a) If *width* = 20, then *length* = 40, so the *volume* = $20 \cdot 20 \cdot 40 = 16,000 \text{ in}^3$.

    (b) In terms of width $V = x \cdot x \cdot 2x = 2x^3$.

    (c) Solve $V = 2x^3 = 6750$ for x. We have $2x^3 = 6750 \quad \Leftrightarrow \quad x^3 = 3375 \quad \Leftrightarrow \quad x = 15$. So *width* = 15 in. and *length* = $2(15) = 30$ in.

Exercises 1.2

2. Commutative Property for multiplication.

4. Distributive Property.

6. Distributive Property.

8. $(a - b)8 = 8a - 8b$

10. $\dfrac{4}{3}(-6y) = \left[\dfrac{4}{3}(-6)\right]y = -8y$

12. $(3a)(b + c - 2d) = 3ab + 3ac - 6ad$

14. (a) $\dfrac{7}{45} + \dfrac{2}{25} = \dfrac{35}{225} + \dfrac{18}{225} = \dfrac{53}{225}$

   (b) $\dfrac{5}{14} - \dfrac{1}{21} + 1 = \dfrac{15}{42} - \dfrac{2}{42} + \dfrac{42}{42} = \dfrac{55}{42}$

16. (a) $\left(\dfrac{1}{8} - \dfrac{1}{9}\right) \div \dfrac{1}{72} = \left(\dfrac{9}{72} - \dfrac{8}{72}\right) \cdot 72 = \dfrac{1}{72} \cdot 72 = 1$

   (b) $\left(2 \div \dfrac{2}{3}\right) - \left(\dfrac{2}{3} \div 2\right) = \left(2 \cdot \dfrac{3}{2}\right) - \left(\dfrac{2}{3} \cdot \dfrac{1}{2}\right) = 3 - \dfrac{1}{3} = 2\dfrac{2}{3} \text{ or } \dfrac{8}{3}$

18. (a) True. $\dfrac{10}{11} = \dfrac{10}{11} \cdot \dfrac{13}{13} = \dfrac{130}{143}$ and $\dfrac{12}{13} = \dfrac{12}{13} \cdot \dfrac{11}{11} = \dfrac{132}{143}$. Therefore $\dfrac{10}{11} < \dfrac{12}{13}$, because $\dfrac{130}{143} < \dfrac{132}{143}$.

   (b) False.

20. (a) False

   (b) True.

22. (a) $y < 0$

   (b) $z > 1$

   (c) $b \le 8$

   (d) $0 < w \le 17$

   (e) $|y - \pi| \ge 2$

24. (a) $B \cup C = \{2, 4, 6, 7, 8, 9, 10\}$

   (b) $B \cap C = \{8\}$

26. (a) $A \cup B \cup C = \{1, 2, 3, 4, 5, 6, 7, 8, 9, 10\}$

   (b) $A \cap B \cap C = \emptyset$

28. (a) $A \cap C = \{x \mid -1 < x \le 5\}$

   (b) $A \cap B = \{x \mid -2 \le x < 4\}$

30. $(2, 8] = \{x \mid 2 < x \le 8\}$

32. $\left[-6, -\frac{1}{2}\right] = \left\{x \mid -6 \le x \le -\frac{1}{2}\right\}$

34. $(-\infty, 1) = \{x \mid x < 1\}$

36. $1 \le x \le 2 \quad \Leftrightarrow \quad x \in [1, 2]$

38. $x \ge -5 \quad \Leftrightarrow \quad x \in [-5, \infty)$

40. $-5 < x < 2 \quad \Leftrightarrow \quad x \in (-5, 2)$

42. $(-2, 0) \cap (-1, 1) = (-1, 0)$

44. $[-4, 6] \cup [0, 8) = [-4, 8)$

46. $(-\infty, 6] \cap (2, 10) = (2, 6]$

48. (a) $\left|\sqrt{5} - 5\right| = -\left(\sqrt{5} - 5\right) = 5 - \sqrt{5}$, since $5 > \sqrt{5}$.

(b) $|10 - \pi| = 10 - \pi$, since $10 > \pi$.

50. (a) $\left| 2 - |-12| \right| = |2 - 12| = |-10| = 10.$

(b) $-1 - \left| 1 - |-1| \right| = -1 - |1 - 1| = -1 - |0| = -1.$

52. (a) $\left| \frac{-6}{24} \right| = \left| \frac{-1}{4} \right| = \frac{1}{4}.$

(b) $\left| \frac{7-12}{12-7} \right| = \left| \frac{-5}{5} \right| = |-1| = 1.$

54. (a) $\left| \frac{7}{15} - \left(-\frac{1}{21} \right) \right| = \left| \frac{49}{105} + \frac{5}{105} \right| = \left| \frac{54}{105} \right| = \left| \frac{18}{35} \right| = \frac{18}{35}.$

(b) $|-38 - (-57)| = |-38 + 57| = |19| = 19.$

(c) $|-2.6 - (-1.8)| = |-2.6 + 1.8| = |-0.8| = 0.8.$

56. (a) Let $x = 5.2323\ldots$ So,

$$100x = 523.2323\ldots$$
$$1x = 5.2323\ldots$$
$$\overline{99x = 518}$$

Thus $x = \frac{518}{99}$

(b) Let $x = 1.3777\ldots$ So,

$$100x = 137.7777\ldots$$
$$10x = 13.7777\ldots$$
$$\overline{90x = 124}$$

Thus $x = \frac{124}{90} = \frac{62}{45}$

(c) Let $x = 2.13535\ldots$ So,

$$1000x = 2135.3535\ldots$$
$$10x = 21.3535\ldots$$
$$\overline{990x = 2114}$$

Thus $x = \frac{2114}{990} = \frac{1057}{495}$

58. Let $x = \dfrac{m_1}{n_1}$ and $y = \dfrac{m_2}{n_2}$ be rational numbers. Then

(i) $x + y = \dfrac{m_1}{n_1} + \dfrac{m_2}{n_2} = \dfrac{m_1 n_2 + m_2 n_1}{n_1 n_2}$

(ii) $x - y = \dfrac{m_1}{n_1} - \dfrac{m_2}{n_2} = \dfrac{m_1 n_2 - m_2 n_1}{n_1 n_2}$

(iii) $x \cdot y = \dfrac{m_1}{n_1} \cdot \dfrac{m_2}{n_2} = \dfrac{m_1 m_2}{n_1 n_2}$

This shows that the sum, difference, and product of two rational numbers are again rational numbers. However the product of two irrational numbers is not necessarily irrational; for example, $\sqrt{2} \cdot \sqrt{2} = 2$, which is rational. Also, the sum of two irrational numbers is not necessarily irrational; for example, $\sqrt{2} + (-\sqrt{2}) = 0$ which is rational.

60. (a) Construct the number $\sqrt{2}$ on the number line by transferring the length of the hypothenuse of a right triangle with legs of length 1 and 1.

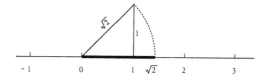

(b) Construct a right triangle with legs of length 1
     and 2. By the Pythagorean Theorem, the
     length of the hypothenuse is $\sqrt{1^2 + 2^2} = \sqrt{5}$.
     Then transfer the length of the hypothenuse to
     the number line.

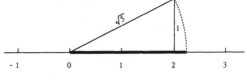
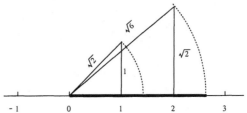

(c) Construct a right triangle with legs of length
     $\sqrt{2}$ and 2, (construct $\sqrt{2}$ as in part (a)). By
     the Pythagorean Theorem, the length of the
     hypothenuse is $\sqrt{(\sqrt{2})^2 + 2^2} = \sqrt{6}$. Then
     transfer the length of the hypothenuse to the
     number line.

Exercises 1.3

2.   (a) $\left(\dfrac{1}{2}\right)^4 4^{-2} = \dfrac{1}{2^4} \cdot \dfrac{1}{4^2} = \dfrac{1}{16} \cdot \dfrac{1}{16} = \dfrac{1}{256}$

     (b) $\left(\dfrac{1}{4}\right)^{-2} = 4^2 = 16$ (c) $\left(\dfrac{1}{4}\right)^0 \cdot 2^{-1} = 1 \cdot \dfrac{1}{2^1} = \dfrac{1}{2}$

4.   (a) $\sqrt{64} = \sqrt{8^2} = 8$ (b) $\sqrt[3]{-64} = \sqrt[3]{(-4)^3} = -4$

     (c) $\sqrt[5]{-32} = \sqrt[5]{(-2)^5} = -2$

6.   (a) $\sqrt{7}\,\sqrt{28} = \sqrt{7}\,\sqrt{4 \cdot 7} = \sqrt{7} \cdot 2 \cdot \sqrt{7} = 2 \cdot 7 = 14$

     (b) $\sqrt[3]{3}\,\sqrt[3]{9} = \sqrt[3]{27} = 3$

     (c) $\sqrt[4]{24}\,\sqrt[4]{54} = \sqrt[4]{8 \cdot 3}\,\sqrt[4]{2 \cdot 27} = \sqrt[4]{2^3 \cdot 3 \cdot 2 \cdot 3^3} = \sqrt[4]{2^4 \cdot 3^4} = 2 \cdot 3 = 6$

8.   (a) $9^{7/2} = \left(9^{1/2}\right)^7 = 3^7 = 2187$ (b) $(-32)^{2/5} = \left[(-2)^5\right]^{2/5} = (-2)^2 = 4$

     (c) $(-125)^{-1/3} = \left[(-5)^3\right]^{-1/3} = (-5)^{-1} = \frac{1}{-5} = -\frac{1}{5}$

10.   (a) $1024^{-0.1} = \left(2^{10}\right)^{-0.1} = 2^{-1} = \frac{1}{2}$ (b) $3^{2/7}\,3^{5/7} = 3^{2/7+5/7} = 3^1 = 3$

      (c) $3^{1/2}\,9^{1/4} = 3^{1/2}\left(3^2\right)^{1/4} = 3^{1/2+2/4} = 3^1 = 3$

12. $\sqrt{8} + \sqrt{50} = \sqrt{2^2 \cdot 2} + \sqrt{5^2 \cdot 2} = 2\sqrt{2} + 5\sqrt{2} = 7\sqrt{2}$

14. $\sqrt[3]{54} - \sqrt[3]{16} = \sqrt[3]{3^3 \cdot 2} - \sqrt[3]{2^3 \cdot 2} = 3\sqrt[3]{2} - 2\sqrt[3]{2} = \sqrt[3]{2}$

16. $(3y^2)(4y^5) = 3 \cdot 4y^{2+5} = 12y^7$ 18. $(6y)^3 = 6^3\,y^3 = 216y^3$

20. $\dfrac{a^{-3}b^4}{a^{-5}b^5} = a^{-3-(-5)}b^{4-5} = a^2 b^{-1} = \dfrac{a^2}{b}$

22. $(2s^3 t^{-1})\left(\dfrac{1}{4}s^6\right)(16t^4) = \dfrac{2 \cdot 16}{4}\,s^{3+6}\,t^{-1+4} = 8s^9 t^3$

24. $(2u^2 v^3)^3 (3u^3 v)^{-2} = 2^3 u^6 v^9 \cdot 3^{-2} u^{-6} v^{-2} = \dfrac{2^3}{3^2} u^{6-6} v^{9-2} = \dfrac{8}{9} v^7$

26. $\dfrac{(2x^3)^2 (3x^4)}{(x^3)^4} = \dfrac{2^2 x^6 \cdot 3x^4}{x^{12}} = 12x^{6+4-12} = 12x^{-2} = \dfrac{12}{x^2}$

28. $\left(\dfrac{c^4 d^3}{cd^2}\right)\left(\dfrac{d^2}{c^3}\right)^3 = \dfrac{c^4 d^3}{cd^2} \cdot \dfrac{d^6}{c^9} = c^{4-1-9} d^{3+6-2} = c^{-6} d^7 = \dfrac{d^7}{c^6}$

30. $\left(\dfrac{xy^{-2}z^{-3}}{x^2 y^3 z^{-4}}\right)^{-3} = \dfrac{x^{-3} y^6 z^9}{x^{-6} y^{-9} z^{12}} = x^{-3-(-6)} y^{6-(-9)} z^{9-12} = x^3 y^{15} z^{-3} = \dfrac{x^3 y^{15}}{z^3}$

32. $(3ab^2 c)\left(\dfrac{2a^2 b}{c^3}\right)^{-2} = 3ab^2 c \cdot \dfrac{2^{-2} a^{-4} b^{-2}}{c^{-6}} = \dfrac{3}{4}\,a^{1-4}\,b^{2-2}\,c^{1-(-6)} = \dfrac{3}{4}\,a^{-3} b^0 c^7 = \dfrac{3c^7}{4a^3}$

34. $\left(-2a^{3/4}\right)\left(5a^{3/2}\right) = -10a^{3/4}a^{3/2} = -10a^{(3/4+6/4)} = -10a^{9/4}$

36. $\left(8x^6\right)^{-2/3} = \left(2^3\right)^{-2/3}\left(x^6\right)^{-2/3} = 2^{-6/3}x^{-12/3} = 2^{-2}x^{-4} = \dfrac{1}{4x^4}$

38. $\left(4x^6y^8\right)^{3/2} = \left(2^2\right)^{3/2}(x^6)^{3/2}(y^8)^{3/2} = 2^{6/2}x^{18/2}y^{24/2} = 2^3x^9y^{12} = 8x^9y^{12}$

40. $\left(a^{2/5}\right)^{-3/4} = a^{(2/5)\cdot(-3/4)} = a^{-6/20} = a^{-3/10} = \dfrac{1}{a^{3/10}}$

42. $\left(x^{-5}y^3z^{10}\right)^{-3/5} = x^{15/5}y^{-9/5}z^{-30/5} = x^3y^{-9/5}z^{-6} = \dfrac{x^3}{y^{9/5}z^6}$

44. $\left(\dfrac{-2x^{1/3}}{y^{1/2}z^{1/6}}\right)^4 = \dfrac{(-2)^4x^{4/3}}{y^{4/2}z^{4/6}} = \dfrac{16x^{4/3}}{y^2z^{2/3}}$

46. $\dfrac{\left(y^{10}z^{-5}\right)^{1/5}}{\left(y^{-2}z^3\right)^{1/3}} = \dfrac{y^2z^{-1}}{y^{-2/3}z} = y^{2-(-2/3)}\,z^{-1-1} = y^{8/3}\,z^{-2} = \dfrac{y^{8/3}}{z^2}$

48. $\left(\dfrac{a^2b^{-3}}{x^{-1}y^2}\right)^3\left(\dfrac{x^{-2}b^{-1}}{a^{3/2}y^{1/3}}\right) = \dfrac{a^6b^{-9}}{x^{-3}y^6}\cdot\dfrac{x^{-2}b^{-1}}{a^{3/2}y^{1/3}} = a^{6-(3/2)}b^{-9-1}x^{-2-(-3)}y^{-6-1/3}$

      $= a^{9/2}b^{-10}x^1y^{-19/3} = \dfrac{a^{9/2}x}{b^{10}y^{19/3}}$

50. $\sqrt[3]{x^3y^6} = \left(x^3y^6\right)^{1/3} = xy^2$ 52. $\sqrt{x^4y^4} = \left(x^4y^4\right)^{1/2} = x^2y^2$

54. $\sqrt[3]{a^2b}\,\sqrt[3]{a^4b} = \sqrt[3]{a^6b^2} = \left(a^6b^2\right)^{1/3} = a^2b^{2/3} = a^2\sqrt[3]{b^2}$

56. $\sqrt[4]{x^4y^2z^2} = \sqrt[4]{x^4}\,\sqrt[4]{y^2z^2} = |x|\sqrt[4]{y^2z^2}$

58.   (a) $\sqrt{\dfrac{x^5}{2}} = \dfrac{\sqrt{x^5}}{\sqrt{2}} = \dfrac{\sqrt{x^4\cdot x}}{\sqrt{2}} = \dfrac{x^2\sqrt{x}}{\sqrt{2}}\cdot\dfrac{\sqrt{2}}{\sqrt{2}} = \dfrac{x^2\sqrt{2x}}{2}$

       (b) $\sqrt{\dfrac{2}{3}} = \dfrac{\sqrt{2}}{\sqrt{3}} = \dfrac{\sqrt{2}}{\sqrt{3}}\cdot\dfrac{\sqrt{3}}{\sqrt{3}} = \dfrac{\sqrt{6}}{3}$

       (c) $\sqrt{\dfrac{1}{2x^3y^5}} = \dfrac{1}{\sqrt{x^2y^4\cdot 2xy}} = \dfrac{1}{xy^2\sqrt{2xy}} = \dfrac{1}{xy^2\sqrt{2xy}}\cdot\dfrac{\sqrt{2xy}}{\sqrt{2xy}} = \dfrac{\sqrt{2xy}}{xy^2\cdot 2xy} = \dfrac{\sqrt{2xy}}{2x^2y^3}$

60.   (a) $\dfrac{1}{\sqrt[3]{x^2}} = \dfrac{1}{\sqrt[3]{x^2}}\cdot\dfrac{\sqrt[3]{x}}{\sqrt[3]{x}} = \dfrac{\sqrt[3]{x}}{x}$ (b) $\dfrac{1}{\sqrt[4]{x^3}} = \dfrac{1}{\sqrt[4]{x^3}}\cdot\dfrac{\sqrt[4]{x}}{\sqrt[4]{x}} = \dfrac{\sqrt[4]{x}}{x}$

       (c) $\dfrac{1}{\sqrt[3]{x^4}} = \dfrac{1}{\sqrt[3]{x^3\cdot x}} = \dfrac{1}{x\sqrt[3]{x}} = \dfrac{1}{x\sqrt[3]{x}}\cdot\dfrac{\sqrt[3]{x^2}}{\sqrt[3]{x^2}} = \dfrac{\sqrt[3]{x^2}}{x\sqrt[3]{x^3}} = \dfrac{\sqrt[3]{x^2}}{x^2}$

62.   (a) $7{,}259{,}000{,}000 = 7.259\times 10^9$ (b) $0.0000000014 = 1.4\times 10^{-9}$

       (c) $0.0007029 = 7.029\times 10^{-4}$

64.   (a) $8.55\times 10^{-3} = 0.00855$ (b) $6\times 10^{12} = 6{,}000{,}000{,}000{,}000$

       (c) $6.257\times 10^{-10} = 0.0000000006257$

66. (a) $93,000,000 \text{ mi} = 9.3 \times 10^7 \text{ mi}$

     (b) $0.000000000000000000000053 \text{ g} = 5.3 \times 10^{-23} \text{ g}$

     (c) $5,970,000,000,000,000,000,000,000 \text{ kg} = 5.97 \times 10^{24} \text{ kg}$

68. $(1.062 \times 10^{24})(8.61 \times 10^{19}) = 1.062 \times 8.61 \times 10^{24} \times 10^{19} \approx 9.14 \times 10^{43}$

70. $\dfrac{(73.1)(1.6341 \times 10^{28})}{0.0000000019} = \dfrac{(7.31 \times 10)(1.6341 \times 10^{28})}{1.9 \times 10^{-9}}$

     $= \dfrac{7.31 \times 1.6341}{1.9} \times 10^{1+28-(-9)} \approx 6.3 \times 10^{38}$

72. $\dfrac{(3.542 \times 10^{-6})^9}{(5.05 \times 10^4)^{12}} = \dfrac{(3.542)^9 \times 10^{-54}}{(5.05)^{12} \times 10^{48}} = \dfrac{87747.96}{275103767.10} \times 10^{-54-48} \approx 3.19 \times 10^{-4} \times 10^{-102}$

     $\approx 3.19 \times 10^{-106}$

74. (a)   Using $f = 0.4$ and substituting $d = 65$, we obtain $s = \sqrt{30fd} = \sqrt{30 \times 0.4 \times 65} \approx 28 \text{ mi/h}$.

     (b)   Using $f = 0.5$ and substituting $s = 50$, we find d. Thus gives $s = \sqrt{30fd} \quad \Leftrightarrow$

         $50 = \sqrt{30 \cdot (0.5)d} \quad \Leftrightarrow \quad 50 = \sqrt{15d} \quad \Leftrightarrow \quad 2500 = 15d \quad \Leftrightarrow \quad d = \dfrac{500}{3} \approx 167 \text{ feet}$.

76. (a) $\dfrac{a^m}{a^n} = \dfrac{a \cdot a \cdot a \cdot \cdots \cdot a \ (m \text{ factors})}{a \cdot a \cdot a \cdot \cdots \cdot a \ (n \text{ factors})} = a \cdot a \cdot a \cdot \cdots \cdot a \ (m - n \text{ factors}) = a^{m-n} \ (a \neq 0)$.

     (b) $\left(\dfrac{a}{b}\right)^n = \dfrac{a}{b} \cdot \dfrac{a}{b} \cdot \cdots \cdot \dfrac{a}{b} \ (n \text{ factors}) = \dfrac{a \cdot a \cdot a \cdot \cdots \cdot a \ (n \text{ factors})}{b \cdot b \cdot b \cdot \cdots \cdot b \ (n \text{ factors})} = \dfrac{a^n}{b^n} \ (b \neq 0)$.

     (c) $\left(\dfrac{a}{b}\right)^{-n} = \left[\left(\dfrac{a}{b}\right)^{-1}\right]^n = \left[\dfrac{1}{\left(\dfrac{a}{b}\right)}\right]^n = \left(\dfrac{b}{a}\right)^n = \dfrac{b^n}{a^n} \ (a \neq 0, b \neq 0)$.

      The first equality follows from Law 3. The second equality is given by the Negative Exponents Law. The third equality is simplification, and the fourth equality follows from Law 5.

78. (a)   Since $\frac{1}{2} > \frac{1}{3}$, $2^{\frac{1}{2}} > 2^{\frac{1}{3}}$.

     (b) $\left(\dfrac{1}{2}\right)^{\frac{1}{2}} = 2^{-\frac{1}{2}}$ and $\left(\dfrac{1}{2}\right)^{\frac{1}{3}} = 2^{-\frac{1}{3}}$. Since $-\frac{1}{2} < -\frac{1}{3}$, we have $\left(\dfrac{1}{2}\right)^{\frac{1}{2}} < \left(\dfrac{1}{2}\right)^{\frac{1}{3}}$.

     (c)   We find a common root: $7^{\frac{1}{4}} = 7^{\frac{3}{12}} = (7^3)^{\frac{1}{12}} = 343^{\frac{1}{12}}$; $4^{\frac{1}{3}} = 4^{\frac{4}{12}} = (4^4)^{\frac{1}{12}} = 256^{\frac{1}{12}}$. So $7^{\frac{1}{4}} > 4^{\frac{1}{3}}$.

     (d)   We find a common root: $\sqrt[3]{5} = 5^{\frac{1}{3}} = 5^{\frac{2}{6}} = (5^2)^{\frac{1}{6}} = 25^{\frac{1}{6}}$; $\sqrt{3} = 3^{\frac{1}{2}} = 3^{\frac{3}{6}} = (3^3)^{\frac{1}{6}} = 27^{\frac{1}{6}}$. So $\sqrt[3]{5} < \sqrt{3}$.

80. $|10^{50} - 10^{10}| < 10^{50}$, whereas $|10^{101} - 10^{100}| = 10^{100}|10 - 1| = 9 \times 10^{100} > 10^{50}$. So 10^{10} is closer to 10^{50} than 10^{100} is to 10^{101}.

Exercises 1.4

2. $(3x^2 + x + 1) - (2x^2 - 3x - 5) = 3x^2 + x + 1 - 2x^2 + 3x + 5 = x^2 + 4x + 6$

4. $3(x - 1) + 4(x + 2) = 3x - 3 + 4x + 8 = 7x + 5$

6. $4(x^2 - 3x + 5) - 3(x^2 - 2x + 1) = 4x^2 - 12x + 20 - 3x^2 + 6x - 3 = x^2 - 6x + 17$

8. $5(3t - 4) - (t^2 + 2) - 2t(t - 3) = 15t - 20 - t^2 - 2 - 2t^2 + 6t = -3t^2 + 21t - 22$

10. $x^{3/2}(\sqrt{x} - 1/\sqrt{x}) = x^{3/2}(x^{1/2} - x^{-1/2}) = x^{3/2}x^{1/2} - x^{3/2}x^{-1/2} = x^2 - x$

12. $(4x - 1)(3x + 7) = 12x^2 + 28x - 3x - 7 = 12x^2 + 25x - 7$

14. $(t + 6)(t + 5) - 3(t + 4) = t^2 + 5t + 6t + 30 - 3t - 12 = t^2 + 8t + 18$

16. $(4x - 3y)(2x + 5y) = 8x^2 + 20xy - 6xy - 15y^2 = 8x^2 + 14xy - 15y^2$

18. $(3x + 4)^2 = (3x)^2 + 2(3x)(4) + (4)^2 = 9x^2 + 24x + 16$

20. $(x^2 + 3)(5x - 6) = 5x^3 - 6x^2 + 15x - 18$

22. $(1 + 2x)(x^2 - 3x + 1) = x^2 - 3x + 1 + 2x^3 - 6x^2 + 2x = 2x^3 - 5x^2 - x + 1$

24. $\left(x^{1/2} + y^{1/2}\right)\left(x^{1/2} - y^{1/2}\right) = \left(x^{1/2}\right)^2 - \left(y^{1/2}\right)^2 = x - y$

26. $\left(\sqrt{h^2 + 1} + 1\right)\left(\sqrt{h^2 + 1} - 1\right) = \left(\sqrt{h^2 + 1}\right)^2 - (1)^2 = h^2 + 1 - 1 = h^2$

28. $(x - 1)(x^2 + x + 1) = x^3 + x^2 + x - x^2 - x - 1 = x^3 - 1$

30. $\left(c + \dfrac{1}{c}\right)^2 = (c)^2 + 2(c)\left(\dfrac{1}{c}\right) + \left(\dfrac{1}{c}\right)^2 = c^2 + 2 + \dfrac{1}{c^2}$

32. $(1 + x + x^2)(1 - x + x^2) = [(x^2 + 1) + x][(x^2 + 1) - x] = (x^2 + 1)^2 - (x)^2$
       $= x^4 + 2x^2 + 1 - x^2 = x^4 + x^2 + 1$

34. $\left(x^{3/2} - x + 1\right)\left(x^2 + x^{1/2} - 2\right) = x^{7/2} + x^2 - 2x^{3/2} - x^3 - x^{3/2} + 2x + x^2 + x^{1/2} - 2$
       $= x^{7/2} - x^3 + 2x^2 - 3x^{3/2} + 2x + x^{1/2} - 2$

36. $(1 + x - x^2)^2 = \left[(1 + x) - x^2\right]^2 = (1 + x)^2 - 2(1 + x)(x^2) + (x^2)^2$
       $= 1 + 2x + x^2 - 2x^2 - 2x^3 + x^4 = 1 + 2x - x^2 - 2x^3 + x^4$

38. $(x^4y - y^5)(x^2 + xy + y^2) = x^6y + x^5y^2 + x^4y^3 - x^2y^5 - xy^6 - y^7$

40. $8x^5 + 4x^3 = 4x^3(2x^2 + 1)$

42. $5ab - 8abc = ab(5 - 8c)$

44. $x^2 - x - 6 = (x - 3)(x + 2)$

46. $x^2 - 14x + 48 = (x - 8)(x - 6)$

48. $z^2 + 6z - 16 = (z - 2)(z + 8)$

50. $2x^2 + 7x - 4 = (2x - 1)(x + 4)$

52. $8x^2 + 10x + 3 = (4x + 3)(2x + 1)$

54. $6 + 5t - 6t^2 = (3 - 2t)(2 + 3t)$

56. $(x + 1)^3 x - 2(x + 1)^2 x^2 + x^3(x + 1) = x(x + 1)\left[(x + 1)^2 - 2(x + 1)x + x^2\right]$

$\quad = x(x + 1)\left[(x + 1) - x\right]^2 = x(x + 1)(1)^2 = x(x + 1)$

58. $n(x - y) + (n - 1)(y - x) = n(x - y) - (n - 1)(x - y) = (x - y)\left[n - (n - 1)\right] = x - y$

60. $(a + b)^2 - (a - b)^2 = \left[(a + b) - (a - b)\right]\left[(a + b) + (a - b)\right] = (a + b - a + b)(a + b + a - b)$

$\quad = (2b)(2a) = 4ab$

62. $4t^2 - 9s^2 = (2t)^2 - (3s)^2 = (2t - 3s)(2t + 3s)$

64. $x^3 - 27 = x^3 - 3^3 = (x - 3)(x^2 + 3x + 9)$

66. $3x^3 - 27x = 3x(x^2 - 9) = 3x(x - 3)(x + 3)$

68. $4r^2 - 12rs + 9s^2 = (2r)^2 - 2(2r \cdot 3s) + (3s)^2 = (2r - 3s)^2$

70. $x^6 + 64 = (x^2)^3 + 4^3 = (x^2 + 4)((x^2)^2 + (x^2)(4) + 4^2) = (x^2 + 4)(x^4 + 4x^2 + 16)$

72. $x^4 + 2x^2 + 1 = (x^2)^2 + 2(x^2) + 1 = (x^2 + 1)^2$

74. $x^3 + 3x^2 - x - 3 = (x^3 + 3x^2) + (-x - 3) = x^2(x + 3) - (x + 3) = (x + 3)(x^2 - 1)$

$\quad = (x + 3)(x - 1)(x + 1)$

76. $y^3 - y^2 + y - 1 = y^2(y - 1) + 1(y - 1) = (y^2 + 1)(y - 1)$

78. $3x^3 + 5x^2 - 6x - 10 = x^2(3x + 5) - 2(3x + 5) = (x^2 - 2)(3x + 5)$

80. $\left(1 + \dfrac{1}{x}\right)^2 - \left(1 - \dfrac{1}{x}\right)^2 = \left[\left(1 + \dfrac{1}{x}\right) - \left(1 - \dfrac{1}{x}\right)\right]\left[\left(1 + \dfrac{1}{x}\right) + \left(1 - \dfrac{1}{x}\right)\right]$

$\quad = \left[1 + \dfrac{1}{x} - 1 + \dfrac{1}{x}\right]\left[1 + \dfrac{1}{x} + 1 - \dfrac{1}{x}\right] = \left(\dfrac{2}{x}\right)(2) = \dfrac{4}{x}$

82. $3x^{-1/2} + 4x^{1/2} + x^{3/2} = x^{-1/2}\left(3 + 4x + x^2\right) = \left(\dfrac{1}{\sqrt{x}}\right)(3 + x)(1 + x)$

84. $(x - 1)^{7/2} - (x - 1)^{3/2} = (x - 1)^{3/2}\left[(x - 1)^2 - 1\right] = (x - 1)^{3/2}\left[(x - 1) - 1\right]\left[(x - 1) + 1\right]$

$\quad = (x - 1)^{3/2}(x - 2)(x)$

86. $x^{-1/2}(x + 1)^{1/2} + x^{1/2}(x + 1)^{-1/2} = x^{-1/2}(x + 1)^{-1/2}[(x + 1) + x] = \dfrac{2x + 1}{\sqrt{x}\,\sqrt{x + 1}}$

88. $(a^2 + 2a)^2 - 2(a^2 + 2a) - 3 = [(a^2 + 2a) - 3][(a^2 + 2a) + 1]$

$\quad = (a^2 + 2a - 3)(a^2 + 2a + 1) = (a - 1)(a + 3)(a + 1)^2$

90. $5(x^2 + 4)^4(2x)(x - 2)^4 + (x^2 + 4)^5(4)(x - 2)^3$

$\quad = 2(x^2 + 4)^4(x - 2)^3[(5)(x)(x - 2) + (x^2 + 4)(2)] = 2(x^2 + 4)^4(x - 2)^3(5x^2 - 10x + 2x^2 + 8)$

$\quad = 2(x^2 + 4)^4(x - 2)^3(7x^2 - 10x + 8)$

92. $\frac{1}{3}(x+6)^{-2/3}(2x-3)^2 + (x+6)^{1/3}(2)(2x-3)(2)$

$= \frac{1}{3}(x+6)^{-2/3}(2x-3)[(2x-3)+(3)(x+6)(4)] = \frac{1}{3}(x+6)^{-2/3}(2x-3)[2x-3+12x+72]$

$= \frac{1}{3}(x+6)^{-2/3}(2x-3)(14x+69)$

94. (a)   Special Product Formula 1. Using FOIL we obtain:

$(A-B)(A+B) = A^2 + AB - AB - B^2 = A^2 - B^2$

Special Product Formula 2. Using FOIL we obtain:

$(A+B)(A+B) = A^2 + AB + AB + B^2 = A^2 + 2AB + B^2$

(b)   Special Product Formula 3. Using FOIL we obtain:

$(A-B)(A-B) = A^2 - AB - AB + B^2 = A^2 - 2AB + B^2$

Special Product Formula 4.

$(A+B)^3 = (A+B)^2(A+B) = (A^2 + 2AB + B^2)(A+B)$

$= A^3 + 2A^2B + AB^2 + A^2B + 2AB^2 + B^3$

$= A^3 + 3A^2B + 3AB^2 + B^3$

(c)   Difference of Cubes.

$(A-B)(A^2 + AB + B^2) = A^3 + A^2B + AB^2 - A^2B - AB^2 - B^3 = A^3 - B^3$

(d)   Sum of Cubes.

$(A+B)(A^2 - AB + B^2) = A^3 - A^2B + AB^2 + A^2B - AB^2 + B^3 = A^3 + B^3$

96.   The volume of the shell is the difference between the volumes of the outside cylinder (with radius R) and the inside cylinder (with radius r). Thus

$$V = \pi R^2 h - \pi r^2 h = \pi(R^2 - r^2)h = \pi(R-r)(R+r)h = 2\pi \cdot \frac{R+r}{2} \cdot h \cdot (R-r).$$

The average radius is $\dfrac{R+r}{2}$ and $2\pi \cdot \dfrac{R+r}{2}$ is the average circumference (length of the rectangular box), h is the height, and $R-r$ is the thickness of the rectangular box. Thus

$$V = \pi R^2 h - \pi r^2 h = 2\pi \cdot \frac{R+r}{2} \cdot h \cdot (R-r) = 2\pi \cdot (\textit{average radius}) \cdot (\textit{height}) \cdot (\textit{thickness})$$

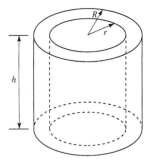 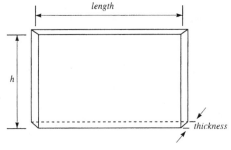

98.

$$
\begin{array}{r}
A + 1 \\
\times \quad A - 1 \\
\hline
-A - 1 \\
A^2 + A \phantom{{}-1} \\
\hline
A^2 - 1
\end{array}
\qquad
\begin{array}{r}
A^2 + A + 1 \\
\times \quad A - 1 \\
\hline
-A^2 - A - 1 \\
A^3 + A^2 + A \phantom{{}-1} \\
\hline
A^3 - 1
\end{array}
\qquad
\begin{array}{r}
A^3 + A^2 + A + 1 \\
\times \quad A - 1 \\
\hline
-A^3 - A^2 - A - 1 \\
A^4 + A^3 + A^2 + A \phantom{{}-1} \\
\hline
A^4 - 1
\end{array}
$$

Based on the pattern: $A^5 - 1 = (A-1)(A^4 + A^3 + A^2 + A + 1)$

$$\begin{array}{r} A^4 + A^3 + A^2 + A + 1 \\ \times \qquad\qquad\qquad A - 1 \\ \hline -A^4 - A^3 - A^2 - A - 1 \\ A^5 + A^4 + A^3 + A^2 + A \qquad\quad \\ \hline A^5 \qquad\qquad\qquad\qquad\qquad - 1 \end{array}$$

The generalized pattern is $A^n - 1 = (A - 1)(A^{n-1} + A^{n-2} + \cdots + A^2 + A + 1)$, where n is a positive integer.

Exercises 1.5

2. $\dfrac{x^2 - x - 2}{x^2 - 1} = \dfrac{(x-2)(x+1)}{(x-1)(x+1)} = \dfrac{x-2}{x-1}$

4. $\dfrac{x^2 - x - 12}{x^2 + 5x + 6} = \dfrac{(x-4)(x+3)}{(x+2)(x+3)} = \dfrac{x-4}{x+2}$

6. $\dfrac{y^2 - 3y - 18}{2y^2 + 5y + 3} = \dfrac{(y-6)(y+3)}{(2y+3)(y+1)}$

8. $\dfrac{1 - x^2}{x^3 - 1} = \dfrac{(1-x)(1+x)}{(x-1)(x^2+x+1)} = \dfrac{-(x-1)(1+x)}{(x-1)(x^2+x+1)} = \dfrac{-(x+1)}{x^2+x+1}$

10. $\dfrac{x^2 - x - 6}{x^2 + 2x} \cdot \dfrac{x^3 + x^2}{x^2 - 2x - 3} = \dfrac{(x-3)(x+2)}{x(x+2)} \cdot \dfrac{x^2(x+1)}{(x-3)(x+1)} = x$

12. $\dfrac{x^2 + 2xy + y^2}{x^2 - y^2} \cdot \dfrac{2x^2 - xy - y^2}{x^2 - xy - 2y^2} = \dfrac{(x+y)(x+y)}{(x-y)(x+y)} \cdot \dfrac{(x-y)(2x+y)}{(x-2y)(x+y)} = \dfrac{2x+y}{x-2y}$

14. $\dfrac{4y^2 - 9}{2y^2 + 9y - 18} \div \dfrac{2y^2 + y - 3}{y^2 + 5y - 6} = \dfrac{4y^2 - 9}{2y^2 + 9y - 18} \cdot \dfrac{y^2 + 5y - 6}{2y^2 + y - 3}$

$= \dfrac{(2y-3)(2y+3)}{(2y-3)(y+6)} \cdot \dfrac{(y-1)(y+6)}{(y-1)(2y+3)} = 1$

16. $\dfrac{\dfrac{2x^2 - 3x - 2}{x^2 - 1}}{\dfrac{2x^2 + 5x + 2}{x^2 + x - 2}} = \dfrac{2x^2 - 3x - 2}{x^2 - 1} \cdot \dfrac{x^2 + x - 2}{2x^2 + 5x + 2} = \dfrac{(x-2)(2x+1)}{(x-1)(x+1)} \cdot \dfrac{(x-1)(x+2)}{(x+2)(2x+1)} = \dfrac{x-2}{x+1}$

18. $\dfrac{x}{y/z} = x \div \dfrac{y}{z} = \dfrac{x}{1} \cdot \dfrac{z}{y} = \dfrac{xz}{y}$

20. $\dfrac{1}{x+1} + \dfrac{1}{x-1} = \dfrac{x-1}{(x+1)(x-1)} + \dfrac{x+1}{(x+1)(x-1)} = \dfrac{x-1+x+1}{(x+1)(x-1)} = \dfrac{2x}{(x+1)(x-1)}$

22. $\dfrac{x}{x-4} - \dfrac{3}{x+6} = \dfrac{x(x+6)}{(x-4)(x+6)} + \dfrac{-3(x-4)}{(x-4)(x+6)} = \dfrac{x^2 + 6x - 3x + 12}{(x-4)(x+6)} = \dfrac{x^2 + 3x + 12}{(x-4)(x+6)}$

24. $\dfrac{5}{2x-3} - \dfrac{3}{(2x-3)^2} = \dfrac{5(2x-3)}{(2x-3)^2} - \dfrac{3}{(2x-3)^2} = \dfrac{10x - 15 - 3}{(2x-3)^2} = \dfrac{10x - 18}{(2x-3)^2} = \dfrac{2(5x-9)}{(2x-3)^2}$

26. $\dfrac{2}{a^2} - \dfrac{3}{ab} + \dfrac{4}{b^2} = \dfrac{2b^2}{a^2 b^2} - \dfrac{3ab}{a^2 b^2} + \dfrac{4a^2}{a^2 b^2} = \dfrac{2b^2 - 3ab + 4a^2}{a^2 b^2}$

28. $\dfrac{1}{x} + \dfrac{1}{x^2} + \dfrac{1}{x^3} = \dfrac{x^2}{x^3} + \dfrac{x}{x^3} + \dfrac{1}{x^3} = \dfrac{x^2 + x + 1}{x^3}$

30. $\dfrac{x}{x^2 - 4} + \dfrac{1}{x-2} = \dfrac{x}{(x-2)(x+2)} + \dfrac{1}{x-2} = \dfrac{x}{(x-2)(x+2)} + \dfrac{x+2}{(x-2)(x+2)}$

$= \dfrac{2x+2}{(x-2)(x+2)} = \dfrac{2(x+1)}{(x-2)(x+2)}$

32. $\dfrac{x}{x^2 + x - 2} - \dfrac{2}{x^2 - 5x + 4} = \dfrac{x}{(x-1)(x+2)} + \dfrac{-2}{(x-1)(x-4)}$

$= \dfrac{x(x-4)}{(x-1)(x+2)(x-4)} + \dfrac{-2(x+2)}{(x-1)(x+2)(x-4)} = \dfrac{x^2 - 4x - 2x - 4}{(x-1)(x+2)(x-4)}$

$= \dfrac{x^2 - 6x - 4}{(x-1)(x+2)(x-4)}$

34. $\dfrac{x}{x^2 - x - 6} - \dfrac{1}{x+2} - \dfrac{2}{x-3} = \dfrac{x}{(x-3)(x+2)} + \dfrac{-1}{x+2} + \dfrac{-2}{x-3}$

$= \dfrac{x}{(x-3)(x+2)} + \dfrac{-1(x-3)}{(x-3)(x+2)} + \dfrac{-2(x+2)}{(x-3)(x+2)} = \dfrac{x - x + 3 - 2x - 4}{(x-3)(x+2)} = \dfrac{-2x - 1}{(x-3)(x+2)}$

36. $\dfrac{1}{x+1} - \dfrac{2}{(x+1)^2} + \dfrac{3}{x^2 - 1} = \dfrac{1}{x+1} + \dfrac{-2}{(x+1)^2} + \dfrac{3}{(x-1)(x+1)}$

$= \dfrac{(x+1)(x-1)}{(x-1)(x+1)^2} + \dfrac{-2(x-1)}{(x-1)(x+1)^2} + \dfrac{3(x+1)}{(x-1)(x+1)^2}$

$= \dfrac{x^2 - 1}{(x-1)(x+1)^2} + \dfrac{-2x + 2}{(x-1)(x+1)^2} + \dfrac{3x + 3}{(x-1)(x+1)^2} = \dfrac{x^2 - 1 - 2x + 2 + 3x + 3}{(x-1)(x+1)^2}$

$= \dfrac{x^2 + x + 4}{(x-1)(x+1)^2}$

38. $x - \dfrac{y}{\dfrac{x}{y} + \dfrac{y}{x}} = x - \dfrac{y}{\dfrac{x}{y} + \dfrac{y}{x}} \cdot \dfrac{xy}{xy} = x - \dfrac{xy^2}{x^2 + y^2} = \dfrac{x(x^2 + y^2)}{x^2 + y^2} - \dfrac{xy^2}{x^2 + y^2} = \dfrac{x^3 + xy^2 - xy^2}{x^2 + y^2}$

$= \dfrac{x^3}{x^2 + y^2}$

40. $1 + \dfrac{1}{1 + \frac{1}{1+x}} = 1 + \dfrac{1}{1 + \frac{1}{1+x}} \cdot \dfrac{1+x}{1+x} = 1 + \dfrac{1+x}{1+x+1} = 1 + \dfrac{1+x}{2+x} = \dfrac{2+x}{2+x} + \dfrac{1+x}{2+x} = \dfrac{3+2x}{2+x}$

42. $\dfrac{\dfrac{a-b}{a} - \dfrac{a+b}{b}}{\dfrac{a-b}{b} + \dfrac{a+b}{a}} = \dfrac{\dfrac{a-b}{a} - \dfrac{a+b}{b}}{\dfrac{a-b}{b} + \dfrac{a+b}{a}} \cdot \dfrac{ab}{ab} = \dfrac{(a-b)b - (a+b)a}{(a-b)a + (a+b)b} = \dfrac{ab - b^2 - a^2 - ab}{a^2 - ab + ab + b^2}$

$= \dfrac{-a^2 - b^2}{a^2 + b^2} = \dfrac{-(a^2 + b^2)}{a^2 + b^2} = -1$

44. $\dfrac{x^{-1} + y^{-1}}{(x+y)^{-1}} = \dfrac{\dfrac{1}{x} - \dfrac{1}{y}}{\dfrac{1}{x+y}} = \dfrac{\dfrac{1}{x} - \dfrac{1}{y}}{\dfrac{1}{x+y}} \cdot \dfrac{xy(x+y)}{xy(x+y)} = \dfrac{y(x+y) - x(x+y)}{xy} = \dfrac{xy + y^2 - x^2 - xy}{xy}$

$= \dfrac{y^2 - x^2}{xy}$

46.
$$\frac{\left(a+\frac{1}{b}\right)^m\left(a-\frac{1}{b}\right)^n}{\left(b+\frac{1}{a}\right)^m\left(b-\frac{1}{a}\right)^n} = \left(\frac{a+\frac{1}{b}}{b+\frac{1}{a}}\right)^m\left(\frac{a-\frac{1}{b}}{b-\frac{1}{a}}\right)^n = \left(\frac{\frac{ab+1}{b}}{\frac{ab+1}{a}}\right)^m\left(\frac{\frac{ab-1}{b}}{\frac{ab-1}{a}}\right)^n = \left(\frac{a}{b}\right)^m\left(\frac{a}{b}\right)^n$$
$$= \left(\frac{a}{b}\right)^{m+n} = \frac{a^{m+n}}{b^{m+n}}$$

48.
$$\frac{(x+h)^{-3}-x^{-3}}{h} = \frac{\frac{1}{(x+h)^3}-\frac{1}{x^3}}{h} = \left(\frac{1}{(x+h)^3}-\frac{1}{x^3}\right)\cdot\frac{1}{h} = \left(\frac{x^3}{(x+h)^3 x^3}+\frac{-(x+h)^3}{(x+h)^3 x^3}\right)\cdot\frac{1}{h}$$
$$= \frac{x^3-(x^3+3x^2h+3xh^2+h^3)}{(x+h)^3 x^3}\cdot\frac{1}{h} = \frac{x^3-x^3-3x^2h-3xh^2-h^3}{h(x+h)^3 x^3} = \frac{-3x^2h-3xh^2-h^3}{h(x+h)^3 x^3}$$
$$= \frac{-h(3x^2+3xh+h^2)}{h(x+h)^3 x^3} = \frac{-(3x^2+3xh+h^2)}{(x+h)^3 x^3}$$

50.
$$\frac{(x+h)^3-7(x+h)-(x^3-7x)}{h} = \frac{x^3+3x^2h+3xh^2+h^3-7x-7h-x^3+7x}{h}$$
$$= \frac{3x^2h+3xh^2+h^3-7h}{h} = \frac{h(3x^2+3xh+h^2-7)}{h} = 3x^2+3xh+h^2-7$$

52.
$$\sqrt{1+\left(x^3-\frac{1}{4x^3}\right)^2} = \sqrt{1+x^6-\frac{2x^3}{4x^3}+\frac{1}{16x^6}} = \sqrt{1+x^6-\frac{1}{2}+\frac{1}{16x^6}}$$
$$= \sqrt{x^6+\frac{1}{2}+\frac{1}{16x^6}} = \sqrt{\left(x^3+\frac{1}{4x^3}\right)^2} = \left|x^3+\frac{1}{4x^3}\right|$$

54.
$$\frac{2x(x+6)^4-x^2(4)(x+6)^3}{(x+6)^8} = \frac{(x+6)^3[2x(x+6)-4x^2]}{(x+6)^8} = \frac{2x^2+12x-4x^2}{(x+6)^5} = \frac{12x-2x^2}{(x+6)^5}$$
$$= \frac{2x(6-x)}{(x+6)^5}$$

56.
$$\frac{(1-x^2)^{1/2}+x^2(1-x^2)^{-1/2}}{1-x^2} = \frac{(1-x^2)^{-1/2}(1-x^2+x^2)}{1-x^2} = \frac{1}{(1-x^2)^{3/2}}$$

58.
$$\frac{(7-3x)^{1/2}+\frac{3}{2}x(7-3x)^{-1/2}}{7-3x} = \frac{(7-3x)^{-1/2}\left(7-3x+\frac{3}{2}x\right)}{7-3x} = \frac{7-\frac{3}{2}x}{(7-3x)^{3/2}}$$

60.
$$\frac{1}{\sqrt{x}+1} = \frac{1}{\sqrt{x}+1}\cdot\frac{\sqrt{x}-1}{\sqrt{x}-1} = \frac{\sqrt{x}-1}{x-1}$$

62.
$$\frac{y}{\sqrt{3}+\sqrt{y}} = \frac{y}{\sqrt{3}+\sqrt{y}}\cdot\frac{\sqrt{3}-\sqrt{y}}{\sqrt{3}-\sqrt{y}} = \frac{y\left(\sqrt{3}-\sqrt{y}\right)}{3-y} = \frac{y\sqrt{3}-y\sqrt{y}}{3-y}$$

64.
$$\frac{\sqrt{3}+\sqrt{5}}{2} = \frac{\sqrt{3}+\sqrt{5}}{2}\cdot\frac{\sqrt{3}-\sqrt{5}}{\sqrt{3}-\sqrt{5}} = \frac{3-5}{2\left(\sqrt{3}-\sqrt{5}\right)} = \frac{-2}{2\left(\sqrt{3}-\sqrt{5}\right)} = \frac{-1}{\sqrt{3}-\sqrt{5}}$$

66.
$$\frac{\sqrt{x}-\sqrt{x+h}}{h\sqrt{x}\sqrt{x+h}} = \frac{\sqrt{x}-\sqrt{x+h}}{h\sqrt{x}\sqrt{x+h}}\cdot\frac{\sqrt{x}+\sqrt{x+h}}{\sqrt{x}+\sqrt{x+h}} = \frac{x-(x+h)}{h\sqrt{x}\sqrt{x+h}\left(\sqrt{x}+\sqrt{x+h}\right)}$$

$$= \frac{-h}{h\sqrt{x}\sqrt{x+h}\left(\sqrt{x}+\sqrt{x+h}\right)} = \frac{-1}{\sqrt{x}\sqrt{x+h}\left(\sqrt{x}+\sqrt{x+h}\right)}$$

68. $\sqrt{x+1}-\sqrt{x} = \dfrac{\sqrt{x+1}-\sqrt{x}}{1} \cdot \dfrac{\sqrt{x+1}+\sqrt{x}}{\sqrt{x+1}+\sqrt{x}} = \dfrac{x+1-x}{\sqrt{x+1}+\sqrt{x}} = \dfrac{1}{\sqrt{x+1}+\sqrt{x}}$

70. This statement is false. For example, take $b=2$ and $c=1$, then LHS $= \dfrac{b}{b-c} = \dfrac{2}{2-1} = 2$, while

RHS $= 1 - \dfrac{b}{c} = 1 - \dfrac{2}{1} = -1$, and $2 \neq -1$.

72. This statement is false. For example, take $x=5$ and $y=2$. Then substituting into the left hand side

we obtain LHS $= \dfrac{x+1}{y+1} = \dfrac{5+1}{2+1} = \dfrac{6}{3} = 2$, while the right hand side yields RHS $= \dfrac{x}{y} = \dfrac{5}{2}$, and

$2 \neq \dfrac{5}{2}$.

74. This statement is false. For example, take $x=1$ and $y=1$. Then substituting into the left hand side

we obtain LHS $= 2\left(\dfrac{a}{b}\right) = 2\left(\dfrac{1}{1}\right) = 2$, while the right hand side yields RHS $= \dfrac{2a}{2b} = \dfrac{2}{2} = 1$, and

$2 \neq 1$.

76. This statement is true: $\dfrac{1+x+x^2}{x} = \dfrac{1}{x} + \dfrac{x}{x} + \dfrac{x^2}{x} = \dfrac{1}{x} + 1 + x.$

78. This statement is true, for $x \neq 1$: $\dfrac{x^2-1}{x-1} = \dfrac{(x-1)(x+1)}{x-1} = x+1.$

80.

x	2.80	2.90	2.95	2.99	2.999	3	3.001	3.01	3.05	3.10	3.20
$\dfrac{x^2-9}{x-3}$	5.80	5.90	5.95	5.99	5.999	?	6.001	6.01	6.05	6.10	6.20

From the table, we see that the expression $\dfrac{x^2-9}{x-3}$ approaches 6 as x approaches 3. We simplify the

expression: $\dfrac{x^2-9}{x-3} = \dfrac{(x-3)(x+3)}{x-3} = x+3 \;\; (x \neq 3)$. Clearly as x approaches $3, x+3$
approaches 6. This explains the result in the table.

82. Answers will vary.

Algebraic Error	Counterexample	
$\dfrac{1}{a} + \dfrac{1}{b} \not= \dfrac{1}{a+b}$	$\dfrac{1}{2} + \dfrac{1}{2} \not= \dfrac{1}{2+2}$	LHS $= \dfrac{1}{2} + \dfrac{1}{2} = 1$ RHS $= \dfrac{1}{2+2} = \dfrac{1}{4}$
$(a+b)^2 \not= a^2 + b^2$	$(1+3)^2 \not= 1^2 + 3^2$	LHS $= (1+3)^2 = 4^2 = 16$ RHS $= 1^2 + 3^2 = 1+9 = 10$
$\sqrt{a^2+b^2} \not= a+b$	$\sqrt{5^2+12^2} \not= 5+12$	LHS $= \sqrt{5^2+12^2} = \sqrt{25+144}$ $= \sqrt{169} = 13$ RHS $= 5+12 = 17$

Algebraic Error	Counterexample	
$\dfrac{a+b}{a} \not\Join b$	$\dfrac{2+6}{2} \not\Join 6$	LHS $= \dfrac{2+6}{2} = \dfrac{8}{2} = 4$ RHS $= 6$
$(a^3+b^3)^{1/3} \not\Join a+b$	$(2^3+2^3)^{1/3} \not\Join 2+2$	LHS $= (a^3+b^3)^{1/3} = (8+8)^{1/3}$ $\quad = 2\sqrt[3]{2}$ RHS $= 2+2 = 4$
$\dfrac{a^m}{a^n} \not\Join a^{m/n}$	$\dfrac{3^5}{3^2} \not\Join 3^{5/2}$	LHS $= \dfrac{3^5}{3^2} = \dfrac{243}{9} = 27$ RHS $= 3^{5/2} = 9\sqrt{3}$
$a^{-1/n} \not\Join \dfrac{1}{a^n}$	$64^{-1/3} \not\Join \dfrac{1}{64^3}$	LHS $= 64^{-1/3} = \left(\dfrac{1}{64}\right)^{1/3} = \dfrac{1}{4}$ RHS $= \dfrac{1}{64^3} = \dfrac{1}{262{,}144}$

Exercises 1.6

2. (a) $4(-3-1)-(2-[-3]) \stackrel{?}{=} 5(-3-2)+4$

$\qquad\qquad 4(-4)-(5) \stackrel{?}{=} 5(-5)+4$

$\qquad\qquad\qquad -16-5 \stackrel{?}{=} -25+4 \qquad$ Yes, a solution.

(b) $4(0-1)-(2-[0]) \stackrel{?}{=} 5(0-2)+4$

$\qquad\qquad 4(-1)-(2) \stackrel{?}{=} 5(-2)+4$

$\qquad\qquad\quad -4-2 \stackrel{?}{=} -10+4 \qquad$ Yes, a solution.

Note: This equation is an identity, so any real number is a solution.

4. (a) $1-[2-(3-\{2\})] \stackrel{?}{=} 4\{2\}-(6+\{2\})$

$\qquad\qquad 1-[2-(1)] \stackrel{?}{=} 8-8$

$\qquad\qquad\qquad 1-(1) \stackrel{?}{=} 0 \qquad$ Yes, a solution.

(b) $1-[2-(3-\{22\})] \stackrel{?}{=} 4\{22\}-(6+\{22\})$

$\qquad\qquad 1-[2-(-19)] \stackrel{?}{=} 88-28$

$\qquad\qquad\qquad 1-(21) \stackrel{?}{=} 60 \qquad\qquad$ No, not a solution.

6. (a) $\dfrac{a(0)-b}{b(0)-a} \stackrel{?}{=} \dfrac{a}{b}$

$\qquad\qquad \dfrac{-b}{-a} \stackrel{?}{=} \dfrac{a}{b}$

$\qquad\qquad \dfrac{b}{a} \stackrel{?}{=} \dfrac{a}{b}$

Since this is true only if
$a=b$, this is not a solution.

(b) $\dfrac{a(1)-b}{b(1)-a} \stackrel{?}{=} \dfrac{a}{b}$

$\qquad\qquad \dfrac{a-b}{b-a} \stackrel{?}{=} \dfrac{a}{b}$

$\qquad\qquad \dfrac{a-b}{-(a-b)} \stackrel{?}{=} \dfrac{a}{b}$

$\qquad\qquad\qquad -1 \stackrel{?}{=} \dfrac{a}{b}$

Since $a > 0$ and $b > 0$, we must have $\dfrac{a}{b} > 0$,
and so this is not a solution.

8. $4x+12=28 \quad\Leftrightarrow\quad 4x=16 \quad\Leftrightarrow\quad x=4$

10. $4x+7=9x-13 \quad\Leftrightarrow\quad 20=5x \quad\Leftrightarrow\quad x=4$

12. $5t-13=12-5t \quad\Leftrightarrow\quad 10t=25 \quad\Leftrightarrow\quad t=\dfrac{5}{2}$

14. $\dfrac{z}{5}=\dfrac{3}{10}z+7 \quad\Leftrightarrow\quad 2z=3z+70 \quad\Leftrightarrow\quad z=-70$

16. $5(x+3)+9=-2(x-2)-1 \quad\Leftrightarrow\quad 5x+15+9=-2x+4-1 \quad\Leftrightarrow\quad 5x+24=-2x+3$
     $\Leftrightarrow\quad 7x=-21 \quad\Leftrightarrow\quad x=-3$

18. $\dfrac{2}{3}y+\dfrac{1}{2}(y-3)=\dfrac{y+1}{4} \quad\Leftrightarrow\quad 8y+6(y-3)=3(y+1) \quad\Leftrightarrow\quad 8y+6y-18=3y+3 \quad\Leftrightarrow$
     $14y-18=3y+3 \quad\Leftrightarrow\quad 11y=21 \quad\Leftrightarrow\quad y=\dfrac{21}{11}$

20. $\dfrac{2x-1}{x+2} = \dfrac{4}{5} \;\Rightarrow\; 5(2x-1) = 4(x+2) \;\Leftrightarrow\; 10x-5 = 4x+8 \;\Leftrightarrow\; 6x = 13 \;\Leftrightarrow\;$
$x = \dfrac{13}{6}$

22. $\dfrac{1}{t-1} + \dfrac{t}{3t-2} = \dfrac{1}{3} \;\Rightarrow\; 3(3t-2) + 3t(t-1) = (t-1)(3t-2) \;\Leftrightarrow\;$
$9t - 6 + 3t^2 - 3t = 3t^2 - 5t + 2 \;\Leftrightarrow\; 11t = 8 \;\Leftrightarrow\; t = \dfrac{8}{11}$

24. $(t-4)^2 = (t+4)^2 + 32 \;\Leftrightarrow\; t^2 - 8t + 16 = t^2 + 8t + 16 + 32 \;\Leftrightarrow\; -16t = 32 \;\Leftrightarrow\;$
$t = -2$

26. $\dfrac{2}{3}x - \dfrac{1}{4} = \dfrac{1}{6}x - \dfrac{1}{9} \;\Leftrightarrow\; 24x - 9 = 6x - 4 \;\Leftrightarrow\; 18x = 5 \;\Leftrightarrow\; x = \dfrac{5}{18}$

28. $\dfrac{6}{x-3} = \dfrac{5}{x+4} \;\Rightarrow\; 6(x+4) = 5(x-3) \;\Leftrightarrow\; 6x + 24 = 5x - 15 \;\Leftrightarrow\; x = -39$

30. $\dfrac{4}{x-1} + \dfrac{2}{x+1} = \dfrac{35}{x^2-1} \;\Rightarrow\; 4(x+1) + 2(x-1) = 35 \;\Leftrightarrow\; 4x + 4 + 2x - 2 = 35 \;\Leftrightarrow\;$
$6x + 2 = 35 \;\Leftrightarrow\; 6x = 33 \;\Leftrightarrow\; x = \dfrac{11}{2}$

32. $\dfrac{12x-5}{6x+3} = 2 - \dfrac{5}{x} \;\Rightarrow\; (12x-5)x = 2x(6x+3) - 5(6x+3) \;\Leftrightarrow\;$
$12x^2 - 5x = 12x^2 + 6x - 30x - 15 \;\Leftrightarrow\; 12x^2 - 5x = 12x^2 - 24x - 15 \;\Leftrightarrow\; 19x = -15$
$\Leftrightarrow\; x = -\dfrac{15}{19}$

34. $2x - \dfrac{x}{2} + \dfrac{x+1}{4} = 6x \;\Leftrightarrow\; 8x - 2x + x + 1 = 24x \;\Leftrightarrow\; 7x + 1 = 24x \;\Leftrightarrow\; 1 = 17x$
$\Leftrightarrow\; x = \dfrac{1}{17}$

36. $\dfrac{1}{1 - \dfrac{3}{2+w}} = 60 \;\Leftrightarrow\; \dfrac{2+w}{2+w-3} = 60$ (Multiplying the LHS by $\dfrac{2+w}{2+w}$). Thus $\dfrac{2+w}{w-1} = 60$
$\Rightarrow\; 2 + w = 60(w-1) \;\Leftrightarrow\; 2 + w = 60w - 60 \;\Leftrightarrow\; 62 = 59w \;\Leftrightarrow\; w = \dfrac{62}{59}$

38. $\dfrac{1}{3-t} + \dfrac{4}{3+t} + \dfrac{16}{9-t^2} = 0 \;\Rightarrow\; (3+t) + 4(3-t) + 16 = 0 \;\Leftrightarrow\;$
$3 + t + 12 - 4t + 16 = 0 \;\Leftrightarrow\; -3t + 31 = 0 \;\Leftrightarrow\; -3t = -31 \;\Leftrightarrow\; t = \dfrac{31}{3}$

40. $\dfrac{1}{x+3} + \dfrac{5}{x^2-9} = \dfrac{2}{x-3} \;\Rightarrow\; (x-3) + 5 = 2(x+3) \;\Leftrightarrow\; x + 2 = 2x + 6 \;\Leftrightarrow\;$
$x = -4$

42. $\dfrac{1}{x} - \dfrac{2}{2x+1} = \dfrac{1}{2x^2+x} \;\Rightarrow\; (2x+1) - 2(x) = 1 \;\Leftrightarrow\; 1 = 1.$ This is an identity for $x \neq 0$
and $x \neq -\frac{1}{2}$, so the solutions are all real numbers except 0 and $-\frac{1}{2}$.

44. $x^2 = 18 \;\Rightarrow\; x = \pm\sqrt{18} = \pm 3\sqrt{2}$

46. $x^2 - 7 = 0 \;\Leftrightarrow\; x^2 = 7 \;\Rightarrow\; x = \pm\sqrt{7}$

48. $5x^2 - 125 = 0 \;\Leftrightarrow\; 5(x^2 - 25) = 0 \;\Leftrightarrow\; x^2 = 25 \;\Rightarrow\; x = \pm 5$

50. $6x^2 + 100 = 0 \;\Leftrightarrow\; 6x^2 = -100 \;\Leftrightarrow\; x^2 = -\frac{50}{3}$, which has no real solutions.

52. $3(x-5)^2 = 15 \quad \Leftrightarrow \quad (x-5)^2 = 5 \quad \Rightarrow \quad x-5 = \pm\sqrt{5} \quad \Leftrightarrow \quad x = 5 \pm \sqrt{5}$

54. $x^5 + 32 = 0 \quad \Leftrightarrow \quad x^5 = -32 \quad \Leftrightarrow \quad x = -32^{1/5} = -2$

56. $64x^6 = 27 \quad \Leftrightarrow \quad x^6 = \frac{27}{64} \quad \Rightarrow \quad x = \pm\left(\frac{27}{64}\right)^{1/6} = \pm\frac{27^{1/6}}{64^{1/6}} = \pm\frac{\sqrt{3}}{2}$

58. $(x-1)^3 + 8 = 0 \quad \Leftrightarrow \quad (x-1)^3 = -8 \quad \Leftrightarrow \quad x-1 = (-8)^{1/3} = -2 \quad \Leftrightarrow \quad x = -1.$

60. $(x+1)^4 + 16 = 0 \quad \Leftrightarrow \quad (x+1)^4 = -16$, which has no real solutions.

62. $4(x+2)^5 = 1 \quad \Leftrightarrow \quad (x+2)^5 = \frac{1}{4} \quad \Rightarrow \quad x+2 = \sqrt[5]{\frac{1}{4}} \quad \Leftrightarrow \quad x = -2 + \sqrt[5]{\frac{1}{4}}$

64. $x^{4/3} - 16 = 0 \quad \Leftrightarrow \quad x^{4/3} = 16 = 2^4 \quad \Leftrightarrow \quad \left(x^{4/3}\right)^3 = (2^4)^3 = 2^{12} \quad \Leftrightarrow \quad x^4 = 2^{12} \quad \Leftrightarrow$
$x = \pm\left(2^{12}\right)^{1/4} = \pm 2^3 = \pm 8.$

66. $6x^{2/3} - 216 = 0 \quad \Leftrightarrow \quad 6x^{2/3} = 216 \quad \Leftrightarrow \quad x^{2/3} = 36 = 6^2 \quad \Leftrightarrow \quad \left(x^{2/3}\right)^{3/2} = (6^2)^{3/2} \quad \Leftrightarrow$
$x = 6^3 = 216$

68. $3.95 - x = 2.32x + 2.00 \quad \Leftrightarrow \quad 1.95 = 3.32x \quad \Leftrightarrow \quad x = \dfrac{1.95}{3.32} \approx 0.59$

70. $\dfrac{0.26x - 1.94}{3.03 - 2.44x} = 1.76 \quad \Rightarrow \quad 0.26x - 1.94 = 1.76(3.03 - 2.44x) \quad \Leftrightarrow$
$0.26x - 1.94 = 5.33 - 4.29x \quad \Leftrightarrow \quad 4.55x = 7.27 \quad \Leftrightarrow \quad x = \dfrac{7.27}{4.55} \approx 1.60$

72. $F = G\dfrac{mM}{r^2} \quad \Leftrightarrow \quad m = \dfrac{Fr^2}{GM}$

74. $P = 2l + 2w \quad \Leftrightarrow \quad 2w = P - 2l \quad \Leftrightarrow \quad w = \dfrac{P - 2l}{2}$

76. $a - 2[b - 3(c - x)] = 6 \quad \Leftrightarrow \quad a - 2(b - 3c + 3x) = 6 \quad \Leftrightarrow \quad a - 2b + 6c - 6x = 6 \quad \Leftrightarrow$
$-6x = 6 - a + 2b - 6c \quad \Leftrightarrow \quad x = \dfrac{6 - a + 2b - 6c}{-6} = -\dfrac{6 - a + 2b - 6c}{6}$

78. $\dfrac{a+1}{b} = \dfrac{a-1}{b} + \dfrac{b+1}{a} \quad \Leftrightarrow \quad a(a+1) = a(a-1) + b(b+1) \quad \Leftrightarrow$
$a^2 + a = a^2 - a + b^2 + b \quad \Leftrightarrow \quad 2a = b^2 + b \quad \Leftrightarrow \quad a = \frac{1}{2}(b^2 + b)$

80. $F = G\dfrac{mM}{r^2} \quad \Leftrightarrow \quad r^2 = G\dfrac{mM}{F} \quad \Rightarrow \quad r = \pm\sqrt{G\dfrac{mM}{F}}$

82. $A = P\left(1 + \dfrac{i}{100}\right)^2 \quad \Leftrightarrow \quad \dfrac{A}{P} = \left(1 + \dfrac{i}{100}\right)^2 \quad \Rightarrow \quad 1 + \dfrac{i}{100} = \pm\sqrt{\dfrac{A}{P}} \quad \Leftrightarrow$
$\dfrac{i}{100} = -1 \pm \sqrt{\dfrac{A}{P}} \quad \Leftrightarrow \quad i = -100 \pm 100\sqrt{\dfrac{A}{P}}$

84. $x^4 + y^4 + z^4 = 100 \quad \Leftrightarrow \quad x^4 = 100 - y^4 - z^4 \quad \Rightarrow \quad x = \pm\sqrt[4]{100 - y^4 - z^4}$

86. (a) $3(0) + k - 5 = k(0) - k + 1 \quad \Leftrightarrow \quad k - 5 = -k + 1 \quad \Leftrightarrow \quad 2k = 6 \quad \Leftrightarrow \quad k = 3$

    (b) $3(1) + k - 5 = k(1) - k + 1 \quad \Leftrightarrow \quad 3 + k - 5 = k - k + 1 \quad \Leftrightarrow \quad k - 2 = 1 \quad \Leftrightarrow$
    $k = 3$

(c) $3(2) + k - 5 = k(2) - k + 1 \quad \Leftrightarrow \quad 6 + k - 5 = 2k - k + 1 \quad \Leftrightarrow \quad k + 1 = k + 1.$ Since both sides of this equation are equal, $x = 2$ is a solution for every value of k. That is, $x = 2$ is a solution to every member of this family of equations.

88.   Using the formulas for volume we have: for the sphere, $V = \frac{4}{3}\pi r^3$; for the cylinder, $V = \pi r^2 h$; for the cone, $V = \frac{1}{3}\pi r^2 h$. Setting the volume of the sphere equal to the volume of the cylinder, we have $\frac{4}{3}\pi r^3 = \pi r^2 h \quad \Leftrightarrow \quad \frac{4}{3}r = h$. So the height of the cylinder is $h = \frac{4}{3}r$.

Likewise, setting the volume of the sphere equal to the volume of the cone, we have $\frac{4}{3}\pi r^3 = \frac{1}{3}\pi r^2 h$ $\Leftrightarrow \quad 4r = h$. So the height of the cone is $h = 4r$.

Review Exercises for Chapter 1

2. Commutative Law for multiplication.

4. Distributive Law.

6. $(-\infty, 4] = \{x \mid x \le 4\}$

8. $1 \le x \le 6 \iff x \in [1, 6]$

10. $1 - |1 - |-1|| = 1 - |1 - 1| = 1 - |0| = 1$

12. $\sqrt[3]{-125} = \sqrt[3]{(-5)^3} = -5$

14. $64^{2/3} = (4^3)^{2/3} = 4^2 = 16$

16. $\sqrt[4]{4}\sqrt[4]{324} = \sqrt[4]{4}\sqrt[4]{4 \cdot 81} = \sqrt[4]{2^2}\sqrt[4]{2^2 \cdot 3^4} = 2 \cdot 3 = 6$

18. $\sqrt{2}\sqrt{50} = \sqrt{100} = 10$

20. $x\sqrt{x} = x^1 \cdot x^{1/2} = x^{3/2}$

22. $\left((x^m)^2\right)^n = (x^{2m})^n = x^{2mn}$

24. $\left((x^a)^b\right)^c = (x^{ab})^c = x^{abc}$

26. $\dfrac{(x^2)^n x^5}{x^n} = \dfrac{x^{2n} \cdot x^5}{x^n} = x^{2n+5-n} = x^{n+5}$

28. $(a^2)^{-3}(a^3b)^2(b^3)^4 = a^{-6} \cdot a^6 b^2 \cdot b^{12} = a^{-6+6}\,b^{2+12} = b^{14}$

30. $\left(\dfrac{r^2 s^{4/3}}{r^{1/3} s}\right)^6 = \dfrac{r^{12} s^8}{r^2 s^6} = r^{12-2} s^{8-6} = r^{10} s^2$

32. $\sqrt{x^2 y^4} = \sqrt{x^2} \cdot \sqrt{(y^2)^2} = |x| y^2$

34. $\dfrac{\sqrt{x}+1}{\sqrt{x}-1} = \dfrac{\sqrt{x}+1}{\sqrt{x}-1} \cdot \dfrac{\sqrt{x}+1}{\sqrt{x}+1} = \dfrac{\left(\sqrt{x}\right)^2 + 2\sqrt{x} + 1}{x-1} = \dfrac{x + 2\sqrt{x} + 1}{x-1}$. Here simplify means to rationalize the denominator.

36. $\left(\dfrac{ab^2 c^{-3}}{2a^3 b^{-4}}\right)^{-2} = \dfrac{a^{-2} b^{-4} c^6}{2^{-2} a^{-6} b^8} = 2^2\, a^{-2-(-6)}\, b^{-4-8}\, c^6 = 4a^4\, b^{-12}\, c^6 = \dfrac{4a^4 c^6}{b^{12}}$

38. $2.08 \times 10^{-8} = 0.0000000208$

40. $80\dfrac{\text{times}}{\text{minute}} \cdot \dfrac{60 \text{ minutes}}{\text{hour}} \cdot \dfrac{24 \text{ hours}}{\text{day}} \cdot \dfrac{365 \text{ day}}{\text{years}} \cdot 90 \text{ years} \approx 3.8 \times 10^9 \text{ times}$

42. $x^2 - 9x + 18 = (x-6)(x-3)$

44. $6x^2 + x - 12 = (3x-4)(2x+3)$

46. $x^4 - 2x^2 + 1 = (x^2 - 1)^2 = [(x-1)(x+1)]^2 = (x-1)^2(x+1)^2$

48. $2y^6 - 32y^2 = 2y^2(y^4 - 16) = 2y^2(y^2 + 4)(y^2 - 4) = 2y^2(y^2 + 4)(y+2)(y-2)$

50. $y^3 - 2y^2 - y + 2 = y^2(y-2) - 1(y-2) = (y-2)(y^2-1) = (y-2)(y-1)(y+1)$

52. $a^4 b^2 + ab^5 = ab^2(a^3 + b^3) = ab^2(a+b)(a^2 - ab + b^2)$

54. $8x^3 + y^6 = (2x)^3 + (y^2)^3 = (2x + y^2)(4x^2 - 2xy^2 + y^4)$

56. $3x^3 - 2x^2 + 18x - 12 = x^2(3x - 2) + 6(3x - 2) = (3x - 2)(x^2 + 6)$

58. $ax^2 + bx^2 - a - b = x^2(a + b) - 1(a + b) = (a + b)(x^2 - 1) = (a + b)(x - 1)(x + 1)$

60. $(a + b)^2 + 2(a + b) - 15 = [(a + b) - 3][(a + b) + 5] = (a + b - 3)(a + b + 5)$

62. $(2y - 7)(2y + 7) = 4y^2 - 49$

64. $(1 + x)(2 - x) - (3 - x)(3 + x) = 2 + x - x^2 - (9 - x^2) = 2 + x - x^2 - 9 + x^2 = -7 + x$

66. $(2x + 1)^3 = (2x)^3 + 3(2x)^2(1) + 3(2x)(1)^2 + (1)^3 = 8x^3 + 12x^2 + 6x + 1$

68. $x^3(x - 6)^2 + x^4(x - 6) = x^3(x - 6)[(x - 6) + x] = x^3(x - 6)(2x - 6) = x^3[2x^2 - 18x + 36]$
     $= 2x^5 - 18x^4 + 36x^3$

70. $\dfrac{x^3 + 2x^2 + 3x}{x} = \dfrac{x(x^2 + 2x + 3)}{x} = x^2 + 2x + 3$

72. $\dfrac{t^3 - 1}{t^2 - 1} = \dfrac{(t - 1)(t^2 + t + 1)}{(t - 1)(t + 1)} = \dfrac{t^2 + t + 1}{t + 1}$

74. $\dfrac{x^3/(x - 1)}{x^2/(x^3 - 1)} = \dfrac{x^3}{x - 1} \cdot \dfrac{x^3 - 1}{x^2} = \dfrac{x^3}{x - 1} \cdot \dfrac{(x - 1)(x^2 + x + 1)}{x^2} = x(x^2 + x + 1) = x^3 + x^2 + x$

76. $x - \dfrac{1}{x + 1} = \dfrac{x(x + 1)}{x + 1} - \dfrac{1}{x + 1} = \dfrac{x^2 + x - 1}{x + 1}$

78. $\dfrac{2}{x} + \dfrac{1}{x - 2} + \dfrac{3}{(x - 2)^2} = \dfrac{2(x - 2)^2}{x(x - 2)^2} + \dfrac{x(x - 2)}{x(x - 2)^2} + \dfrac{3x}{x(x - 2)^2}$
     $= \dfrac{2(x^2 - 4x + 4) + x^2 - 2x + 3x}{x(x - 2)^2} = \dfrac{2x^2 - 8x + 8 + x^2 - 2x + 3x}{x(x - 2)^2} = \dfrac{3x^2 - 7x + 8}{x(x - 2)^2}$

80. $\dfrac{1}{x + 2} + \dfrac{1}{x^2 - 4} - \dfrac{2}{x^2 - x - 2} = \dfrac{1}{x + 2} + \dfrac{1}{(x - 2)(x + 2)} - \dfrac{2}{(x - 2)(x + 1)}$
     $= \dfrac{(x - 2)(x + 1)}{(x - 2)(x + 1)(x + 2)} + \dfrac{x + 1}{(x - 2)(x + 1)(x + 2)} - \dfrac{2(x + 2)}{(x - 2)(x + 1)(x + 2)}$
     $= \dfrac{x^2 - x - 2 + x + 1 - 2x - 4}{(x - 2)(x + 1)(x + 2)} = \dfrac{x^2 - 2x - 5}{(x - 2)(x + 1)(x + 2)}$

82. $\dfrac{\dfrac{1}{x} - \dfrac{1}{x + 1}}{\dfrac{1}{x} + \dfrac{1}{x + 1}} = \dfrac{\dfrac{1}{x} - \dfrac{1}{x + 1}}{\dfrac{1}{x} + \dfrac{1}{x + 1}} \cdot \dfrac{x(x + 1)}{x(x + 1)} = \dfrac{(x + 1) - x}{(x + 1) + x} = \dfrac{1}{2x + 1}$

84. $\dfrac{\sqrt{x + h} - \sqrt{x}}{h} = \dfrac{\sqrt{x + h} - \sqrt{x}}{h} \cdot \dfrac{\sqrt{x + h} + \sqrt{x}}{\sqrt{x + h} + \sqrt{x}} = \dfrac{(x + h) - x}{h\left(\sqrt{x + h} + \sqrt{x}\right)}$
     $= \dfrac{h}{h\left(\sqrt{x + h} + \sqrt{x}\right)} = \dfrac{1}{\sqrt{x + h} + \sqrt{x}}$

86. $5x - 7 = 42 \quad \Leftrightarrow \quad 5x = 35 \quad \Leftrightarrow \quad x = 7.$

88. $8 - 2x = 14 + x \quad \Leftrightarrow \quad -3x = 6 \quad \Leftrightarrow \quad x = -2.$

90. $\frac{2}{3}x + \frac{3}{5} = \frac{1}{5} - 2x$ $\Leftrightarrow$ $10x + 9 = 3 - 30x$ $\Leftrightarrow$ $40x = -6$ $\Leftrightarrow$ $x = -\frac{6}{40} = -\frac{3}{20}$.

92. $\dfrac{x-5}{2} - \dfrac{2x+5}{3} = \dfrac{5}{6}$ $\Leftrightarrow$ $3(x-5) - 2(2x+5) = 5$ $\Leftrightarrow$ $3x - 15 - 4x - 10 = 5$ $\Leftrightarrow$
$-x = 30$ $\Leftrightarrow$ $x = -30$.

94. $\dfrac{x}{x+2} - 3 = \dfrac{1}{x+2}$ $\Leftrightarrow$ $x - 3(x+2) = 1$ $\Leftrightarrow$ $x - 3x - 6 = 1$ $\Leftrightarrow$ $-2x = 7$ $\Leftrightarrow$
$x = -\frac{7}{2}$.

96. $x^3 - 27 = 0$ $\Leftrightarrow$ $x^3 = 27$ $\Rightarrow$ $x = 3$.

98. $6x^4 + 15 = 0$ $\Leftrightarrow$ $6x^4 = -15$ $\Leftrightarrow$ $x^4 = -\frac{5}{2}$. Since x^4 must be non-negative, there is no real
solution.

100. $(x+2)^2 - 2 = 0$ $\Leftrightarrow$ $(x+2)^2 = 2$ $\Leftrightarrow$ $x + 2 = \pm\sqrt{2}$ $\Leftrightarrow$ $x = -2 \pm \sqrt{2}$.

102. $x^{2/3} - 4 = 0$ $\Leftrightarrow$ $\left(x^{1/3}\right)^2 = 4$ $\Rightarrow$ $x^{1/3} = \pm 2$ $\Leftrightarrow$ $x = \pm 8$.

104. $(x-2)^{1/5} = 2$ $\Leftrightarrow$ $x - 2 = 2^5 = 32$ $\Leftrightarrow$ $x = 2 + 32 = 34$.

106.   This statement is true, for $a \neq 1$: $\dfrac{1 + \sqrt{a}}{1 - a} = \dfrac{1 + \sqrt{a}}{1 - a} \cdot \dfrac{1 - \sqrt{a}}{1 - \sqrt{a}} = \dfrac{1 - a}{(1-a)(1 - \sqrt{a})} = \dfrac{1}{1 - \sqrt{a}}$.

108.   This statement is false. For example, take $a = 1$ and $b = 1$, then LHS $= \sqrt[3]{a+b} = \sqrt[3]{1+1}$
$= \sqrt[3]{2}$, while RHS $= \sqrt[3]{a} + \sqrt[3]{b} = \sqrt[3]{1} + \sqrt[3]{1} = 1 + 1 = 2$, and $\sqrt[3]{2} \neq 2$.

110.   This statement is false. For example, take $x = 1$, then LHS $= \dfrac{1}{x+4} = \dfrac{1}{1+4} = \dfrac{1}{5}$, while
RHS $= \dfrac{1}{x} + \dfrac{1}{4} = \dfrac{1}{1} + \dfrac{1}{4} = \dfrac{5}{4}$, and $\dfrac{1}{5} \neq \dfrac{5}{4}$.

112.   Substituting for a and b we obtain $a^2 + b^2 = (2mn)^2 + (m^2 - n^2)^2$
$= 4m^2n^2 + m^4 - 2m^2n^2 + n^4 = m^4 + 2m^2n^2 + n^4 = (m^2 + n^2)^2$. Since this last expression is
c^2, we have $a^2 + b^2 = c^2$ for these values.

114.   The fourth step is obtained by dividing both sides by the quantity $(a - b)$. However, since we are
assuming that $a = b$, this means we divided both sides by zero.

Principles of Problem Solving

2. Let r be the rate of the descent. We use the formula $time = \dfrac{distance}{rate}$; the ascent takes $\dfrac{1}{15}$ hr, the descent takes $\dfrac{1}{r}$ hr, and the total trip should take $\dfrac{2}{30} = \dfrac{1}{15}$ hr. Thus we have $\dfrac{1}{15} + \dfrac{1}{r} = \dfrac{1}{15}$ $\Leftrightarrow$ $\dfrac{1}{r} = 0$, which is impossible. So the car can not go fast enough to average 30 mi/h for the 2 mile trip.

4. Let us start with a given price P. After a discount of 40%, the price decreases to $0.6P$. After a discount of 20%, the price decreases to $0.8P$, and after another 20% discount, it becomes $0.8(0.8P) = 0.64P$. Since $0.6P < 0.64P$, a 40% discount is better.

6. $\dfrac{\sqrt{2}+\sqrt{6}}{\sqrt{2+\sqrt{3}}} = \sqrt{\dfrac{\left(\sqrt{2}+\sqrt{6}\right)^2}{2+\sqrt{3}}} = \sqrt{\dfrac{2+2\sqrt{12}+6}{2+\sqrt{3}}} = \sqrt{\dfrac{8+4\sqrt{3}}{2+\sqrt{3}}} = \sqrt{\dfrac{4\left(2+\sqrt{3}\right)}{2+\sqrt{3}}} = 2$

8. George's speed is $\dfrac{1}{50}$ lap/s, and Sue's is $\dfrac{1}{30}$ lap/s. So after t seconds, George has run $\dfrac{t}{50}$ laps, and Sue has run $\dfrac{t}{30}$ laps. They will next be side by side when Sue has run exactly one more lap than George, that is, when $\dfrac{t}{30} = \dfrac{t}{50} + 1$. We solve for t by first multiplying by 150, so $50t = 30t + 150$ $\Leftrightarrow$ $20t = 150$ $\Leftrightarrow$ $t = 75$. Therefore, they will be even after 75 s.

10. The north pole is such a point. And there are others: Consider a point a_1 near the south pole such that the parallel passing through a_1 forms a circle C_1 with circumference exactly one mile. Any point P_1 exactly one mile north of the circle C_1 along a meridian is a point satisfying the conditions in the problem: starting at P_1 she walks one mile south to the point a_1 on the circle C_1, then one mile east along C_1 returning to the point a_1, then north for one mile to P_1. That's not all. If a point a_2 (or $a_3, a_4, a_5, \dots$) is chosen near the south pole so that the parallel passing through it forms a circle C_2 ($C_3, C_4, C_5, \dots$) with a circumference of exactly $\frac{1}{2}$ mile ($\frac{1}{3}$ mi, $\frac{1}{4}$ mi, $\frac{1}{5}$ mi, $\dots$), then the point P_2 ($P_3, P_4, P_5, \dots$) one mile north of a_2 ($a_3, a_4, a_5, \dots$) along a meridian satisfies the conditions of the problem: she walks one mile south from P_2 ($P_3, P_4, P_5, \dots$) arriving at a_2 ($a_3, a_4, a_5, \dots$) along the circle C_2 ($C_3, C_4, C_5, \dots$), walks east along the circle for one mile thus traversing the circle twice (three times, four times, five times, $\dots$) returning to a_2 ($a_3, a_4, a_5, \dots$), and then walks north one mile to P_2 ($P_3, P_4, P_5, \dots$).

12. It remains the same. The weight of the ice cube is the same as the weight of the volume of water it displaces. Thus as the ice cube melts, it becomes water that fits exactly into the space displaced by the floating ice cube.

14. Let h_1 be the height of the pyramid whose square base length is a. Then $h_1 - h$ is the height of the pyramid whose square base length is b. Thus the volume of the truncated pyramid is $V = \frac{1}{3}h_1 a^2 - \frac{1}{3}(h_1 - h)b^2 = \frac{1}{3}h_1 a^2 - \frac{1}{3}h_1 b^2 + \frac{1}{3}hb^2 = \frac{1}{3}h_1(a^2 - b^2) + \frac{1}{3}hb^2$. Next we must find a relationship between h_1 and the other variables. Using geometry, the ratio of the height to the base of the two pyramids must be the same. Thus $\dfrac{h_1}{a} = \dfrac{h_1 - h}{b}$ $\Leftrightarrow$ $bh_1 = ah_1 - ah$ $\Leftrightarrow$ $ah = ah_1 - bh_1 = (a-b)h_1$ $\Leftrightarrow$ $\dfrac{ah}{a-b} = h_1$. Substituting for h_1 we have

$$V = \tfrac{1}{3}\left(\frac{ah}{a-b}\right)(a^2 - b^2) + \tfrac{1}{3}hb^2 = \tfrac{1}{3}(ah)(a+b) + \tfrac{1}{3}hb^2 = \tfrac{1}{3}ha^2 + \tfrac{1}{3}hab + \tfrac{1}{3}hb^2$$
$$= \tfrac{1}{3}h(a^2 + ab + b^2).$$

16. What is wrong is that the terms of the will have not been carried out. The oldest son receives $\frac{9}{17}$ of the nobleman's horses, and $\frac{9}{17} \neq \frac{1}{2}$. Similarly $\frac{6}{17} \neq \frac{1}{3}$ and $\frac{2}{17} \neq \frac{1}{9}$. The executor's horse is irrelevant to the problem.

18. The first few powers of 3 are $3^1 = 3$, $3^2 = 9$, $3^3 = 27$, $3^4 = 81$, $3^5 = 243$, $3^6 = 729$. It appears that the final digit cycles in a pattern, namely $3 \to 9 \to 7 \to 1 \to 3 \to 9 \to 7 \to 1$, of length 4. Since $459 = 4 \times 114 + 3$, the final digit is the third in the cycle, namely 7.

20. Let us see what happens when we square similar numbers with fewer 9's:

$$39^2 = 1521, \quad 399^2 = 159201, \quad 3999^2 = 15992001, \quad 39999^2 = 1599920001.$$

The pattern is that the square always seems to start with 15 and end with 1, and if $39\cdots9$ has n 9's, then the 2 in the middle of its square is preceded by $(n-1)$ 9's and followed by $(n-1)$ 0's. From this pattern, we make the guess that

$$3{,}999{,}999{,}999{,}999^2 = 15{,}999{,}999{,}999{,}992{,}000{,}000{,}000{,}001$$

This can be verified by writing the number as follows:

$3{,}999{,}999{,}999{,}999^2 = (4{,}000{,}000{,}000{,}000 - 1)^2$
$= 4{,}000{,}000{,}000{,}000^2 - 2 \cdot 4{,}000{,}000{,}000{,}000 + 1$
$= 16{,}000{,}000{,}000{,}000{,}000{,}000{,}000{,}000 - 8{,}000{,}000{,}000{,}000 + 1$
$= 15{,}999{,}999{,}999{,}992{,}000{,}000{,}000{,}001$

22. Let r be the radius of the earth in feet. Then the circumference (length of the ribbon) is $2\pi r$. When we increase the radius by 1 foot, the new radius is $r + 1$, so the new circumference is $2\pi(r+1)$. Thus you need $2\pi(r+1) - 2\pi r = 2\pi$ extra feet of ribbon.

Chapter Two
Exercises 2.1

2. $A\,(5,\,1)$ $B\,(1,\,2)$ $C\,(-2,\,6)$ $D\,(-6,\,2)$
    $E\,(-4,\,-1)$ $F\,(-2,\,0)$ $G\,(-1,\,-3)$ $H\,(2,\,-2)$

4. (a)   (b) $d = \sqrt{(2-4)^2 + (-1-3)^2}$

$$= \sqrt{(-2)^2 + (-4)^2} = \sqrt{4+16}$$
$$= \sqrt{20} = 2\sqrt{5}$$

(c)   midpoint: $\left(\frac{2+4}{2}, \frac{-1+3}{2}\right) = (3, 1)$

6. (a)   (b) $d = \sqrt{(1-(-1))^2 + (-6-(-3))^2}$

$$= \sqrt{2^2 + (-3)^2} = \sqrt{4+9} = \sqrt{13}$$

(c)   midpoint: $\left(\frac{1+(-1)}{2}, \frac{-6+(-3)}{2}\right) = \left(0, -\frac{9}{2}\right)$

8. (a)   (b) $d = \sqrt{(5-0)^2 + (0-6)^2}$

$$= \sqrt{5^2 + (-6)^2} = \sqrt{25 + 36}$$
$$= \sqrt{61}$$

(c)   midpoint: $\left(\frac{5+0}{2}, \frac{0+6}{2}\right) = \left(\frac{5}{2}, 3\right)$

10. The area of a parallelogram = *base · height*. Since two sides are parallel to the x-axis, we use the length of one of these as the *base*. Thus *base* is

$$d(A, B) = \sqrt{(1-5)^2 + (2-2)^2} = \sqrt{(-4)^2} = 4.$$

The height is the change in the y coordinates, thus, the *height* is $6 - 2 = 4$. So the area of the parallelogram is *base · height* $= 4 \cdot 4 = 16$.

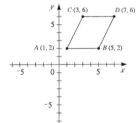

12. The point S must be located at $(0, -4)$. To find the area, we find the length of one side and square it. This gives

$$d(Q, R) = \sqrt{(-5-0)^2 + (1-6)^2} = \sqrt{(-5)^2 + (-5)^2}$$
$$= \sqrt{25 + 25} = \sqrt{50} = 5\sqrt{2}.$$

So the area is $\left(5\sqrt{2}\right)^2 = 50.$

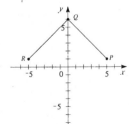

14.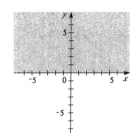

16.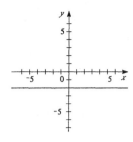

18.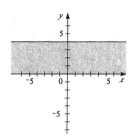

20. $xy > 0 \quad \Leftrightarrow \quad x < 0$ and $y < 0$ or $x > 0$ and $y > 0$.

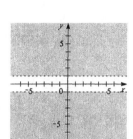

22.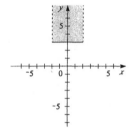

24.

26. $d(E, C) = \sqrt{(-6 - (-2))^2 + (3 - 1)^2} = \sqrt{(-4)^2 + 2^2} = \sqrt{16 + 4} = \sqrt{20}.$

   $d(E, D) = \sqrt{(3 - (-2))^2 + (0 - 1)^2} = \sqrt{5^2 + (-1)^2} = \sqrt{25 + 1} = \sqrt{26}.$

   Thus point C is closer to point E.

28. (a) The distance from $(7, 3)$ to the origin is

   $\sqrt{(7 - 0)^2 + (3 - 0)^2} = \sqrt{7^2 + 3^2} = \sqrt{49 + 9} = \sqrt{58}.$ The distance from $(3, 7)$ to the origin is $\sqrt{(3 - 0)^2 + (7 - 0)^2} = \sqrt{3^2 + 7^2} = \sqrt{9 + 49} = \sqrt{58}.$ So the points are the same distance from the origin.

   (b) The distance from (a, b) to the origin is $\sqrt{(a - 0)^2 + (b - 0)^2} = \sqrt{a^2 + b^2}.$ The distance from (b, a) to the origin is $\sqrt{(b - 0)^2 + (a - 0)^2} = \sqrt{b^2 + a^2} = \sqrt{a^2 + b^2}.$ So the points are the same distance from the origin.

30. Since the side AB is parallel to the x-axis, we use this as the *base* in the formula *Area* $= \frac{1}{2}(base \cdot height)$. The *height* is the change in the y coordinates. The *base* is $|-2 - 4| = 6$, and the *height* is $|4 - 1| = 3$. So *Area* is $\frac{1}{2}(6 \cdot 3) = 9$.

32. $d(A, B) = \sqrt{(11 - 6)^2 + (-3 - (-7))^2} = \sqrt{5^2 + 4^2} = \sqrt{25 + 16} = \sqrt{41};$

   $d(A, C) = \sqrt{(2 - 6)^2 + (-2 - (-7))^2} = \sqrt{(-4)^2 + 5^2} = \sqrt{16 + 25} = \sqrt{41};$

   $d(B, C) = \sqrt{(2 - 11)^2 + (-2 - (-3))^2} = \sqrt{(-9)^2 + 1^2} = \sqrt{81 + 1} = \sqrt{82}.$

   Since $[d(A, B)]^2 + [d(A, C)]^2 = [d(B, C)]^2$, we conclude that the triangle is a right triangle. The *Area* is $\frac{1}{2}\left(\sqrt{41} \cdot \sqrt{41}\right) = \frac{41}{2}$.

34. $d(A, B) = \sqrt{(3 - (-1))^2 + (11 - 3)^2} = \sqrt{4^2 + 8^2} = \sqrt{16 + 64} = \sqrt{80} = 4\sqrt{5}.$

   $d(B, C) = \sqrt{(5 - 3)^2 + (15 - 11)^2} = \sqrt{2^2 + 4^2} = \sqrt{4 + 16} = \sqrt{20} = 2\sqrt{5}.$

   $d(A, C) = \sqrt{(5 - (-1))^2 + (15 - 3)^2} = \sqrt{6^2 + 12^2} = \sqrt{36 + 144} = \sqrt{180} = 6\sqrt{5}.$ So

$d(A, B) + d(B, C) = d(A, C)$, and the points are collinear.

36. The midpoint of AB is $C' = \left(\dfrac{1+3}{2}, \dfrac{0+6}{2}\right) = (2, 3)$. So the length of the median CC' is

$d(C, C') = \sqrt{(2-8)^2 + (3-2)^2} = \sqrt{37}$. The midpoint of AC is $B' = \left(\dfrac{1+8}{2}, \dfrac{0+2}{2}\right)$

$= \left(\frac{9}{2}, 1\right)$. So the length of the median BB' is $d(B, B') = \sqrt{\left(\frac{9}{2} - 3\right)^2 + (1-6)^2} = \dfrac{\sqrt{109}}{2}$. The

midpoint of BC is $A' = \left(\dfrac{3+8}{2}, \dfrac{6+2}{2}\right) = \left(\dfrac{11}{2}, 4\right)$. So the length of the median AA' is

$d(A, A') = \sqrt{\left(\frac{11}{2} - 1\right)^2 + (4-0)^2} = \dfrac{\sqrt{145}}{2}$.

38. Points on a perpendicular bisector of PQ are the same distance from the points P and Q.

For point A, $d(P, A) = \sqrt{(5 - (-2))^2 + (-7 - 1)^2} =$
$\sqrt{7^2 + (-8)^2} = \sqrt{113}$, and
$d(Q, A) = \sqrt{(5 - 12)^2 + (-7 - (-1))^2} = \sqrt{(-7)^2 + (-6)^2} = \sqrt{85}$.
Since $d(P, A) \neq d(Q, A)$, point A does not lie on the perpendicular
bisector of PQ.
For point B, $d(P, B) = \sqrt{(6 - (-2))^2 + (7 - 1)^2} = \sqrt{8^2 + 6^2} = 10$,
and $d(Q, B) = \sqrt{(6 - 12)^2 + (7 - (-1))^2} = \sqrt{(-6)^2 + 8^2} = 10$.

Since $d(P, B) = d(Q, B)$, point B lies on the perpendicular bisector of PQ.

40. We solve the equation $6 = \dfrac{2+x}{2}$ to find the x coordinate of B. This gives $6 = \dfrac{2+x}{2} \quad \Leftrightarrow$

$12 = 2 + x \quad \Leftrightarrow \quad x = 10$. Likewise, $8 = \dfrac{3+y}{2} \quad \Leftrightarrow \quad 16 = 3 + y \quad \Leftrightarrow \quad y = 13$. Thus,
$B = (10, 13)$.

42. We have $M = \left(\dfrac{a+0}{2}, \dfrac{b+0}{2}\right) = \left(\dfrac{a}{2}, \dfrac{b}{2}\right)$. Thus,

$d(C, M) = \sqrt{\left(\dfrac{a}{2} - 0\right)^2 + \left(\dfrac{b}{2} - 0\right)^2} = \sqrt{\dfrac{a^2}{4} + \dfrac{b^2}{4}} = \dfrac{\sqrt{a^2 + b^2}}{2}$;

$d(A, M) = \sqrt{\left(\dfrac{a}{2} - a\right)^2 + \left(\dfrac{b}{2} - 0\right)^2} = \sqrt{\left(-\dfrac{a}{2}\right)^2 + \left(\dfrac{b}{2}\right)^2} = \sqrt{\dfrac{a^2}{4} + \dfrac{b^2}{4}} = \dfrac{\sqrt{a^2 + b^2}}{2}$;

$d(B, M) = \sqrt{\left(\dfrac{a}{2} - 0\right)^2 + \left(\dfrac{b}{2} - b\right)^2} = \sqrt{\left(\dfrac{a}{2}\right)^2 + \left(-\dfrac{b}{2}\right)^2} = \sqrt{\dfrac{a^2}{4} + \dfrac{b^2}{4}} = \dfrac{\sqrt{a^2 + b^2}}{2}$.

44. (a) The point $(3, 7)$ is reflected to the point $(-3, 7)$.

(b) The point (a, b) is reflected to the point $(-a, b)$.

(c) Since the point $(-a, b)$ is the reflection of (a, b), the point $(-4, -1)$ is the reflection of
$(4, -1)$.

(d) $A = (3, 3)$ so $A' = (-3, 3)$;
$B = (6, 1)$ so $B' = (-6, 1)$;

$C = (1, -4)$ so $C' = (-1, -4)$.

46.   We need to find a point $S(x_1, y_1)$ such that $PQRS$ is a parallelogram.
As indicated by Example 5, this will be the case if the diagonals PR and
QS bisect each other. So the midpoints of PR and QS are the same.

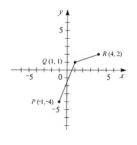

Thus $\left(\dfrac{(-1) + 4}{2}, \dfrac{(-4) + 2}{2} \right) = \left(\dfrac{x_1 + 1}{2}, \dfrac{y_1 + 1}{2} \right)$. Setting the

x-coordinates equal, we get $\dfrac{4 + (-1)}{2} = \dfrac{x_1 + 1}{2} \quad \Leftrightarrow \quad 4 - 1 = x_1 + 1$

$\Leftrightarrow \quad x_1 = 2$. Setting the y-coordinates equal, we get

$\dfrac{2 + (-4)}{2} = \dfrac{y_1 + 1}{2} \quad \Leftrightarrow \quad 2 - 4 = y_1 + 1 \quad \Leftrightarrow \quad y_1 = -3$.

Thus $S = (2, -3)$.

Exercises 2.2

2. $(1,0)$: $0 \overset{?}{=} \sqrt{(1)+1}$ $\Leftrightarrow$ $0 \overset{?}{=} \sqrt{2}$ No.
   $(0,1)$: $1 \overset{?}{=} \sqrt{(0)+1}$ $\Leftrightarrow$ $1 \overset{?}{=} \sqrt{1}$ Yes.
   $(3,2)$: $2 \overset{?}{=} \sqrt{(3)+1}$ $\Leftrightarrow$ $2 \overset{?}{=} \sqrt{4}$ Yes.
   So $(0,1)$ and $(3,2)$ are points on the graph of this equation.

4. $(1,1)$: $(1)[(1)^2+1] \overset{?}{=} 1$ $\Leftrightarrow$ $1(2) \overset{?}{=} 1$ No.
   $(1,\frac{1}{2})$: $(\frac{1}{2})[(1)^2+1] \overset{?}{=} 1$ $\Leftrightarrow$ $\frac{1}{2}(2) \overset{?}{=} 1$ Yes.
   $(-1,\frac{1}{2})$: $(\frac{1}{2})[(-1)^2+1] \overset{?}{=} 1$ $\Leftrightarrow$ $\frac{1}{2}(2) \overset{?}{=} 1$ Yes.
   So both $(1,\frac{1}{2})$ and $(-1,\frac{1}{2})$ are points on the graph of this equation.

6. $(0,1)$: $(0)^2+(1)^2-1 \overset{?}{=} 0$ $\Leftrightarrow$ $0+1-1 \overset{?}{=} 0$. Yes.
   $(\frac{1}{\sqrt{2}},\frac{1}{\sqrt{2}})$: $(\frac{1}{\sqrt{2}})^2+(\frac{1}{\sqrt{2}})^2-1 \overset{?}{=} 0$ $\Leftrightarrow$ $\frac{1}{2}+\frac{1}{2}-1 \overset{?}{=} 0$. Yes.
   $(\frac{3}{\sqrt{2}},\frac{1}{2})$: $(\frac{3}{\sqrt{2}})^2+(\frac{1}{2})^2-1 \overset{?}{=} 0$ $\Leftrightarrow$ $\frac{3}{4}+\frac{1}{4}-1 \overset{?}{=} 0$. Yes.
   So $(0,1)$, $(\frac{1}{\sqrt{2}},\frac{1}{\sqrt{2}})$ and $(\frac{3}{\sqrt{2}},\frac{1}{2})$, are all points on the graph of this equation.

8. To find x-intercepts, set $y=0$. This gives $0=x^2-5x+6$ $\Leftrightarrow 0=(x-2)(x-3)$. So $x-2=0$ and $x=2$ or $x-3=0$ and $x=3$, and the x-intercepts are at 2 and 3. To find y-intercepts, set $x=0$. This gives $y=0^2-0+6$ $\Leftrightarrow$ $y=6$, so the y-intercept is 6.

10. To find x-intercepts, set $y=0$. This gives $0-2x(0)+2x=1$ $\Leftrightarrow$ $2x=1$ $\Leftrightarrow$ $x=\frac{1}{2}$, so the x-intercept is $\frac{1}{2}$. To find y-intercepts, set $x=0$. This gives $y-2(0)y+2(0)=1$ $\Leftrightarrow$ $y=1$, so the y-intercept is 1.

12. To find x-intercepts, set $y=0$. This gives $0=\sqrt{x+1}$ $\Leftrightarrow$ $0=x+1$ $\Leftrightarrow$ $x=-1$, so the x-intercept is -1. To find y-intercepts, set $x=0$. This gives $y=\sqrt{0+1}$ $\Leftrightarrow$ $y=1$, so the y-intercept is 1.

14. To find x-intercepts, set $y=0$. This gives $x^2-x(0)+(0)=1$ $\Leftrightarrow$ $x^2=1$ $\Rightarrow$ $x=\pm 1$, so the x-intercepts are -1 and 1. To find y-intercepts, set $x=0$. This gives $y=(0)^2-(0)y+y=1$ $\Leftrightarrow$ $y=1$, so the y-intercept is 1.

16. $y=-x$

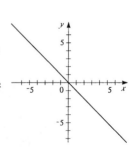

x	y
-4	4
-2	2
0	0
1	-1
2	-2
3	-3
4	-4

$y=0$ $\Leftrightarrow$ $x=0$. So the x-intercept is 0, and the y-intercept is also 0.
x-axis symmetry: $(-y)=-x$ $\Leftrightarrow$ $y=x$, which is not the same as $y=-x$, so not symmetric with respect to the x-axis.
y-axis symmetry: $y=-(-x)$ $\Leftrightarrow$ $y=x$, which is not the same as $y=-x$, so not symmetric with respect to the y-axis.
Origin symmetry: $(-y)=-(-x)$ is the same as $y=-x$, so it is symmetric with respect to the origin.

18. $y = 2x + 5$

x	y
-3	-1
-2	1
-1	3
0	5
1	7
2	9
3	11

$y = 0 \Rightarrow 0 = 2x + 5 \Leftrightarrow 2x = -5$, so the x-intercept is $-\frac{5}{2}$, and $x = 0 \Rightarrow y = 2(0) + 5 = 5$, so the y-intercept is 5.

x-axis symmetry: $(-y) = 2x + 5 \Leftrightarrow -y = 2x + 5$, which is not the same as $y = 2x + 5$, so not symmetric with respect to the x-axis.

y-axis symmetry: $y = 2(-x) + 5 \Leftrightarrow y = -2x + 5$, which is not the same as $y = 2x + 5$, so not symmetric with respect to the y-axis.

Origin symmetry: $(-y) = 2(-x) + 5 \Leftrightarrow y = -2x + 5$, which is not the same as $y = 2x + 5$, so not symmetric with respect to the origin.

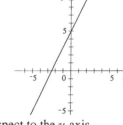

20. Solve for y: $x + y = 3 \Leftrightarrow y = -x + 3$.

x	y
-2	5
-1	4
0	3
1	2
2	1
3	0
4	-1

$y = 0 \Rightarrow 0 = -x + 3 \Leftrightarrow x = 3$, so the x-intercept is 3, and $x = 0 \Rightarrow y = -(0) + 3 = 3$, so the y-intercept is 3.

x-axis symmetry: $x + (-y) = 3 \Leftrightarrow x - y = 3$, which is not the same as $x + y = 3$, so not symmetric with respect to the x-axis.

y-axis symmetry: $(-x) + y = 5 \Leftrightarrow -x + y = 3$, which is not the same as $x + y = 3$, so not symmetric with respect to the y-axis.

Origin symmetry: $(-x) + (-y) = 3 \Leftrightarrow -x - y = 3$, which is not the same as $x + y = 3$, so not symmetric with respect to the origin.

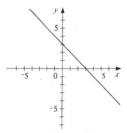

22. $y = x^2 + 2$

x	y
-3	11
-2	6
-1	3
0	2
1	3
2	6
3	11

$y = 0 \Rightarrow 0 = x^2 + 2 \Leftrightarrow -2 = x^2$, since $x^2 \geq 0$, there are no x-intercepts, and $x = 0 \Rightarrow y = (0)^2 + 2 = 2$, so the y-intercept is 2.

x-axis symmetry: $(-y) = x^2 + 2 \Leftrightarrow -y = x^2 + 2$, which is not the same, so not symmetric with respect to the x-axis.

y-axis symmetry: $y = (-x)^2 + 2 = x^2 + 2$, so it is symmetric with respect to the y-axis.

Origin symmetry: $(-y) = (-x)^2 + 2 \Leftrightarrow -y = x^2 + 2$, which is not the same, so not symmetric with respect to the origin.

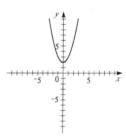

24. $8y = x^3 \Leftrightarrow y = \frac{1}{8}x^3$

x	y
-6	-27
-4	-8
-2	-1
0	0
2	1
4	8
3	27

$y = 0 \Rightarrow 0 = \frac{1}{8}x^3 \Leftrightarrow x^3 = 0 \Rightarrow x = 0$, so the x-intercept is 0, and $x = 0 \Rightarrow y = \frac{1}{8}(0)^3 = 0$, so the y-intercept is 0.

x-axis symmetry: $(-y) = \frac{1}{8}x^3$, which is not the same as $y = \frac{1}{8}x^3$, so not symmetric with respect to the x-axis.

y-axis symmetry: $y = \frac{1}{8}(-x)^3 = -\frac{1}{8}x^3$, which is not the same as $y = \frac{1}{8}x^3$, so not symmetric with respect to the y-axis.

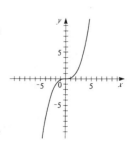

Origin symmetry: $(-y) = \frac{1}{8}(-x)^3 \quad \Leftrightarrow \quad -y = -\frac{1}{8}x^3$, which is the same as $y = \frac{1}{8}x^3$, so it is symmetric with respect to the origin.

26. $y = 9 - x^2$

x	y
-4	-7
-3	0
-2	5
-1	8
0	9
1	8
2	5
3	0
4	-7

$y = 0 \quad \Rightarrow \quad 0 = 9 - x^2 \quad \Leftrightarrow \quad x^2 = 9 \quad \Rightarrow \quad x = \pm 3$, so the x-intercepts are -3 and 3, and $x = 0 \quad \Rightarrow$ $y = 9 - (0)^2 = 9$, so the y-intercept is 9.

x-axis symmetry: $(-y) = 9 - x^2$, which is not the same as $y = 9 - x^2$, so not symmetric with respect to the x-axis.

y-axis symmetry: $y = 9 - (-x)^2 = 9 - x^2$, so it is symmetric with respect to the y-axis.

Origin symmetry: $(-y) = 9 - (-x)^2 \quad \Leftrightarrow \quad -y = 9 - x^2$, which is not the same as $y = 9 - x^2$, so not symmetric with respect to the origin.

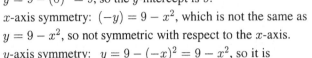

28. Solve for x in terms of y: $x + y^2 = 4 \quad \Leftrightarrow \quad x = 4 - y^2$

x	y
-12	-4
-5	-3
0	-2
3	-1
4	0
3	1
0	2
-5	3
-12	4

$y = 0 \quad \Rightarrow \quad x + 0^2 = 4 \quad \Leftrightarrow \quad x = 4$, so the x-intercept is 4, and $x = 0 \quad \Rightarrow \quad 0 + y^2 = 4 \quad \Rightarrow \quad y = \pm 2$, so the y-intercepts are -2 and 2.

x-axis symmetry: $x + (-y)^2 = 4 \quad \Leftrightarrow \quad x + y^2 = 4$, so it is symmetric with respect to the x-axis.

y-axis symmetry: $(-x) + y^2 = 4 \quad \Leftrightarrow \quad -x + y^2 = 4$, which is not the same, so not symmetric with respect to the y-axis.

Origin symmetry: $(-x) + (-y)^2 = 4 \quad \Leftrightarrow \quad -x + y^2 = 4$, which is not the same as $x + y^2 = 4$, so not symmetric with respect to the origin.

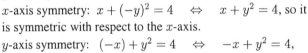

30. $x^2 + y^2 = 9$

x	y
-3	0
-2	$\pm\sqrt{5}$
-1	$\pm 2\sqrt{2}$
0	± 3
1	$\pm 2\sqrt{2}$
2	$\pm\sqrt{5}$
3	0

$y = 0 \quad \Rightarrow \quad x^2 + 0^2 = 9 \quad \Leftrightarrow \quad x = \pm 3$, so the x-intercepts are -3 and 3, and $x = 0 \quad \Rightarrow \quad 0^2 + y^2 = 9$ $\Leftrightarrow \quad y = \pm 3$, so the y-intercepts are -3 and 3.

x-axis symmetry: $x^2 + (-y)^2 = 9 \quad \Leftrightarrow$ $x^2 + y^2 = 9$, so it is symmetric with respect to the x-axis.

y-axis symmetry: $(-x)^2 + y^2 = 9 \quad \Leftrightarrow$ $x^2 + y^2 = 9$, so it is symmetric with respect to the y-axis.

Origin symmetry: $(-x)^2 + (-y)^2 = 9 \quad \Leftrightarrow$ $x^2 + y^2 = 9$, so it is symmetric with respect to the origin.

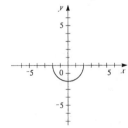

32. Since the radicand (the inside of the square root) cannot be negative, we must have $4 - x^2 \geq 0$ $\Leftrightarrow \quad x^2 \leq 4 \quad \Leftrightarrow \quad |x| \leq 2$. So $-2 \leq x \leq 2$ is the only portion of the x-axis where this equation is defined.

x	y
-2	0
-1	$-\sqrt{3}$
0	-4
1	$-\sqrt{3}$
2	0

$y = 0 \quad \Rightarrow \quad 0 = -\sqrt{4 - x^2} \quad \Leftrightarrow \quad 4 - x^2 = 0 \quad \Leftrightarrow$ $x^2 = 4 \quad \Rightarrow \quad x = \pm 2$, so the x-intercepts are -2 and 2, and $x = 0 \quad \Rightarrow \quad y = -\sqrt{4 - (0)^2} = -\sqrt{4} = -2$, so the y-intercept is -2.

x-axis symmetry: Since $y \leq 0$, this graph is not symmetric with respect to the x-axis.

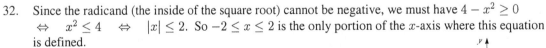

y-axis symmetry: $y = -\sqrt{4 - (-x)^2} = -\sqrt{4 - x^2}$, so it is symmetric with respect to the y-axis. Origin symmetry: Since $y \le 0$, the graph is not symmetric with respect to the origin.

34. $x = |y|$. Here we insert values of y and find the corresponding value of x.

x	y
3	-3
2	-2
1	-1
0	0
1	1
2	2
3	3

$y = 0 \Rightarrow x = |0| = 0$, so the x-intercept is 0, and $x = 0$ $\Rightarrow 0 = |y| \Leftrightarrow y = 0$, so the y-intercept is 0. x-axis symmetry: $x = |-y| = |y|$, so the graph is symmetric with respect to the x-axis. y-axis symmetry: Since $x \ge 0$, the graph is not symmetric with respect to the y-axis. Origin symmetry: Since $x \ge 0$, the graph is not symmetric with respect to the origin.

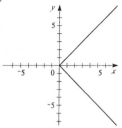

36. $y = |4 - x|$

x	y
-6	10
-4	8
-2	6
0	4
2	2
4	0
6	2
8	4
10	6

$y = 0 \Rightarrow 0 = |4 - x| \Leftrightarrow 4 - x = 0 \Rightarrow x = 4$, so the x-intercept is 4, and $x = 0 \Rightarrow y = |4 - 0| = |4| = 4$, so the y-intercept is 4. x-axis symmetry: $y = |4 - (-x)| = |4 + x|$, which is not the same as $y = |4 - x|$, so not symmetric with respect to the x-axis. y-axis symmetry: $(-y) = |4 - x| \Leftrightarrow -y = |4 - x|$, which is not the same as $y = |4 - x|$, so not symmetric with respect to the y-axis. Origin symmetry: $(-y) = |4 - (-x)| \Leftrightarrow -y = |4 + x|$, which is not the same as $y = |4 - x|$, so not symmetric with respect to the origin.

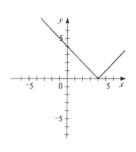

38. $y = x^3 - 1$

x	y
-3	-28
-2	-9
-1	-2
0	-1
1	1
2	7
3	26

$y = 0 \Rightarrow 0 = x^3 - 1 = (x - 1)(x^2 + x + 1)$. So $x - 1 = 0 \Leftrightarrow x = 1$, while $x^2 + x + 1 = 0$ has no real solution, so the x-intercept is 1. And $x = 0 \Rightarrow y = (0)^3 - 1 = -1$, so the y-intercept is -1. x-axis symmetry: $-y = x^3 - 1$, which is not the same as $y = x^3 - 1$, so not symmetric with respect to the x-axis. y-axis symmetry: $y = (-x)^3 - 1 = -x^3 - 1$, which is not the same as $y = x^3 - 1$, so not symmetric with respect to the y-axis.

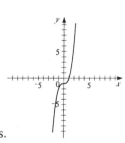

Origin symmetry: $(-y) = (-x)^3 - 1 \Leftrightarrow -y = -x^3 - 1 \Leftrightarrow y = x^3 + 1$ which is not the same. Not symmetric with respect to the origin.

40. $y = 16 - x^4$

x	y
-3	-65
-2	0
-1	15
0	16
1	15
2	0
3	-65

$y = 0 \Rightarrow 0 = 16 - x^4 \Rightarrow x^4 = 16 \Rightarrow x^2 = 4 \Rightarrow x = \pm 2$, so the x-intercepts are ± 2, and so $x = 0 \Rightarrow y = 16 - 0^4 = 16$, so the y-intercept is 16. x-axis symmetry: $(-y) = 16 - x^4 \Leftrightarrow y = -16 + x^4$, which is not the same as $y = 16 - x^4$, so not symmetric with respect to the x-axis. y-axis symmetry: $y = 16 - (-x)^4 = 16 - x^4$, so it is symmetric with respect to the y-axis.

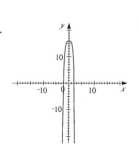

Origin symmetry: $(-y) = 16 - (-x)^4 \quad \Leftrightarrow \quad -y = 16 - x^4$, which is not the same as $y = 16 - x^4$, so not symmetric with respect to the origin.

42. x-axis symmetry: $x = (-y)^4 - (-y)^2 = y^4 - y^2$, so it is symmetric with respect to the x-axis.

     y-axis symmetry: $(-x) = y^4 - y^2$, which is not the same as $x = y^4 - y^2$, so not symmetric with respect to the y-axis.

     Origin symmetry: $(-x) = (-y)^4 - (-y)^2 \quad \Leftrightarrow \quad -x = y^4 - y^2$, which is not the same as $x = y^4 - y^2$, so not symmetric with respect to the origin.

44. x-axis symmetry: $x^4(-y)^4 + x^2(-y)^2 = 1 \quad \Leftrightarrow \quad x^4y^4 + x^2y^2 = 1$, so it is symmetric with respect to the x-axis.

     y-axis symmetry: $(-x)^4y^4 + (-x)^2y^2 = 1 \quad \Leftrightarrow x^4y^4 + \quad x^2y^2 = 1$, so it is symmetric with respect to the y-axis.

     Origin symmetry: $(-x)^4(-y)^4 + (-x)^2(-y)^2 = 1 \quad \Leftrightarrow \quad x^4y^4 + x^2y^2 = 1$, so it is symmetric with respect to the origin.

46. x-axis symmetry: $(-y) = x^2 + |x| \quad \Leftrightarrow \quad y = -x^2 - |x|$, which is not the same as $y = x^2 + |x|$, so not symmetric with respect to the x-axis.

     y-axis symmetry: $y = (-x)^2 + |-x| \quad \Leftrightarrow \quad y = x^2 + |x|$, so it is symmetric with respect to the y-axis. Note: $|-x| = |x|$

     Origin symmetry: $(-y) = (-x)^2 + |-x| \quad \Leftrightarrow \quad -y = x^2 + |x| \quad \Leftrightarrow \quad y = -x^2 - |x|$, which is not the same as $y = x^2 + |x|$, so not symmetric with respect to the origin.

48.   Symmetric with respect to the x-axis.   50.   Symmetric with respect to the origin.

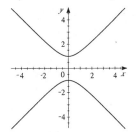   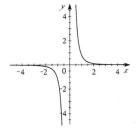

52.   Using $h = -1$, $k = -4$, and $r = 8$ we get $(x - (-1))^2 + (y - (-4))^2 = 8^2 \quad \Leftrightarrow$
     $(x + 1)^2 + (y + 4)^2 = 64$.

54.   Using $h = -1$ and $k = 5$ we get $(x - (-1))^2 + (y - 5)^2 = r^2 \quad \Leftrightarrow \quad (x + 1)^2 + (y - 5)^2 = r^2$.
     Next, using the point $(-4, -6)$, we solve for r^2. This gives $(-4 + 1)^2 + (-6 - 5)^2 = r^2 \quad \Leftrightarrow$
     $130 = r^2$. Thus, the equation of the circle is $(x + 1)^2 + (y - 5)^2 = 130$.

56.   The center is at the midpoint of the line segment, which is $\left(\frac{-1+7}{2}, \frac{3+-5}{2}\right) = (3, -1)$. The radius is one half the diameter, so $r = \frac{1}{2}\sqrt{(-1 - 7)^2 + (3 - (-5))^2} = 4\sqrt{2}$. Thus, the equation of the circle is $(x - 3)^2 + (y + 1)^2 = 32$.

58.   Since the circle with $r = 5$ lies in the first quadrant and is tangent to both the x-axis and the y-axis, the center of the circle is at $(5, 5)$. Therefore, the equation of the circle is $(x - 5)^2 + (y - 5)^2 = 25$.

60.   From the figure, the center of the circle is at $(-1, 1)$. The radius is the distance from the center to the point $(2, 0)$. Thus $r = \sqrt{(-1 - 2)^2 + (1 - 0)^2} = \sqrt{9 + 1} = \sqrt{10}$, and the equation of the circle is $(x + 1)^2 + (y - 1)^2 = 10$.

62. Completing the square gives $x^2 + y^2 - 2x - 2y = 2 \quad \Leftrightarrow \quad x^2 - 2x + \_\_ + y^2 - 2y + \_\_ = 2$
$\Leftrightarrow \quad x^2 - 2x + \left(\frac{-2}{2}\right)^2 + y^2 - 2y + \left(\frac{-2}{2}\right)^2 = 2 + \left(\frac{-2}{2}\right)^2 + \left(\frac{-2}{2}\right)^2 \quad \Leftrightarrow$
$x^2 - 2x + 1 + y^2 - 2y + 1 = 2 + 1 + 1 \quad \Leftrightarrow \quad (x-1)^2 + (y-1)^2 = 4$. Thus, the center is at $(1, 1)$, and the radius is 2.

64. Completing the square gives $x^2 + y^2 + 6y + 2 = 0 \quad \Leftrightarrow \quad x^2 + y^2 + 6y + \_\_ = -2 \quad \Leftrightarrow$
$x^2 + y^2 + 6y + \left(\frac{6}{2}\right)^2 = -2 + \left(\frac{6}{2}\right)^2 \quad \Leftrightarrow \quad x^2 + y^2 + 6y + 9 = -2 + 9 \quad \Leftrightarrow \quad x^2 + (y+3)^2 = 7$.
Thus, the center is at $(0, -3)$, and the radius is $\sqrt{7}$.

66. Completing the square gives $x^2 + y^2 + 2x + y + 1 = 0 \quad \Leftrightarrow \quad x^2 + 2x + \_\_ + y^2 + y = -1 \quad \Leftrightarrow$
$x^2 + 2x + \left(\frac{2}{2}\right)^2 + y^2 + y + \left(\frac{1}{2}\right)^2 = -1 + 1 + \left(\frac{1}{2}\right)^2 \quad \Leftrightarrow \quad x^2 + 2x + 1 + y^2 + y + \frac{1}{4} = \frac{1}{4} \quad \Leftrightarrow$
$(x+1)^2 + \left(y + \frac{1}{2}\right)^2 = \frac{1}{4}$. Thus, the center is at $\left(-1, -\frac{1}{2}\right)$, and the radius is $\frac{1}{2}$.

68. Completing the square gives $x^2 + y^2 + \frac{1}{2}x + 2y + \frac{1}{16} = 0 \quad \Leftrightarrow$
$x^2 + \frac{1}{2}x + \_\_ + y^2 + 2y + \_\_ = -\frac{1}{16} \quad \Leftrightarrow$
$x^2 + \frac{1}{2}x + \left(\frac{1/2}{2}\right)^2 + y^2 + 2y + \left(\frac{2}{2}\right)^2 = -\frac{1}{16} + \left(\frac{1/2}{2}\right)^2 + \left(\frac{2}{2}\right)^2 \quad \Leftrightarrow \quad \left(x + \frac{1}{4}\right)^2 + (y+1)^2 = 1$.
Thus, the center is at $\left(-\frac{1}{4}, -1\right)$, and the radius is 1.

70. First divide by 4, then complete the square. This gives
$4x^2 + 4y^2 + 2x = 0 \quad \Leftrightarrow \quad x^2 + y^2 + \frac{1}{2}x = 0 \quad \Leftrightarrow$
$x^2 + \frac{1}{2}x + \_\_ + y^2 = 0 \quad \Leftrightarrow \quad x^2 + \frac{1}{2}x + \left(\frac{1/2}{2}\right)^2 + y^2 = \left(\frac{1/2}{2}\right)^2 \quad \Leftrightarrow$
$\left(x + \frac{1}{4}\right)^2 + y^2 = \frac{1}{16}$.
Thus, the center is at $\left(-\frac{1}{4}, 0\right)$, and the radius is $\frac{1}{4}$.

72. $x^2 + y^2 - 16x + 12y + 200 = 0 \quad \Leftrightarrow \quad x^2 - 16x + \_\_ + y^2 + 12y + \_\_ = -200 \quad \Leftrightarrow$
$x^2 - 16x + \left(\frac{-16}{2}\right)^2 + y^2 + 12y + \left(\frac{12}{2}\right)^2 = -200 + \left(\frac{-16}{2}\right)^2 + \left(\frac{12}{2}\right)^2 \quad \Leftrightarrow$
$(x-8)^2 + (y+6)^2 = -200 + 64 + 36 = -100$. Since completing the square gives $r^2 = -100$, this is not the equation of a circle. There is no graph.

74. $\{(x, y) \mid x^2 + y^2 > 4\}$. This is the set of points outside the circle $x^2 + y^2 = 4$.

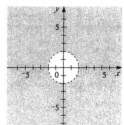

76. $\{(x, y) \mid 2x < x^2 + y^2 \le 4\}$. Completing the square gives
$2x < x^2 + y^2 \quad \Leftrightarrow \quad 0 < x^2 - 2x + \_\_ + y^2 \quad \Leftrightarrow$
$1 < x^2 + 2x + 1 + y^2 \quad \Leftrightarrow \quad 1 < (x+1)^2 + y^2$. Thus, this is the set of points outside the circle $(x+1)^2 + y^2 = 1$ and inside the circle $x^2 + y^2 = 4$.

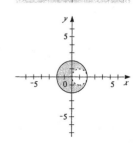

78. This is the top quarter of the circle of radius 3. Thus, the area is
$\frac{1}{4}(9\pi) = \frac{9\pi}{4}$.

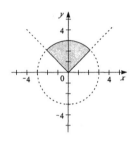

80. (a) (i) $(x - 2)^2 + (y - 1)^2 = 9$, the center is at $(2, 1)$, and the radius is 3.
$(x - 6)^2 + (y - 4)^2 = 16$, the center is at $(6, 4)$, and the radius is 4.
The distance between centers is
$$\sqrt{(2 - 6)^2 + (1 - 4)^2} = \sqrt{(-4)^2 + (-3)^2} = \sqrt{16 + 9} = \sqrt{25} = 5.$$
Since $5 < 3 + 4$, these circles intersect.

(ii) $x^2 + (y - 2)^2 = 4$, the center is at $(0, 2)$, and the radius is 2.
$(x - 5)^2 + (y - 14)^2 = 9$, the center is at $(5, 14)$, and the radius is 3.
The distance between centers is
$$\sqrt{(0 - 5)^2 + (2 - 14)^2} = \sqrt{(-5)^2 + (-12)^2} = \sqrt{25 + 144} = \sqrt{169} = 13.$$
Since $13 > 2 + 3$, these circles do not intersect.

(iii) $(x - 3)^2 + (y + 1)^2 = 1$, the center is at $(3, -1)$, and the radius is 1.
$(x - 2)^2 + (y - 2)^2 = 25$, the center is at $(2, 2)$, and the radius is 5.
The distance between centers is
$$\sqrt{(3 - 2)^2 + (-1 - 2)^2} = \sqrt{1^2 + (-3)^2} = \sqrt{1 + 9} = \sqrt{10}.$$
Since $\sqrt{10} < 1 + 5$, these circles intersect.

(b) As shown in the diagram, if two circles intersect, then the centers of the circles and one point of intersection form a triangle. So because in any triangle each side has length less than the sum of the other two, the two circles will intersect only if distance between their centers, d, is less than or equal to the sum of the radii, r_1 and r_2. That is, the circles will intersect if $d \le r_1 + r_2$.

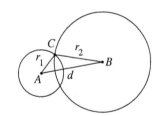

Exercises 2.3

2. $y = \sqrt{8 - x}$

    (a) $[-2, 2]$ by $[-2, 2]$

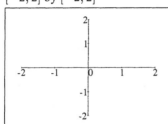

    (b) $[-4, 4]$ by $[-1, 4]$

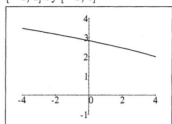

    (c) $[-10, 10]$ by $[-10, 10]$

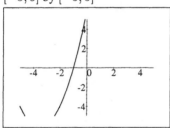

    (d) $[-20, 20]$ by $[-20, 20]$

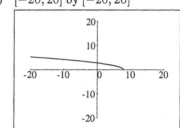

    The viewing rectangle in part (c) produces the most appropriate graph of the equation.

4. $y = x^2 + 7x + 6$

    (a) $[-5, 5]$ by $[-5, 5]$

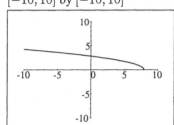

    (b) $[0, 10]$ by $[-20, 100]$

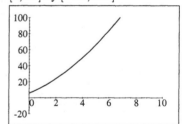

    (c) $[-15, 8]$ by $[-20, 100]$

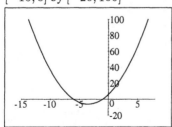

    (d) $[-10, 3]$ by $[-100, 20]$

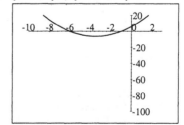

    The viewing rectangle in part (c) produces the most appropriate graph of the equation.

6. $y = 2x^2 - 1000$

(a) $[-10, 10]$ by $[-10, 10]$

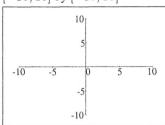

(b) $[-10, 10]$ by $[-100, 100]$

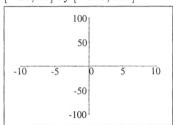

(c) $[-10, 10]$ by $[-1000, 1000]$

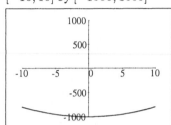

(d) $[-25, 25]$ by $[-1200, 200]$

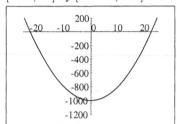

The viewing rectangle in part (d) produces the most appropriate graph of the equation.

8. $y = \sqrt{8x - x^2}$

(a) $[-4, 4]$ by $[-4, 4]$

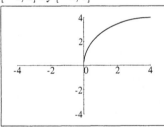

(b) $[-5, 5]$ by $[0, 100]$

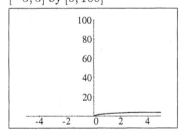

(c) $[-10, 10]$ by $[-10, 40]$

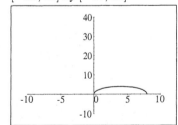

(d) $[-2, 10]$ by $[-2, 6]$

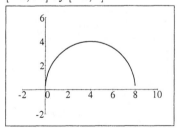

From the graphs we see that the viewing rectangle in (d) produces the most appropriate graph of the equation. Note: Squaring both sides yields the equation $y^2 = 8x - x^2 \quad \Leftrightarrow \quad (x - 4)^2 + y^2 = 16$. Since this gives a circle, the original equation represents the top half of a circle.

10. $y = -100x^2$
     $[-5, 5]$ by $[-1000, 100]$

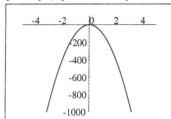

12. $y = 0.3x^2 + 1.7x - 3$
     $[-10, 5]$ by $[-10, 20]$

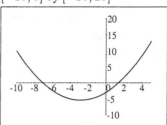

14. $y = \sqrt{12x - 17}$
     $[0, 10]$ by $[0, 20]$

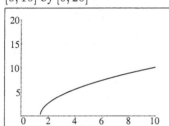

16. $y = x(x + 6)(x - 9)$
     $[-10, 10]$ by $[-250, 150]$

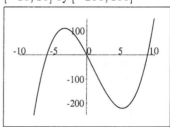

18. $y = \dfrac{x}{x^2 + 25}$
     $[-10, 10]$ by $[-0.2, 0.2]$

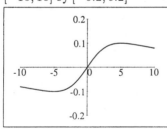

20. $y = x^3 + \dfrac{1}{x}$
     $[-5, 5]$ by $[-20, 20]$

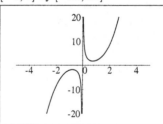

22. $y = 2x - |x^2 - 5|$
     $[-10, 10]$ by $[-10, 10]$

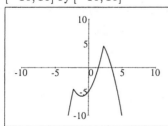

24. $y = x^{1/3} - 8x^{-1/3}$
     $[-20, 20]$ by $[-20, 20]$

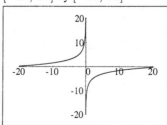

26. $(y-1)^2 + x^2 = 1 \quad \Leftrightarrow \quad (y-1)^2 = 1 - x^2$
$\Rightarrow \quad y - 1 = \pm\sqrt{1 - x^2} \quad \Leftrightarrow$
$y = 1 \pm \sqrt{1 - x^2}$. So we graph the functions
$y_1 = 1 + \sqrt{1 - x^2}$ and $y_2 = 1 - \sqrt{1 - x^2}$ in
the viewing rectangle $[-2, 2]$ by $[0, 3]$.

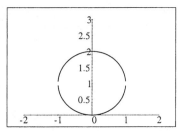

28. $y^2 - 9x^2 = 1 \quad \Leftrightarrow \quad y^2 = 1 + 9x^2 \quad \Rightarrow$
$y = \pm\sqrt{1 + 9x^2}$. So we graph the functions
$y_1 = \sqrt{1 + 9x^2}$ and $y_2 = -\sqrt{1 + 9x^2}$ in the
viewing rectangle $[-5, 5]$ by $[-5, 5]$.

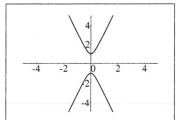

30. Although the graphs of $y = \sqrt{49 - x^2}$ and
$y = \frac{1}{5}(41 - 3x)$ appear to intersect in the viewing
rectangle $[-8, 8]$ by $[-1, 8]$, there are no points of
intersection. You can verify that this is not an
intersection by zooming in.

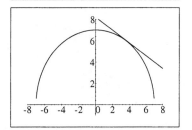

32. The graphs of $y = x^3 - 4x$ and $y = x + 5$
appears to have one point of intersection in the
viewing rectangle $[-4, 4]$ by $[-15, 15]$. The
solution is $x \approx 2.627$.

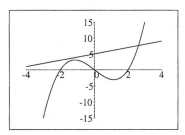

34. Calculators follow the following order of operations: exponents are applied before division and
division is applied before addition. Therefore, $Y_1 = x\verb|^|1/3$ is interpreted as
$y = (x\verb|^|1)/3 = \dfrac{x\verb|^|1}{3} = \frac{1}{3}x$, which is the equation of a line. Likewise, $Y_2 = x/x + 4$ is interpreted as
$y = (x/x) + 4 = 1 + 4 = 5$, again, the equation of a line. The student should have entered the
following information into his calculator:

$Y_1 = x\verb|^|(1/3)$

$Y_2 = x/(x + 4)$.

Exercises 2.4

2. $m = \dfrac{y_2 - y_1}{x_2 - x_1} = \dfrac{0 - (-6)}{0 - (2)} = \dfrac{6}{-2} = -3.$

4. $m = \dfrac{y_2 - y_1}{x_2 - x_1} = \dfrac{2 - (3)}{1 - (3)} = \dfrac{-1}{-2} = \dfrac{1}{2}.$

6. $m = \dfrac{y_2 - y_1}{x_2 - x_1} = \dfrac{3 - (-5)}{(-4) - (2)} = \dfrac{8}{-6}.$

8. $m = \dfrac{y_2 - y_1}{x_2 - x_1} = \dfrac{0 - (-4)}{6 - (-1)} = \dfrac{4}{7}.$

10. (a)

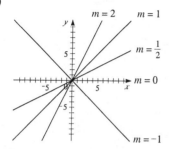

(b)

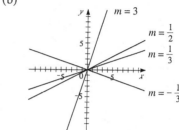

12. We find two points on the graph, $(0, 4)$ and $(-2, 0)$. So the slope is $m = \dfrac{0 - 4}{-2 - 0} = 2.$ Since the y-intercept is 4, the equation of the line is $y = mx + b = 2x + 4$, so $y = 2x + 4 \quad \Leftrightarrow \quad 2x - y + 4 = 0.$

14. We choose the two intercepts, $(0, -4)$ and $(-3, 0)$. So the slope is $m = \dfrac{0 - (-4)}{-3 - 0} = -\dfrac{4}{3}.$ Since the y-intercept is -4, the equation of the line is $y = mx + b = -\dfrac{4}{3}x - 4 \quad \Leftrightarrow \quad 4x + 3y + 12 = 0.$

16. Using the equation $y - y_1 = m(x - x_1)$, we get $y - 4 = -1(x - (-2)) \quad \Leftrightarrow \quad y - 4 = -x - 2 \quad \Leftrightarrow \quad x + y - 2 = 0.$

18. Using the equation $y - y_1 = m(x - x_1)$, we get $y - (-5) = -\dfrac{7}{2}(x - (-3)) \quad \Leftrightarrow \quad 2y + 10 = -7x - 21 \quad \Leftrightarrow \quad 7x + 2y + 31 = 0.$

20. First we find the slope, which is $m = \dfrac{y_2 - y_1}{x_2 - x_1} = \dfrac{3 - (-2)}{4 - (-1)} = \dfrac{5}{5} = 1.$ Substituting into $y - y_1 = m(x - x_1)$, we get $y - 3 = 1(x - 4) \quad \Leftrightarrow \quad y - 3 = x - 4 \quad \Leftrightarrow \quad x - y - 1 = 0.$

22. Using $y = mx + b$, we have $y = \dfrac{2}{5}x + 4 \quad \Leftrightarrow \quad 2x - 5y + 20 = 0.$

24. We are given two points, $(-8, 0)$ and $(0, 6)$. Thus, the slope is $m = \dfrac{y_2 - y_1}{x_2 - x_1} = \dfrac{6 - 0}{0 - (-8)} = \dfrac{6}{8} = \dfrac{3}{4}.$ Using the y-intercept we have $y = \dfrac{3}{4}x + 6 \quad \Leftrightarrow \quad 3x - 4y + 24 = 0.$

26. Any line parallel to the y-axis will have undefined slope and be of the form $x = a$. Since the graph of the line passes through the point $(4, 5)$, the equation of the line is $x = 4$.

28. Since $2x + 3y + 4 = 0$ $\Leftrightarrow$ $3y = -2x - 4$ $\Leftrightarrow$ $y = -\frac{2}{3}x - \frac{4}{3}$, the slope of this line is
     $m = -\frac{2}{3}$. Substituting $m = -\frac{2}{3}$ and $b = 6$ into the slope intercept formula, the line we seek is given
     by $y = -\frac{2}{3}x + 6$ $\Leftrightarrow$ $2x + 3y - 18 = 0$.

30. Any line perpendicular to $y = 1$ has undefined slope and is of the form $x = a$. Since the graph of
     the line passes through the point $(2, 6)$, the equation of the line is $x = 2$.

32. First find the slope of the line $4x - 8y = 1$. This gives $4x - 8y = 1$ $\Leftrightarrow$ $-8y = -4x + 1$ $\Leftrightarrow$
     $y = \frac{1}{2}x - \frac{1}{8}$. So the slope of the line that is perpendicular to $4x - 8y = 1$ is $m = -\frac{1}{1/2} = -2$. The
     equation of the line we seek is $y - \left(-\frac{2}{3}\right) = -2\left(x - \frac{1}{2}\right)$ $\Leftrightarrow$ $y + \frac{2}{3} = -2x + 1$ $\Leftrightarrow$
     $6x + 3y - 1 = 0$.

34. First find the slope of the line passing through $(1, 1)$ and $(5, -1)$. This gives
     $m = \dfrac{-1 - 1}{5 - 1} = \dfrac{-2}{4} = -\dfrac{1}{2}$, and so the slope of the line that is perpendicular is $m = -\dfrac{1}{-1/2} = 2$.
     Thus the equation of the line we seek is $y + 11 = 2(x + 2)$ $\Leftrightarrow$ $2x - y - 7 = 0$.

36. (a)   (b) $y - (-1) = -2(x - 4)$ $\Leftrightarrow$ $y + 1 = -2x + 8$ $\Leftrightarrow$
                                                             $2x + y - 7 = 0$.

38.   They have the same slope, so they are parallel.

40. $3x - 2y = 12$ $\Leftrightarrow$ $-2y = -3x + 12$
     $\Leftrightarrow$ $y = \frac{3}{2}x - 6$. So the slope is $\frac{3}{2}$, and the
     y-intercept is -6.

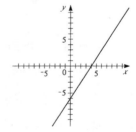

42. $2x - 5y = 0 \quad \Leftrightarrow \quad -5y = -2x \quad \Leftrightarrow$
$y = \frac{2}{5}x.$ So the slope is $\frac{2}{5}$, and the y-intercept
is 0.

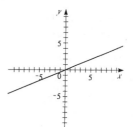

44. $-3x - 5y + 30 = 0 \quad \Leftrightarrow \quad -5y = 3x - 30$
$\Leftrightarrow \quad y = -\frac{3}{5}x + 6.$ So the slope is $-\frac{3}{5}$, and
the y-intercept is 6.

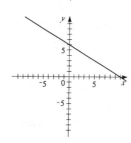

46. $4y + 8 = 0 \quad \Leftrightarrow \quad 4y = -8 \quad \Leftrightarrow \quad y = -2,$
which can also be expressed as $y = 0x - 2.$
So the slope is 0, and the y-intercept is -2.

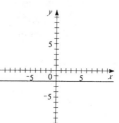

48. $x = -5$ cannot be expressed in the form
$y = mx + b.$ So the slope is undefined, and
there is no y-intercept. This is a vertical line.

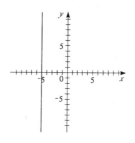

50. $4x + 5y = 10 \quad \Leftrightarrow \quad 5y = -4x + 10 \quad \Leftrightarrow$
$y = -\frac{4}{5}x + 2.$ So the slope is $-\frac{4}{5}$, and the
y-intercept is 2.

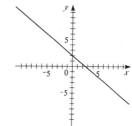

52. We first plot the points to determine the perpendicular sides. Next find
     the slopes of the sides.

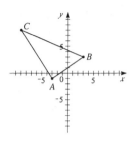

The slope of AB is $\frac{3-(-1)}{3-(-3)} = \frac{4}{6} = \frac{2}{3}$, and the slope of AC is
$\frac{8-(-1)}{-9-(-3)} = \frac{9}{-6} = -\frac{3}{2}$. Since the (slope of AB) × (slope of AC)
$= \left(\frac{2}{3}\right)\left(-\frac{3}{2}\right) = -1$, the sides are perpendicular, and ABC is a right
triangle.

54. (a) The slope of the line passing through $(1, 1)$ and $(3, 9)$ is $\frac{9-1}{3-1} = \frac{8}{2} = 4$. The slope of the line
          passing through $(1, 1)$ and $(6, 21)$ is $\frac{21-1}{6-1} = \frac{20}{5} = 4$. Since the slopes are equal, the points are
          collinear.

     (b) The slope of the line passing through $(-1, 3)$ and $(1, 7)$ is $\frac{7-3}{1-(-1)} = \frac{4}{2} = 2$. The slope of the
          line passing through $(-1, 3)$ and $(4, 15)$ is $\frac{15-3}{4-(-1)} = \frac{12}{5}$. Since the slopes are not equal, the
          points are not collinear.

56. We find the intercepts (the length of the sides). When $x = 0$, we have $2y + 3(0) - 6 = 0$ ⇔
     $2y = 6$ ⇔ $y = 3$, and when $y = 0$, we have $2(0) + 3x - 6 = 0$ ⇔ $3x = 6$ ⇔ $x = 2$.
     Thus, the area of the triangle is $\frac{1}{2}(3)(2) = 3$.

58. (a) The line tangent at $(3, -4)$ will be perpendicular to the line passing through the points $(0, 0)$
          and $(3, -4)$. The slope of this line is $\frac{-4-0}{3-0} = -\frac{4}{3}$. Thus, the slope of the tangent line will be
          $-\frac{1}{(-4/3)} = \frac{3}{4}$. Then the equation of the tangent line is $y - (-4) = \frac{3}{4}(x - 3)$ ⇔
          $4(y + 4) = 3(x - 3)$ ⇔ $3x - 4y - 25 = 0$.

     (b) Since diametrically opposite points on the circle have parallel tangent lines, the other point is
          $(-3, 4)$.

60. (a) The slope represents the increase in the average surface temperature in degrees in °C per year.
          The T-intercept is the average surface temperature in 1900, or 8.5°C.

     (b) In 2100, $T = 2100 - 1900 = 200$, so $T = 0.02(200) + 8.50 = 12.5$°C.

62. (a)   (b) The slope, -4, represents the decline in number of spaces
                                                       sold for each $1 increase in rent. The y-intercept is the
                                                       number of spaces at the flea market, 200, and the x-intercept
                                                       is the cost per space when the manager rents no spaces, $50.

64. (a)

C	$-30°$	$-20°$	$-10°$	$0°$	$10°$	$20°$	$30°$
F	$-22°$	$-4°$	$14°$	$32°$	$50°$	$68°$	$86°$

     (b) Substituting a for both F and C, we have $a = \frac{9}{5}a + 32$ ⇔ $-\frac{4}{5}a = 32$ ⇔ $a = -40°$.
          Thus both scales agree at $-40°$.

66. (a) Using t in place of x and V in place of y, we find the slope of the line using the points $(0, 4000)$ and $(4, 200)$. Thus, the slope is $m = \frac{200-4000}{4-0} = \frac{-3800}{4} = -950$. Using the V-intercept, the linear equation is $V = -950t + 4000$.

   (b) When $t = 3$, the value of the computer is given by $V = -950(3) + 4000 = 1150$.

68. (a) Using $rate = \frac{distance}{time}$, we have $rate = \dfrac{40}{50/60} = 48\,\text{mi/h}$. So $d = 48t$.

   (b)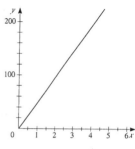

   (c) The slope of the line is 48 and it represents the speed in mi/h.

70. (a) Using the points $(100, 2200)$ and $(300, 4800)$, we find that the slope is $\frac{4800-2200}{300-100} = \frac{2600}{200} = 13$. So $y - 2200 = 13(x - 100) \quad\Leftrightarrow\quad y = 13x + 900$.

   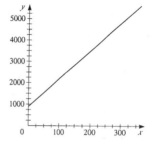

   (b) The slope of the line in part (a) is 13, and it represents the cost of producing each additional chair.

   (c) The y-intercept is 900, and it represents the fixed daily costs of operating the factory.

72. (a) Viewing rectangle $[0, 50]$ by $[0, 300]$.

   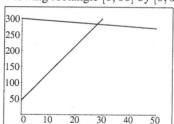

   (b) $(p, y) = (28.02, 283.26)$

   (c) Setting the y-coordinates in the two equations equal, we have $8.5p + 45 = -0.6p + 300 \quad\Leftrightarrow\quad 9.1p = 255 \quad\Rightarrow\quad p \approx 28.02$. So the price is \$28.02. Substituting p into the equation, we find $y = 8.5(28.02) + 45 = 283.17$.

74. We label the three points A, B, and C.

   If the slope of the line segment $\overline{AB}$ is equal to the slope of the line segment $\overline{BC}$, then the points A, B, and C are collinear.

   Using the distance formula, we find the distance between A and B, between B and C, and between A and C. If the sum of the two smaller distances equals the largest distance, the points A, B, and C are collinear.

   Another method: Find an equation for the line through A and B. Then check if C satisfies the equation. If so, the points are collinear.

Review Exercises for Chapter 2

2. (a)

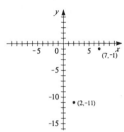

(b) The distance from P to Q is $d(P, Q) = \sqrt{(2-7)^2 + (-11+1)^2} = \sqrt{25 + 100} = \sqrt{125}$
$= 5\sqrt{5}$.

(c) The midpoint is $\left(\frac{2+7}{2}, \frac{-11-1}{2}\right) = \left(\frac{9}{2}, -6\right)$.

(d) The line has slope $m = \frac{-11+1}{2-7} = \frac{-10}{-5} = 2$, and its equation is $y + 11 = 2(x - 2)$ $\Leftrightarrow$
$y + 11 = 2x - 4$ $\Leftrightarrow$ $y = 2x - 15$.

(e) The radius of this circle was found in
part (b). It is $r = d(P, Q) = 5\sqrt{5}$. So
the equation is

$(x - 7)^2 + (y + 1)^2 = \left(5\sqrt{5}\right)^2$ $\Leftrightarrow$
$(x - 7)^2 + (y + 1)^2 = 125$.

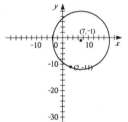

4. $\{(x, y) \mid x \geq 4 \text{ or } y \geq 2\}$

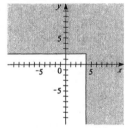

6. The circle with center at $(2, -5)$ and radius $\sqrt{2}$ has equation $(x - 2)^2 + (y + 5)^2 = \left(\sqrt{2}\right)^2$ $\Leftrightarrow$
$(x - 2)^2 + (y + 5)^2 = 2$.

8. The midpoint of segment PQ is $\left(\frac{2-1}{2}, \frac{3+8}{2}\right) = \left(\frac{1}{2}, \frac{11}{2}\right)$, and the radius is $\frac{1}{2}$ of the distance from P to
Q, or $r = \frac{1}{2} \cdot d(P, Q) = \frac{1}{2}\sqrt{(2 - (-1))^2 + (3 - 8)^2} = \frac{1}{2}\sqrt{(2 + 1)^2 + (3 - 8)^2}$ $\Leftrightarrow$
$r = \frac{1}{2}\sqrt{34}$. Thus the equation is $(x - \frac{1}{2})^2 + (y - \frac{11}{2})^2 = \frac{17}{2}$.

10. $2x^2 + 2y^2 - 2x + 8y = \frac{1}{2}$ $\Leftrightarrow$ $x^2 - x + y^2 + 4y = \frac{1}{4}$ $\Leftrightarrow$
$\left(x^2 - x + \frac{1}{4}\right) + (y^2 + 4y + 4) = \frac{1}{4} + \frac{1}{4} + 4$ $\Leftrightarrow$ $\left(x - \frac{1}{2}\right)^2 + (y + 2)^2 = \frac{9}{2}$. This is the equation
of a circle whose center is $\left(\frac{1}{2}, -2\right)$ and radius is $\frac{3}{\sqrt{2}}$.

12. $x^2 + y^2 - 6x - 10y + 34 = 0 \quad \Leftrightarrow \quad x^2 - 6x + y^2 - 10y = -34 \quad \Leftrightarrow$
$(x^2 - 6x + 9) + (y^2 - 10y + 25) = -34 + 9 + 25 \quad \Leftrightarrow \quad (x-3)^2 + (y-5)^2 = 0$. This is the
equation of the point $(3, 5)$.

14. $2x - y + 1 = 0 \quad \Leftrightarrow \quad y = 2x + 1$

x-axis symmetry: $(-y) = 2x + 1 \quad \Leftrightarrow \quad y = -2x - 1$, which is not the same as the original
equation, so not symmetric with respect to the x-axis.

y-axis symmetry: $y = 2(-x) + 1 \quad \Leftrightarrow \quad y = -2x + 1$, which is not the same as the original
equation, so not symmetric with respect to the y-axis.

Origin symmetry: $(-y) = 2(-x) + 1 \quad \Leftrightarrow \quad -y = -2x + 1 \quad \Leftrightarrow$
$y = 2x - 1$, which is not the same as the original equation,
so not symmetric with respect to the origin.

x	y
-2	-3
0	1
$-\frac{1}{2}$	0

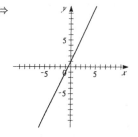

16. $x = 2y + 12 \quad \Leftrightarrow \quad 2y = x - 12 \quad \Leftrightarrow \quad y = \frac{1}{2}x - 6$

x-axis symmetry: $(-y) = \frac{1}{2}x - 6 \quad \Leftrightarrow \quad y = -\frac{1}{2}x + 6$, which is not the same as the original
equation, so not symmetric with respect to the x-axis.

y-axis symmetry: $y = \frac{1}{2}(-x) - 6 \quad \Leftrightarrow \quad y = -\frac{1}{2}x - 6$, which is not the same as the original
equation, so not symmetric with respect to the y-axis.

Origin symmetry: $(-y) = \frac{1}{2}(-x) - 6 \quad \Leftrightarrow \quad y = \frac{1}{2}x + 6$,
which is not the same as the original equation, so not
symmetric with respect to the origin.

x	y
-4	-8
0	-6
12	0

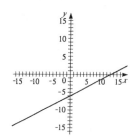

18. $\dfrac{x}{4} + \dfrac{y}{5} = 0 \quad \Leftrightarrow \quad 5x + 4y = 0$

x-axis symmetry: $5x + 4(-y) = 0 \quad \Leftrightarrow \quad 5x - 4y = 0$, which is not the same as the original
equation, so not symmetric with respect to the x-axis.

y-axis symmetry: $5(-x) + 4y = 0 \quad \Leftrightarrow \quad -5x + 4y = 0$, which is not the same as the original
equation, so not symmetric with respect to the y-axis.

Origin symmetry: $5(-x) + 4(-y) = 0 \quad \Leftrightarrow$
$-5x - 4y = 0 \quad \Leftrightarrow \quad 5x + 4y = 0$, which is the original
equation, so it is symmetric with respect to the origin.

x	y
-4	5
0	0
4	-5

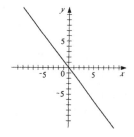

20. $8x + y^2 = 0$ $\Leftrightarrow$ $y^2 = -8x$

x-axis symmetry: $(-y)^2 = -8x$ $\Leftrightarrow$ $y^2 = -8x$, which is the same as the original equation, so it is symmetric with respect to the x-axis.

y-axis symmetry: $y^2 = -8(-x)$ $\Leftrightarrow$ $y^2 = 8x$, which is not the same as the original equation, so not symmetric with respect to the y-axis.

Origin symmetry: $(-y)^2 = -8(-x)$ $\Leftrightarrow$ $y^2 = 8x$, which is not the same as the original equation, so not symmetric with respect to the origin.

x	y
-8	± 8
-2	± 4
0	0

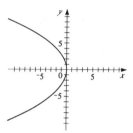

22. $y = -\sqrt{1 - x^2}$

x-axis symmetry: $(-y) = -\sqrt{1 - x^2}$ $\Leftrightarrow$ $y = \sqrt{1 - x^2}$, which is not the same as the original equation, so not symmetric with respect to the x-axis.

y-axis symmetry: $y = -\sqrt{1 - (-x)^2}$ $\Leftrightarrow$ $y = -\sqrt{1 - x^2}$, which is the same as the original equation, so it is symmetric with respect to the y-axis.

Origin symmetry: $(-y) = -\sqrt{1 - (-x)^2}$ $\Leftrightarrow$ $y = \sqrt{1 - x^2}$, which is not the same as the original equation, so not symmetric with respect to the origin.

x	y
-1	0
$\frac{1}{2}$	$-\frac{\sqrt{3}}{2}$
0	-1
1	0

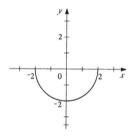

24. $y = \sqrt{5 - x}$;
Viewing rectangle $[-10, 6]$ by $[-1, 5]$.

26. $\dfrac{x^2}{4} + y^2 = 1$ $\Leftrightarrow$ $y^2 = 1 - \dfrac{x^2}{4}$ $\Rightarrow$

$y = \pm\sqrt{1 + \dfrac{x^2}{4}}$

Viewing rectangle $[-3, 3]$ by $[-2, 2]$.

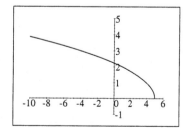

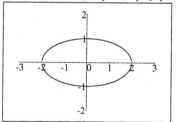

28. Using the point slope formula, the equation is $y + 3 = -\frac{1}{2}(x - 6)$ $\Leftrightarrow$ $y + 3 = -\frac{1}{2}x + 3$ $\Leftrightarrow$
$y = -\frac{1}{2}x$ or $x + 2y = 0$.

30. $x - 3y + 16 = 0 \quad \Leftrightarrow \quad -3y = -x - 16 \quad \Leftrightarrow \quad y = \frac{1}{3}x + \frac{16}{3}$. So the slope of the perpendicular line we seek is $m = -\dfrac{1}{(1/3)} = -3$. Then the equation of the perpendicular line passing through the point $(1, 7)$ is $y - 7 = -3(x - 1) \quad \Leftrightarrow \quad y = -3x + 10$ or $3x + y - 10 = 0$.

32. The line passing through the points $(-1, -3)$ and $(3, 2)$ has slope $m = \frac{2+3}{3+1} = \frac{5}{4}$. Therefore the equation of the parallel line passing through the point $(5, 2)$ is $y - 2 = \frac{5}{4}(x - 5) \quad \Leftrightarrow \quad 4y - 8 = 5x - 25 \quad \Leftrightarrow \quad 5x - 4y - 17 = 0$.

34. (a) We use the information to find two points, $(0, 60000)$ and $(3, 70500)$. Then the slope is $m = \frac{70500-60000}{3-0} = \frac{10500}{3} = 3,500$. So $s = 3,500t + 60,000$.

     (b) The slope represents her annual increase, $\$3,500$, and the s-intercept represents her initial salary, $\$60,000$.

     (c) When $t = 12$, her salary will be $s = 3,500(12) + 60,000 = 42,000 + 60,000 = \$102,000$.

36. Since the circle is tangent to the x-axis at the point $(5, 0)$ and tangent to the y-axis at the point $(0, 5)$, the center is at $(5, 5)$ and the radius is 5. Thus the equation is $(x - 5)^2 + (y - 5)^2 = 5^2 \quad \Leftrightarrow \quad (x - 5)^2 + (y - 5)^2 = 25$. The slope of the line passing through the points $(8, 1)$ and $(5, 5)$ is $m = \frac{5-1}{5-8} = \frac{4}{-3} = -\frac{4}{3}$, so the equation of the line we seek is $y - 8 = -\frac{4}{3}(x - 1) \quad \Leftrightarrow \quad 4x + 3y - 28 = 0$.

Principles of Modeling

2. (a)

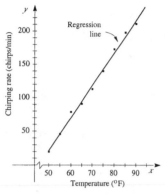

(b) Using a graphing calculator, we obtain the regression line $y = 4.857x - 220.97$.

(c) Using $x = 100°F$ in the equation $y = 4.857x - 220.97$, we get $y \approx 265$ chirps per minute.

4. (a)

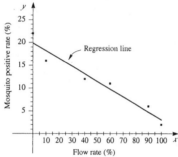

(b) Using a graphing calculator, we obtain the regression line $y = -0.168x + 19.89$.

(c) Using the regression line equation $y = -0.168x + 19.89$, we get $y \approx 8.13\%$ when $x = 70\%$.

6. (a) Let x be the education level and y be the ulcer rate. Then the scatter plot of the data is:

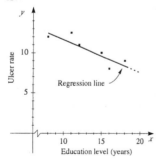

(b) Using a graphing calculator, we obtain the regression line $y = -0.413x + 15.93$.

(c) Using the regression line equation $y = -0.413x + 15.93$, we get $y = 7.67$ when $x = 20$ years.

8. (a)

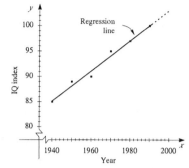

(b) Using a graphing calculator, we obtain the regression line $y = 0.297x - 491.2$.

(c) Using the regression line equation $y = 0.297x - 491.2$, we get an estimated IQ of 103.

10. (a)

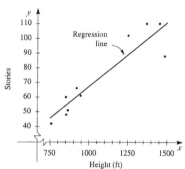

(b) Using a graphing calculator, we obtain the regression line $y = 0.0867x - 19.3$.

(c) The slope indicates the fraction of a story represented by one foot of height in the building. Since $\dfrac{1}{0.0867} \approx 12$, each story is about 12 feet.

12. (a) For the men's data the regression equation is $y = -0.181x + 65.0$. For the women's data, the regression equation is $y = -0.288x + 79.5$.

(b)

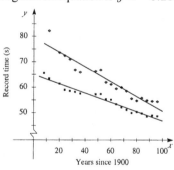

These lines predict that the women will overtake the men in this event when
$$-0.181x + 65.0 = -0.288x + 79.5 \quad \Leftrightarrow$$
$$0.107x = 14.5 \quad \Leftrightarrow \quad x = 135.5, \text{ or in } 2036.$$

14. Results will depend on student surveys in each class.

Chapter Three
Exercises 3.1

2. Algebraically: $3x + 7 = 31 \iff 3x = 24 \iff x = 8$.
    Graphically: We graph the two equations $y_1 = 3x + 7$ and
    $y_2 = 31$ in the viewing rectangle $[5, 10]$ by $[30, 32]$.
    Zooming in we see that solution is $x = 8$.

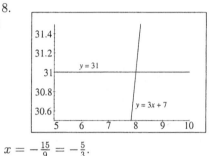

4. Algebraically: $6x + 15 = -3x \iff 15 = -9x \iff x = -\frac{15}{9} = -\frac{5}{3}$.
    Graphically: We graph the two equations $y_1 = 6x + 15$ and
    $y_2 = -3x$ in the viewing rectangle $[-5, 5]$ by $[-5, 10]$.
    Zooming in we see that solution is $x \approx -1.67$.

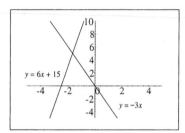

6. Algebraically: $\frac{3}{2}x + 2(x + 1) = -\frac{5}{2}x + 14 \iff \frac{3}{2}x + 2x + 2 = -\frac{5}{2}x + 14 \iff$
    $\frac{7}{2}x + 2 = -\frac{5}{2}x + 14 \iff 6x = 12 \iff x = 2$.
    Graphically: We graph the two equations $y_1 = \frac{3}{2}x + 2(x + 1)$
    and $y_2 = -\frac{5}{2}x + 14$ in the viewing rectangle $[-5, 5]$ by
    $[-5, 10]$. Zooming in we see that solution is $x = 2$.

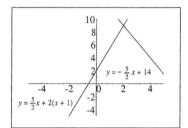

8. Algebraically: $\dfrac{4}{x + 2} - \dfrac{6}{2x} = \dfrac{5}{2x + 4} \iff 2x(x + 2)\left(\dfrac{4}{x + 2} - \dfrac{6}{2x}\right) = 2x(x + 2)\left(\dfrac{5}{2x + 4}\right)$
    $\iff 2x(4) - (x + 2)(6) = x(5) \iff 8x - 6x - 12 = 5x \iff -12 = 3x \iff$
    $-4 = x$.

    Graphically: We graph the two equations $y_1 = \dfrac{4}{x + 2} - \dfrac{6}{2x}$
    and $y_2 = \dfrac{5}{2x + 4}$ in the viewing rectangle $[-5, 5]$ by $[-10, 10]$.
    Zooming in we see that there is only one solution at $x = -4$.

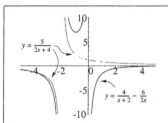

10. Algebraically: $x^3 + 16 = 0 \Leftrightarrow x^3 = -16 \Leftrightarrow x = -2\sqrt[3]{2}$.

Graphically: We graph the equation $y = x^3 + 16$ and determine where this curve intersects the x-axis. We use the viewing rectangle $[-5, 5]$ by $[-5, 5]$. Zooming in, we see that solution is $x \approx -2.52$.

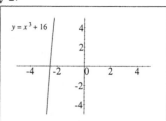

12. Algebraically: $2x^5 - 243 = 0 \Leftrightarrow 2x^5 = 243 \Leftrightarrow x^5 = \frac{243}{2} \Leftrightarrow x = \sqrt[5]{\frac{243}{2}} = \frac{3}{2}\sqrt[5]{16}$.

Graphically: We graph the equation $y = 2x^5 - 243$ and determine where this curve intersects the x-axis. We use the viewing rectangle $[-5, 10]$ by $[-5, 5]$. Zooming in, we see that solution is $x \approx 2.61$.

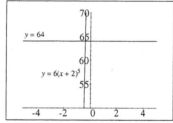

14. Algebraically: $6(x + 2)^5 = 64 \Leftrightarrow (x + 2)^5 = \frac{64}{6} = \frac{32}{3} \Leftrightarrow x + 2 = \sqrt[5]{\frac{32}{3}} = \frac{2}{3}\sqrt[5]{81} \Leftrightarrow$
$x = -2 + \frac{2}{3}\sqrt[5]{81}$.

Graphically: We graph the two equations $y_1 = 6(x + 2)^5$ and $y_2 = 64$ in the viewing rectangle $[-5, 5]$ by $[50, 70]$. Zooming in, we see that solution is $x \approx -0.39$.

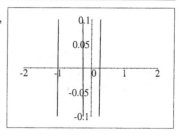

16. We graph $y = x^2 - 0.75x + 0.125$ in the viewing rectangle $[-2, 2]$ by $[-0.1, 0.1]$. The solutions are $x = 0.25$ and $x = 0.50$.

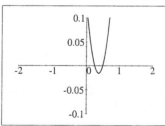

18. Since $16x^3 + 16x^2 = x + 1 \Leftrightarrow 16x^3 + 16x^2 - x - 1 = 0$, we graph $y = 16x^3 + 16x^2 - x - 1$ in the viewing rectangle $[-2, 2]$ by $[-0.1, 0.1]$. The solutions are: $x = -1.00$, $x = -0.25$, and $x = 0.25$.

20. $1 + \sqrt{x} = \sqrt{1 + x^2}$ $\Leftrightarrow$ $1 + \sqrt{x} - \sqrt{1 + x^2} = 0$. Since $\sqrt{x}$ is only defined for $x \geq 0$, we start with the viewing rectangle $[-1, 5]$ by $[-1, 1]$. In this rectangle, we see a solution at $x = 0.00$ and another one between $x = 2$ and $x = 2.5$.

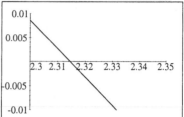

We then use the viewing rectangle $[2.3, 2.35]$ by $[-.01, .01]$, and isolate the second solution as $x \approx 2.314$.
Thus the solutions are $x = 0.00$ and $x \approx 2.31$.

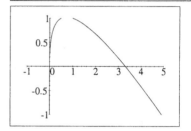

22. Since $x^{1/2}$ is only defined for $x \geq 0$, we start by graphing $y = x^{1/2} + x^{1/3} - x$ in the viewing rectangle $[-1, 5]$ by $[-1, 1]$. We see a solution at $x = 0.00$ and another one between $x = 3$ and $x = 3.5$.

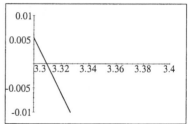

We then use the viewing rectangle $[3.3, 3.4]$ by $[-.01, .01]$, and isolate the second solution as $x \approx 3.31$.
Thus, the solutions are $x = 0$ and $x \approx 3.31$.

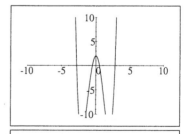

24. $x^4 - 8x^2 + 2 = 0$. We start by graphing the function $y = x^4 - 8x^2 + 2$ in the viewing rectangle $[-10, 10]$ by $[-10, 10]$. There appears to be four solutions between $x = -3$ and $x = 3$.

We then use the viewing rectangle $[-1, 5]$ by $[-1, 1]$, and zoom to find the four solutions $x \approx -2.78$, $x \approx -0.51$, . $x \approx 0.51$, and $x \approx 2.78$.

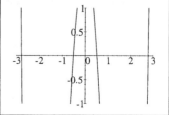

26. $x^4 = 16 - x^3$. We start by graphing the functions $y_1 = x^4$ and $y_2 = 16 - x^3$ in the viewing rectangle $[-10, 10]$ by $[-5, 40]$. There appears to be two solutions, one near $x = -2$ and another one near $x = 2$.

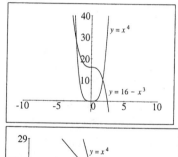

We then use the viewing rectangle $[-2.4, -2.2]$ by $[27, 29]$, and zoom in to find the solution at $x \approx -2.31$.

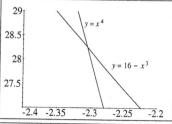

We then use the viewing rectangle $[1.7, 1.8]$ by $[9.5, 10.5]$, and zoom in to find the solution at $x \approx 1.79$.

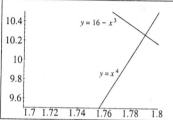

28. Answers will vary.

Exercises 3.2

2. If n is the middle integer, then $n - 1$ is the first integer, and $n + 1$ is the third integer. So the sum of the three consecutive integer is $(n - 1) + n + (n + 1) = 3n$.

4. If x dollars are invested at 7% simple interest, then each year you will receive $0.07x$ dollars in interest. After two years, this amounts to $2(0.07x) = 0.14x$ dollars.

6. Since w is the width of the rectangle, the length is $w + 5$. The perimeter is $2 \times length + 2 \times width = 2(w + 5) + 2(w) = 4w + 10$.

8. If d is the given distance, in miles, and $distance = rate \times time$, we have $time = \dfrac{distance}{rate} = \dfrac{d}{55}$.

10. If x is the gallons of pure water added, the mixture will contain 25 oz of salt and $3 + x$ gallons of water. Thus the concentration is $\dfrac{25}{3 + x}$.

12. If p is the number of pennies in the purse, then the number of nickels is $2p$, the number of dimes is $4 + 2p$, and the number of quarters is $(2p) + (4 + 2p) = 4p + 4$. Thus the value (in cents) of the change in the purse is $1 \cdot p + 5 \cdot 2p + 10 \cdot (4 + 2p) + 25 \cdot (4p + 4)$
$= p + 10p + 40 + 20p + 100p + 100 = 131p + 140$.

14. Let s be the husband's annual salary. Then her annual salary is $1.15s$. Since *husband's annual salary + wife's annual salary = total annual income*, we have $s + 1.15s = 69{,}875 \quad \Leftrightarrow \quad 2.15s = 69{,}875 \quad \Leftrightarrow \quad s = 32{,}500$. Thus the husband's annual salary is \$32,500.

16. Let a be the daughter's age now. Then her father's age now is $4a$. In 6 years, her age will $a + 6$, and her father's age will be $3(a + 6)$. But her father's age in 6 years is also $4a + 6$. So $3(a + 6) = 4a + 6 \quad \Leftrightarrow \quad 3a + 18 = 4a + 6 \quad \Leftrightarrow \quad 12 = a$. Thus the daughter is 12 years old.

18. All ages are in terms of the daughter's age 7 years ago. Let y be age of the daughter 7 years ago. Then $11y$ is the age of the movie star 7 years ago. Today, the daughter is $y + 7$, and the movie star is $11y + 7$. But the movie star is also 4 times his daughter's age today. So $4(y + 7) = 11y + 7$
$\Leftrightarrow \quad 4y + 28 = 11y + 7 \quad \Leftrightarrow \quad 21 = 7y \quad \Leftrightarrow \quad y = 3$. Thus the movie star's age today is $11(3) + 7 = 40$ years.

20. Let x be the first consecutive odd integer. Then $x + 2$, $x + 4$, and $x + 6$ are the next consecutive odd integers. So $x + (x + 2) + (x + 4) + (x + 6) = 272 \quad \Leftrightarrow \quad 4x + 12 = 272 \quad \Leftrightarrow \quad 4x = 260$
$\Leftrightarrow \quad x = 65$. Thus the consecutive odd integers are $65, 67, 69,$ and 71.

22. Let x be overtime hours Helen works. Since *gross pay = regular salary + overtime pay*, we obtain the equation $352.50 = 7.50 \times 35 + 7.50 \times 1.5 \times x \quad \Leftrightarrow \quad 352.50 = 262.50 + 11.25x \quad \Leftrightarrow$
$90 = 11.25x \quad \Leftrightarrow \quad x = \dfrac{90}{11.25} = 8$. Thus Helen worked 8 hours of overtime.

24. Let h be number of home runs Babe Ruth hit. Then $h + 31$ is the number of home runs that Hank Aaron hit. So $1459 = h + h + 31 \quad \Leftrightarrow \quad 1428 = 2h \quad \Leftrightarrow \quad h = 714$. Thus Babe Ruth hit 714 home runs.

26. Let m be amount invested at $5\frac{1}{2}\%$. Then $4000 + m$ is the total amount invested. Thus the *interest earned at $4\frac{1}{2}\% =$ interest earned at $4\% +$ the interest earned at $5\frac{1}{2}\%$.* So $0.045(4000 + m) = 0.04(4000) + 0.055m \iff 180 + 0.045m = 160 + 0.055m \iff 20 = 0.01m \iff m = \frac{20}{0.01} = 2000$. Thus $2,000 needs to be invested at $5\frac{1}{2}\%$.

28. Let p be the number of pennies. Then p is the number of nickels and p is the number of dimes. So the *value of the coins in the purse = value of the pennies + value of the nickels + value of the dimes.* Thus $1.44 = 0.01p + 0.05p + 0.10p \iff 1.44 = 0.16p \iff p = \frac{1.44}{0.16} = 9$. So the purse contains 9 pennies, 9 nickels, and 9 dimes.

30. Let x be the number of pounds of $3.00/lb. tea Then $80 - x$ is the number of pounds of $2.75/lb. tea.

	3.00 tea	2.75 tea	mixture
pounds	x	$80 - x$	80
rate (cost per pound)	3.00	2.75	2.90
value	$3.00x$	$2.75(80 - x)$	$2.90(80)$

So $3.00x + 2.75(80 - x) = 2.90(80) \iff 3.00x + 220 - 2.75x = 232 \iff 0.25x = 12 \iff x = 48$. The mixture uses 48 pounds of $3.00/lb. tea and $80 - 48 = 32$ pounds of $2.75/lb. tea.

32. Let x be initial number of fruit flies. After the first day, Dr. Plath will have $x + \frac{1}{2}x - 200$ or $\frac{3}{2}x - 200$. After the second day, Dr. Plath will have $\left(\frac{3}{2}x - 200\right) + \frac{1}{2}\left(\frac{3}{2}x - 200\right) - 200$ $= \frac{3}{2}x - 200 + \frac{3}{4}x - 100 - 200 = \frac{9}{4}x - 500$. And after the third day, Dr. Plath will have $\left[\frac{9}{4}x - 500\right] + \frac{1}{2}\left[\frac{9}{4}x - 500\right] - 200 = \frac{9}{4}x - 500 + \frac{9}{8}x - 250 - 200 = \frac{27}{8}x - 950$. So $\frac{27}{8}x - 950 = 3100 \iff \frac{27}{8}x = 4050 \iff x = 1200$. Thus Dr. Plath started with 1200 fruit flies.

34. Let x be Rochelle's final exam score. Since the final counts twice as much as a midterm, her average score will be $\dfrac{82 + 75 + 71 + 2x}{5}$. For her to get a B, her average must be at least 80. Thus we solve $80 = \dfrac{82 + 75 + 71 + 2x}{5} \iff 400 = 82 + 75 + 71 + 2x \iff 172 = 2x \iff x = 86$. For her to get an A, her average must at least 90. Thus we solve $90 = \dfrac{82 + 75 + 71 + 2x}{5} \iff 82 + 75 + 71 + 2x = 450 \iff 2x = 222 \iff x = 111$, which is impossible. So for her to get a B in the class, she must score at least 86 on the final, and Rochelle cannot get an A.

36. Let x be highway miles he drove. Then he drove $400 - x$ city miles. He used $\frac{x}{30}$ gallons in highway driving and $\frac{400-x}{25}$ gallons in the city driving. So $\dfrac{x}{30} + \dfrac{400 - x}{25} = 14 \iff 5(x) + 6(400 - x) = 150 \cdot 14 \iff 5x + 2400 - 6x = 2100 \iff -x = -300 \iff x = 300$. Hence, William drove 300 highway miles on this trip.

38. Let w be the largest weight that can be hung. In this exercise, the edge of the building acts as the fulcrum, so the 240 lb man is sitting 25 feet from the fulcrum. Then substituting the known values into the formula given in Exercise 37, we have $240(25) = 5w \iff 6000 = 5w \iff w = 1200$. Therefore, 1200 pounds is the largest weight that can be hung.

40. Let x be the length of a side of the square plot. As
     shown in the figure to the right,
     area of the plot = area of the building +
                          area of the parking lot
     So $x^2 = 60(40) + 12{,}000 = 2{,}400 + 12{,}000 = 14{,}400$
     $\Rightarrow$ $x = \pm 120$. So the plot of land is 120 feet by
     120 feet.

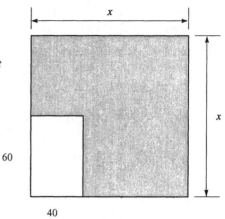

42. The figure is a trapezoid, so the *area* $= \dfrac{base_1 + base_2}{2}(height)$. Putting in the known quantities we
     have $120 = \dfrac{y + 2y}{2}(y) = \frac{3}{2}y^2$ $\Leftrightarrow$ $y^2 = 80$ $\Rightarrow$ $y = \pm\sqrt{80} = \pm 4\sqrt{5}$. Since length is
     positive, $y = 4\sqrt{5} \approx 8.94$.

44. Let x be the height of the tall tree. Here we use the property that corresponding sides in similar
     triangles are proportional. The base of the similar triangles starts at eye level of the woodcutter, 5
     feet. Thus we obtain the proportion $\dfrac{x - 5}{15} = \dfrac{150}{25}$ $\Leftrightarrow$ $25(x - 5) = 15(150)$ $\Leftrightarrow$
     $25x - 125 = 2250$ $\Leftrightarrow$ $25x = 2375$ $\Leftrightarrow$ $x = 95$. Thus the tree is 95 feet tall.

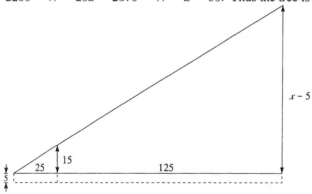

46. Let x be the number of liters of water to be boiled off. The result will contain $6 - x$ liters.

	Original	Water	Final
liters	6	$-x$	$6 - x$
concentration	120	0	200
amount	120(6)	0	200(6 − x)

So $120(6) + 0 = 200(6 - x)$ $\Leftrightarrow$ $720 = 1200 - 200x$ $\Leftrightarrow$ $200x = 480$ $\Leftrightarrow$ $x = 2.4$.
Thus 2.4 liters need to be boiled off.

48. Let x be the number of gallons of 2% bleach removed from the tank. This is also the number of gallons of pure bleach added to make the 5% mixture.

	original 2%	pure bleach	5% mixture
gallons	$100 - x$	x	100
concentration	0.02	1	0.05
bleach	$0.02(100 - x)$	$1x$	$0.05 \cdot 100$

So $0.02(100 - x) + x = 0.05 \cdot 100$ $\Leftrightarrow$ $2 - 0.02x + x = 5$ $\Leftrightarrow$ $0.98x = 3$ $\Leftrightarrow$ $x = 3.06$. Thus 3.06 gallons need to removed and replaced with pure bleach.

50. Let c be the concentration of fruit juice in the cheaper brand. The new mixture that Jill makes will consist of 650 ml of the original fruit punch and 100 ml of the cheaper fruit punch.

	Fruit Punch	Cheaper FP	mixture
ml	650	100	750
concentration	0.50	c	0.48
juice	$0.50 \cdot 650$	$100c$	$0.48 \cdot 750$

So $0.50 \cdot 650 + 100c = 0.48 \cdot 750$ $\Leftrightarrow$ $325 + 100c = 360$ $\Leftrightarrow$ $100c = 35$ $\Leftrightarrow$ $c = 0.35$. Thus the cheaper brand is only 35% fruit juice.

52. Let t be the time it takes Hilda, in minutes, to mow the lawn. Since Hilda is twice as fast as Stan, it takes Stan $2t$ minutes to mow the lawn by himself. Thus $40 \cdot \dfrac{1}{t} + 40 \cdot \dfrac{1}{2t} = 1$ $\Leftrightarrow$ $40 + 20 = t$ $\Leftrightarrow$ $t = 60$. So it would take Stan $2(60) = 120$ minutes to mow the lawn.

54. Let h be the time, in hours, to fill the swimming pool using Jim's hose alone. Since Bob's hose takes 20% less time, it uses only 80% of the time, or $0.8h$. Thus $18 \cdot \dfrac{1}{h} + 18 \cdot \dfrac{1}{0.8h} = 1$ $\Leftrightarrow$ $18 \cdot 0.8 + 18 = 0.8h$ $\Leftrightarrow$ $14.4 + 18 = 0.8h$ $\Leftrightarrow$ $32.4 = 0.8h$ $\Leftrightarrow$ $h = 40.5$. Jim's hose takes 40.5 hours, and Bob's hose takes 32.4 hours to fill the pool alone.

56. Let t be the time, in hours, it takes the marshal to catch the bank robber. Since the bank robber get a ten minute head start, his time, in hours, is $t + \frac{1}{6}$.

	Rate	Time	Distance
Bank robber	14	$t + \frac{1}{6}$	$14\left(t + \frac{1}{6}\right)$
Marshal	16	t	$16t$

When the marshal catches the bank robber, they will have traveled the same distance, so $14\left(t + \frac{1}{6}\right) = 16t$ $\Leftrightarrow$ $14t + \frac{7}{3} = 16t$ $\Leftrightarrow$ $\frac{7}{3} = 2t$ $\Leftrightarrow$ $t = \frac{7}{6}$. Thus the marshal catches the robber 1 hour 10 minutes later.

58. Let d be the distance, in miles, that he travels upstream. (This is the same as the distance downstream.) His rate upstream is $20 - 4 = 16$ knots, and his rate downstream is $20 + 4 = 24$ knots.

	Rate	Time	Distance
Upstream	16	$\frac{d}{16}$	d
Downstream	24	$\frac{d}{24}$	d

Since the total time is 6 hours, we have $6 = \dfrac{d}{16} + \dfrac{d}{24}$ $\Leftrightarrow$ $48 \cdot 6 = 3d + 2d$ $\Leftrightarrow$ $288 = 5d$ $\Leftrightarrow$ $d = 57.6$. So the captain travels 57.6 miles upstream.

60. Let r be the speed of the slower cyclist, in mi/h. Then the speed of the faster cyclist is $2r$.

	Rate	Time	Distance
Slower cyclist	r	2	$2r$
Faster cyclist	$2r$	2	$4r$

When they meet, they will have traveled a total of 90 miles, so $2r + 4r = 90$ ⇔ $6r = 90$ ⇔ $r = 15$. The speed of the slower cyclist is 15 mi/h while, the speed of the faster cyclist is $2(15) = 30$ mi/h.

62. Let x be the speed of the car in mi/h. Since a mile contains 5280 ft and an hour contains 3600 s, $1 \text{ mi/h} = \dfrac{5280 \text{ ft}}{3600 \text{sec}} = \dfrac{22}{15}$ feet/second. The truck is traveling at $50 \cdot \dfrac{22}{15} = \dfrac{220}{3}$ ft/s. So in 6 seconds, the truck travels $6 \cdot \frac{220}{3} = 440$ feet. Thus the back end of the car must travel the length of the car, the length of the truck, and the 440 feet in 6 seconds, so its speed must be $\frac{14+30+440}{6} = \frac{242}{3}$ ft/s. Converting to mi/h, we have that the speed of the car is $\frac{242}{3} \cdot \frac{15}{22} = 55$ mi/h.

64. Let y be the length of one leg of the right triangle. Then $y + 3$ is the length of the hypotenuse. Thus $y^2 + 10^2 = (y + 3)^2$ ⇔ $y^2 + 100 = y^2 + 6y + 9$ ⇔ $91 = 6y$ ⇔ $y = 15.17$. The triangle has legs 10 cm and 15.17 cm long and a hypotenuse that is 18.17 cm long.

66. Let h be the height in feet of the structure. The structure is composed of a right cylinder with radius 10 and height $\frac{2}{3}h$ and a cone with base radius 10 and height $\frac{1}{3}h$. Using the formulas for the volume of a cylinder and that of a cone, we obtain the equation $1400\pi = \pi(10)^2\left(\frac{2}{3}h\right) + \frac{1}{3}\pi(10)^2\left(\frac{1}{3}h\right)$ ⇔ $1400\pi = \frac{200\pi}{3}h + \frac{100\pi}{9}h$ ⇔ $126 = 6h + h$ (multiply both sides by $\frac{9}{100\pi}$) ⇔ $126 = 7h$ ⇔ $h = 18$. Thus the height of the structure is 18 feet.

Exercises 3.3

2. $x^2 + 2x - 8 = 0$ $\Leftrightarrow$ $(x-2)(x+4) = 0$ $\Leftrightarrow$ $x - 2 = 0$ or $x + 4$. Thus $x = 2$ or $x = -4$.

4. $x^2 + 6x + 8 = 0$ $\Leftrightarrow$ $(x+2)(x+4) = 0$ $\Leftrightarrow$ $x + 2 = 0$ or $x + 4 = 0$. Thus $x = -2$ or $x = -4$.

6. $4w^2 = 4w + 3$ $\Leftrightarrow$ $4w^2 - 4w - 3 = 0$ $\Leftrightarrow$ $(2w+1)(2w-3) = 0$ $\Leftrightarrow$ $2w + 1 = 0$ or $2w - 3 = 0$. If $2w + 1 = 0$, then $w = -\frac{1}{2}$; if $2w - 3 = 0$, then $w = \frac{3}{2}$.

8. $3x^2 + 1 = 4x$ $\Leftrightarrow$ $3x^2 - 4x + 1 = 0$ $\Leftrightarrow$ $(3x-1)(x-1) = 0$ $\Leftrightarrow$ $3x - 1 = 0$ or $x - 1 = 0$. If $3x - 1 = 0$, then $x = \frac{1}{3}$; if $x - 1 = 0$, then $x = 1$.

10. $a^2x^2 + 2ax + 1 = 0$ $\Leftrightarrow$ $(ax+1)^2 = 0$ $\Leftrightarrow$ $ax + 1 = 0$ $\Leftrightarrow$ $ax = -1$ $\Leftrightarrow$ $x = -\frac{1}{a}$.

12. $x^2 - 4x + 2 = 0$ $\Leftrightarrow$ $x^2 - 4x = -2$ $\Leftrightarrow$ $x^2 - 4x + 4 = -2 + 4$ $\Leftrightarrow$ $(x-2)^2 = 2$ $\Rightarrow$ $x - 2 = \pm\sqrt{2}$ $\Leftrightarrow$ $x = 2 \pm \sqrt{2}$.

14. $x^2 + x - \dfrac{3}{4} = 0$ $\Leftrightarrow$ $x^2 + x = \dfrac{3}{4}$ $\Leftrightarrow$ $x^2 + x + \dfrac{1}{4} = \dfrac{3}{4} + \dfrac{1}{4}$ $\Leftrightarrow$ $\left(x + \dfrac{1}{2}\right)^2 = 1$ $\Rightarrow$ $x + \frac{1}{2} = \pm 1$ $\Leftrightarrow$ $x = \frac{1}{2} \pm 1$, so $x = \frac{3}{2}$ or $x = -\frac{1}{2}$.

16. $x^2 - 18x = 19$ $\Leftrightarrow$ $x^2 - 18x + (-9)^2 = 19 + (-9)^2 = 19 + 81$ $\Leftrightarrow$ $(x-9)^2 = 100$ $\Rightarrow$ $x - 9 = \pm 10$ $\Leftrightarrow$ $x = 9 \pm 10$, so $x = -1$ or $x = 19$.

18. $3x^2 - 6x - 1 = 0$ $\Leftrightarrow$ $x^2 - 2x - \frac{1}{3} = 0$ $\Leftrightarrow$ $x^2 - 2x = \frac{1}{3}$ $\Leftrightarrow$ $x^2 - 2x + 1 = \frac{1}{3} + 1$ $\Leftrightarrow$ $(x-1)^2 = \dfrac{4}{3}$ $\Rightarrow$ $x - 1 = \pm\sqrt{\dfrac{4}{3}}$ $\Leftrightarrow$ $x = 1 \pm \dfrac{2\sqrt{3}}{3}$.

20. $x^2 = \frac{3}{4}x - \frac{1}{8}$ $\Leftrightarrow$ $x^2 - \frac{3}{4}x = -\frac{1}{8}$ $\Leftrightarrow$ $x^2 - \frac{3}{4}x + \frac{9}{64} = -\frac{1}{8} + \frac{9}{64}$ $\Leftrightarrow$ $\left(x - \frac{3}{8}\right)^2 = \frac{1}{64}$ $\Rightarrow$ $x - \frac{3}{8} = \pm\frac{1}{8}$ $\Leftrightarrow$ $x = \frac{3}{8} \pm \frac{1}{8}$, so $x = \frac{1}{2}$ or $x = \frac{1}{4}$.

22. $2x^2 + x - 3 = 0$ $\Leftrightarrow$ $(x-1)(2x+3) = 0$ $\Leftrightarrow$ $x - 1 = 0$ or $2x + 3 = 0$. If $x - 1 = 0$, then $x = 1$; if $2x + 3 = 0$, then $x = -\frac{3}{2}$.

24. $8x^2 - 6x - 9 = 0$ $\Leftrightarrow$ $(2x-3)(4x+3) = 0$ $\Leftrightarrow$ $2x - 3 = 0$ or $4x + 3 = 0$. If $2x - 3 = 0$, then $x = \frac{3}{2}$; if $4x + 3 = 0$, then $x = -\frac{3}{4}$.

26. $x^2 - 6x + 1 = 0$ $\Rightarrow$ $x = \dfrac{-b \pm \sqrt{b^2 - 4ac}}{2a} = \dfrac{-(-6) \pm \sqrt{(-6)^2 - 4(1)(1)}}{2(1)} = \dfrac{6 \pm \sqrt{36 - 4}}{2}$
$= \dfrac{6 \pm \sqrt{32}}{2} = \dfrac{6 \pm 4\sqrt{2}}{2} = 3 \pm 2\sqrt{2}$.

28. $\theta^2 - \dfrac{3}{2}\theta + \dfrac{9}{16} = 0$ $\Leftrightarrow$ $\left(\theta - \dfrac{3}{4}\right)^2 = 0$ $\Leftrightarrow$ $\theta - \dfrac{3}{4} = 0$ $\Leftrightarrow$ $\theta = \dfrac{3}{4}$

30. $0 = x^2 - 4x + 1 = 0$ $\Rightarrow$ $x = \dfrac{-b \pm \sqrt{b^2 - 4ac}}{2a} = \dfrac{-(-4) \pm \sqrt{(-4)^2 - 4(1)(1)}}{2(1)} =$
$\dfrac{4 \pm \sqrt{16 - 4}}{2} = \dfrac{4 \pm \sqrt{12}}{2} = \dfrac{4 \pm 2\sqrt{3}}{2} = 2 \pm \sqrt{3}$.

32. $w^2 = 3(w-1) \quad \Leftrightarrow \quad w^2 - 3w + 3 = 0 \quad \Rightarrow$

$w = \frac{-(-3)\pm\sqrt{(-3)^2-4(1)(3)}}{2(1)} = \frac{3\pm\sqrt{9-12}}{2} = \frac{3\pm\sqrt{-3}}{2}$. Since the discriminant is less than 0, the equation has no real solutions.

34. $\sqrt{6}x^2 + 2x - \sqrt{\dfrac{3}{2}} = 0 \quad \Rightarrow \quad x = \dfrac{-b\pm\sqrt{b^2-4ac}}{2a} = \dfrac{-(2)\pm\sqrt{(2)^2 - 4\left(\sqrt{6}\right)\left(-\sqrt{\frac{3}{2}}\right)}}{2\left(\sqrt{6}\right)} =$

$\dfrac{-2\pm\sqrt{4+12}}{2\sqrt{6}} = \dfrac{-2\pm\sqrt{16}}{2\sqrt{6}} = \dfrac{-2\pm 4}{2\sqrt{6}}$. So $x = -\dfrac{\sqrt{6}}{2}$ or $x = \dfrac{\sqrt{6}}{6}$.

36. $25x^2 + 70x + 49 = 0 \quad \Leftrightarrow \quad (5x+7)^2 = 0 \quad \Leftrightarrow \quad 5x+7 = 0 \quad \Leftrightarrow \quad 5x = -7 \quad \Leftrightarrow$
    $x = -\frac{7}{5}$.

38. $5x^2 - 7x + 5 \quad \Rightarrow \quad x = \dfrac{-b\pm\sqrt{b^2-4ac}}{2a} = \dfrac{-(-7)\pm\sqrt{(-7)^2 - 4(5)(5)}}{2(5)}$

$= \dfrac{7\pm\sqrt{49-100}}{10} = = \dfrac{7\pm\sqrt{-51}}{10}$. Since the discriminant is less than 0, the equation has no real solutions.

40. $bx^2 + 2x + \frac{1}{b} = 0 \quad \Leftrightarrow \quad b^2x^2 + 2bx + 1 = 0 \quad \Leftrightarrow \quad (bx+1)^2 = 0 \quad \Leftrightarrow \quad bx + 1 = 0 \quad \Leftrightarrow$
    $\Leftrightarrow \quad x = -\frac{1}{b}$.

42. $2.232x^2 - 4.112x = 6.219 \quad \Leftrightarrow \quad 2.232x^2 - 4.112x - 6.219 = 0 \quad \Rightarrow$

$x = \dfrac{-(-4.112)\pm\sqrt{(-4.112)^2 - 4(2.232)(-6.219)}}{2(2.232)} = \dfrac{4.112\pm\sqrt{16.908544 + 55.523232}}{4.464}$

$= \dfrac{4.112\pm\sqrt{72.431776}}{4.464} \approx \dfrac{4.112\pm 8.511}{4.464}$. Thus $x \approx \dfrac{4.112 + 8.511}{4.464} = 2.828$ or

$x \approx \dfrac{4.112 - 8.511}{4.464} = -0.985$.

44. $x^2 - 2.450x + 1.501 = 0 \quad \Rightarrow \quad x = \dfrac{-(-2.450)\pm\sqrt{(-2.450)^2 - 4(1)(1.501)}}{2(1)}$

$= \dfrac{2.450\pm\sqrt{6.0025 - 6.004}}{2} = \dfrac{2.450\pm\sqrt{-0.0015}}{2}$. Thus there are no real solutions.

46. $S = \dfrac{n(n+1)}{2} \quad \Leftrightarrow \quad 2S = n^2 + n \quad \Leftrightarrow \quad n^2 + n - 2S = 0$. Using the quadratic formula,

$n = \dfrac{-1\pm\sqrt{(1)^2 - 4(1)(-2S)}}{2(1)} = \dfrac{-1\pm\sqrt{1+8S}}{2}$.

48. $\dfrac{1}{s+a} + \dfrac{1}{s+b} = \dfrac{1}{c} \quad \Leftrightarrow \quad c(s+b) + c(s+a) = (s+a)(s+b) \quad \Leftrightarrow$
    $cs + bc + cs + ac = s^2 + as + bs + ab \quad \Leftrightarrow \quad s^2 + (a+b-2c)s + (ab - ac - bc) = 0$. Using
    the quadratic formula, $s = \dfrac{-(a+b-2c)\pm\sqrt{(a+b-2c)^2 - 4(1)(ab - ac - bc)}}{2(1)}$

$$= \frac{-(a+b-2c) \pm \sqrt{a^2+b^2+4c^2+2ab-4ac-4bc-4ab+4ac+4bc}}{2}$$

$$= \frac{-(a+b-2c) \pm \sqrt{a^2+b^2+4c^2-2ab}}{2}.$$

50. We graph the equation $y = 0.24x^2 - 4.66x - 10.51$ in the viewing rectangle $[-10, 25]$ by $[-15, 5]$. Using Zoom and/or Trace, we get the solutions $x \approx -2.04$ and $x \approx 21.46$.

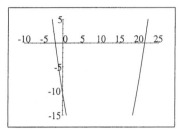

52. We graph the equation $y = 8.3x^2 + 0.4x + 1.5$ in the viewing rectangle $[-5, 5]$ by $[-5, 5]$. We can see from this viewing rectangle that the graph does not intersect the x-axis, so there are no real solutions to the equation.

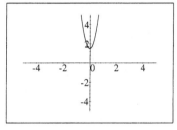

54. $x^2 = 6x - 9 \Leftrightarrow x^2 - 6x + 9$, so $D = b^2 - 4ac = (-6)^2 - 4(1)(9) = 36 - 36 = 0$. Since $D = 0$, this equation has one real solution.

56. $D = b^2 - 4ac = (2.21)^2 - 4(1)(1.21) = 4.8841 - 4.84 = 0.0441$. Since D is positive, this equation has two real solutions.

58. $D = b^2 - 4ac = (-r)^2 - 4(1)(s) = r^2 - 4s > 0$, (since $r > 2\sqrt{s}$). Since D is positive, this equation has two real solutions.

60. We want to find the values of k that make the discriminant 0. Thus $D = 36^2 - 4(k)(k) = 0 \Leftrightarrow 4k^2 = 36^2 \Rightarrow 2k = \pm 36 \Leftrightarrow k = \pm 18$.

62. Let n be one even number. Then the next even number is $n + 2$. Thus we get the equation $n^2 + (n+2)^2 = 1252 \Leftrightarrow n^2 + n^2 + 4n + 4 = 1252 \Leftrightarrow 0 = 2n^2 + 4n - 1248 = 2(n^2 + 2n - 624) = 2(n - 24)(n + 26)$. So $n = 24$ or $n = -26$. Thus the consecutive even integers are 24 and 26 or -26 and -24.

64. Let w be the width of the bedroom. Then it's length is $w + 7$. Since $area = length \times width$, we have $228 = (w+7)w = w^2 + 7w \Leftrightarrow w^2 + 7w - 228 = 0 \Leftrightarrow (w+19)(w-12) = 0 \Leftrightarrow w + 19 = 0$ or $w - 12 = 0$. Thus $w = -19$ or $w = 12$. Since the width must be positive, the width is 12 feet.

66. The shaded area can be broken down into three rectangles as shown in the on the next page. So $160 = 14x + x^2 + 13x \Leftrightarrow x^2 + 27x - 160 = 0 \Leftrightarrow (x-5)(x+32) = 0 \Leftrightarrow x - 5 = 0$ or $x + 32 = 0$. Thus $x = 5$ or $x = -32$. Since x represents a length, it must be positive, so x is 5 in.

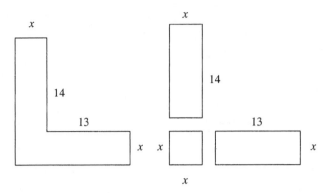

68.   Setting $P = 1250$ and solving for x, we have $1250 = \dfrac{1}{10}x(300 - x) = 30x - \dfrac{1}{10}x^2 \quad \Leftrightarrow$

$\dfrac{1}{10}x^2 - 30x + 1250 = 0$. Using quadratic formula $x = \dfrac{-(-30) \pm \sqrt{(-30)^2 - 4\left(\frac{1}{10}\right)(1250)}}{2\left(\frac{1}{10}\right)}$

$= \dfrac{30 \pm \sqrt{900 - 500}}{0.2} = \dfrac{30 \pm 20}{0.2}$. Thus $x = \dfrac{30 - 20}{0.2} = 50$ or $x = \dfrac{30 + 20}{0.2} = 250$. Since he must have

$0 \le x \le 200$, he should make 50 ovens per week.

70.   Let r be the radius of the can. Now using the formula $V = \pi r^2 h$ with $V = 40\pi$ cm^3 and $h = 10$, we
solve for r. Thus $40\pi = \pi r^2(10) \quad \Leftrightarrow \quad 4 = r^2 \quad \Rightarrow \quad r = \pm 2$. Since r represents radius, $r > 0$.
Thus $r = 2$, and the diameter is 4 cm.

72.   Let h be the height of the flagpole, in feet. Then the length of each guy wire is $h + 5$. Since the
distance between the points where the wires are fixed to the ground is equal to one guy wire, the
triangle is equilateral, and the flagpole is the perpendicular bisector of the base. Thus from the
Pythagorean Theorem, we get $\left[\frac{1}{2}(h + 5)\right]^2 + h^2 = (h + 5)^2 \quad \Leftrightarrow$

$h^2 + 10h + 25 + 4h^2 = 4h^2 + 40h + 100 \quad \Leftrightarrow \quad h^2 - 30h - 75 = 0 \quad \Rightarrow$

$h = \dfrac{-(-30) \pm \sqrt{(-30)^2 - 4(1)(-75)}}{2(1)} = \dfrac{30 \pm \sqrt{900 + 300}}{2} = \dfrac{30 \pm \sqrt{1200}}{2} = \dfrac{30 \pm 20\sqrt{3}}{2}$. Since

$h = \dfrac{30 - 20\sqrt{3}}{2} < 0$, we reject it. Thus the height is $h = \dfrac{30 + 20\sqrt{3}}{2} = 15 + 10\sqrt{3} \approx 32.32$ feet ≈ 32
feet 4 inches.

74.   (a)   Using $h_0 = 96$, half the distance is 48, so we solve the equation $48 = -16t^2 + 96 \quad \Leftrightarrow$

        $-48 = -16t^2 \quad \Leftrightarrow \quad 3 = t^2 \quad \Rightarrow \quad t = \pm\sqrt{3}$. Since $t \ge 0$, it takes $\sqrt{3} \approx 1.732$ sec.

       (b)   The ball hits the ground when $h = 0$, so we solve the equation $0 = -16t^2 + 96 \quad \Leftrightarrow$

        $16t^2 = 96 \quad \Leftrightarrow \quad t^2 = 6 \quad \Rightarrow \quad t = \pm\sqrt{6}$. Since $t \ge 0$, it takes $\sqrt{6} \approx 2.449$ sec.

76.   If the maximum height is 100 feet, then the discriminant of the equation, $16t^2 - v_o t + 100 = 0$,
must equal zero. So $0 = b^2 - 4ac = (-v_o)^2 - 4(16)(100) \quad \Leftrightarrow \quad v_o^2 = 6400 \quad \Rightarrow \quad v_o = \pm 80$.
Since $v_o = -80$ does not make sense, we must have $v_o = 80$ ft/s.

78.   Let y be the circumference of the circle, so $360 - y$ is the perimeter of the square. Use the
circumference to find the radius, r, in terms of y: $y = 2\pi r \quad \Rightarrow \quad r = \dfrac{y}{2\pi}$. Thus the area of the

circle is $\pi\left(\dfrac{y}{2\pi}\right)^2 = \dfrac{y^2}{4\pi}$. Now if the perimeter of the square is $360 - y$, the length of each side is

$\frac{1}{4}(360 - y)$, and the area of the square is $\left(\frac{360-y}{4}\right)^2$. Setting these areas equal, we obtain

$$\frac{y^2}{4\pi} = \left(\frac{360 - y}{4}\right)^2 \quad \Leftrightarrow \quad \frac{y}{2\sqrt{\pi}} = \frac{360 - y}{4} \quad \Leftrightarrow \quad 2y = 360\sqrt{\pi} - \sqrt{\pi}\,y \quad \Leftrightarrow$$

$(2 + \sqrt{\pi})y = 360\sqrt{\pi}$. Therefore, $y = \dfrac{360\sqrt{\pi}}{2 + \sqrt{\pi}} \approx 169.1$. Thus one wire is 169.1 in long and the other is 190.9 in long.

80. Let x be the rate, in mi/h, at which Kiran drove from Tortula to Cactus.

Cities	Distance	Rate	Time
Tortula $\to$ Cactus	250	x	$\dfrac{250}{x}$
Cactus $\to$ Dry Junction	360	$x + 10$	$\dfrac{360}{x + 10}$

We have used $Time = \frac{Distance}{Rate}$ to fill in the "Time" column of the table. We are given that the sum of the times is 11 hours. Thus we get the equation $\dfrac{250}{x} + \dfrac{360}{x + 10} = 11 \quad \Leftrightarrow$

$250(x + 10) + 360x = 11x(x + 10) \quad \Leftrightarrow \quad 250x + 2500 + 360x = 11x^2 + 110x \quad \Leftrightarrow$

$11x^2 - 500x - 2500 = 0 \quad \Rightarrow$

$$x = \frac{-(-500) \pm \sqrt{(-500)^2 - 4(11)(-2500)}}{2(11)} = \frac{500 \pm \sqrt{250000 + 110000}}{22} = \frac{500 \pm \sqrt{360000}}{22}$$

$= \dfrac{500 \pm 600}{22}$. Hence, Kiran drove either -4.54 mi/h (impossible) or 50 mi/h between Tortula and Cactus.

82. Let w be the uniform width of the lawn. With w cut off each end, the area of the factory is $(240 - 2w)(180 - 2w)$. Since the lawn and the factory are equal in size this area, is $\frac{1}{2} \cdot 240 \cdot 180$. So $21600 = 43200 - 480w - 360w + 4w^2 \quad \Leftrightarrow \quad 0 = 4w^2 - 840w + 21600$ $= 4(w^2 - 210w + 5400) = 4(w - 30)(w - 180) \quad \Rightarrow \quad w = 30$ or $w = 180$. Since 180 is too wide, the width of the lawn is 30 feet, and the factory is 120 by 180.

84. Let t be the time, in hours, it takes Kay to deliver all the flyers alone. Then it takes Lynn $t + 1$ hours to deliver all the flyers alone, and it takes the group $0.4t$ hours to do it together. Thus $\frac{1}{4} + \frac{1}{t} + \frac{1}{t+1} = \frac{1}{0.4t} \quad \Leftrightarrow \quad \frac{1}{4}(0.4t) + \frac{1}{t}(0.4t) + \frac{1}{t+1}(0.4t) = 1 \quad \Leftrightarrow \quad t + 4 + \frac{4t}{t+1} = 10 \quad \Leftrightarrow$ $t(t + 1) + 4(t + 1) + 4t = 10(t + 1) \quad \Leftrightarrow \quad t^2 + t + 4t + 4 + 4t = 10t + 10 \quad \Leftrightarrow$ $t^2 - t - 6 = 0 \quad \Leftrightarrow \quad (t - 3)(t + 2) = 0$. So $t = 3$ or $t = -2$. Since $t = -2$ is impossible, it takes Kay 3 hours to deliver all the flyers alone.

86. $x^2 - 9x + 20 = (x - 4)(x - 5) = 0$, so $x = 4$ or $x = 5$. The roots are 4 and 5. The product is $4 \cdot 5 = 20$, and the sum is $4 + 5 = 9$.

$x^2 - 2x - 8 = (x - 4)(x + 2) = 0$, so $x = 4$ or $x = -2$. The roots are 4 and -2. The product is $4 \cdot (-2) = -8$, and the sum is $4 + (-2) = 2$.

$x^2 + 4x + 2 = 0$, so using the quadratic formula, $x = \dfrac{-4 \pm \sqrt{4^2 - 4(1)(2)}}{2(1)} = \dfrac{-4 \pm \sqrt{8}}{2}$

$= \dfrac{-4 \pm 2\sqrt{2}}{2} = -2 \pm \sqrt{2}$. The roots are $-2 - \sqrt{2}$ and $-2 + \sqrt{2}$. The product is $(-2 - \sqrt{2}) \cdot (-2 + \sqrt{2}) = 4 - 2 = 2$, and the sum is $(-2 - \sqrt{2}) + (-2 + \sqrt{2}) = -4$.

In general, if $x = r_1$ and $x = r_2$ are roots, then
$x^2 + bx + c = (x - r_1)(x - r_2) = x^2 - r_1 x - r_2 x + r_1 r_2 = x^2 - (r_1 + r_2)x + r_1 r_2$. Equating the coefficients, we get $c = r_1 r_2$ and $b = -(r_1 + r_2)$.

Exercises 3.4

2. $\dfrac{2+4i}{3} = \dfrac{2}{3} + \dfrac{4}{3}\,i$: real part $\dfrac{2}{3}$, imaginary part $\dfrac{4}{3}$.

4. $\dfrac{1}{2}$: real part $\dfrac{1}{2}$, imaginary part 0.

6. $\dfrac{2+4i}{\sqrt{-16}} = \dfrac{2+4i}{4i} = \dfrac{2+4i}{4i}\cdot\dfrac{i}{i} = \dfrac{2i+4i^2}{4i^2} = \dfrac{-4+2i}{-4} = 1 - \dfrac{1}{2}\,i$: real part 1, imaginary part $-\dfrac{1}{2}$.

8. $(7-6i)+(-3+7i) = (7-3)+(-6+7)i = 4+i.$

10. $(-4+i)-(2-5i) = -4+i-2+5i = (-4-2)+(1+5)i = -6+6i.$

12. $6i-(4-i) = 6i-4+i = (-4)+(6+1)i = -4+7i.$

14. $2i\left(\dfrac{1}{2}-i\right) = i-2i^2 = 2+i.$

16. $(5-3i)(1+i) = 5+5i-3i-3i^2 = (5+3)+(5-3)i = 8+2i.$

18. $\left(\dfrac{2}{3}+12i\right)\left(\dfrac{1}{6}+24i\right) = \dfrac{1}{9}+16i+2i+288i^2 = \left(\dfrac{1}{9}-288\right)+(16+2)i = -\dfrac{2591}{9}+18i.$

20. $(-2+i)(3-7i) = -6+14i+3i-7i^2 = (-6+7)+(14+3)i = 1+17i.$

22. $\dfrac{1}{1+i} = \dfrac{1}{1+i}\cdot\dfrac{1-i}{1-i} = \dfrac{1-i}{1-i^2} = \dfrac{1-i}{1+1} = \dfrac{1-i}{2} = \dfrac{1}{2}-\dfrac{1}{2}\,i.$

24. $\dfrac{5-i}{3+4i} = \dfrac{5-i}{3+4i}\cdot\dfrac{3-4i}{3-4i} = \dfrac{15-20i-3i+4i^2}{9-16i^2} = \dfrac{(15-4)+(-20-3)i}{9+16} = \dfrac{11-23i}{25}$
$= \dfrac{11}{25}-\dfrac{23}{25}\,i.$

26. $\dfrac{25}{4-3i} = \dfrac{25}{4-3i}\cdot\dfrac{4+3i}{4+3i} = \dfrac{100+75i}{16-9i^2} = \dfrac{100+75i}{16+9} = \dfrac{100+75i}{25} = \dfrac{25(4+3i)}{25} = 4+3i.$

28. $(2-3i)^{-1} = \dfrac{1}{2-3i} = \dfrac{1}{2-3i}\cdot\dfrac{2+3i}{2+3i} = \dfrac{2+3i}{4-9i^2} = \dfrac{2+3i}{4+9} = \dfrac{2+3i}{13} = \dfrac{2}{13}+\dfrac{3}{13}\,i.$

30. $\dfrac{-3+5i}{15i} = \dfrac{-3+5i}{15i}\cdot\dfrac{i}{i} = \dfrac{-3i+5i^2}{15i^2} = \dfrac{-5-3i}{-15} = \dfrac{-5}{-15}+\dfrac{-3}{-15}\,i = \dfrac{1}{3}+\dfrac{1}{5}\,i.$

32. $\dfrac{(1+2i)(3-i)}{2+i} = \dfrac{3-i+6i-2i^2}{2+i} = \dfrac{5+5i}{2+i}\cdot\dfrac{2-i}{2-i} = \dfrac{10-5i+10i-5i^2}{4-i^2} =$
$\dfrac{(10+5)+(-5+10)i}{5} = \dfrac{15+5i}{5} = \dfrac{15}{5}+\dfrac{5}{5}\,i = 3+i.$

34. $(2i)^4 = 2^4\cdot i^4 = 16\cdot(1) = 16.$

36. $i^{1002} = \left(i^4\right)^{250}\cdot i^2 = (1)^{250}\cdot(-1) = -1.$

38. $\sqrt{-\dfrac{9}{4}} = \dfrac{3}{2}\,i.$

40. $\sqrt{\dfrac{1}{3}}\,\sqrt{-27} = \sqrt{\dfrac{1}{3}}\cdot 3\sqrt{3}\,i = 3i.$

42. $\dfrac{1 - \sqrt{-1}}{1 + \sqrt{-1}} = \dfrac{1 - i}{1 + i} = \dfrac{1 - i}{1 + i} \cdot \dfrac{1 - i}{1 - i} = \dfrac{1 - i - i + i^2}{1 - i^2} = \dfrac{(1 - 1) + (-1 - 1)i}{1 + 1} = \dfrac{-2i}{2} = -i.$

44. $\left(\sqrt{3} - \sqrt{-4}\right)\left(\sqrt{6} - \sqrt{-8}\right) = \left(\sqrt{3} - 2i\right)\left(\sqrt{6} - 2\sqrt{2}\,i\right)$

   $= \sqrt{18} - 2\sqrt{6}\,i - 2\sqrt{6}\,i + 4\sqrt{2}\,i^2 = \left(3\sqrt{2} - 4\sqrt{2}\right) + \left(-2\sqrt{6} - 2\sqrt{6}\right)i = -\sqrt{2} - 4\sqrt{6}\,i.$

46. $\dfrac{\sqrt{-7}\,\sqrt{-49}}{\sqrt{28}} = \dfrac{\left(\sqrt{7}\,i\right)(7i)}{2\sqrt{7}} = \dfrac{7i^2}{2} = \dfrac{-7}{2}.$

48. $9x^2 + 4 = 0 \quad \Leftrightarrow \quad 9x^2 = -4 \quad \Leftrightarrow \quad x^2 = -\dfrac{4}{9} \quad \Rightarrow \quad x = \pm\dfrac{2}{3}\,i.$

50. $x^2 + 2x + 2 = 0 \quad \Rightarrow \quad x = \dfrac{-(2) \pm \sqrt{(2)^2 - 4(1)(2)}}{2(1)} = \dfrac{-2 \pm \sqrt{4 - 8}}{2} = \dfrac{-2 \pm \sqrt{-4}}{2} =$

   $\dfrac{-2 \pm 2i}{2} = -1 \pm i.$

52. $x^2 - 3x + 3 = 0 \quad \Rightarrow \quad x = \dfrac{-(-3) \pm \sqrt{(-3)^2 - 4(1)(3)}}{2(1)} = \dfrac{3 \pm \sqrt{9 - 12}}{2} = \dfrac{3 \pm \sqrt{-3}}{2} =$

   $\dfrac{3 \pm \sqrt{3}\,i}{2} = \dfrac{3}{2} \pm \dfrac{\sqrt{3}}{2}\,i.$

54. $2x^2 + 3 = 2x \quad \Leftrightarrow \quad 2x^2 - 2x + 3 = 0 \quad \Rightarrow \quad x = \dfrac{-(-2) \pm \sqrt{(-2)^2 - 4(2)(3)}}{2(2)}$

   $= \dfrac{2 \pm \sqrt{4 - 24}}{4} = \dfrac{2 \pm \sqrt{-20}}{4} = \dfrac{2 \pm 2\sqrt{5}\,i}{4} = \dfrac{1}{2} \pm \dfrac{\sqrt{5}}{2}\,i.$

56. $z + 4 + \dfrac{12}{z} = 0 \quad \Leftrightarrow \quad z^2 + 4z + 12 = 0 \quad \Rightarrow \quad z = \dfrac{-(4) \pm \sqrt{(4)^2 - 4(1)(12)}}{2(1)}$

   $= \dfrac{-4 \pm \sqrt{16 - 48}}{2} = \dfrac{-4 \pm \sqrt{-32}}{2} = \dfrac{-4 \pm 4\sqrt{2}\,i}{2} = -2 \pm 2\sqrt{2}\,i.$

58. $4x^2 - 16x + 19 = 0 \quad \Rightarrow \quad x = \dfrac{-(-16) \pm \sqrt{(-16)^2 - 4(4)(19)}}{2(4)} = \dfrac{16 \pm \sqrt{256 - 304}}{8}$

   $= \dfrac{16 \pm \sqrt{-48}}{8} = \dfrac{16 \pm 4\sqrt{3}\,i}{8} = \dfrac{16}{8} \pm \dfrac{4\sqrt{3}}{8}\,i = 2 \pm \dfrac{\sqrt{3}}{2}\,i.$

60. $x^2 + \tfrac{1}{2}x + 1 = 0 \quad \Rightarrow \quad x = \dfrac{-\left(\tfrac{1}{2}\right) \pm \sqrt{\left(\tfrac{1}{2}\right)^2 - 4(1)(1)}}{2(1)} = \dfrac{-\tfrac{1}{2} \pm \sqrt{\tfrac{1}{4} - 4}}{2} = \dfrac{-\tfrac{1}{2} \pm \sqrt{-\tfrac{15}{4}}}{2}$

   $= \dfrac{-\tfrac{1}{2} \pm \tfrac{1}{2}\sqrt{15}\,i}{2} = -\dfrac{1}{4} \pm \dfrac{\sqrt{15}}{4}\,i.$

62. LHS $= \overline{zw} = \overline{(a + bi)(c + di)} = \overline{ac + adi + bci + bd\,i^2} = \overline{(ac - bd) + (ad + bc)\,i} = $
   $(ac - bd) - (ad + bc)\,i.$

   RHS $= \bar{z} \cdot \bar{w} = \overline{a + bi} \cdot \overline{c + di} = (a - bi)(c - di) = ac - adi - bci + bd\,i^2$
   $= (ac - bd) - (ad + bc)\,i.$

Since LHS = RHS, this proves the statement.

64. $\bar{\bar{z}} = \overline{\overline{a+bi}} = \overline{a-bi} = a+bi = z.$

66. $z - \bar{z} = (a+bi) - \overline{(a+bi)} = a+bi - (a-bi) = a+bi-a+bi = 2bi$, which is a pure imaginary number.

68. Suppose $z = \bar{z}$. Then we have $(a+bi) = \overline{(a+bi)}$ $\Rightarrow$ $a+bi = a-bi$ $\Rightarrow$ $0 = -2bi$
     $\Rightarrow$ $b = 0$, so z is real. Now if z is real, then $z = a + 0i$ (where a is real). Since $\bar{z} = a - 0i$, we
     have $z = \bar{z}$.

70. $\begin{aligned} i &= i \\ i^2 &= -1 \\ i^3 &= -i \\ i^4 &= 1 \end{aligned}$
     $\qquad \begin{aligned} i^5 &= i^4 \cdot i = i \\ i^6 &= i^4 \cdot i^2 = -1 \\ i^7 &= i^4 \cdot i^3 = -i \\ i^8 &= i^4 \cdot i^4 = 1 \end{aligned}$
     $\qquad \begin{aligned} i^9 &= i^8 \cdot i = i \\ i^{10} &= i^8 \cdot i^2 = -1 \\ i^{11} &= i^8 \cdot i^3 = -i \\ i^{12} &= i^8 \cdot i^4 = 1 \end{aligned}$

     Because $i^4 = 1$, we have $i^n = i^r$, where r is the remainder when n is divided by 4, that is,
     $n = 4 \cdot k + r$, where k is an integer and $0 \le r < 4$.
     Since $4446 = 4 \cdot 1111 + 2$, we must have $i^{4446} = i^2 = -1$.

Exercises 3.5

2. $x^5 = 64x^2$ $\Leftrightarrow$ $0 = x^5 - 64x^2 = x^2(x^3 - 64)$ $\Leftrightarrow$ $x^2 = 0$ or $x^3 - 64 = 0$. If $x^2 = 0$, then $x = 0$. If $x^3 - 64 = 0$, then $x^3 = 64$ $\Leftrightarrow$ $x = 4$. The solutions are 0 and 4.

4. $0 = x^6 - 16x^2 = x^2(x^4 - 16) = x^2(x^2 + 4)(x^2 - 4) = x^2(x^2 + 4)(x - 2)(x + 2)$. Since $x^2 + 4 = 0$ has no real solution, thus either $x^2 = 0$, so $x = 0$, or $x = 2$, or $x = -2$. The solutions are 0, 2, and -2.

6. $0 = x^4 - x^3 - 2x^2 = x^2(x^2 - x - 2) = x^2(x - 2)(x + 1)$. Thus either $x^2 = 0$, so $x = 0$,or $x = 2$, or $x = -1$. The solutions are $0, 2$, and -1.

8. $0 = (x - 2)^5 - 9(x - 2)^3 = (x - 2)^3[(x - 2)^2 - 9] = (x - 2)^3[(x - 2) - 3][(x - 2) + 3]$ $= (x - 2)^3(x - 5)(x + 1)$. Thus either $x = 2$,or $x = 5$, or $x = -1$. The solutions are $2, 5$, and -1.

10. $0 = 2x^3 + x^2 - 18x - 9 = x^2(2x + 1) - 9(2x + 1) = (2x + 1)(x^2 - 9)$ $= (2x + 1)(x - 3)(x + 3)$. The solutions are $-\frac{1}{2}$, 3, and -3.

12. $7x^3 - x + 1 = x^3 + 3x^2 + x$ $\Leftrightarrow$ $0 = 6x^3 - 3x^2 - 2x + 1 = 3x^2(2x - 3) - (2x - 3)$ $= (2x - 3)(3x^2 - 1)$ $\Leftrightarrow$ $2x - 3 = 0$ or $3x^2 - 1 = 0$. If $2x - 3 = 0$, then $x = \frac{3}{2}$. If $3x^2 - 1 = 0$, then $3x^2 = 1$ $\Leftrightarrow$ $x^2 = \frac{1}{3}$ $\Rightarrow$ $x = \pm\sqrt{\frac{1}{3}}$. The solutions are $\frac{3}{2}$ and $\pm\sqrt{\frac{1}{3}}$.

14. $\dfrac{10}{x} - \dfrac{12}{x - 3} + 4 = 0$ $\Leftrightarrow$ $x(x - 3)\left(\dfrac{10}{x} - \dfrac{12}{x - 3} + 4\right) = 0$ $\Leftrightarrow$ $(x - 3)10 - 12x + 4x(x - 3) = 0$ $\Leftrightarrow$ $10x - 30 - 12x + 4x^2 - 12x = 0$ $\Leftrightarrow$ $4x^2 - 14x - 30 = 0$. Using the quadratic formula, we have $x = \dfrac{-(-14)\pm\sqrt{(-14)^2 - 4(4)(30)}}{2(4)} = \dfrac{14\pm\sqrt{196 - 480}}{8} = \dfrac{14\pm\sqrt{-284}}{8}$. Since the radicand is negative, there are no real solutions.

16. $1 + \dfrac{2x}{(x + 3)(x + 4)} = \dfrac{2}{x + 3} + \dfrac{4}{x + 4}$ $\Rightarrow$ $(x + 3)(x + 4) + 2x = 2(x + 4) + 4(x + 3)$ $\Leftrightarrow$ $x^2 + 7x + 12 + 2x = 2x + 8 + 4x + 12$ $\Leftrightarrow$ $x^2 + 3x - 8 = 0$. Using the quadratic formula, we have $x = \dfrac{-(3)\pm\sqrt{(3)^2 - 4(1)(-8)}}{2(1)} = \dfrac{-3\pm\sqrt{9 + 32}}{2} = \dfrac{-3\pm\sqrt{41}}{2}$. The solutions are $\dfrac{-3\pm\sqrt{41}}{2}$.

18. $\dfrac{x}{2x + 7} - \dfrac{x + 1}{x + 3} = 1$ $\Leftrightarrow$ $x(x + 3) - (x + 1)(2x + 7) = (2x + 7)(x + 3)$ $\Leftrightarrow$ $x^2 + 3x - 2x^2 - 9x - 7 = 2x^2 + 13x + 21$ $\Leftrightarrow$ $3x^2 + 19x + 28 = 0$ $\Leftrightarrow$ $(3x + 7)(x + 4) = 0$. Thus either $3x + 7 = 0$, so $x = -\frac{7}{3}$, or $x = -4$. The solutions are $-\frac{7}{3}$ and -4.

20. $\dfrac{x + \frac{2}{x}}{3 + \frac{4}{x}} = 5x$ $\Rightarrow$ $\left(\dfrac{x + \frac{2}{x}}{3 + \frac{4}{x}}\right) \cdot \dfrac{x}{x} = \dfrac{x^2 + 2}{3x + 4} = 5x$ $\Rightarrow$ $x^2 + 2 = 5x(3x + 4)$ $\Leftrightarrow$ $x^2 + 2 = 15x^2 + 20x$ $\Leftrightarrow$ $0 = 14x^2 + 20x - 2$ $\Rightarrow$ $x = \dfrac{-(20)\pm\sqrt{(20)^2 - 4(14)(-2)}}{2(14)}$ $= \dfrac{-20\pm\sqrt{400 + 112}}{28} = \dfrac{-20\pm\sqrt{512}}{28} = \dfrac{-20\pm16\sqrt{2}}{28} = \dfrac{-5\pm4\sqrt{2}}{7}$. The solutions are $\dfrac{-5\pm4\sqrt{2}}{7}$.

22. Let $w = \dfrac{x+1}{x}$. Then $0 = \left(\dfrac{x+1}{x}\right)^2 + 4\left(\dfrac{x+1}{x}\right) + 3$ becomes

$0 = w^2 + 4w + 3 = (w+1)(w+3)$. Now if $w+1 = 0$, then $\dfrac{x+1}{x} + 1 = 0 \quad \Leftrightarrow \quad \dfrac{x+1}{x} = -1$

$\Leftrightarrow \quad x+1 = -x \quad \Leftrightarrow \quad x = -\frac{1}{2}$, and if $w+3 = 0$, then $\dfrac{x+1}{x} + 3 = 0 \quad \Leftrightarrow \quad \dfrac{x+1}{x} = -3$

$\Leftrightarrow \quad x+1 = -3x \quad \Leftrightarrow \quad x = -\frac{1}{4}$. The solutions are $-\frac{1}{2}$ and $-\frac{1}{4}$.

24. Let $w = \dfrac{x}{x+2}$. Then $\left(\dfrac{x}{x+2}\right)^2 = \dfrac{4x}{x+2} - 4$ becomes $w^2 = 4w - 4 \quad \Leftrightarrow$

$0 = w^2 - 4w + 4 = (w-2)^2$. Now if $w - 2 = 0$, then $\dfrac{x}{x+2} - 2 = 0 \quad \Leftrightarrow \quad \dfrac{x}{x+2} = 2 \quad \Leftrightarrow$

$x = 2x + 4 \quad \Leftrightarrow \quad x = -4$. The solution is -4.

26. $0 = x^4 - 5x^2 + 4 = (x^2 - 4)(x^2 - 1) = (x-2)(x+2)(x-1)(x+1)$. So $x = 2$, $x = -2$, or $x = 1$, or $x = -1$. The solutions are -2, 2, -1, and 1.

28. $0 = x^6 - 2x^3 - 3 = (x^3 - 3)(x^3 + 1)$. If $x^3 - 3 = 0$, then $x^3 = 3 \quad \Leftrightarrow \quad x = \sqrt[3]{3}$, or if $x^3 = -1$ $\Leftrightarrow \quad x = -1$. Thus $x = \sqrt[3]{3}$ or $x = -1$. The solutions are $\sqrt[3]{3}$ and -1.

30. Let $u = \sqrt[4]{x}$; then $0 = \sqrt{x} - 3\sqrt[4]{x} - 4 = u^2 - 3u - 4 = (u-4)(u+1)$. So $u - 4 = \sqrt[4]{x} - 4 = 0 \quad \Leftrightarrow \quad \sqrt[4]{x} = 4 \quad \Rightarrow \quad x = 4^4 = 256$, or $u + 1 = \sqrt[4]{x} + 1 = 0 \quad \Leftrightarrow$ $\sqrt[4]{x} = -1$. However, $\sqrt[4]{x}$ is the positive fourth root, so this cannot equal -1. The only solution is 256.

32. $x^{1/2} + 3x^{-1/2} = 10x^{-3/2} \quad \Leftrightarrow \quad 0 = x^{1/2} + 3x^{-1/2} - 10x^{-3/2} = x^{-3/2}(x^2 + 3x - 10)$ $= x^{-3/2}(x - 2)(x + 5)$. Now $x^{-3/2}$ never equals 0, and no solution can be negative, because we cannot take the $\frac{1}{2}$ power of a negative number. Thus 2 is the only solution.

34. Let $u = \sqrt{x}$. Then $0 = x - 5\sqrt{x} + 6$ becomes $u^2 - 5u + 6 = (u - 3)(u - 2) = 0$. If $u - 3 = 0$, then $\sqrt{x} - 3 = 0 \quad \Leftrightarrow \quad \sqrt{x} = 3 \quad \Rightarrow \quad x = 9$. If $u - 2 = 0$, then $\sqrt{x} - 2 = 0 \quad \Leftrightarrow$ $\sqrt{x} = 2 \quad \Rightarrow \quad x = 4$. The solutions are 9 and 4.

36. $0 = 4x^{-4} - 16x^{-2} + 4$. Multiplying by $\dfrac{x^4}{4}$ we get, $0 = 1 - 4x^2 + x^4$. Substituting $u = x^2$, we get

$0 = 1 - 4u + u^2$, and using the quadratic formula, we get $u = \dfrac{-(-4) \pm \sqrt{(-4)^2 - 4(1)(1)}}{2(1)}$

$= \dfrac{4 \pm \sqrt{16 - 4}}{2} = \dfrac{4 \pm \sqrt{12}}{2} = \dfrac{4 \pm 2\sqrt{3}}{2} = 2 \pm \sqrt{3}$. Substituting back, we have $x^2 = 2 \pm \sqrt{3}$,

and since $2 + \sqrt{3}$ and $2 - \sqrt{3}$ are both positive we have $x = \pm\sqrt{2 + \sqrt{3}}$ or $x = \pm\sqrt{2 - \sqrt{3}}$.

Thus the solutions are $-\sqrt{2 - \sqrt{3}}$, $\sqrt{2 - \sqrt{3}}$, $-\sqrt{2 + \sqrt{3}}$, and $\sqrt{2 + \sqrt{3}}$.

38. $x - \sqrt{9 - 3x} = 0 \quad \Leftrightarrow \quad x = \sqrt{9 - 3x} \quad \Rightarrow \quad x^2 = 9 - 3x \quad \Leftrightarrow \quad 0 = x^2 + 3x - 9$. Using the quadratic formula to find the potential solutions, we have $x = \dfrac{-3 \pm \sqrt{3^2 - 4(1)(-9)}}{2(1)} = \dfrac{-3 \pm \sqrt{45}}{2}$ $= \dfrac{-3 \pm 3\sqrt{5}}{2}$. Substituting each of these solutions into the original equation, we see that $x = \dfrac{-3 + 3\sqrt{5}}{2}$ is a solution, but $x = \dfrac{-3 - 3\sqrt{5}}{2}$ is not. Thus $x = \dfrac{-3 + 3\sqrt{5}}{2}$ is the only solution.

40. $2x + \sqrt{x+1} = 8 \quad \Leftrightarrow \quad \sqrt{x+1} = 8 - 2x \quad \Rightarrow \quad x + 1 = (8 - 2x)^2 \quad \Leftrightarrow$
$x + 1 = 64 - 32x + 4x^2 \quad \Leftrightarrow \quad 0 = 4x^2 - 33x + 63 = (4x - 21)(x - 3)$. Potential solutions are
$x = \frac{21}{4}$ and $x = 3$. Substituting each of these solutions into the original equation, we see that $x = 3$
is a solution , but $x = \frac{21}{4}$ is not. Thus 3 is the only solution.

42. $\sqrt[3]{4x^2 - 4x} = x \quad \Leftrightarrow \quad 4x^2 - 4x = x^3 \quad \Leftrightarrow$
$0 = x^3 - 4x^2 + 4x = x(x^2 - 4x + 4) = x(x - 2)^2$. So $x = 0$ or $x = 2$. The solutions are 0 and 2.

44. Let $u = \sqrt{11 - x^2}$. By definition of u we require it to be nonnegative. Now
$\sqrt{11 - x^2} - \dfrac{2}{\sqrt{11 - x^2}} = 1 \quad \Leftrightarrow \quad u - \dfrac{2}{u} = 1$. Multiplying both sides by u we obtain
$u^2 - 2 = u \quad \Leftrightarrow \quad 0 = u^2 - u - 2 = (u - 2)(u + 1)$. So $u = 2$ or $u = -1$. But since u must be
nonnegative, we only have $u = 2 \quad \Leftrightarrow \quad \sqrt{11 - x^2} = 2 \quad \Rightarrow \quad 11 - x^2 = 4 \quad \Leftrightarrow \quad x^2 = 7$
$\Leftrightarrow \quad x = \pm\sqrt{7}$. The solutions are $\pm\sqrt{7}$.

46. $\sqrt{1 + \sqrt{x + \sqrt{2x + 1}}} = \sqrt{5 + \sqrt{x}}$. We square both sides to get $1 + \sqrt{x + \sqrt{2x + 1}} = 5 + \sqrt{x}$
$\Rightarrow \quad x + \sqrt{2x + 1} = \left(4 + \sqrt{x}\right)^2 = 16 + 8\sqrt{x} + x \quad \Leftrightarrow \quad \sqrt{2x + 1} = 16 + 8\sqrt{x}$. Again,
squaring both sides, we obtain $2x + 1 = \left(16 + 8\sqrt{x}\right)^2 = 256 + 256\sqrt{x} + 64x \quad \Leftrightarrow$
$-62x - 255 = 256\sqrt{x}$. We could continue squaring both sides until we found possible solutions;
however, consider the last equation. Since we are working with real numbers, for $\sqrt{x}$ to be defined,
we must have $x \geq 0$. Then $-62x - 255 < 0$ while $256\sqrt{x} \geq 0$, so there is no solution.

48. $0 = x^4 - 16 = (x^2 - 4)(x^2 + 4) = (x - 2)(x + 2)(x - 2\,i)(x + 2\,i)$. Setting each factor in turn
equal to zero, we see that the solutions are ± 2 and $\pm 2\,i$.

50. $x^4 + x^3 + x^2 + x = 0 \quad \Leftrightarrow$
$0 = x(x^3 + x^2 + x + 1) = x[x^2(x + 1) + (x + 1)] = x(x + 1)(x^2 + 1) = x(x + 1)(x - i)(x + i)$.
Setting each factor in turn equal to zero, we see that the solutions are $0, -1$, and $\pm i$.

52. $0 = x^3 + 3x^2 + 9x + 27 = x^2(x + 3) + 9(x + 3) = (x + 3)(x^2 + 9) = (x + 3)(x - 3\,i)(x + 3\,i)$.
Setting each factor in turn equal to zero, we see that the solutions are -3 and $\pm 3\ i$.

54. $0 = x^6 + 9x^4 - 4x^2 - 36 = x^4(x^2 + 9) - 4(x^2 + 9) = (x^2 + 9)(x^4 - 4)$
$= (x - 3\,i)(x + 3\,i)(x^2 - 2)(x^2 + 2)$
$= (x - 3\,i)(x + 3\,i)\left(x - \sqrt{2}\right)\left(x + \sqrt{2}\right)\left(x - \sqrt{2}\,i\right)\left(x - \sqrt{2}\,i\right)$. The six solutions are $\pm 3\ i$,
$\pm\sqrt{2}$, and $\pm\sqrt{2}\ i$.

56. $1 - \sqrt{x^2 + 7} = 6 - x^2 \quad \Leftrightarrow \quad x^2 - 5 = \sqrt{x^2 + 7}$. Squaring both sides, we get
$x^4 - 10x^2 + 25 = x^2 + 7 \quad \Leftrightarrow \quad 0 = x^4 - 11x^2 + 18 = (x^2 - 9)(x^2 - 2) =$
$(x - 3)(x + 3)(x - \sqrt{2})(x + \sqrt{2})$. The possible solutions are $x = \pm 3$ and $x = \pm\sqrt{2}$.
Checking $x = \pm 3$, we have LHS $= 1 - \sqrt{(\pm 3)^2 + 7} = 1 - \sqrt{16} = -3$;
RHS $= 6 - (\pm 3)^2 = -3$. Since LHS $=$ RHS these are solutions.

Checking $\pm\sqrt{2}$,we have LHS $= 1 - \sqrt{\left(\pm\sqrt{2}\right)^2 + 7} = 1 - \sqrt{9} = -2$;

RHS $= 6 - \left(\pm\sqrt{2}\right)^2 = 4$. Since LHS $\neq$ RHS these are not solutions. Thus the only solutions are
± 3.

58. Let n be the number of people in the group, so each person now pays $\dfrac{120{,}000}{n}$. If one person joins the group, then there would be $n + 1$ members in the group, and each person would pay $\dfrac{120{,}000}{n} - 6000$. So $(n + 1)\left(\dfrac{120{,}000}{n} - 6000\right) = 120{,}000 \quad \Leftrightarrow$

$\left[\left(\dfrac{n}{6000}\right)\left(\dfrac{120{,}000}{n} - 6000\right)\right](n + 1) = \left(\dfrac{n}{6000}\right)120{,}000 \quad \Leftrightarrow \quad (20 - n)(n + 1) = 20n \quad \Leftrightarrow$

$-n^2 + 19n + 20 = 20n \quad \Leftrightarrow \quad 0 = n^2 + n - 20 = (n - 4)(n + 5)$. Thus $n = 4$ or $n = -5$. Since n must be positive, there are now 4 friends in the group.

60. Let d be the distance from the lens to the object. Then the distance from the lens to the image is $d - 4$. So substituting $F = 4.8$, $x = d$, and $y = d - 4$, and then solving for x, we have

$\dfrac{1}{4.8} = \dfrac{1}{d} + \dfrac{1}{d - 4}$. Now we multiply by the LCD, $4.8d(d - 4)$, to get

$d(d - 4) = 4.8(d - 4) + 4.8d \quad \Leftrightarrow \quad d^2 - 4d = 9.6d - 19.2 \quad \Leftrightarrow \quad 0 = d^2 - 13.6d + 19.2$

$\Rightarrow \quad d = \dfrac{13.6 \pm 10.4}{2}$. So $d = 1.6$ or $d = 12$. Since $d - 4$ must also be positive, the object is 12 cm from the lens.

62. Let r be the radius of the larger sphere, in mm. Equating the volumes, we have

$\frac{4}{3}\pi r^3 = \frac{4}{3}\pi(2^3 + 3^3 + 4^3) \quad \Leftrightarrow \quad r^3 = 2^3 + 3^3 + 4^3 \quad \Leftrightarrow \quad r^3 = 99 \quad \Leftrightarrow \quad r = \sqrt[3]{99} \approx 4.63$. Therefore, the radius of the larger sphere is about 4.63 mm.

64. Let x be the distance, in feet, that he goes on the boardwalk before veering off onto the sand. The distance along the boardwalk from where he started to the point on the boardwalk closest to the umbrella is $\sqrt{750^2 - 210^2} = 720$ ft. Thus the distance that he walks on the sand is

$\sqrt{(720 - x)^2 + 210^2} = \sqrt{518400 - 1440x + x^2 + 44100} = \sqrt{x^2 - 1440x + 562500}$

	Distance	Rate	Time
Along Boardwalk	x	4	$\dfrac{x}{4}$
Across Sand	$\sqrt{x^2 - 1440x + 562500}$	2	$\dfrac{\sqrt{x^2 - 1440x + 562500}}{2}$

Since 4 minutes 45 seconds $= 285$ seconds, we equate the time it takes to walk along the Boardwalk and across the sand to the total time to get $285 = \dfrac{x}{4} + \dfrac{\sqrt{x^2 - 1440x + 562500}}{2} \quad \Leftrightarrow$

$1140 - x = 2\sqrt{x^2 - 1440x + 562500}$. Squaring both sides, we get

$(1140 - x)^2 = 4(x^2 - 1440x + 562500) \quad \Leftrightarrow$

$1299600 - 2280x + x^2 = 4x^2 - 5760x + 2250000 \quad \Leftrightarrow \quad 0 = 3x^2 - 3480x + 950400$

$= 3(x^2 - 1160x + 316800) = 3(x - 720)(x - 440)$. So $x - 720 = 0 \quad \Leftrightarrow \quad x = 720$, and $x - 440 = 0 \quad \Leftrightarrow \quad x = 440$. Checking $x = 720$, the distance across the sand is 210 feet. So $\dfrac{720}{4} + \dfrac{210}{2} = 180 + 105 = 285$ seconds. Checking $x = 440$, the distance across the sand is $\sqrt{(720 - 440)^2 + 210^2} = 350$ feet. So $\dfrac{440}{4} + \dfrac{350}{2} = 110 + 175 = 285$ seconds. Since both solutions are less than or equal to 720 feet, we have two solutions: he walks 440 feet down the boardwalk and then heads towards his umbrella, or he walks 720 feet down the boardwalk and then heads toward his umbrella.

66. Let r be the radius of the tank, in feet. The volume of the spherical tank is $\frac{4}{3}\pi r^3$ and is also

$750 \times 0.1337 = 100.275$. So $\frac{4}{3}\pi r^3 = 100.275$ $\Leftrightarrow$ $r^3 = 23.938$ $\Leftrightarrow$ $r = 2.88$ feet.

68. Let h be the height of the screens in inches. Hence, the width of the smaller screen is $h + 5$ inches, and the width of the bigger screen is $2.4h$ inches. The diagonal measure of the smaller screen is $\sqrt{h^2 + (h+5)^2}$, and the diagonal measure of the larger screen is $\sqrt{h^2 + (2.4\,h)^2} = \sqrt{6.76\,h^2}$ $= 2.6h$. Thus $\sqrt{h^2 + (h+5)^2} + 14 = 2.6\,h$ $\Leftrightarrow$ $\sqrt{h^2 + (h+5)^2} = 2.6\,h - 14$. Squaring both sides yields $h^2 + h^2 + 10h + 25 = 6.76h^2 - 72.8h + 196$ $\Leftrightarrow$ $0 = 4.76h^2 - 82.80h + 171$. Applying the quadratic formula, we obtain

$h = \dfrac{82.8 \pm \sqrt{(-82.8)^2 - 4(4.76)(171)}}{2(4.76)} = \dfrac{82.8 \pm \sqrt{3600}}{9.52} = \dfrac{82.8 \pm 60}{9.52}$. So $h = 15$ or

$h = 2.395$, and since $h \geq 10$, the height of the screens is 15 inches.

70. $0 = x^4 + 5ax^2 + 4a^2 = (x^2 + a)(x^2 + 4a)$. Since a is positive, $x^2 + a = 0$ $\Leftrightarrow$ $x^2 = -a$ $\Leftrightarrow$ $x = \pm i\sqrt{a}$. Again, since a is positive, $x^2 + 4a = 0$ $\Leftrightarrow$ $x^2 = -4a$ $\Leftrightarrow$ $x = \pm 2i\sqrt{a}$. Thus the four solutions are: $\pm i\sqrt{a}, \pm 2i\sqrt{a}$.

72. $\sqrt{x + a} + \sqrt{x - a} = \sqrt{2}\,\sqrt{x + 6}$. Squaring both sides, we have

$x + a + 2\left(\sqrt{x+a}\right)\left(\sqrt{x-a}\right) + x - a = 2(x + 6)$ $\Leftrightarrow$

$2x + 2\left(\sqrt{x+a}\right)\left(\sqrt{x-a}\right) = 2x + 12$ $\Leftrightarrow$ $2\left(\sqrt{x+a}\right)\left(\sqrt{x-a}\right) = 12$ $\Leftrightarrow$

$\left(\sqrt{x+a}\right)\left(\sqrt{x-a}\right) = 6$. Squaring both sides again we have: $(x+a)(x-a) = 36$ $\Leftrightarrow$

$x^2 - a^2 = 36$ $\Leftrightarrow$ $x^2 = a^2 + 36$ $\Leftrightarrow$ $x = \pm\sqrt{a^2 + 36}$. Checking these answers, we see that $x = -\sqrt{a^2 + 36}$ is not a solution (for example, try substituting $a = 8$), but $x = \sqrt{a^2 + 36}$ is a solution.

74. (a) Method 1: Let $u = \sqrt{x}$, so $u^2 = x$. Thus $x - \sqrt{x} - 2 = 0$ becomes $u^2 - u - 2 = 0$ $\Leftrightarrow$
$(u - 2)(u + 1) = 0$. So $u = 2$ or $u = -1$. If $u = 2$, then $\sqrt{x} = 2$ $\Rightarrow$ $x = 4$. If $u = -1$, then $\sqrt{x} = -1$ $\Rightarrow$ $x = 1$. So the possible solutions are 4 and 1. Checking $x = 4$ we have $4 - \sqrt{4} - 2 = 4 - 2 - 2 = 0$. Checking $x = 1$ we have $1 - \sqrt{1} - 2 = 1 - 1 - 2 \neq 0$. The only solution is 4.

Method 2: $x - \sqrt{x} - 2 = 0$ $\Leftrightarrow$ $x - 2 = \sqrt{x}$ $\Rightarrow$ $x^2 - 4x + 4 = x$ $\Leftrightarrow$ $x^2 - 5x + 4 = 0$ $\Leftrightarrow$ $(x - 4)(x - 1) = 0$. So the possible solutions are 4 and 1. Checking will result in the same solution.

(b) Method 1: Let $u = \dfrac{1}{x - 3}$, so $u^2 = \dfrac{1}{(x-3)^2}$. Thus $\dfrac{12}{(x-3)^2} + \dfrac{10}{x - 3} + 1 = 0$ becomes

$12u^2 + 10u + 1 = 0$. Using the quadratic formula, we have

$u = \frac{-10 \pm \sqrt{10^2 - 4(12)(1)}}{2(12)} = \frac{-10 \pm \sqrt{52}}{24} = \frac{-10 \pm 2\sqrt{13}}{24} = \frac{-5 \pm \sqrt{13}}{12}$. If $u = \frac{-5 - \sqrt{13}}{12}$, then

$\dfrac{1}{x - 3} = \dfrac{-5 - \sqrt{13}}{12}$ $\Leftrightarrow$ $x - 3 = \dfrac{12}{-5 - \sqrt{13}} \cdot \dfrac{-5 + \sqrt{13}}{-5 + \sqrt{13}} = \dfrac{12(-5 + \sqrt{13})}{12} = -5 + \sqrt{13}$. So

$x = -2 + \sqrt{13}$.

If $u = \frac{-5 + \sqrt{13}}{12}$, then $\dfrac{1}{x - 3} = \dfrac{-5 + \sqrt{13}}{12}$ $\Leftrightarrow$

$x - 3 = \frac{12}{-5+\sqrt{13}} \cdot \frac{-5-\sqrt{13}}{-5-\sqrt{13}} = \frac{12(-5-\sqrt{13})}{12} = -5 - \sqrt{13}.$ So $x = -2 - \sqrt{13}.$
The solutions are $-2 \pm \sqrt{13}.$

<u>Method 2:</u> Multiply by LCD, $(x-3)^2$, we get

$(x-3)^2 \left(\frac{12}{(x-3)^2} + \frac{10}{x-3} + 1 \right) = 0 \cdot (x-3)^2 \quad \Leftrightarrow \quad 12 + 10(x-3) + (x-3)^2 = 0$

$\Leftrightarrow \quad 12 + 10x - 30 + x^2 - 6x + 9 = 0 \quad \Leftrightarrow \quad x^2 + 4x - 9 = 0.$ Using the quadratic

formula, we have $u = \frac{-4 \pm \sqrt{4^2 - 4(1)(-9)}}{2} = \frac{-4 \pm \sqrt{52}}{2} = \frac{-4 \pm 2\sqrt{13}}{22} = -2 \pm \sqrt{13}.$ The solutions are

$-2 \pm \sqrt{13}.$

Exercises 3.6

2. $x = -1$: $(-1) - 2 \overset{?}{<} 0$. Yes.　　　　$x = 0$: $(0) - 2 \overset{?}{<} 0$. Yes.

$x = \frac{1}{2}$: $\left(\frac{1}{2}\right) - 2 \overset{?}{<} 0$. Yes.　　　　$x = \sqrt{2}$: $(\sqrt{2}) - 2 \overset{?}{<} 0$. Yes.

$x = 2$: $(2) - 2 \overset{?}{<} 0$. No.　　　　The solutions are: $-1, 0, \frac{1}{2}$, and $\sqrt{2}$.

4. $x = -1$: $4(-1) + 1 \overset{?}{\leq} 2(-1)$. Yes.　　　　$x = 0$: $4(0) + 1 \overset{?}{\leq} 2(0)$. No.

$x = \frac{1}{2}$: $4\left(\frac{1}{2}\right) + 1 \overset{?}{\leq} 2\left(\frac{1}{2}\right)$. No.　　　　$x = \sqrt{2}$: $4(\sqrt{2}) + 1 \overset{?}{\leq} 2(\sqrt{2})$. No.

$x = 2$: $4(2) + 1 \overset{?}{\leq} 2(2)$. No.　　　　The solution is -1.

6. $x = -1$: $(-1)^2 + 2 \overset{?}{<} 4$. Yes.　　　　$x = 0$: $(0)^2 + 2 \overset{?}{<} 4$. Yes.

$x = \frac{1}{2}$: $\left(\frac{1}{2}\right)^2 + 2 \overset{?}{<} 4$. Yes.　　　　$x = \sqrt{2}$: $(\sqrt{2})^2 + 2 \overset{?}{<} 4$. No.

$x = 2$: $(2)^2 + 2 \overset{?}{<} 4$. No.　　　　The solutions are $-1, 0$, and $\frac{1}{2}$.

8. $-4x > 16 \Leftrightarrow x < -4$. Interval: $(-\infty, -4)$.　　　Graph:

10. $-1 \geq 7x \Leftrightarrow -\frac{1}{7} \geq x$. Interval: $\left(-\infty, -\frac{1}{7}\right]$.　　　Graph:

12. $3x + 11 < 5 \Leftrightarrow 3x < -6 \Leftrightarrow x < -2$.　　　Interval: $(-\infty, -2)$.
Graph:

14. $5 - 3x \leq -16 \Leftrightarrow -3x \leq -21 \Leftrightarrow x \geq 7$. Interval: $[7, \infty)$.
Graph:

16. $0 < 5 - 2x \Leftrightarrow 2x < 5 \Leftrightarrow x < \frac{5}{2}$.　　　Interval: $\left(-\infty, \frac{5}{2}\right)$.
Graph:

18. $6 - x \geq 2x + 9 \Leftrightarrow -3 \geq 3x \Leftrightarrow -1 \geq x$. Interval: $(-\infty, -1]$.
Graph:

20. $4 - 3x \geq 6 \Leftrightarrow -3x \geq 2 \Leftrightarrow x \leq -\frac{2}{3}$.　　　Interval: $\left(-\infty, -\frac{2}{3}\right]$.
Graph:

22. $\frac{2}{5}x + 1 < \frac{1}{5} - 2x \Leftrightarrow \frac{12}{5}x < -\frac{4}{5} \Leftrightarrow x < -\frac{1}{3}$. Interval: $\left(-\infty, -\frac{1}{3}\right)$.
Graph:

24. $3\left(1 - \frac{3}{4}x\right) > 5 - \frac{1}{4}x \Leftrightarrow 3 - \frac{9}{4}x > 5 - \frac{1}{4}x \Leftrightarrow -2 > 2x \Leftrightarrow -1 > x$.
Interval: $(-\infty, -1)$.　　　Graph:

26. $2(7x - 3) \leq 12x + 16 \Leftrightarrow 14x - 6 \leq 12x + 16 \Leftrightarrow 2x \leq 22 \Leftrightarrow x \leq 11$.
Interval: $(-\infty, 11]$.　　　Graph:

28. $5 \leq 3x - 4 \leq 14 \Leftrightarrow 9 \leq 3x \leq 18 \Leftrightarrow 3 \leq x \leq 6$.
Interval: $[3, 6]$.　　　Graph:

30. $1 < 3x + 4 \leq 16$ $\Leftrightarrow$ $-3 < 3x \leq 12$ $\Leftrightarrow$ $-1 < x \leq 4$. Interval: $(-1, 4]$.
     Graph:

32. $-5 \leq 3 - 2x \leq 9$ $\Leftrightarrow$ $-8 \leq -2x \leq 6$ $\Leftrightarrow$ (multiply by -2, reverse the inequalities)
     $4 \geq x \geq -3$ $\Leftrightarrow$ $-3 \leq x \leq 4$.   Interval: $[-3, 4.]$

     Graph:

34. $-3 \leq 3x + 7 \leq \frac{1}{2}$ $\Leftrightarrow$ $-10 \leq 3x \leq -\frac{13}{2}$ $\Leftrightarrow$ $-\frac{10}{3} \leq x \leq -\frac{13}{6}$.
     Interval: $\left[-\frac{10}{3}, -\frac{13}{6}\right]$.   Graph:

36. $-\dfrac{1}{2} < \dfrac{4 - 3x}{5} \leq \dfrac{1}{4}$ $\Leftrightarrow$ (multiply each expression by 20) $-10 < 4(4 - 3x) \leq 5$ $\Leftrightarrow$
     $-10 < 16 - 12x \leq 5$ $\Leftrightarrow$ $-26 < -12x \leq -11$ $\Leftrightarrow$ $\frac{13}{6} > x \geq \frac{11}{12}$ $\Leftrightarrow$ (expressing in
     standard form) $\frac{11}{12} \leq x < \frac{13}{6}$.   Interval: $\left[\frac{11}{12}, \frac{13}{6}\right)$ Graph:

38. Let m be the number of minutes of long-distance calls placed per month. Then under Plan A, the
     cost will be $25 + 0.05m$, and under Plan B, the cost will be $5 + 0.12m$. To determine when Plan B
     is advantageous, we must solve $25 + 0.05m > 5 + 0.12m$ $\Leftrightarrow$ $20 > 0.07m$ $\Leftrightarrow$ $285.7 > m$
     So Plan B is advantageous if a person places less than 286 minutes of long-distance calls during a
     month.

40. Inserting the relationship $F = \frac{9}{5}C + 32$, we have $50 \leq F \leq 95$ $\Leftrightarrow$ $50 \leq \frac{9}{5}C + 32 \leq 95$ $\Leftrightarrow$
     $18 \leq \frac{9}{5}C \leq 63$ $\Leftrightarrow$ $10 \leq C \leq 35$.

42. (a) $T = 20 - \frac{h}{100}$, where T is the temperature in °C, and h is the height in meters.
     (b) Solving the expression in part (a) for h, we get $h = 100(20 - T)$. So $0 \leq h \leq 5000$ $\Leftrightarrow$
     $0 \leq 100(20 - T) \leq 5000$ $\Leftrightarrow$ $0 \leq 20 - T \leq 50$ $\Leftrightarrow$ $-20 \leq -T \leq 30$ $\Leftrightarrow$
     $20 \geq T \geq -30$. Thus the range of temperature is from 20°C down to -30°C.

44. If the customer buys x pounds of coffee at \$6.50 per pound, then his cost c will be $6.50x$. Thus
     $x = \frac{c}{6.5}$. Since the scale's accuracy is ± 0.03 lb, and the scale shows 3 lb, we have
     $3 - 0.03 \leq x \leq 3 + 0.03$ $\Leftrightarrow$ $2.97 \leq \frac{c}{6.5} \leq 3.03$ $\Leftrightarrow$ $(6.50)2.97 \leq c \leq (6.50)3.03$ $\Leftrightarrow$
     $19.305 \leq c \leq 19.695$. Since the customer paid \$19.50, he could have been over- or undercharged
     by as much as $19\frac{1}{2}$¢.

46. We have $a \leq bx + c < 2a$, where $a, b, c > 0$ $\Leftrightarrow$ $a - c \leq bx < 2a - c$ $\Leftrightarrow$
     $\dfrac{a - c}{b} \leq x < \dfrac{2a - c}{b}$.

48. We have $\dfrac{ax + b}{c} \leq b$, where $a, b, c < 0$ $\Leftrightarrow$ $ax + b \geq bc$ $\Leftrightarrow$ $ax \geq bc - b$ $\Leftrightarrow$
     $x \leq \dfrac{bc - b}{a}$.

50. If $0 < a < b$, then since $a > 0$, we can multiply both sides by a and obtain $a \cdot a < a \cdot b$, or $a^2 < ab$.
     Likewise, since $b > 0$, we can multiply both sides by b and obtain $a \cdot b < b \cdot b$, or $ab < b^2$. Putting
     these two together, we have $a^2 < ab < b^2$, which we reduce to $a^2 < b^2$.

52. (a) $(-2, 5) < (-1, 4) < (0, 2) < (2, -3) < (2, 0) < (2, 5) < (4, -2)$.

(b) $S = \{(x, y) \,|\, (0, 3) < (x, y)\}.$
By the definition, $(0, 3) < (x, y)$
if $0 < x$ or if $0 = x$ <u>and</u> $3 < y$.

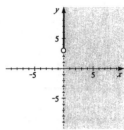

$T = \{(x, y) \,|\, (-2, 2) < (x, y) \leq (4, 0)\}.$
Now $(-2, 2) < (x, y) \leq (4, 0)$
if $-2 < x \leq 4$, or
if $-2 = x$ <u>and</u> $2 < y$, or
if $x = 4$ <u>and</u> $y \leq 0$.

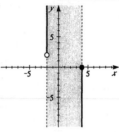

Exercises 3.7

2. $(3x+1)(x-1) \geq 0$. The expression on the left of the inequality changes sign when $x = -\frac{1}{3}$ and $x = 1$. Thus we must check the intervals in the following table.

Interval	$(-\infty, -\frac{1}{3})$	$(-\frac{1}{3}, 1)$	$(1, \infty)$
Sign of $3x + 1$	$-$	$+$	$+$
Sign of $x - 1$	$-$	$-$	$+$
Sign of $(3x+1)(x-1)$	$+$	$-$	$+$

From the table, the solution set is $\left\{x \mid \ x \leq -\frac{1}{3} \text{ or } 1 \leq x\right\}$.

Solution: $\left(-\infty, -\frac{1}{3}\right] \cup [1, \infty)$.   Graph:

4. $x^2 + 5x + 6 > 0 \quad \Leftrightarrow \quad (x+3)(x+2) > 0$. The expression on the left of the inequality changes sign when $x = -3$ and $x = -2$. Thus we must check the intervals in the following table.

Interval	$(-\infty, -3)$	$(-3, -2)$	$(-2, \infty)$
Sign of $x + 3$	$-$	$+$	$+$
Sign of $x + 2$	$-$	$-$	$+$
Sign of $(x+3)(x+2)$	$+$	$-$	$+$

From the table, the solution set is $\{x \mid \ x < -3 \text{ or } -2 < x\}$.

Solution: $(-\infty, -3) \cup (-2, \infty)$.   Graph:

6. $x^2 < x + 2 \quad \Leftrightarrow \quad x^2 - x - 2 < 0 \quad \Leftrightarrow \quad (x+1)(x-2) < 0$. The expression on the left of the inequality changes sign when $x = -1$ and $x = 2$. Thus we must check the intervals in the following table.

Interval	$(-\infty, -1)$	$(-1, 2)$	$(2, \infty)$
Sign of $x + 1$	$-$	$+$	$+$
Sign of $x - 2$	$-$	$-$	$+$
Sign of $(x+1)(x-2)$	$+$	$-$	$+$

From the table, the solution set is $\{x \mid \ -1 < x < 2\}$.

Solution: $(-1, 2)$.   Graph:

8. $5x^2 + 3x \geq 3x^2 + 2 \quad \Leftrightarrow \quad 2x^2 + 3x - 2 \geq 0 \quad \Leftrightarrow \quad (2x - 1)(x + 2) \geq 0$. The expression on the left of the inequality changes sign when $x = \frac{1}{2}$ and $x = -2$. Thus we must check the intervals in the following table.

Interval	$(-\infty, -2)$	$(-2, \frac{1}{2})$	$(\frac{1}{2}, \infty)$
Sign of $2x - 1$	$-$	$-$	$+$
Sign of $x + 2$	$-$	$+$	$+$
Sign of $(2x-1)(x+2)$	$+$	$-$	$+$

From the table, the solution set is $\left\{x \mid \ x \leq -2 \text{ or } \frac{1}{2} \leq x\right\}$.

Solution: $(-\infty, -2] \cup \left[\frac{1}{2}, \infty\right)$.   Graph:

10. $x^2 + 2x > 3 \quad \Leftrightarrow \quad x^2 + 2x - 3 > 0 \quad \Leftrightarrow \quad (x+3)(x-1) > 0$. The expression on the left of the inequality changes sign when $x = -3$ and $x = 1$. Thus we must check the intervals in the following table.

Interval	$(-\infty, -3)$	$(-3, 1)$	$(1, \infty)$
Sign of $x + 3$	$-$	$+$	$+$
Sign of $x - 1$	$-$	$-$	$+$
Sign of $(x + 3)(x - 1)$	$+$	$-$	$+$

From the table, the solution set is $\{x \mid x < -3 \text{ or } 1 < x\}$.

Solution: $(-\infty, -3) \cup (1, \infty)$.   Graph: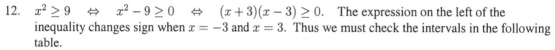

12. $x^2 \geq 9$ $\Leftrightarrow$ $x^2 - 9 \geq 0$ $\Leftrightarrow$ $(x + 3)(x - 3) \geq 0$.   The expression on the left of the inequality changes sign when $x = -3$ and $x = 3$. Thus we must check the intervals in the following table.

Interval	$(-\infty, -3)$	$(-3, 3)$	$(3, \infty)$
Sign of $x + 3$	$-$	$+$	$+$
Sign of $x - 3$	$-$	$-$	$+$
Sign of $(x + 3)(x - 3)$	$+$	$-$	$+$

From the table, the solution set is $\{x \mid x \leq -3 \text{ or } 3 \leq x\}$.

Solution: $(-\infty, -3] \cup [3, \infty)$.   Graph:

14. $(x + 2)(x - 1)(x - 3) \leq 0$. The expression on the left of the inequality changes sign when $x = -2$, $x = 1$, and $x = 3$. Thus we must check the intervals in the following table.

Interval	$(-\infty, -2)$	$(-2, 1)$	$(1, 3)$	$(3, \infty)$
Sign of $x + 2$	$-$	$+$	$+$	$+$
Sign of $x - 1$	$-$	$-$	$+$	$+$
Sign of $x - 3$	$-$	$-$	$-$	$+$
Sign of $(x + 2)(x - 1)(x - 3)$	$-$	$+$	$-$	$+$

From the table, the solution set is $\{x \mid x \leq -2 \text{ or } 1 \leq x \leq 3\}$.

Solution: $(-\infty, -2] \cup [1, 3]$.   Graph:

16. $x^3 > x$ $\Leftrightarrow$ $x^3 - x > 0$ $\Leftrightarrow$ $x(x^2 - 1) > 0$ $\Leftrightarrow$ $x(x - 1)(x + 1) > 0$. The expression on the left of the inequality changes sign when $x = 0$, $x = 1$, and $x = -1$. Thus we must check the intervals in the following table.

Interval	$(-\infty, -1)$	$(-1, 0)$	$(0, 1)$	$(1, \infty)$
Sign of x	$-$	$-$	$+$	$+$
Sign of $x - 1$	$-$	$-$	$-$	$+$
Sign of $x + 1$	$-$	$+$	$+$	$+$
Sign of $x(x - 1)(x + 1)$	$-$	$+$	$-$	$+$

From the table, the solution set is $\{x \mid -1 < x < 0 \text{ or } 1 < x\}$.

Solution: $(-1, 0) \cup (1, \infty)$.   Graph:

18. $\dfrac{2x + 6}{x - 2} < 0$. The expression on the left of the inequality changes sign when $x = -3$ and $x = 2$. Thus we must check the intervals in the following table.

Interval	$(-\infty, -3)$	$(-3, 2)$	$(2, \infty)$
Sign of $2x + 6$	$-$	$+$	$+$
Sign of $x - 2$	$-$	$-$	$+$
Sign of $\dfrac{2x + 6}{x - 2}$	$+$	$-$	$+$

From the table, the solution set is $\{x \mid -3 < x < 2\}$.

Solution: $(-3, 2)$.　　　　Graph:

20. $-2 < \dfrac{x+1}{x-3} \Leftrightarrow 0 < \dfrac{x+1}{x-3} + 2 \Leftrightarrow 0 < \dfrac{x+1}{x-3} + \dfrac{2(x-3)}{x-3} \Leftrightarrow 0 < \dfrac{3x-5}{x-3}$. The expression on the left of the inequality changes sign when $x = \frac{5}{3}$ and $x = 3$. Thus we must check the intervals in the following table.

Interval	$\left(-\infty, \frac{5}{3}\right)$	$\left(\frac{5}{3}, 3\right)$	$(3, \infty)$
Sign of $3x - 5$	$-$	$+$	$+$
Sign of $x - 3$	$-$	$-$	$+$
Sign of $\dfrac{3x - 5}{x - 3}$	$+$	$-$	$+$

From the table, the solution set is $\left\{x \mid x < \frac{5}{3} \text{ or } 3 < x < \infty\right\}$.

Solution: $\left(-\infty, \frac{5}{3}\right) \cup (3, \infty)$.　　　　Graph:

22. $\dfrac{3+x}{3-x} \geq 1 \Leftrightarrow \dfrac{3+x}{3-x} - 1 \geq 0 \Leftrightarrow \dfrac{3+x}{3-x} - \dfrac{3-x}{3-x} \geq 0 \Leftrightarrow \dfrac{2x}{3-x} \geq 0$. The expression on the left of the inequality changes sign when $x = 0$ and $x = 3$. Thus we must check the intervals in the following table.

Interval	$(-\infty, 0)$	$(0, 3)$	$(3, \infty)$
Sign of $3 - x$	$+$	$+$	$-$
Sign of $2x$	$-$	$+$	$+$
Sign of $\dfrac{2x}{3 - x}$	$-$	$+$	$-$

Since the denominator cannot equal 0, we must have $x \neq 3$. The solution set is $\{x \mid 0 \leq x < 3\}$.

Solution: $[0, 3)$.　　　　Graph:

24. $\dfrac{x}{x+1} > 3x \Leftrightarrow \dfrac{x}{x+1} - 3x > 0 \Leftrightarrow \dfrac{x}{x+1} - \dfrac{3x(x+1)}{x+1} > 0 \Leftrightarrow \dfrac{-2x - 3x^2}{x+1} > 0$

$\Leftrightarrow \dfrac{-x(2+3x)}{x+1} > 0$. The expression on the left of the inequality changes sign when $x = 0$, $x = -\frac{2}{3}$, and $x = -1$. Thus we must check the intervals in the following table.

Interval	$(-\infty, -1)$	$\left(-1, -\frac{2}{3}\right)$	$\left(-\frac{2}{3}, 0\right)$	$(0, \infty)$
Sign of $-x$	$+$	$+$	$+$	$-$
Sign of $2 + 3x$	$-$	$-$	$+$	$+$
Sign of $x + 1$	$-$	$+$	$+$	$+$
Sign of $\dfrac{(2 - x)(2 + x)}{x}$	$+$	$-$	$+$	$-$

From the table, the solution set is $\left\{x \mid x < -1 \text{ or } -\frac{2}{3} < x < 0\right\}$.

Solution: $(-\infty, -1) \cup \left(-\frac{2}{3}, 0\right)$.　　　　Graph:

26. $\dfrac{x}{x+2} \le \dfrac{1}{x} \quad\Leftrightarrow\quad \dfrac{x}{x+2} - \dfrac{1}{x} \le 0 \quad\Leftrightarrow\quad \dfrac{x \cdot x}{(x+2)x} - \dfrac{x+2}{x(x+2)} \le 0 \quad\Leftrightarrow\quad \dfrac{x^2 - x - 2}{x(x+2)} \le 0$

$\Leftrightarrow \dfrac{(x-2)(x+1)}{x(x+2)} \le 0.$ The expression on the left of the inequality changes sign when $x = -2$,

$x = -1, x = 0$, and $x = 2$. Thus we must check the intervals in the following table.

Interval	$(-\infty, -2)$	$(-2, -1)$	$(-1, 0)$	$(0, 2)$	$(2, \infty)$
Sign of $x - 2$	$-$	$-$	$-$	$-$	$+$
Sign of $x + 1$	$-$	$-$	$+$	$+$	$+$
Sign of x	$-$	$-$	$-$	$+$	$+$
Sign of $x + 2$	$-$	$+$	$+$	$+$	$+$
Sign of $\dfrac{(x-2)(x+1)}{x(x+2)}$	$+$	$-$	$+$	$-$	$+$

From the table, the solution set is $\{x \mid\ -2 < x \le -1 \text{ or } 0 < x \le 2\}$. The values $x = -2$ and $x = 0$ are excluded because the expressions in the original inequality are undefined there.

Solution: $(-2, -1] \cup (0, 2]$.   Graph:

28. $\dfrac{3}{x-1} - \dfrac{4}{x} \ge 1 \quad\Leftrightarrow\quad \dfrac{3}{x-1} - \dfrac{4}{x} - 1 \ge 0 \quad\Leftrightarrow\quad \dfrac{3x}{x(x-1)} - \dfrac{4(x-1)}{x(x-1)} - \dfrac{x(x-1)}{x(x-1)} \ge 0 \Leftrightarrow$

$\dfrac{3x - 4x + 4 - x^2 + x}{x(x-1)} \ge 0 \quad\Leftrightarrow\quad \dfrac{4 - x^2}{x(x-1)} \ge 0 \quad\Leftrightarrow\quad \dfrac{(2-x)(2+x)}{x(x-1)} \ge 0.$ The expression

on the left of the inequality changes sign when $x = 2$, $x = -2$, $x = 0$, and $x = 1$. Thus we must check the intervals in the following table.

Interval	$(-\infty, -2)$	$(-2, 0)$	$(0, 1)$	$(1, 2)$	$(2, \infty)$
Sign of $2 - x$	$+$	$+$	$+$	$+$	$-$
Sign of $2 + x$	$-$	$+$	$+$	$+$	$+$
Sign of x	$-$	$-$	$+$	$+$	$+$
Sign of $x - 1$	$-$	$-$	$-$	$+$	$+$
Sign of $\dfrac{(2-x)(2+x)}{x(x-1)}$	$-$	$+$	$-$	$+$	$-$

Since $x = 0$ and $x = 1$ yield undefined expressions, we cannot include them in the solution. From the table, the solution set is $\{x \mid\ -2 \le x < 0 \text{ or } 1 < x \le 2\}$.

Solution: $[-2, 0) \cup (1, 2]$.   Graph:

30. $\dfrac{(x-1)^2}{(x+1)(x+2)} > 0.$ The expression on the left of the inequality changes sign when $x = 1$, $x = -1$, and $x = -2$. Thus we must check the intervals in the following table.

Interval	$(-\infty, -2)$	$(-2, -1)$	$(-1, 1)$	$(1, \infty)$
Sign of $(x - 1)^2$	$+$	$+$	$+$	$+$
Sign of $x + 1$	$-$	$-$	$+$	$+$
Sign of $x + 2$	$-$	$+$	$+$	$+$
Sign of $\dfrac{(x-1)^2}{(x+1)(x+2)}$	$+$	$-$	$+$	$+$

The solution set is $\{x \mid\ x < -2 \text{ or } -1 < x < 1 \text{ or } 1 < x\}$.

Solution: $(-\infty, -2) \cup (-1, 1) \cup (1, \infty)$.   Graph:

32. $\dfrac{x^2 - 16}{x^4 - 16} < 0 \quad \Leftrightarrow \quad \dfrac{(x-4)(x+4)}{(x-2)(x+2)(x^2+4)} < 0$. Since $x^2 + 4 = 0$ has no real solution, the expression on the left of the inequality changes sign when $x = 4$, $x = -4$, $x = 2$, and $x = -2$. Thus we must check the intervals in the following table.

Interval	$(-\infty, -4)$	$(-4, -2)$	$(-2, 2)$	$(2, 4)$	$(4, \infty)$
Sign of $x - 4$	$-$	$-$	$-$	$-$	$+$
Sign of $x + 4$	$-$	$+$	$+$	$+$	$+$
Sign of $x - 2$	$-$	$-$	$-$	$+$	$+$
Sign of $x + 2$	$-$	$-$	$+$	$+$	$+$
Sign of $x^2 + 4$	$+$	$+$	$+$	$+$	$+$
Sign of $\dfrac{(x-4)(x+4)}{(x-2)(x+2)(x^2+4)}$	$+$	$-$	$+$	$-$	$+$

From the table, the solution set is $\{x \mid\ -4 < x < -2 \text{ or } 2 < x < 4\}$.

Solution: $(-4, -2) \cup (2, 4)$.   Graph:

34. $\dfrac{1}{x} + \dfrac{1}{x+1} < \dfrac{2}{x+2} \quad \Leftrightarrow \quad \dfrac{1}{x} + \dfrac{1}{x+1} - \dfrac{2}{x+2} < 0 \quad \Leftrightarrow$

$\dfrac{(x+1)(x+2)}{x(x+1)(x+2)} + \dfrac{x(x+2)}{x(x+1)(x+2)} - \dfrac{2x(x+1)}{x(x+1)(x+2)} < 0 \quad \Leftrightarrow$

$\dfrac{x^2 + 3x + 2 + x^2 + 2x - 2x^2 - 2x}{x(x+1)(x+2)} < 0 \quad \Leftrightarrow \quad \dfrac{3x + 2}{x(x+1)(x+2)} < 0$. The expression on the left of the inequality changes sign when $x = -\frac{2}{3}$, $x = 0$, $x = -1$, and $x = -2$. Thus we must check the intervals in the following table.

Interval	$(-\infty, -2)$	$(-2, -1)$	$(-1, -\frac{2}{3})$	$(-\frac{2}{3}, 0)$	$(0, \infty)$
$3x + 2$	$-$	$-$	$-$	$+$	$+$
x	$-$	$-$	$-$	$-$	$+$
$x + 1$	$-$	$-$	$+$	$+$	$+$
$x + 2$	$-$	$+$	$+$	$+$	$+$
expression	$+$	$-$	$+$	$-$	$+$

From the table, the solution set is $\{x \mid\ -2 < x < -1 \text{ or } -\frac{2}{3} < x < 0\}$.

Solution: $(-2, -1) \cup (-\frac{2}{3}, 0)$.   Graph:

36. $\dfrac{x}{2} \ge \dfrac{5}{x+1} + 4 \quad \Leftrightarrow \quad \dfrac{x}{2} - \dfrac{5}{x+1} - 4 \ge 0 \quad \Leftrightarrow \quad \dfrac{x(x+1)}{2(x+1)} - \dfrac{2 \cdot 5}{2(x+1)} - \dfrac{4(2)(x+1)}{2(x+1)} \ge 0$

$\Leftrightarrow \quad \dfrac{x^2 + x - 10 - 8x - 8}{2(x+1)} \ge 0 \quad \Leftrightarrow \quad \dfrac{x^2 - 7x - 18}{2(x+1)} \ge 0 \quad \Leftrightarrow \quad \dfrac{(x-9)(x+2)}{2(x+1)} \ge 0$. The expression on the left of the inequality changes sign when $x = 9$, $x = -2$, and $x = -1$. Thus we must check the intervals in the following table.

Interval	$(-\infty, -2)$	$(-2, -1)$	$(-1, 9)$	$(9, \infty)$
Sign of $x - 9$	$-$	$-$	$-$	$+$
Sign of $x + 2$	$-$	$+$	$+$	$+$
Sign of $x + 1$	$-$	$-$	$+$	$+$
Sign of $\dfrac{(x-9)(x+2)}{2(x+1)}$	$-$	$+$	$-$	$+$

From the table, the solution set is $\{x|\ -2 \le x < -1 \text{ or } 9 \le x\}$. The point $x = -1$ is excluded from the solution set because it makes the expression undefined.

Solution: $[-2, -1) \cup [9, \infty)$ Graph:

38. $\dfrac{1}{x+1} + \dfrac{1}{x+2} \le 0 \quad \Leftrightarrow \quad \dfrac{x+2}{(x+1)(x+2)} + \dfrac{x+1}{(x+1)(x+2)} \le 0 \quad \Leftrightarrow \quad \dfrac{x+2+x+1}{(x+1)(x+2)} \le 0$

$\Leftrightarrow \dfrac{2x+3}{(x+1)(x+2)} \le 0$. The expression on the left of the inequality changes sign when

$x = -\frac{3}{2}$, $x = -1$, and $x = -2$. Thus we must check the intervals in the following table.

Interval	$(-\infty, -2)$	$\left(-2, -\frac{3}{2}\right)$	$\left(-\frac{3}{2}, -1\right)$	$(-1, \infty)$
Sign of $2x+3$	$-$	$-$	$+$	$+$
Sign of $x+1$	$-$	$-$	$-$	$+$
Sign of $x+2$	$-$	$+$	$+$	$+$
Sign of $\dfrac{2x+3}{(x+1)(x+2)}$	$-$	$+$	$-$	$+$

From the table, the solution set is $\left\{x|\ x < -2 \text{ or } -\frac{3}{2} \le x < -1\right\}$. The points $x = -2$ and $x = -1$ are excluded from the solution because the expression is undefined at those values.

Solution: $(-\infty, -2) \cup \left[-\frac{3}{2}, -1\right)$.   Graph:

40. $x^5 > x^2 \quad \Leftrightarrow \quad x^5 - x^2 > 0 \quad \Leftrightarrow \quad x^2(x^3 - 1) > 0 \quad \Leftrightarrow \quad x^2(x-1)(x^2 + x + 1) > 0$. The expression on the left of the inequality changes sign when $x = 0$ and $x = 1$. But the solution of $x^2 + x + 1 = 0$ are $x = \dfrac{-1 \pm \sqrt{(1)^2 - 4(1)(1)}}{2(1)} = \dfrac{-1 \pm \sqrt{-3}}{2}$. Since these are not real solutions. The expression $x^2 + x + 1$ does not changes signs, so we must check the intervals in the following table.

Interval	$(-\infty, 0)$	$(0, 1)$	$(1, \infty)$
Sign of x^2	$+$	$+$	$+$
Sign of $x-1$	$-$	$-$	$+$
Sign of $x^2 + x + 1$	$+$	$+$	$+$
Sign of $x^2(x-1)(x^2 + x + 1)$	$-$	$-$	$+$

From the table, the solution set is $\{x|\ 1 < x\}$.

Solution: $(1, \infty)$.   Graph:

42. Since $0.5x^2 + 0.875x \le 0.25 \quad \Leftrightarrow$
$0.5x^2 + 0.875x - 0.25 \le 0$, we graph
$y = 0.5x^2 + 0.875x - 0.25$ in the viewing rectangle $[-3, 1]$ by
$[-5, 5]$. Thus the solution to the inequality is $-2 \le x \le 0.25$.

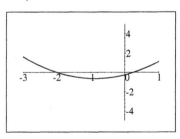

44. Since $16x^3 + 24x^2 > -9x - 1 \quad \Leftrightarrow$
     $16x^3 + 24x^2 + 9x + 1 > 0$, we graph
     $y = 16x^3 + 24x^2 + 9x + 1$ in the viewing rectangle $[-3, 1]$ by
     $[-5, 5]$. From this rectangle, we see that $x = -1$ is an x-
     intercept, but it is unclear what is occurring between $x = -0.5$
     and $x = 0$.

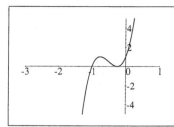

     We then use the viewing rectangle $[-1, 0]$ by $[-0.01, 0.01]$. It
     shows $y = 0$ at $x = -0.25$. Thus in interval notation, the
     solution is $(-1, -0.25) \cup (-0.25, \infty)$.

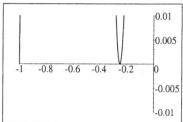

46. Since $\sqrt{0.5x^2 + 1} \le 2|x| \quad \Leftrightarrow \quad \sqrt{0.5x^2 + 1} - 2|x| \le 0$, we
     graph $y = \sqrt{0.5x^2 + 1} - 2|x|$ in the viewing rectangle $[-1, 1]$
     by $[-1, 1]$. We locate the x-intercepts at $x \approx \pm 0.535$. Thus in
     interval notation, the solution is $(-\infty, -0.535] \cup [0.535, \infty)$.

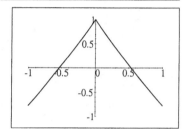

48. Since $(x + 1)^2 \le x^3 \quad \Leftrightarrow \quad (x + 1)^2 - x^3 \le 0$, we graph
     $y = (x + 1)^2 - x^3$ in the viewing rectangle $[-4, 4]$ by $[-1, 1]$.
     The x-intercept is close to $x = 2$.

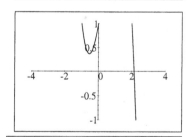

     We then use the viewing rectangle $[2, 2.5]$ by $[-0.1, 0.1]$, and
     obtain $x \approx 2.148$.
     Thus the solution is $[2.148, \infty)$.

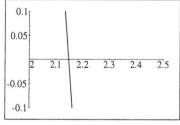

50. $0.004 \le \dfrac{4{,}000{,}000}{d^2} \le 0.01$. Since $d^2 \ge 0$ and $d \ne 0$, we can multiply each expression by d^2 to
     obtain $0.004d^2 \le 4{,}000{,}000 \le 0.01d^2$. Solving each pair, we have $0.004d^2 \le 4{,}000{,}000 \quad \Leftrightarrow$
     $d^2 \le 1{,}000{,}000{,}000 \quad \Rightarrow \quad d \le 10{,}000\sqrt{10}$ (recall that d represents distance, so it is always
     nonnegative). Solving $4{,}000{,}000 \le 0.01d^2 \quad \Leftrightarrow \quad 400{,}000{,}000 \le d^2 \Rightarrow 20{,}000 \le d$. Putting these
     together, we have $20{,}000 \le d \le 10{,}000\sqrt{10}$.

52.   Solve $30 \leq 10 + 0.9v - 0.01v^2$ for $10 \leq v \leq 75$. We have $30 \leq 10 + 0.9v - 0.01v^2$ $\Leftrightarrow$ $0.01v^2 - 0.9v + 20 \leq 0$ $\Leftrightarrow$ $(0.1v - 4)(0.1v - 5) \leq 0$. The possible endpoints are $0.1v - 4 = 0$ $\Leftrightarrow$ $0.1v = 4$ $\Leftrightarrow$ $v = 40$ and $0.1v - 5 = 0$ $\Leftrightarrow$ $0.1v = 5$ $\Leftrightarrow$ $v = 50$.

Interval	$(10, 40)$	$(40, 50)$	$(50, 75)$
Sign of $0.1v - 4$	$-$	$+$	$+$
Sign of $0.1v - 5$	$-$	$-$	$+$
Sign of $(0.1v - 4)(0.1v - 5)$	$+$	$-$	$+$

Thus he must drive between 40 and 50 mi/h.

54.   Solve $2400 \leq 20x - (2000 + 8x + 0.0025x^2)$ $\Leftrightarrow$ $2400 \leq 20x - 2000 - 8x - 0.0025x^2$ $\Leftrightarrow$ $0.0025x^2 - 12x + 4400 \leq 0$ $\Leftrightarrow$ $(0.0025x - 1)(x - 4400) \leq 0$. The expression on the left of the inequality changes sign when $x = 400$ and $x = 4400$. Since the manufacturer can only sell positive units, we check the intervals in the following table.

Interval	$(0, 400)$	$(400, 4400)$	$(4400, \infty)$
Sign of $0.0025x - 1$	$-$	$+$	$+$
Sign of $x - 4400$	$-$	$-$	$+$
Sign of $(0.0025x - 1)(x - 4400)$	$+$	$-$	$+$

So the manufacturer must sell between 400 and 4400 units to enjoy a profit of at least $2400.

56.   Let n be the number of people in the group. Then the bus fare is $\dfrac{360}{n}$, and the cost of the theater tickets is $30 - 0.25n$. We want the total cost to be less than $39 per person, that is, $\dfrac{360}{n} + (30 - 0.25n) < 39$. If we multiply this inequality by n, we will not change the direction of the inequality; n is positive since it represents the number of people. So we get $360 + n(30 - 0.25n) < 39n$ $\Leftrightarrow$ $-0.25n^2 + 30n + 360 < 39n$ $\Leftrightarrow$ $-0.25n^2 - 9n + 360 < 0$ $\Leftrightarrow$ $(0.25n + 15)(-n + 24)$. The expression on the left of the inequality changes sign when $n = -60$ and $n = 24$. Since $n > 0$, we check the intervals in the following table.

Interval	$(0, 24)$	$(24, \infty)$
Sign of $0.25n + 15$	$+$	$+$
Sign of $-n + 24$	$+$	$-$
Sign of $(0.25n + 15)(-n + 24)$	$+$	$-$

So the group must have more than 24 people in order that the cost of the theater tour is less than $39.

58.   For $\sqrt{3x^2 - 5x + 2}$ to be defined as a real number, we must have $3x^2 - 5x + 2 \geq 0$ $\Leftrightarrow$ $(3x - 2)(x - 1) \geq 0$. The expression on the left of the inequality changes sign when $x = \frac{2}{3}$ and $x = 1$. Thus we must check the intervals in the following table.

Interval	$\left(-\infty, \frac{2}{3}\right)$	$\left(\frac{2}{3}, 1\right)$	$(1, \infty)$
Sign of $3x - 2$	$-$	$+$	$+$
Sign of $x - 1$	$-$	$-$	$+$
Sign of $(3x - 2)(x - 1)$	$+$	$-$	$+$

Thus $x \leq \frac{2}{3}$ or $1 \leq x$.

60. For $\sqrt[4]{\dfrac{1-x}{2+x}}$ to be defined as a real number we must have $\dfrac{1-x}{2+x} \geq 0$. The expression on the left of the inequality changes sign when $x = 1$ and $x = -2$. Thus we must check the intervals in the following table.

Interval	$(-\infty, -2)$	$(-2, 1)$	$(1, \infty)$
Sign of $1 - x$	$+$	$+$	$-$
Sign of $2 + x$	$-$	$+$	$+$
Sign of $\dfrac{1-x}{2+x}$	$-$	$+$	$-$

Thus $-2 < x \leq 1$. Note that $x = -2$ has been excluded from the solution set because the expression is undefined at that value.

62. Case 1: $a < b < 0$. We have $a \cdot a > a \cdot b$, since $a < 0$, and $b \cdot a > b \cdot b$, since $b < 0$. So $a^2 > a \cdot b > b^2$, that is $a < b < 0 \Rightarrow a^2 > b^2$. Continuing, we have $a \cdot a^2 < a \cdot b^2$, since $a < 0$ and $b^2 \cdot a < b^2 \cdot b$, since $b^2 > 0$. So $a^3 < ab^2 < b^3$. Thus $a < b < 0 \Rightarrow a^3 > b^3$. So $a < b < 0 \Rightarrow a^n > b^n$, if n is even, and $a^n < b$, if n is odd.

Case 2: $0 < a < b$. We have $a \cdot a < a \cdot b$, since $a > 0$, and $b \cdot a < b \cdot b$, since $b < 0$. So $a^2 < a \cdot b < b^2$. Thus $0 < a < b \Rightarrow a^2 < b^2$. Likewise, $a^2 \cdot a < a^2 \cdot b$ and $b \cdot a^2 < b \cdot b^2$, thus $a^3 < b^3$. So $0 < a < b \Rightarrow a^n < b^n$, for all positive integers n.

Case 3: $a < 0 < b$. If n is odd, then $a^n < b^n$, because a^n is negative and b^n is positive. If n is even, then we could have either $a^n < b^n$ or $a^n > b^n$. For example, $-1 < 2$ and $(-1)^2 < 2^2$, but $-3 < 2$ and $(-3)^2 > 2^2$.

Exercises 3.8

2. $4|x| = 24$ $\Leftrightarrow$ $|x| = 6$ $\Leftrightarrow$ $x = \pm 6$.

4. $|2x - 3| = 7$ is equivalent to either $2x - 3 = 7$ $\Leftrightarrow$ $2x = 10$ $\Leftrightarrow$ $x = 5$; or $2x - 3 = -7$
    $\Leftrightarrow$ $2x = -4$ $\Leftrightarrow$ $x = -2$. The two solutions are $x = 5$ and $x = -2$.

6. $|x + 4| = -3$. Since the absolute value is always nonnegative, there is no solution.

8. $\left|\frac{1}{2}x - 2\right| = 1$ is equivalent to either $\frac{1}{2}x - 2 = 1$ $\Leftrightarrow$ $\frac{1}{2}x = 3$ $\Leftrightarrow$ $x = 6$; or $\frac{1}{2}x - 2 = -1$
    $\Leftrightarrow$ $\frac{1}{2}x = 1$ $\Leftrightarrow$ $x = 2$. The two solutions are $x = -1$ and $x = 2$.

10. $|5 - 2x| + 6 = 14$ $\Leftrightarrow$ $|5 - 2x| = 8$ which is equivalent to either $5 - 2x = 8$ $\Leftrightarrow$ $-2x = 3$
    $\Leftrightarrow$ $x = -\frac{3}{2}$; or $5 - 2x = -8$ $\Leftrightarrow$ $-2x = -13$ $\Leftrightarrow$ $x = \frac{13}{2}$. The two solutions are
    $x = -\frac{3}{2}$ and $x = \frac{13}{2}$.

12. $20 + |2x - 4| = 15$ $\Leftrightarrow$ $|2x - 4| = -5$. Since the absolute value is always nonnegative, there is
    no solution.

14. $\left|\frac{3}{5}x + 2\right| - \frac{1}{2} = 4$ $\Leftrightarrow$ $\left|\frac{3}{5}x + 2\right| = \frac{9}{2}$ which is equivalent to either $\frac{3}{5}x + 2 = \frac{9}{2}$ $\Leftrightarrow$ $\frac{3}{5}x = \frac{5}{2}$
    $\Leftrightarrow$ $x = \frac{25}{6}$; or $\frac{3}{5}x + 2 = -\frac{9}{2}$ $\Leftrightarrow$ $\frac{3}{5}x = -\frac{13}{2}$ $\Leftrightarrow$ $x = -\frac{65}{6}$. The two solutions are $x = \frac{25}{6}$
    and $x = -\frac{65}{6}$.

16. $|x + 3| = |2x + 1|$ is equivalent to either $x + 3 = 2x + 1$ $\Leftrightarrow$ $-x = -2$ $\Leftrightarrow$ $x = 2$ or to
    $x + 3 = -(2x + 1)$ $\Leftrightarrow$ $x + 3 = -2x - 1$ $\Leftrightarrow$ $3x = -4$ $\Leftrightarrow$ $x = -\frac{4}{3}$. The two
    solutions are $x = 2$ and $x = -\frac{4}{3}$.

18. $|x| \geq 4$ is equivalent to $x \geq 4$ or $x \leq -4$. Interval: $(-\infty, -4] \cup [4, \infty)$.

20. $|x - 9| > 9$ is equivalent to $x - 9 > 9$ $\Leftrightarrow$ $x > 18$, or $x - 9 < -9$ $\Leftrightarrow$ $x < 0$.
    Interval: $(-\infty, 0) \cup (18, \infty)$.

22. $|x + 4| \leq 0$ is equivalent to $|x + 4| = 0$ $\Leftrightarrow$ $x + 4 = 0$ $\Leftrightarrow$ $x = -4$. The solution is just the
    point $x = -4$.

24. $|x + 1| \geq 3$ is equivalent either to $x + 1 \geq 3$ $\Leftrightarrow$ $x \geq 2$, or to $x + 1 \leq -3$ $\Leftrightarrow$ $x \leq -4$.
    Interval: $(-\infty, -4] \cup [2, \infty)$.

26. $|5x - 2| < 6$ $\Leftrightarrow$ $-6 < 5x - 2 < 6$ $\Leftrightarrow$ $-4 < 5x < 8$ $\Leftrightarrow$ $-\frac{4}{5} < x < \frac{8}{5}$.
    Interval: $\left(-\frac{4}{5}, \frac{8}{5}\right)$.

28. $\left|\frac{x + 1}{2}\right| \geq 4$ $\Leftrightarrow$ $\left|\frac{1}{2}(x + 1)\right| \geq 4$ $\Leftrightarrow$ $\frac{1}{2}|x + 1| \geq 4$ $\Leftrightarrow$ $|x + 1| \geq 8$ which is equivalent
    either to $x + 1 \geq 8$ $\Leftrightarrow$ $x \geq 7$, or to $x + 1 \leq -8$ $\Leftrightarrow$ $x \leq -9$.
    Interval: $(-\infty, -9] \cup [7, \infty)$.

30. $|x - a| < d$ $\Leftrightarrow$ $-d < x - a < d$ $\Leftrightarrow$ $a - d < x < a + d$. Interval: $(a - d, a + d)$.

32. $3 - |2x + 4| \leq 1$ $\Leftrightarrow$ $-|2x + 4| \leq -2$ $\Leftrightarrow$ $|2x + 4| \geq 2$ which is equivalent to either
    $2x + 4 \geq 2$ $\Leftrightarrow$ $2x \geq -2$ $\Leftrightarrow$ $x \geq -1$; or $2x + 4 \leq -2$ $\Leftrightarrow$ $2x \leq -6$ $\Leftrightarrow$ $x \leq -3$.
    Interval: $(-\infty, -3] \cup [-1, \infty)$.

34. $7|x + 2| + 5 > 4$ $\Leftrightarrow$ $7|x + 2| > -1$ $\Leftrightarrow$ $|x + 2| > -\frac{1}{7}$. Since the absolute value is always nonnegative, the inequality is true for all real numbers. In interval notation, we have $(-\infty, \infty)$.

36. $2\left|\frac{1}{2}x + 3\right| + 3 \le 51$ $\Leftrightarrow$ $2\left|\frac{1}{2}x + 3\right| \le 48$ $\Leftrightarrow$ $\left|\frac{1}{2}x + 3\right| \le 24$ $\Leftrightarrow$ $-24 < \frac{1}{2}x + 3 < 24$
     $\Leftrightarrow$ $-27 < \frac{1}{2}x < 21$ $\Leftrightarrow$ $-54 < x < 42$. Interval: $(-54, 42)$.

38. $0 < |x - 5| \le \frac{1}{2}$. For $x \ne 5$, this is equivalent to $-\frac{1}{2} \le x - 5 \le \frac{1}{2}$ $\Leftrightarrow$ $\frac{9}{2} \le x \le \frac{11}{2}$. Since
     $x = 5$ is excluded, the solution is $\left[\frac{9}{2}, 5\right) \cup \left(5, \frac{11}{2}\right]$.

40. $\dfrac{1}{|2x - 3|} \le 5$ $\Leftrightarrow$ $\frac{1}{5} \le |2x - 3|$, since $|2x - 3| > 0$, provided $2x - 3 \ne 0$ $\Leftrightarrow$ $x \ne \frac{3}{2}$. Now
     for $x \ne \frac{3}{2}$, we have $\frac{1}{5} \le |2x - 3|$ is equivalent to $\frac{1}{5} \le 2x - 3$ $\Leftrightarrow$ $\frac{16}{5} \le 2x$ $\Leftrightarrow$ $\frac{8}{5} \le x$; or
     $2x - 3 \le -\frac{1}{5}$ $\Leftrightarrow$ $2x \le \frac{14}{5}$ $\Leftrightarrow$ $x \le \frac{7}{5}$. Interval: $\left(-\infty, \frac{7}{5}\right] \cup \left[\frac{8}{5}, \infty\right)$.

42. We graph the equations $y_1 = |x^2 - 16|$ and $y_2 = 9$ in the viewing rectangle $[-10, 10]$ by $[0, 15]$. Using Zoom and/or Trace, we get the solutions $x = -5$, $x = 5$, $x \approx -2.65$, and $x \approx 2.65$.

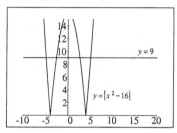

44. We graph the equations $y_1 = ||x - 2| - 10|$ and $y_2 = 5$ in the viewing rectangle $[-20, 20]$ by $[0, 10]$. Using Zoom and/or Trace, we get the solutions $x = -13$, $x = -3$, $x = 7$, and $x = 17$.

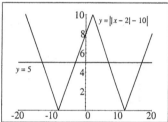

46. We graph the equations $y_1 = |x^2 - 25|$ and $y_2 = |x^2 - 4|$ in the viewing rectangle $[-20, 20]$ by $[0, 10]$. Using Zoom and/or Trace we find that the points of intersection are at $x \approx -3.8$ and $x \approx 3.8$. Since we want $|x^2 - 25| \ge |x^2 - 4|$, the solution is the interval $(-3.8, 3.8)$.

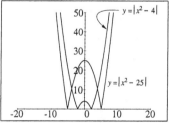

48. We graph the equations $y_1 = ||x - 3| - 12|$ and $y_2 = 6$ in the viewing rectangle $[-20, 20]$ by $[0, 10]$. We find that the points of intersection are at $x = -15$, $x = -3$, $x = 9$, and $x = 21$. Since we want $||x - 3| - 12| < 6$ the solution is $(-15, -3) \cup (9, 21)$.

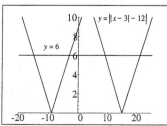

Review Exercises for Chapter 3

2. (a) Algebraically: $3 - x = 5 + 3x$ $\Leftrightarrow$ $-4x = 2$ $\Leftrightarrow$ $x = -\frac{1}{2}$.

   (b) Graphically: We graph the two equations $y_1 = 5x + 11$ and $y_2 = 5 + 3x$ in the viewing rectangle $[-5, 5]$ by $[-5, 5]$. Zooming in, we see that solution is $x = -\frac{1}{2}$.

   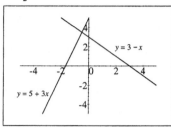

4. (a) Algebraically: $5x^4 - 16 = 0$ $\Leftrightarrow$ $5x^4 = 16$ $\Leftrightarrow$ $x^4 = \frac{16}{5}$ $\Rightarrow$ $x^2 = \pm\frac{4}{\sqrt{5}}$. Now

   $x^2 = -\frac{4}{\sqrt{5}}$ has no real solutions, so we solve $x^2 = \frac{4}{\sqrt{5}}$ $\Rightarrow$ $x = \pm\frac{2}{\sqrt[4]{5}} = \pm\frac{2\sqrt[4]{5^3}}{5}$.

   (b) Graphically: We graph the equation $y = 5x^4 - 16$ in the viewing rectangle $[-5, 5]$ by $[-5, 5]$. Zooming in, we see that solutions are $x \approx \pm 1.34$.

   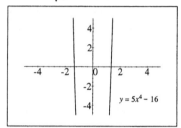

6. $(x + 2)^2 = (x - 4)^2$ $\Leftrightarrow$ $(x + 2)^2 - (x - 4)^2 = 0$ $\Leftrightarrow$
   $[(x + 2) - (x - 4)][(x + 2) + (x - 4)] = 0$ $\Leftrightarrow$
   $[x + 2 - x + 4][x + 2 + x - 4] = 6(2x - 2) = 0$ $\Leftrightarrow$ $2x - 2 = 0$ $\Leftrightarrow$ $x = 1$.

8. $x^2 + 24x + 144 = 0$ $\Leftrightarrow$ $(x + 12)^2 = 0$ $\Leftrightarrow$ $x + 12 = 0$ $\Leftrightarrow$ $x = -12$.

10. $3x^2 + 5x - 2 = 0$ $\Leftrightarrow$ $(3x - 1)(x + 2) = 0$ $\Leftrightarrow$ $x = \frac{1}{3}$ or $x = -2$.

12. $x^3 - 2x^2 - 5x + 10 = 0$ $\Leftrightarrow$ $x^2(x - 2) - 5(x - 2) = 0$ $\Leftrightarrow$ $(x - 2)(x^2 - 5) = 0$ $\Leftrightarrow$
   $x = 2$ or $x = \pm\sqrt{5}$.

14. $x^2 - 3x + 9 = 0$ $\Rightarrow$ $x = \dfrac{-b \pm \sqrt{b^2 - 4ac}}{2a} = \dfrac{-(-3) \pm \sqrt{(-3)^2 - 4(1)(9)}}{2(1)} = \dfrac{3 \pm \sqrt{9 - 36}}{2}$

   $= \dfrac{3 \pm \sqrt{-27}}{2}$, which are not real numbers. There are no real solutions.

16. $\dfrac{x}{x - 2} + \dfrac{1}{x + 2} = \dfrac{8}{x^2 - 4}$ $\Leftrightarrow$ $x(x + 2) + (x - 2) = 8$ $\Leftrightarrow$ $x^2 + 2x + x - 2 = 8$ $\Leftrightarrow$
   $x^2 + 3x - 10 = 0$ $\Leftrightarrow$ $(x - 2)(x + 5) = 0$ $\Leftrightarrow$ $x = 2$ or $x = -5$. However, since $x = 2$
   makes the expression undefined, we reject this solution. Hence the only solution is $x = -5$.

18. $x - 4\sqrt{x} = 32$. Let $u = \sqrt{x}$. Then $u^2 - 4u = 32$ $\Leftrightarrow$ $u^2 - 4u - 32 = 0$ $\Leftrightarrow$
   $(u - 8)(u + 4) = 0$. So $u - 8 = 0$ $\Rightarrow$ $\sqrt{x} - 8 = 0$ $\Leftrightarrow$ $\sqrt{x} = 8$ $\Rightarrow$ $x = 64$, or
   $u + 4 = 0$ $\Rightarrow$ $\sqrt{x} + 4 = 0$ $\Leftrightarrow$ $\sqrt{x} = -4$, which has no real solution. The only solution is
   $x = 64$.

20. $(1 + \sqrt{x})^2 - 2(1 + \sqrt{x}) - 15 = 0$. Let $u = 1 + \sqrt{x}$, then the equation becomes
$u^2 - 2u - 15 = 0 \quad \Leftrightarrow \quad (u - 5)(u + 3) = 0$. So $u - 5 = 1 + \sqrt{x} - 5 = 0 \quad \Leftrightarrow \quad \sqrt{x} = 4$
$\Rightarrow \quad x = 16$; or $u + 3 = 1 + \sqrt{x} + 3 = 0 \quad \Leftrightarrow \quad \sqrt{x} = -4$, which has no real solution. The only solution is $x = 16$.

22. $|3x| = 18$ is equivalent to $3x = \pm 18 \quad \Leftrightarrow \quad x = \pm 6$.

24. $4|3 - x| + 3 = 15 \quad \Leftrightarrow \quad 4|3 - x| = 12 \quad \Leftrightarrow \quad |3 - x| = 3 \quad \Leftrightarrow \quad 3 - x = \pm 3$. So $3 - x = 3$
$\Leftrightarrow \quad -x = 0 \quad \Leftrightarrow \quad x = 0$; or $3 - x = -3 \quad \Leftrightarrow \quad -x = -6 \quad \Leftrightarrow \quad x = 6$. The solutions are
$x = 0$ and $x = 6$.

26. $\sqrt{x + 4} = x^2 - 5$. We graph the equations $y_1 = \sqrt{x + 4}$
and $y_2 = x^2 - 5$ in the viewing rectangle $[-4, 5]$ by
$[0, 10]$. Using Zoom and/or Trace, we get the solutions
$x \approx -2.50$ and $x \approx 2.76$.

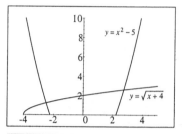

28. $||x + 3| - 5| = 2$. We graph the equations
$y_1 = ||x + 3| - 5|$ and $y_2 = 2$ in the viewing rectangle
$[-20, 20]$ by $[0, 10]$. Using Zoom and/or Trace, we get the
solutions $x = -10$, $x = -6$, $x = 0$, and $x = 4$.

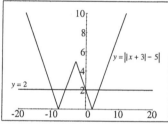

30. Let t be the number of hours that Anthony drives. Then Helen drives for $t - \frac{1}{4}$ hours.

	Rate	Time	Distance
Anthony	45	t	$45t$
Helen	40	$t - \frac{1}{4}$	$40\left(t - \frac{1}{4}\right)$

When they pass each other, they will have traveled a total of 160 miles. So $45t + 40\left(t - \frac{1}{4}\right) = 160$
$\Leftrightarrow \quad 45t + 40t - 10 = 160 \quad \Leftrightarrow \quad 85t = 170 \quad \Leftrightarrow \quad t = 2$. Since Anthony leaves at 2:00 P.M.
and travels for 2 hours, they pass each other at 4:00 P.M.

32. Substituting 75 for d, we have $75 = x + \dfrac{x^2}{20} \quad \Leftrightarrow \quad 1500 = 20x + x^2 \quad \Leftrightarrow$
$x^2 + 20x - 1500 = 0 \quad \Leftrightarrow \quad (x - 30)(x + 50) = 0$. So $x = 30$ or $x = -50$. Since x is the speed
of the car, $x > 0$, the speed of the car must have been 30 mi/h.

34. Let t be the time it would take Abbie to paint a living room if she works alone. It would take Beth
$2t$ hours to paint the living room alone, and it would take $3t$ for Cathie to paint the living room.
Thus Abbie does $\dfrac{1}{t}$ of the job per hour, Beth does $\dfrac{1}{2t}$ of the job per hour, and Cathie does $\dfrac{1}{3t}$ of the
job per hour. So $\dfrac{1}{t} + \dfrac{1}{2t} + \dfrac{1}{3t} = 1 \quad \Leftrightarrow \quad 6 + 3 + 2 = 6t \quad \Leftrightarrow \quad 6t = 11 \quad \Leftrightarrow \quad t = \dfrac{11}{6}$. So it
would Abbie 1 hour and 50 minutes to paint the living room alone.

36. Let l be length of each garden plot. The width of each plot is then $\dfrac{80}{l}$ and the total amount of

fencing material is $4(l) + 6\left(\dfrac{80}{l}\right) = 88$. Thus $4l + \dfrac{480}{l} = 88 \quad \Leftrightarrow \quad 4l^2 + 480 = 88l \quad \Leftrightarrow$

$4l^2 - 88l + 480 = 0 \quad \Leftrightarrow \quad 4(l^2 - 22l + 120) = 0 \quad \Leftrightarrow \quad 4(l - 10)(l - 12) = 0$. So $l = 10$ or
$l = 12$. If $l = 10$ feet, then the width of each plot is $\frac{80}{10} = 8$ feet. If $l = 12$ feet, then the width of
each plot is $\frac{80}{12} = 6.67$ feet. Both solutions are possible.

38. $(-2 + 3\,i) + (\frac{1}{2} - i) = -2 + 3\,i + \frac{1}{2} - i = -\frac{3}{2} + 2\,i$.

40. $3(5 - 2\,i)\dfrac{i}{5} = (15 - 6\,i)\dfrac{i}{5} = 3i - \dfrac{6}{5}i^2 = \dfrac{6}{5} + 3\,i$.

42. $\dfrac{2 + i}{4 - 3\,i} = \dfrac{2 + i}{4 - 3\,i} \cdot \dfrac{4 + 3\,i}{4 + 3\,i} = \dfrac{8 + 6\,i + 4\,i + 3\,i^2}{16 - 9\,i^2} = \dfrac{8 + 10\,i - 3}{16 + 9} = \dfrac{5 + 10\,i}{25} = \dfrac{1}{5} + \dfrac{2}{5}\,i$.

44. $(3 - i)^3 = (3)^3 - 3(3)^2(i) + 3(3)(i)^2 + (i)^3\,i = 27 - 27\,i + 9i^2 + i^3 = 27 - 27\,i - 9 - i$
    $= 18 - 28\,i$.

46. $\sqrt{-5} \cdot \sqrt{-20} = \sqrt{5}\,i \cdot 2\sqrt{5}\,i = 10\,i^2 = -10$.

48. $x^2 = -12 \quad \Rightarrow \quad x = \pm\sqrt{-12} = \pm 2\sqrt{3}\,i$.

50. $2x^2 - 3x + 2 = 0 \quad \Rightarrow \quad x = \dfrac{-(-3) \pm \sqrt{(-3)^2 - 4(2)(2)}}{2(2)} = \dfrac{3 \pm \sqrt{9 - 16}}{4} = \dfrac{3 \pm \sqrt{-7}}{4}$

$= \dfrac{3 \pm \sqrt{7}\,i}{4}$.

52. $x^3 - 2x^2 + 4x - 8 = 0 \quad \Leftrightarrow \quad x^2(x - 2) + 4(x - 2) = 0 \quad \Leftrightarrow \quad (x - 2)(x^2 + 4) = 0 \quad \Leftrightarrow$
    $x = 2$, or $x^2 + 4 = 0 \quad \Leftrightarrow \quad x^2 = -4 \quad \Rightarrow \quad x = \pm\sqrt{-4} = \pm 2i$. The solutions are 2 and $\pm 2i$.

54. $x^3 = 125 \quad \Leftrightarrow \quad x^3 - 125 = 0 \quad \Leftrightarrow \quad (x - 5)(x^2 + 5x + 25) = 0$. So $x = 5$, or
    $x = \dfrac{-5 \pm \sqrt{5^2 - 4(1)(25)}}{2(1)} = \dfrac{-5 \pm \sqrt{25 - 100}}{2} = \dfrac{-5 \pm \sqrt{-75}}{2} = \dfrac{-5 \pm 5\sqrt{3}\,i}{2}$.

    The solutions are 5 and $\dfrac{-5 \pm 5\sqrt{3}\,i}{2}$.

56. $12 - x \geq 7x \quad \Leftrightarrow \quad 12 \geq 8x \quad \Leftrightarrow \quad \frac{3}{2} \geq x$. Interval: $\left(-\infty, \frac{3}{2}\right]$

    Graph: _____
                              $\frac{3}{2}$

58. $3 - x \leq 2x - 7 \quad \Leftrightarrow \quad 10 \leq 3x \quad \Leftrightarrow \quad \frac{10}{3} \leq x$. Interval: $\left[\frac{10}{3}, \infty\right)$

    Graph: _____
                $\frac{10}{3}$

60. $x^2 \leq 1 \quad \Leftrightarrow \quad x^2 - 1 \leq 0 \quad \Leftrightarrow \quad (x - 1)(x + 1) \leq 0$. The expression on the left of the inequality
    changes sign when $x = -1$ and $x = 1$. Thus we must check the intervals in the following table.

Interval	$(-\infty, -1)$	$(-1, 1)$	$(1, \infty)$
Sign of $x - 1$	$-$	$-$	$+$
Sign of $x + 1$	$-$	$+$	$+$
Sign of $(x - 1)(x + 1)$	$+$	$-$	$+$

Interval: $[-1, 1]$ Graph: _____
                                              -1 1

62. $2x^2 \geq x + 3 \quad \Leftrightarrow \quad 2x^2 - x - 3 \geq 0 \quad \Leftrightarrow \quad (2x - 3)(x + 1) \geq 0$. The expression on the left of the inequality changes sign when -1 and $\frac{3}{2}$. Thus we must check the intervals in the following table.

Interval	$(-\infty, -1)$	$(-1, \frac{3}{2})$	$(\frac{3}{2}, \infty)$
Sign of $2x - 3$	$-$	$-$	$+$
Sign of $x + 1$	$-$	$+$	$+$
Sign of $(2x - 3)(x + 1)$	$+$	$-$	$+$

Interval: $(-\infty, -1] \cup \left[\frac{3}{2}, \infty\right)$ Graph: ━━━━━━● ●━━━━━
                                                                        -1 $\frac{3}{2}$

64. $\dfrac{5}{x^3 - x^2 - 4x + 4} < 0 \quad \Leftrightarrow \quad \dfrac{5}{x^2(x - 1) - 4(x - 1)} < 0 \quad \Leftrightarrow \quad \dfrac{5}{(x - 1)(x^2 - 4)} < 0 \quad \Leftrightarrow$

$\dfrac{5}{(x - 1)(x - 2)(x + 2)} < 0$. The expression on the left of the inequality changes sign when $-2, 1$, and 2. Thus we must check the intervals in the following table.

Interval	$(-\infty, -2)$	$(-2, 1)$	$(1, 2)$	$(2, \infty)$
Sign of $x - 1$	$-$	$-$	$+$	$+$
Sign of $x - 2$	$-$	$-$	$-$	$+$
Sign of $x + 2$	$-$	$+$	$+$	$+$
Sign of $\dfrac{5}{(x - 1)(x - 2)(x + 2)}$	$-$	$+$	$-$	$+$

Interval: $(-\infty, -2) \cup (1, 2)$ Graph: ━━━━━━○   ○━━●━━
                                                       -2 1 2

66. $|x - 4| < 0.02 \quad \Leftrightarrow \quad -0.02 < x - 4 < 0.02 \quad \Leftrightarrow \quad 3.98 < x < 4.02$. Interval: $(3.98, 4.02)$.
Graph: ━━━━○━━━━━○━━━━
          3.98 4.02

68. $|x - 1|$ is the distance between x and 1 on the number line, and $|x - 3|$ is the distance between x and 3. We want those points that are closer to 1 than to 3. Since 2 is midway between 1 and 3, we get $x \in (-\infty, 2)$ as the solution.   Graph: ━━━━━━━○━━━━━
                                                                           2

70. $x^3 - 4x^2 - 5x > 2$. We graph the equations $y_1 = x^3 - 4x^2 - 5x$ and $y_2 = 2$ in the viewing rectangle $[-10, 10]$ by $[-5, 5]$. We find that the point of intersection is at $x \approx 5.07$. Since we want $x^3 - 4x^2 - 5x > 2$, the solution is the interval $(5.07, \infty)$.

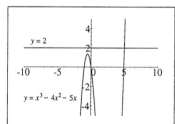

72. $|x^2 - 16| - 10 \geq 0$. We graph the equation $y = |x^2 - 16| - 10$ in the viewing rectangle $[-10, 10]$ by $[-10, 10]$. Using Zoom and/or Trace, we find that the points of intersection are at $x \approx \pm 5.10$ and $x \approx \pm 2.45$. Since we want $|x^2 - 16| - 10 \geq 0$, the solution is $(-\infty, -5.10] \cup [-2.45, 2.45] \cup [5.10, \infty)$.

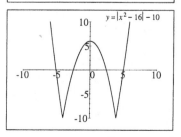

74. We have $8 \leq \dfrac{4}{3}\pi r^3 \leq 12 \quad \Leftrightarrow \quad \dfrac{6}{\pi} \leq r^3 \leq \dfrac{9}{\pi} \quad \Leftrightarrow \quad \sqrt[3]{\dfrac{6}{\pi}} \leq r \leq \sqrt[3]{\dfrac{9}{\pi}}$. Thus $r \in \left[\sqrt[3]{\dfrac{6}{\pi}}, \sqrt[3]{\dfrac{9}{\pi}}\right]$.

Focus on Problem Solving

2. We know that $\sqrt{2}$ is irrational. Now $\sqrt{2}^{\sqrt{2}}$ is either rational or irrational. If $\sqrt{2}^{\sqrt{2}}$ is rational, we would be done because we would have found an irrational number raised to an irrational number which is rational. If $\sqrt{2}^{\sqrt{2}}$ is not rational, then consider $\left(\sqrt{2}^{\sqrt{2}}\right)^{\sqrt{2}} = \sqrt{2}^{\sqrt{2}\cdot\sqrt{2}} = \sqrt{2}^{2} = 2$. So, again we would have found an irrational number (namely $\sqrt{2}^{\sqrt{2}}$) raised to an irrational number (namely $\sqrt{2}$) which is rational (namely 2).

4.   ABCDE
        $\underline{\quad\quad\quad 4}$
      EDCBA

   A must be 1 or 2, since 4A consists of just a single digit. Since A is also the last digit of 4E, it must be even, and so A = 2. Now E $\geq$ 4A = 8 (since E is the first digit of the product), and since 4E ends in the digit A = 2, E must be 8. So far we have

      2BCD8
        $\underline{\quad\quad\quad 4}$
      8DCB2 .

   Now B must be odd, since it is the last digit of 4D + 3. Also, 4B consists of just a single digit (since there is no "carry" added to the final product $4 \cdot 2 = 8$). Thus B = 1, and so 4D + 3 ends in an 8 ($11 - 3 = 8$, $21 - 3 = 18$, and so on). The only possibilities are D = 2 or 7, but since 2 is already used, D = 7. Now we have

      21C78
        $\underline{\quad\quad\quad 4}$
      87C12 .

   The digit 7 in the product could only have resulted from the preceding product ($7 = 4 \cdot 1 + \underline{3}$). Thus the product that results in the C must have a 3 as its first digit; that is, $4C + 3 = 30 + C$. So $3C = 27$ and C = 9. The product is

      21978
        $\underline{\quad\quad\quad 4}$
      87912 .

6. For convenience, let us label the eggs 1, 2, 3, ... , 9. First we weigh $\{1, 2, 3\}$ against $\{4, 5, 6\}$.
   Case 1: If the first weighing is equal, then the light egg is in $\{7, 8, 9\}$, and so we weigh 7 against 8. If this second weighing is unequal, then we can tell whether 7 or 8 is lighter. If not, 9 is the light egg.
   Case 2: If the first weighing is unequal, consider the lighter group, and suppose it is $\{1, 2, 3\}$. Weigh 1 against 2. If this second weighing is unequal, then we can tell whether 1 or 2 is lighter. If not, 3 is the light egg.
   The method is displayed in a *decision* tree below.

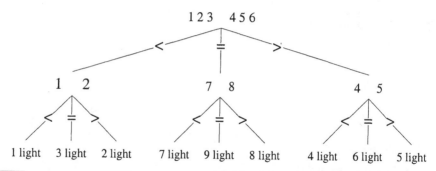

8.   Since $\sqrt{1800} \approx 42.4$ and $\sqrt{1900} \approx 43.6$, Augustus DeMorgan must have been 43 in the year $43^2 = 1849$. He then lived 22 more years, so he died in the year $1849 + 22 = 1871$.

10. You can see infinitely far in this forest, because if your vision is blocked by a tree (at the rational point (a, b), say), then the slope of the line of sight from you to this tree is $\frac{b-0}{a-0} = \frac{b}{a}$, which is a rational number. Thus if you look along a line of irrational slope, you will see infinitely far.

12. We consider four cases corresponding to each quadrant.
     Case (i), $x \geq 0$ and $y \geq 0$: $|x| + |y| \leq 1$ becomes $x + y \leq 1$.
     Case (ii), $x \leq 0$ and $y \geq 0$: $|x| + |y| \leq 1$ becomes $-x + y \leq 1$.
     Case (iii), $x \geq 0$ and $y \leq 0$: $|x| + |y| \leq 1$ becomes $x - y \leq 1$.
     Case (iv), $x \leq 0$ and $y \leq 0$: $|x| + |y| \leq 1$ becomes $-x - y \leq 1$
     $\Leftrightarrow \quad x + y \geq -1$.

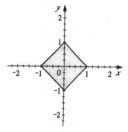

14. Let r and R be the radius of the smaller circle and larger circle, respectively. Since the line is tangent to the smaller circle, using the Pythagorean Theorem, we get the following relationship between the radii: $R^2 = 1^2 + r^2$. Thus the area of the shaded region is $\pi R^2 - \pi r^2 = \pi(1 + r^2) - \pi r^2 = \pi$.

16. Label the figures as shown. The unshaded area is c^2 in the first figure and $a^2 + b^2$ in the second figure. These unshaded areas are equal, since in each case they equal the area of the large square minus the areas of the four shaded triangles. Thus $a^2 + b^2 = c^2$. Finally, note that a, b, and c are the legs and hypotenuse of the shaded triangle.

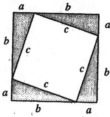
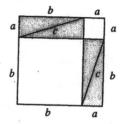

Chapter Four

Exercises 4.1

2. $f(x) = \dfrac{x-5}{7}$

4. $f(x) = \sqrt{x^2+1}$

6. Subtract 5, then divide by 3.

8. Multiply by 2, add 1, then take the square root.

10. Machine diagram for $f(x) = \dfrac{2}{x}$.

12. $g(x) = |2x-3|$

x	$g(x)$
-2	$|2(-2)-3| = 7$
0	$|2(0)-3| = 3$
1	$|2(1)-3| = 1$
3	$|2(3)-3| = 3$
5	$|2(5)-3| = 7$

14. $f(0) = 0^2 + 2(0) = 0;\quad f(3) = 3^2 + 2(3) = 9 + 6 = 15;\quad f(-3) = (-3)^2 + 2(-3) = 9 - 6 = 3;$
$f(a) = a^2 + 2(a) = a^2 + 2a;\quad f(-x) = (-x)^2 + 2(-x) = x^2 - 2x;$
$f\left(\dfrac{1}{a}\right) = \left(\dfrac{1}{a}\right)^2 + 2\left(\dfrac{1}{a}\right) = \dfrac{1}{a^2} + \dfrac{2}{a}.$

16. $h(1) = (1) + \dfrac{1}{(1)} = 2;\quad h(-1) = (-1) + \dfrac{1}{-1} = -1 - 1 = -2;\quad h(2) = 2 + \dfrac{1}{2} = \dfrac{5}{2};$
$h(\tfrac{1}{2}) = \dfrac{1}{2} + \dfrac{1}{\frac{1}{2}} = \dfrac{1}{2} + 2 = \dfrac{5}{2};\quad h(x) = x + \dfrac{1}{x};\quad h\left(\dfrac{1}{x}\right) = \dfrac{1}{x} + \dfrac{1}{\frac{1}{x}} = \dfrac{1}{x} + x.$

18. $f(0) = 0^3 - 4(0)^2 = 0 + 0 = 0;\quad f(1) = 1^3 - 4(1)^2 = 1 - 4 = -3;$
$f(-1) = (-1)^3 - 4(-1)^2 = -1 - 4 = -5;\quad f\left(\tfrac{3}{2}\right) = \left(\tfrac{3}{2}\right)^3 - 4\left(\tfrac{3}{2}\right)^2 = \dfrac{27}{8} - 9 = -\dfrac{45}{8};$
$f\left(\dfrac{x}{2}\right) = \left(\dfrac{x}{2}\right)^3 - 4\left(\dfrac{x}{2}\right)^2 = \dfrac{x^3}{8} - x^2;\quad f(x^2) = (x^2)^3 - 4(x^2)^2 = x^6 - 4x^4.$

20. $f(-2) = \dfrac{|-2|}{-2} = \dfrac{2}{-2} = -1;\quad f(-1) = \dfrac{|-1|}{-1} = \dfrac{1}{-1} = -1;\quad f(x)$ is not defined at $x = 0$;
$f(5) = \dfrac{|5|}{5} = \dfrac{5}{5} = 1;\quad f(x^2) = \dfrac{|x^2|}{x^2} = \dfrac{x^2}{x^2} = 1$ since $x^2 > 0,\, x \neq 0;\quad f\left(\dfrac{1}{x}\right) = \dfrac{\left|\frac{1}{x}\right|}{\frac{1}{x}} = \dfrac{x}{|x|}.$

22. Since $-3 \leq 2$, we have $f(-3) = 5$. Since $0 \leq 2$, we have $f(0) = 5$. Since $2 \leq 2$, we have $f(2) = 5$. Since $3 > 2$, we have $f(3) = 2(3) - 3 = 3$. Since $5 > 2$, we have $f(5) = 2(5) - 3 = 7$.

24. Since $-5 < 0$, we have $f(-5) = 3(-5) = -15$. Since $0 \leq 0 \leq 2$, we have $f(0) = 0 + 1 = 1$. Since $0 \leq 1 \leq 2$, we have $f(1) = 1 + 1 = 2$. Since $0 \leq 2 \leq 2$, we have $f(2) = 2 + 1 = 3$. Since $5 > 2$, we have $f(5) = (5 - 2)^2 = 9$.

26. $f(2x) = 3(2x) - 1 = 6x - 1; \quad 2f(x) = 2(3x - 1) = 6x - 2.$

28. $f\left(\dfrac{x}{3}\right) = 6\left(\dfrac{x}{3}\right) - 18 = 2x - 18; \quad \dfrac{f(x)}{3} = \dfrac{6x - 18}{3} = \dfrac{3(2x - 6)}{3} = 2x - 6.$

30. $f(a) = (a)^2 + 1 = a^2 + 1; \quad f(a + h) = (a + h)^2 + 1 = a^2 + 2ah + h^2 + 1;$

$$\dfrac{f(a + h) - f(a)}{h} = \dfrac{(a^2 + 2ah + h^2 + 1) - (a^2 + 1)}{h} = \dfrac{a^2 + 2ah + h^2 + 1 - a^2 - 1}{h}$$

$$= \dfrac{2ah + h^2}{h} = \dfrac{h(2a + h)}{h} = 2a + h.$$

32. $f(a) = \dfrac{1}{a + 1}; \quad f(a + h) = \dfrac{1}{a + h + 1};$

$$\dfrac{f(a + h) - f(a)}{h} = \dfrac{\dfrac{1}{a + h + 1} - \dfrac{1}{a + 1}}{h} = \dfrac{\dfrac{a + 1}{(a + 1)(a + h + 1)} - \dfrac{a + h + 1}{(a + 1)(a + h + 1)}}{h}$$

$$= \dfrac{\dfrac{-h}{(a + 1)(a + h + 1)}}{h} = \dfrac{-1}{(a + 1)(a + h + 1)}.$$

34. $f(a) = a^3; \quad f(a + h) = (a + h)^3 = a^3 + 3a^2 h + 3ah^2 + h^3;$

$$\dfrac{f(a + h) - f(a)}{h} = \dfrac{(a^3 + 3a^2 h + 3ah^2 + h^3) - (a^3)}{h}$$

$$= \dfrac{3a^2 h + 3ah^2 + h^3}{h} = \dfrac{h(3a^2 + 3ah + h^2)}{h} = 3a^2 + 3ah + h^2.$$

36. $f(x) = x^2 + 1$. Since there is no restrictions, the domain is all real numbers.

38. $f(x) = x^2 + 1$. The domain is restricted by the exercise to $[0, 5]$.

40. $f(x) = \dfrac{1}{3x - 6}$. Since the denominator cannot equal 0, we have $3x - 6 \neq 0 \quad \Leftrightarrow \quad 3x \neq 6 \quad \Leftrightarrow \quad x \neq 2$. In interval notation, the domain is $(-\infty, 2) \cup (2, \infty)$.

42. $f(x) = \dfrac{x^4}{x^2 + x - 6}$. Since the denominator cannot equal 0, $x^2 + x - 6 \neq 0 \quad \Leftrightarrow \quad (x + 3)(x - 2) \neq 0 \quad \Rightarrow \quad x \neq -3$ or $x \neq 2$. In interval notation, the domain is $(-\infty, -3) \cup (-3, 2) \cup (2, \infty)$.

44. $f(x) = \sqrt[4]{x + 9}$. Since even roots are only defined for non-negative numbers, we must have $x + 9 \geq 0 \quad \Leftrightarrow \quad x \geq -9$, so the domain is $[-9, \infty)$.

46. $g(x) = \sqrt{7 - 3x}$. For the square root to be defined, we must have $7 - 3x \geq 0$ $\Leftrightarrow$ $7 \geq 3x$
     $\Leftrightarrow$ $\frac{7}{3} \geq x$. Thus the domain is $(-\infty, \frac{7}{3}]$.

48. $G(x) = \sqrt{x^2 - 9}$. We must have $x^2 - 9 \geq 0$ $\Leftrightarrow$ $x^2 \geq 9$ $\Leftrightarrow$ $|x| \geq 3$ $\Rightarrow$ $x \geq 3$ or
     $x \leq -3$. Thus the domain is $(-\infty, -3] \cup [3, \infty)$.

50. $g(x) = \dfrac{\sqrt{x}}{2x^2 + x - 1}$. We must have $x \geq 0$ for the numerator and $2x^2 + x - 1 \neq 0$ for the
     denominator. So $2x^2 + x - 1 \neq 0$ $\Leftrightarrow$ $(2x - 1)(x + 1) \neq 0$ $\Rightarrow$ $2x - 1 \neq 0$ or $x + 1 \neq 0$
     $\Leftrightarrow$ $x \neq \frac{1}{2}$ or $x \neq -1$. Thus the domain is $[0, \frac{1}{2}) \cup (\frac{1}{2}, \infty)$.

52. $g(x) = \sqrt{x^2 - 2x - 8}$. We must have $x^2 - 2x - 8 \geq 0$ $\Leftrightarrow$ $(x - 4)(x + 2) \geq 0$. Using the
     methods from Section 3.7, we have

	$(-\infty, -2)$	$(-2, 4)$	$(4, \infty)$
Sign of $x - 4$	$-$	$-$	$+$
Sign of $x + 2$	$-$	$+$	$+$
Sign of $(x - 4)(x + 2)$	$+$	$-$	$+$

     Thus the domain is $(-\infty, -2] \cup [4, \infty)$.

54. The salesman travels away from home and stops to make a sales call between 9 a.m. and 10 a.m.,
     and then travels further from home for a sales call between 12 noon and 1 p.m. Next he travels
     along a route that takes him closer to home before taking him further away from home. He then
     makes a final sales call between 5 p.m. and 6 p.m. and then returns home.

56. We assume the grass grows linearly.

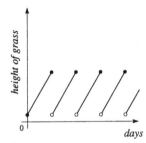

58. 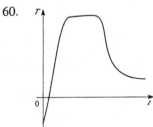   60.

62. (a) The first noticeable movements occurred 5 seconds after the start of the earthquake.

     (b) It seemed to end 30 seconds after the start of the earthquake.

     (c) Maximum intensity was reached 17 seconds after the start of the earthquake.

64.

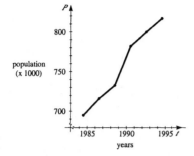

66.   Answers will vary

Exercises 4.2

2. (a) $g(-4) = 3$; $g(-2) = 2$; $g(0) = -2$; $g(2) = 1$; $g(4) = 0$.
    (b) Domain: $[-4, 4]$. Range: $[-2, 3]$.

4. (a) $f(0.5) \approx 1.2$
    (b) $f(3) \approx 2.1$
    (c) $x = 0.4$ and $x = 3.6$ are the only solutions to the equation $f(x) = 1$.

6. The curves in parts (b) and (c) are graphs of functions of x.

8. No, the given curve is not the graph of a function of x.

10. The given curve is the graph of a function of x. Domain: $[-3, 2]$. Range: $\{-2\} \cup (0, 3]$.

12. (a) $f(x) = \frac{1}{2}(x + 1)$ (b) Domain: All real numbers.

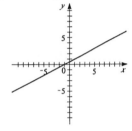

14. (a) $f(x) = x^2 - 4x + 4$ (b) Domain: All real numbers.

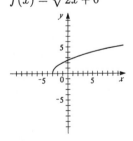

16. (a) $f(x) = \sqrt{2x + 6}$ (b) $2x + 6 \geq 0$ $\Leftrightarrow$ $2x \geq -6$ $\Leftrightarrow$ $x \geq -3$.
                                                                 Domain: $[-3, \infty)$.

18. (a) $f(x) = -\sqrt{25 - x^2}$

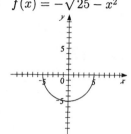

(b) $25 - x^2 \geq 0$ $\Leftrightarrow$ $25 \geq x^2$ $\Leftrightarrow$ $5 \geq |x|$
$\Leftrightarrow$ $-5 \leq x \leq 5$. Therefore, the domain is
$[-5, 5]$.

20. $f(x) = -5$

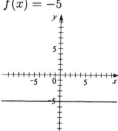

22. $f(x) = 6 - 3x$

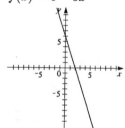

24. $f(x) = \dfrac{x + 3}{2}, \; -2 \leq x \leq 2$

26. $f(x) = x^2 - 4$

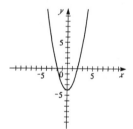

28. $g(x) = 4x^2 - x^4$

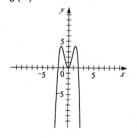

30. $g(x) = \sqrt{6 - 2x}$

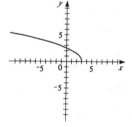

32. $F(x) = \dfrac{2}{x+4}$

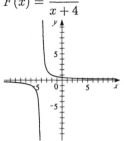

34. $H(x) = |x+1|$

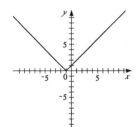

36. $G(x) = |x| - x$

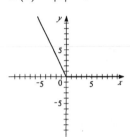

38. $f(x) = \dfrac{x}{|x|}$

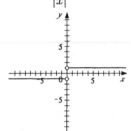

40. $g(x) = \dfrac{|x|}{x^2}$

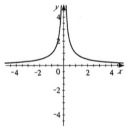

42. Solving for y in terms of x gives: $3x + 7y = 21 \quad \Leftrightarrow \quad 7y = -3x + 21 \quad \Leftrightarrow \quad y = -\frac{3}{7}x + 3$.
     This defines y as a function of x.

44. Solving for y in terms of x gives: $x^2 + (y-1)^2 = 4 \quad \Leftrightarrow \quad (y-1)^2 = 4 - x^2 \quad \Leftrightarrow$
     $y - 1 = \pm\sqrt{4 - x^2} \quad \Leftrightarrow \quad y = 1 \pm \sqrt{4 - x^2}$. The last equation gives two values of y for a given
     value of x. Thus, this equation does not define y as a function of x.

46. Solving for y in terms of x gives: $x^2 + y = 9 \quad \Leftrightarrow \quad y = 9 - x^2$. This defines y as a function of x.

48. Solving for y in terms of x gives: $\sqrt{x} + y = 12 \quad \Leftrightarrow \quad y = 12 - \sqrt{x}$. This defines y as a
     function of x.

50. Solving for y in terms of x gives: $2x + |y| = 0 \quad \Leftrightarrow \quad |y| = -2x$. Since $|a| = |-a|$, the last
     equation gives two values of y for a given value of x. Thus, this equation does not define y as a
     function of x.

52. Solving for y in terms of x gives: $x = y^4 \quad \Leftrightarrow \quad y = \pm\sqrt[4]{x}$. The last equation gives two values of
     y for a given value of x. Thus, this equation does not define y as a function of x.

54. (a) $f(x) = (x - c)^2$, for $c = 0, 1, 2$, and 3.   (b) $f(x) = (x - c)^2$, for $c = 0, -1, -2$, and -3.

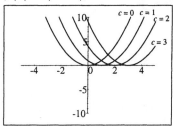   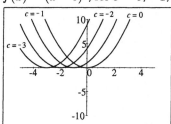

(c) The graphs in part (a) are obtained by shifting the graph of $y = x^2$ to the right 1, 2, and 3 units, while the graphs in part (b) are obtained by shifting the graph of $y = x^2$ to the left 1, 2, and 3 units.

56. (a) $f(x) = cx^2$, for $c = 1, \frac{1}{2}, 2$, and 4.   (b) $f(x) = cx^2$, for $c = 1, -1, -\frac{1}{2}$, and -2.

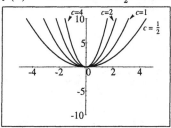   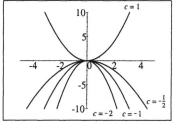

(c) As $|c|$ increases, the graph of $f(x) = cx^2$ is stretched vertically. As $|c|$ decreases, the graph of f is flattened. When $c < 0$, the graph is reflected about the x-axis.

58. (a) $f(x) = \dfrac{1}{x^n}$, for $n = 1$ and 3.   (b) $f(x) = \dfrac{1}{x^n}$, for $n = 2$ and 4.

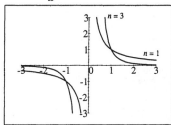   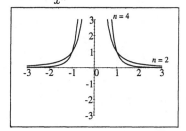

(c) As n increases, the graphs of $y = \dfrac{1}{x^n}$ go to zero faster for x large. Also, as n increases and x goes to 0, the graphs of $y = \dfrac{1}{x^n}$ go to infinity faster. The graphs of $y = \dfrac{1}{x^n}$ for n odd are similar to each other. Likewise, the graphs for n even are similar to each other.

60. $f(x) = \begin{cases} 1 & \text{if } x \leq 1 \\ x+1 & \text{if } x > 1 \end{cases}$

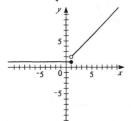

62. $f(x) = \begin{cases} 1-x & \text{if } x < -2 \\ 5 & \text{if } x \geq -2 \end{cases}$

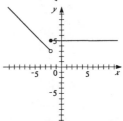

64. $f(x) = \begin{cases} 2x+3 & \text{if } x < -1 \\ 3-x & \text{if } x \geq -1 \end{cases}$

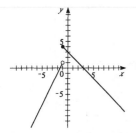

66. $f(x) = \begin{cases} -1 & \text{if } x < -1 \\ x & \text{if } -1 \leq x \leq 1 \\ 1 & \text{if } x > 1 \end{cases}$

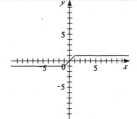

68. $f(x) = \begin{cases} 1-x^2 & \text{if } x \leq 2 \\ x & \text{if } x > 2 \end{cases}$

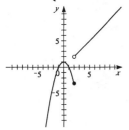

70. $f(x) = \begin{cases} x^2 & \text{if } |x| \leq 1 \\ 1 & \text{if } |x| > 1 \end{cases}$

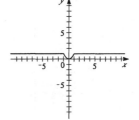

72. $f(x) = \begin{cases} -x & \text{if } x \leq 0 \\ 9-x^2 & \text{if } 0 < x \leq 3 \\ x-3 & \text{if } x > 3 \end{cases}$

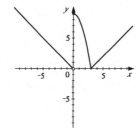

74. $f(x) = \begin{cases} 2x - x^2 & \text{if } x > 1 \\ (x-1)^3 & \text{if } x \leq 1 \end{cases}$

The viewing rectangle below shows the output of a typical graphing device. However, the graph of this function is also shown below, and its difference from the graphing device's version should be noted.

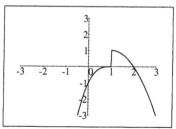   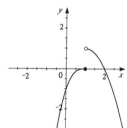

76. $P(x) = \begin{cases} 0.33 & \text{if } 0 < x \leq 1 \\ 0.55 & \text{if } 1 < x \leq 2 \\ 0.77 & \text{if } 2 < x \leq 3 \\ \quad \vdots \\ 2.75 & \text{if } 11 < x \leq 12 \end{cases}$

78. The slope of the line containing the points $(-3, -2)$ and $(6, 3)$ is $m = \frac{-2-3}{-3-6} = \frac{-5}{-9} = \frac{5}{9}$. Using the point-slope equation of the line, we have $y - 3 = \frac{5}{9}(x - 6)$ $\Leftrightarrow$ $y = \frac{5}{9}x - \frac{10}{3} + 3 = \frac{5}{9}x - \frac{1}{3}$. Thus the function is $f(x) = \frac{5}{9}x - \frac{1}{3}$, for $-3 \leq x \leq 6$.

80. First solve for y. This gives $(x-1)^2 + y^2 = 1$ $\Leftrightarrow$ $y^2 = 1 - (x-1)^2$ $\Rightarrow$ $y = \pm\sqrt{1 - (x-1)^2}$. Since we are interested in the top half of the circle we want $y \geq 0$. Thus the function is $f(x) = \sqrt{1 - (x-1)^2} = \sqrt{2x - x^2}$, for $0 \leq x \leq 2$.

82. Answers vary. Some examples are almost anything we purchase based on weight, volume, length, or time, for example gasoline. Although the amount delivered by the pump is continuous, the amount we pay is rounded to the penny. An example involving time would be the cost of a telephone call.

84. (a) The graphs of $f(x) = x^2 + x - 6$ and $g(x) = |x^2 + x - 6|$ are shown in the viewing rectangle $[-10, 10]$ by $[-10, 10]$.

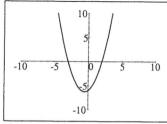   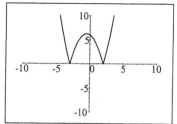

For those values of x where $f(x) \geq 0$, the graphs of f and g coincide, and for those values of x where $f(x) < 0$, the graph of g is obtained from that of f by reflecting the part below the x-axis about the x-axis.

(b) The graphs of $f(x) = x^4 - 6x^2$ and $g(x) = |x^4 - 6x^2|$ are shown in the viewing rectangle $[-5, 5]$ by $[-10, 15]$.

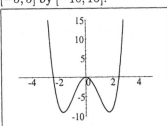   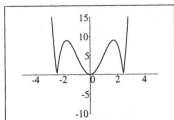

For those values of x where $f(x) \geq 0$, the graphs of f and g coincide, and for those values of x where $f(x) < 0$, the graph of g is obtained from that of f by reflecting the part below the x-axis above the x-axis.

(c) In general, if $g(x) = |f(x)|$, then for those values of x where $f(x) \geq 0$, the graphs of f and g coincide, and for those values of x where $f(x) < 0$, the graph of g is obtained from that of f by reflecting the part below the x-axis above the x-axis.

$y = f(x)$ $y = g(x)$

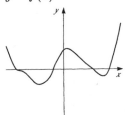   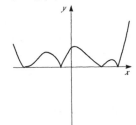

Exercises 4.3

2. $P = ku$, where k is constant.

4. $w = kmn$, where k is constant.

6. $P = \dfrac{k}{T}$, where k is constant.

8. $A = k\dfrac{t^2}{x^3}$, where k is constant.

10. $S = kr^2\theta^2$, where k is constant.

12. $A = k\sqrt{xy}$, where k is constant.

14. $z = \dfrac{k}{t}$. Since $z = 5$ when $t = 3$, we have $5 = \dfrac{k}{3}$ $\Leftrightarrow$ $k = 15$, so $z = \dfrac{15}{t}$.

16. $S = kpq$. Since $S = 180$ when $p = 4$ and $q = 5$, we have $180 = k(4)(5)$ $\Leftrightarrow$ $180 = 20k$ $\Leftrightarrow$ $k = 9$. So $S = 9pq$.

18. $t = k\dfrac{xy}{r}$. Since $t = 25$ when $x = 2$, $y = 3$, and $r = 12$, we have $25 = k\frac{(2)(3)}{12}$ $\Leftrightarrow$ $k = 50$. So $t = 50\dfrac{xy}{r}$.

20. $H = kl^2w^2$. Since $H = 36$ when $l = 2$ and $w = \frac{1}{3}$, we have $36 = k(2)^2\left(\frac{1}{3}\right)^2$ $\Leftrightarrow$ $36 = \frac{4}{9}k$ $\Leftrightarrow$ $k = 81$. So $H = 81l^2w^2$.

22. $M = k\dfrac{abc}{d}$. Since $M = 128$ when $a = d$ and $b = c = 2$, we have $128 = k\dfrac{a(2)(2)}{a} = 4k$ $\Leftrightarrow$ $k = 32$. So $M = 32\dfrac{abc}{d}$.

24. (a) Let T and l be the period and the length of the pendulum, respectively. Then $T = k\sqrt{l}$.

   (b) $T = k\sqrt{l}$ $\Rightarrow$ $T^2 = k^2l$ $\Leftrightarrow$ $l = \dfrac{T^2}{k^2}$. If the period is doubled, the new length is $\dfrac{(2T)^2}{k^2} = 4\dfrac{T^2}{k^2} = 4l$. So we would quadruple the length l to double the period T.

26. (a) $P = \dfrac{kT}{V}$.

   (b) Substituting $P = 33.2$, $T = 400$, and $V = 100$, we get $33.2 = \frac{k(400)}{100}$ $\Leftrightarrow$ $k = 8.3$. Thus the equation is $P = \dfrac{8.3T}{V}$.

   (b) Substituting $T = 500$ and $V = 80$, we have $P = \frac{8.3(500)}{80} = 51.875$ kPa. Hence the pressure of the sample of gas is about 51.9 kPa.

28. (a) $T^2 = kd^3$.

   (b) Substituting $T = 365$ and $d = 93 \times 10^6$, we get $365^2 = k \cdot (93 \times 10^6)^3$ $\Leftrightarrow$ $k = 1.66 \times 10^{-19}$.

   (c) $T^2 = 1.66 \times 10^{-19}(2.79 \times 10^9)^3 = 3.60 \times 10^9$ $\Rightarrow$ $T = 6.00 \times 10^4$. Hence the period of Neptune is 6.00×10^4 days ≈ 164 years.

30. Let S be the final size of the cabbage, in pounds, let N be the amount of nutrients it receives, in ounces, and let c be the number of other cabbages around it. Then $S = k\dfrac{N}{c}$. When $N = 20$ and

$c = 12$, we have $S = 30$, so substituting, we have $30 = k\frac{20}{12}$ $\Leftrightarrow$ $k = 18$. Thus $S = 18\frac{N}{c}$.
When $N = 10$ and $c = 5$, the final size is $S = 18\left(\frac{10}{5}\right) = 36$ lb.

32. Let H be the heat experienced by a hiker at a campfire, let A be the amount of wood, and let d be
the distance from campfire. So $H = k\dfrac{A}{d^3}$. When the hiker is 20 feet from the fire, the heat
experienced is $H = k\dfrac{A}{20^3}$, and when the amount of wood is doubled, the heat experienced is
$H = k\dfrac{2A}{d^3}$. So $k\dfrac{A}{8,000} = k\dfrac{2A}{d^3}$ $\Leftrightarrow$ $d^3 = 16,000$ $\Leftrightarrow$ $d = 20\sqrt[3]{2} \approx 25.2$ feet.

Exercises 4.4

2. Average rate of change $= \dfrac{g(5) - g(1)}{5 - 1} = \dfrac{[5 + \frac{1}{2}(5)] - [5 + \frac{1}{2}(1)]}{4} = \dfrac{\frac{15}{2} - \frac{11}{2}}{4} = \dfrac{2}{4} = \dfrac{1}{2}.$

4. Average rate of change $= \dfrac{f(0) - f(-2)}{0 - (-2)} = \dfrac{[1 - 3(0)^2] - [1 - 3(-2)^2]}{2} = \dfrac{1 - (-11)}{3} = \dfrac{12}{3} = 4.$

6. Average rate of change $= \dfrac{f(3) - f(-1)}{3 - (-1)} = \dfrac{[3 + 3^4] - [(-1) + (-1)^4]}{4} = \dfrac{3 + 81}{4} = \dfrac{84}{4} = 21.$

8. Average rate of change $= \dfrac{f(1 + h) - f(1)}{(1 + h) - 1} = \dfrac{[4 - (1 + h)^2] - [4 - 1^2]}{h} = \dfrac{3 - 2h - h^2 - 3}{h}$

$\qquad\qquad = \dfrac{-2h - h^2}{h} = \dfrac{h(-2 - h)}{h} = -2 - h.$

10. Average rate of change $= \dfrac{g(h) - g(0)}{h - 0} = \dfrac{\frac{2}{h + 1} - \frac{2}{0 + 1}}{h} \cdot \dfrac{(h + 1)}{(h + 1)} = \dfrac{2 - 2(h + 1)}{h(h + 1)}$

$\qquad\qquad = \dfrac{-2h}{h(h + 1)} = \dfrac{-2}{h + 1}.$

12. Average rate of change $= \dfrac{f(a + h) - f(a)}{(a + h) - a} = \dfrac{\sqrt{a + h} - \sqrt{a}}{h} \cdot \dfrac{\sqrt{a + h} + \sqrt{a}}{\sqrt{a + h} + \sqrt{a}}$

$\qquad\qquad = \dfrac{(a + h) - a}{h\left(\sqrt{a + h} + \sqrt{a}\right)} = \dfrac{h}{h\left(\sqrt{a + h} + \sqrt{a}\right)} = \dfrac{1}{\sqrt{a + h} + \sqrt{a}}.$

14. (a) Average rate of change $= \dfrac{g(a + h) - g(a)}{(a + h) - a} = \dfrac{[-4(a + h) + 2] - [-4a + 2]}{h}$

$\qquad\qquad = \dfrac{-4a - 4h + 2 + 4a - 2}{h} = \dfrac{-4h}{h} = -4.$

(b) The slope of the line $g(x) = -4x + 2$ is -4, which is also the average rate of change.

16. We use the points $(1, 4)$ and $(5, 2)$, so the average rate of change $= \frac{2-4}{5-1} = \frac{-2}{4} = -\frac{1}{2}.$

18. We use the points $(-1, 0)$ and $(5, 4)$, so the average rate of change $= \frac{4-0}{5-(-1)} = \frac{4}{6} = \frac{2}{3}.$

20. (a) Average speed $= \frac{800-400}{152-68} = \frac{400}{84} = \frac{100}{21} \approx 4.76$ m/s.

(b) Average speed $= \frac{1,600-1,200}{412-263} = \frac{400}{149} \approx 2.68$ m/s.

(c)

Lap	Length of time to run lap	Average speed of lap.
1	32	6.25 m/s
2	36	5.56 m/s
3	40	5.00 m/s
4	44	4.55 m/s
5	51	3.92 m/s
6	60	3.33 m/s
7	72	2.78 m/s
8	77	2.60 m/s

The man is slowing down throughout the run.

22.

Year	Number of books
1980	420
1981	460
1982	500
1985	620
1990	820
1992	900
1995	1020
1997	1100
1998	1140
1999	1180
2000	1220

24.   The function is increasing on $[0, 1]$. It is decreasing on $[-2, 0]$ and $[1, 3]$.

26.   The function is increasing on $[-1, 1]$. It is decreasing on $[-2, -1]$ and $[1, 2]$.

28.   (a) $f(x) = 4 - x^{2/3}$ is graphed in the viewing rectangle $[-10, 10]$ by $[-10, 10]$.

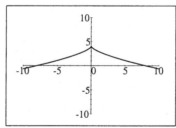

(b)   The function is increasing on $(-\infty, 0]$. It is decreasing on $[0, \infty)$.

30.   (a) $f(x) = x^3 - 4x$ is graphed in the viewing rectangle $[-10, 10]$ by $[-10, 10]$.

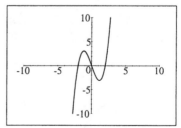

(b)   The function is increasing on $(-\infty, -1.15]$ and $[1.15, \infty)$. It is decreasing on $[-1.15, 1.15]$.

32. (a) $f(x) = x^4 - 16x^2$ is graphed in the
    viewing rectangle $[-10, 10]$ by $[-70, 10]$.

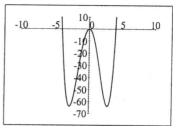

(b) The function is increasing on $[-2.83, 0]$ and $[2.83, \infty)$. It is decreasing on $(-\infty, -2.83]$ and $[0, 2.83]$.

34. (a) $f(x) = x^4 - 4x^3 + 2x^2 + 4x - 3$
    is graphed in the viewing rectangle
    $[-3, 5]$ by $[-5, 5]$.

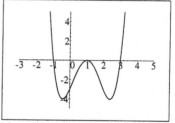

(b) The function is increasing on $(-0.4, 1]$ and $[2.4, \infty)$. It is decreasing on $[-\infty, -0.4]$ and $[1, 2.4]$.

36. (a) $f(x)$ is always increasing, and $f(x) > 0$ for all x.

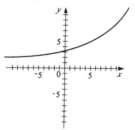

   (b) $f(x)$ is always decreasing, and $f(x) > 0$ for all x.

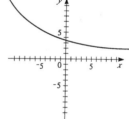

   (c) $f(x)$ is always increasing, and $f(x) < 0$ for all x.

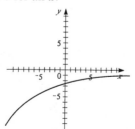

   (d) $f(x)$ is always decreasing, and $f(x) < 0$ for all x.

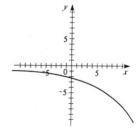

Exercises 4.5

2. (a) Shift the graph of $y = f(x)$ to the left 5 units.
   (b) Shift the graph of $y = f(x)$ upward 5 units.

4. (a) Reflect the graph of $y = f(x)$ about the x-axis.
   (b) Reflect the graph of $y = f(x)$ about the y-axis.

6. (a) Refect the graph of $y = f(x)$ about the x-axis, and stretch it by a factor of 4.
   (b) Refect the graph of $y = f(x)$ about the x-axis, and shrink it by a factor of $\frac{1}{4}$.

8. (a) Shrink the graph of $y = f(x)$ vertically by a factor of $\frac{1}{2}$, and then shift upward 10 units.
   (b) Shift the graph of $y = f(x)$ to the left 10 units, then shrink it vertically by a factor of $\frac{1}{2}$.

10. (a) $y = f(x - 4)$ is graph #3.   (b) $y = f(x) + 3$ is graph #1.
    (c) $y = \frac{1}{3}f(x)$ is graph #4.   (d) $y = -f(x + 4)$ is graph #5.
    (e) $y = 2f(x + 6)$ is graph #2.

12. (a) $f(x) = \sqrt[3]{x}$

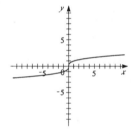

(b) (i) $\sqrt[3]{x} - 2$. Shift the graph of $f(x) = \sqrt[3]{x}$ to the right 2 units.

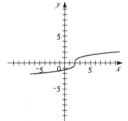

(ii) $y = \sqrt[3]{x + 2} + 2$. Shift the graph of $f(x) = \sqrt[3]{x}$ to the left 2 units and upward 2 units.

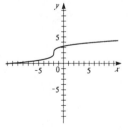

(iii) $y = 1 - \sqrt[3]{x}$. Reflect the graph of $f(x) = \sqrt[3]{x}$ about the x-axis, and then shift it upward 1 unit.

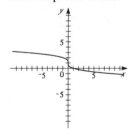

14. (a) The graph of $g(x) = (x - 4)^3$ is obtained by shifting the graph of $f(x)$ to the right 4 units.

(b) The graph of $g(x) = x^3 - 4$ is obtained by shifting the graph of $f(x)$ downward 4 units.

16. (a) The graph of $g(x) = 3|x| + 1$ is obtained by stretching the graph of $f(x)$ vertically by 3 units and then shifting the graph upward 1 unit.

(b) The graph of $g(x) = -|x + 1|$ is obtained by shifting the graph of $f(x)$ right 1 units and then reflecting the graph about the x-axis.

18. $f(x) = (x + 7)^2$. Shift the graph of $y = x^2$ to the left 7 units.

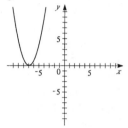

20. $f(x) = 1 - x^2$. Reflect the graph of $y = x^2$ about the x-axis, then shift it upward 1 unit.

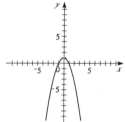

22. $f(x) = -x^3$. Reflect the graph of $y = x^3$ about the x-axis.

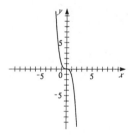

24. $y = 2 - \sqrt{x + 1}$. Shift the graph of $y = \sqrt{x}$ to the left 1 unit, reflect it about the x-axis, and finally shift it upward 2 units.

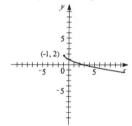

26. $y = 3 - 2(x - 1)^2$. Shift the graph of $y = x^2$ to the right 1 unit, reflect it about the x-axis, stretch it vertically by a factor of 2, and then shift it upward 3 units.

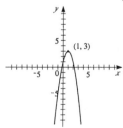

28. $y = \frac{1}{3}x^3 - 1$. Shrink the graph of $y = x^3$ vertically by a factor of $\frac{1}{3}$, then shift it downward 1 unit.

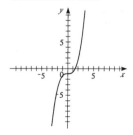

30. $y = |x - 1|$. Shift the graph of $y = |x|$
     to the right 1 unit.

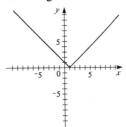

32. $y = 2 - |x|$. Reflect the graph of $y = |x|$ about
     the x-axis, and then shift it upward 2 units.

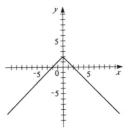

34.

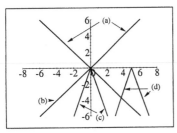

For (b), reflect the graph in (a) about the x-axis; for
(c), stretch the graph in (a) vertically by a factor of 3
and reflect about the x-axis; for (d), shift the graph in
(a) to the right 5 units, stretch it vertically by a factor
of 3, and reflect it about the x-axis. The order in
which each operation is applied to the graph in (a) is
not important to obtain the graphs in part (c) and (d).

36.

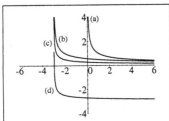

For (b), shift the graph in (a) to the left 3 units; for
(c), shift the graph in (a) to the left 3 units and shrink
it vertically by a factor of $\frac{1}{2}$; for (d), shift the graph in
(a) to the left 3 units, shrink it vertically by a factor of
$\frac{1}{2}$, and then shift it downward 3 units. The order in
which each operation is applied to the graph in (a) is
not important to sketch (c), while it is important in
(d).

38. $f(x) = x^{-3}$. $f(-x) = (-x)^{-3}$
     $= -x^{-3} = -f(x)$. Thus $f(x)$ is odd.

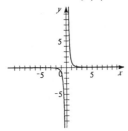

40. $f(x) = x^4 - 4x^2$. $f(-x) = (-x)^4 - 4(-x)^2$
     $= x^4 - 4x^2 = f(x)$. Thus $f(x)$ is even.

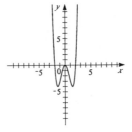

42. $f(x) = 3x^3 + 2x^2 + 1$.
     $f(-x) = 3(-x)^3 + 2(-x)^2 + 1$
     $= -3x^3 + 2x^2 + 1$. Thus $f(-x) \neq f(x)$.
     Also $f(-x) \neq -f(x)$, so $f(x)$ is neither odd
     nor even.

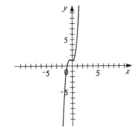

44. $f(x) = x + \dfrac{1}{x}$.

$f(-x) = (-x) + \dfrac{1}{(-x)} = -x - \dfrac{1}{x}$

$= -\left(x + \dfrac{1}{x}\right) = -f(x)$. Thus $f(x)$ is odd.

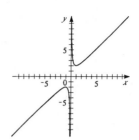

46. $g(x) = |x^4 - 4x^2|$

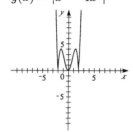

48. (a) $f(x) = x^3$ (b) $g(x) = |x^3|$

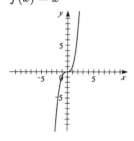   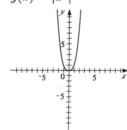

50. f even implies $f(-x) = f(x)$; g even implies $g(-x) = g(x)$; f odd implies $f(-x) = -f(x)$; and g odd implies $g(-x) = -g(x)$.

If f and g are both even, then $(fg)(-x) = f(-x) \cdot g(-x) = f(x) \cdot g(x) = (fg)(x)$. Thus fg is even.

If f and g are both odd, then $(fg)(-x) = f(-x) \cdot g(-x) = -f(x) \cdot (-g(x)) = f(x) \cdot g(x)$ $= (fg)(x)$. Thus fg is even

If f if odd and g is even, then $(fg)(-x) = f(-x) \cdot g(-x) = f(x) \cdot (-g(x)) = -f(x) \cdot g(x)$ $= -(fg)(x)$. Thus fg is odd.

52. (a) $y = f(x) = \sqrt{2x - x^2}$, $y = f(2x) = \sqrt{2(2x) - (2x)^2} = \sqrt{4x - 4x^2}$, and

$y = f(\tfrac{1}{2}x) = \sqrt{2(\tfrac{1}{2}x) - (\tfrac{1}{2}x)^2} = \sqrt{x - \tfrac{1}{4}x^2}$.

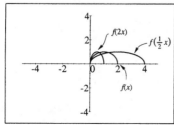

The graph $y = f(2x)$ is obtained by horizontally shrinking the graph $y = f(x)$ by a factor of $\frac{1}{2}$ (so the graph is $\frac{1}{2}$ as wide). The graph $y = f(\frac{1}{2}x)$ is obtained by horizontally stretching the graph $y = f(x)$ by a factor of 2 (so the graph is twice as wide).

(b) For $a > 0$, the graph $y = f(ax)$ is obtained by horizontally shrinking the graph $y = f(x)$ by a factor of a (so the graph is $\frac{1}{a}$ as wide). For $0 < a < 1$, the graph $y = f(ax)$ is obtained by horizontally stretching the graph $y = f(x)$ by a factor of $\frac{1}{a}$.

(c) $y = g(2x)$

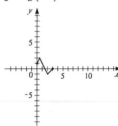

$y = g(\frac{1}{2}x)$

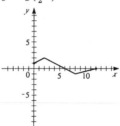

(d) $y = h(3x)$

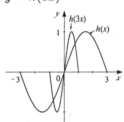

$y = h\left(\frac{1}{3}x\right)$

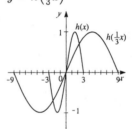

(e) $y = [\![2x]\!]$

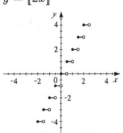

$y = [\![\frac{1}{4}x]\!]$

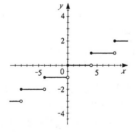

Exercises 4.6

2. $y = x^2 + 6x$

Vertex: $y = x^2 + 6x = x^2 + 6x + 9 - 9 = (x+3)^2 - 9$. Vertex is at $(-3, -9)$.

x-intercept: $y = 0 \Rightarrow x(x+6) = 0 \Leftrightarrow x = -6$ or $x = 0$. The x-intercepts are at $x = -6$ and $x = 0$.

y-intercept: $x = 0 \Rightarrow y = 0$. The y-intercept is at $y = 0$.

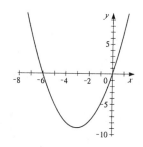

4. $y = -x^2 + 10x$

Vertex: $y = -x^2 + 10x = -(x^2 - 10x + 25) + 25 = -(x-5)^2 + 25$. Vertex is at $(5, 25)$.

x-intercept: $y = 0 \Rightarrow 0 = -x^2 + 10x = -x(x-10) = 0 \Rightarrow x = 0$ or $x = 10$. The x-intercepts are at $x = 0$ and $x = 10$

y-intercept: $x = 0 \Rightarrow y = 0$. The y-intercept is at $y = 0$.

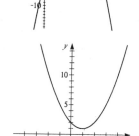

6. $y = x^2 - 2x + 2$

Vertex: $y = x^2 - 2x + 2 = x^2 - 2x + 1 + 1 = (x-1)^2 + 1$. Vertex is at $(1, 1)$.

x-intercept: $y = 0 \Rightarrow (x-1)^2 + 1 = 0 \Leftrightarrow (x-1)^2 = -1$. Since this last equation has no real solution, there is no x-intercept.

y-intercept: $x = 0 \Rightarrow y = 2$. The y-intercept is at $y = 2$.

8. $y = -x^2 - 4x + 4$

Vertex: $y = -x^2 - 4x + 4 = -(x^2 + 4x) + 4 = -(x^2 + 4x + 4) + 4 + 4 = -(x+2)^2 + 8$. Vertex is at $(-2, 8)$.

x-intercept: $y = 0 \Rightarrow 0 = -x^2 - 4x + 4 \Leftrightarrow 0 = x^2 + 4x - 4$. Using the quadratic formula, $x = \frac{-4 \pm \sqrt{(4)^2 - 4(1)(-4)}}{2(1)} = \frac{-4 \pm \sqrt{32}}{2} = \frac{2(-2 \pm 2\sqrt{2})}{2} = -2 \pm 2\sqrt{2}$. The x-intercepts are at $x = -2 + 2\sqrt{2}$ and $x = -2 - 2\sqrt{2}$.

y-intercept: $x = 0 \Rightarrow y = 4$. The y-intercept is at $y = 4$.

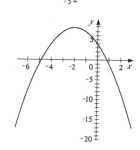

10. $y = -3x^2 + 6x - 2$

Vertex: $y = -3x^2 + 6x - 2 = -3(x^2 - 2x) - 2 = -3(x^2 - 2x + 1) - 2 + 3 = -3(x-1)^2 + 1$. Vertex is at $(1, 1)$.

x-intercept: $y = 0 \Rightarrow 0 = -3(x-1)^2 + 1 = 0 \Leftrightarrow (x-1)^2 = \frac{1}{3} \Rightarrow x - 1 = \pm\sqrt{\frac{1}{3}} \Leftrightarrow x = 1 \pm \sqrt{\frac{1}{3}}$. The x-intercepts are at $x = 1 + \sqrt{\frac{1}{3}}$ and $x = 1 - \sqrt{\frac{1}{3}}$.

y-intercept: $x = 0 \Rightarrow y = -2$. The y-intercept is at $y = -2$.

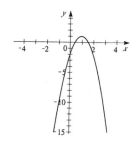

12. $y = 2x^2 + x - 6$

Vertex: $y = 2x^2 + x - 6 = 2(x^2 + \frac{1}{2}x) - 6 =$
$2(x^2 + \frac{1}{2}x + \frac{1}{16}) - 6 - \frac{1}{8} = 2(x + \frac{1}{4})^2 - \frac{49}{8}$. Vertex is at $\left(-\frac{1}{4}, -\frac{49}{8}\right)$.

x-intercept: $y = 0$ $\Rightarrow$ $0 = 2x^2 + x - 6 = (2x - 3)(x + 2)$ $\Rightarrow$
$x = \frac{3}{2}$ or $x = -2$. The x-intercepts are at $x = \frac{3}{2}$ and at $x = -2$.

y-intercept: $x = 0$ $\Rightarrow$ $y = -6$. The y-intercept is at $y = -6$.

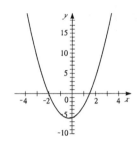

14. $y = 6x^2 + 12x - 5$

Vertex: $y = 6x^2 + 12x - 5 = 6(x^2 + 2x) - 5$
$= 6(x^2 + 2x + 1) - 5 - 6 = 6(x + 1)^2 - 11$. Vertex is at $(-1, -11)$.

x-intercept: $y = 0$ $\Rightarrow$ $0 = 6x^2 + 12x - 5$. Using the quadratic

formula, $x = \frac{-12 \pm \sqrt{(12)^2 - 4(6)(-5)}}{2(6)} = \frac{-12 \pm \sqrt{264}}{12} = \frac{-12 \pm 2\sqrt{66}}{12} = \frac{2(-6 \pm \sqrt{2})}{12}$

$= \frac{-6 \pm \sqrt{2}}{6}$. The x-intercepts are at $x = \frac{-6 - \sqrt{2}}{6}$ and at $x = \frac{-6 + \sqrt{2}}{6}$.

y-intercept: $x = 0$ $\Rightarrow$ $y = -6$. The y-intercept is at $y = 0$.

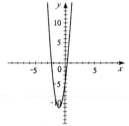

16. $f(x) = x + x^2 = (x^2 + x + \frac{1}{4}) - \frac{1}{4} = (x + \frac{1}{2})^2 - \frac{1}{4}$.

Therefore, the minimum value is $f\left(-\frac{1}{2}\right) = -\frac{1}{4}$.

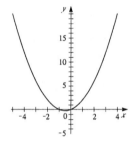

18. $f(x) = x^2 - 8x + 8 = (x^2 - 8x + 16) + 8 - 16 = (x - 4)^2 - 8$.

Therefore, the minimum value is $f(4) = -8$.

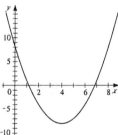

20. $f(x) = 1 - 6x - x^2 = -(x^2 + 6x) + 1 = -(x^2 + 6x + 9) + 1 + 9$
$= -(x + 3)^2 + 10$.

Therefore, the maximum value is $f(-3) = 10$.

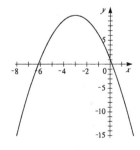

22. $g(x) = 2x^2 + 8x + 11 = 2(x^2 + 4x) + 11$
    $= 2(x^2 + 4x + 4) + 11 - 8 = 2(x + 2)^2 + 3.$

    Therefore, the minimum value is $g(-2) = 3$.

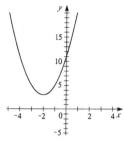

24. $h(x) = 3 - 4x - 4x^2 = -4(x^2 + x) + 3 = -4\left(x^2 + x + \frac{1}{4}\right) + 3 + 1$
    $= -4\left(x + \frac{1}{2}\right)^2 + 4.$

    Therefore, the maximum value is $h\left(-\frac{1}{2}\right) = 4$.

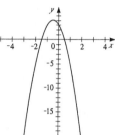

26. $f(x) = 1 + 3x - x^2 = -(x^2 - 3x) + 1 = -\left(x^2 - 3x + \frac{9}{4}\right) + 1 + \frac{9}{4} = -\left(x - \frac{3}{2}\right)^2 + \frac{13}{4}.$
    Therefore, the maximum value is $f\left(\frac{3}{2}\right) = \frac{13}{4}$.

28. $f(t) = 10t^2 + 40t + 113 = 10(t^2 + 4t) + 113 = 10(t^2 + 4t + 4) + 113 - 40 = 10(t + 2)^2 + 73.$
    Therefore, the minimum value is $f(-2) = 73$.

30. $g(x) = 100x^2 - 1500x = 100(x^2 - 15x) = 100\left(x^2 - 15x + \frac{225}{4}\right) - 5625 = 10\left(x - \frac{15}{2}\right)^2 - 5625.$
    Therefore, the minimum value is $g\left(\frac{15}{2}\right) = -5625$.

32. $f(x) = -\frac{x^2}{3} + 2x + 7 = -\frac{1}{3}(x^2 + 6x) + 7 = -\frac{1}{3}(x^2 + 6x + 9) + 7 + 3 = -\frac{1}{3}(x + 3)^2 + 10.$

    Therefore, the maximum value is $f(-3) = 10$.

34. $g(x) = 2x(x - 4) + 7 = 2x^2 - 8x + 7 = 2(x^2 - 4x) + 7 = 2(x^2 - 4x + 4) + 7 - 8$
    $= 2(x - 2)^2 - 1.$ Therefore, the minimum value is $g(2) = -1$.

36. Since the vertex is $(3, 4)$, the function is of the form $y = a(x - 3)^2 + 4$. Since the parabola passes
    through the point $(1, -8)$, it must satisfy $-8 = a(1 - 3)^2 + 4 \quad \Leftrightarrow \quad -8 = 4a + 4 \quad \Leftrightarrow$
    $4a = -12 \quad \Leftrightarrow \quad a = -3$. So the function is $y = -3(x - 3)^2 + 4 = -3x^2 + 18x - 23$.

38. $f(x) = x^2 - 2x - 3 = (x^2 - 2x + 1) - 3 - 1 = (x - 1)^2 - 4$. Then the domain of the function is
    all real numbers, and since the minimum value of the function is $f(1) = -4$, the range of the
    function is $[-4, \infty)$.

40. (a) $y = -0.005x^2 + x + 5 = -0.005(x^2 - 200x) + 5$
    $= -0.005(x^2 - 200x + 10,000) + 5 + 50$
    $= -0.005(x - 100)^2 + 55$

    Thus the maximum height attained by the football is 55 ft.

    (b) We solve for $y = 0$: $0 = -0.005x^2 + x + 5$. Using the quadratic formula, we have
    $x = \frac{-1 \pm \sqrt{1^2 - (4)(-0.005)(5)}}{2(-0.005)} = \frac{-1 \pm \sqrt{1.1}}{-0.01} = 100 \pm 100\sqrt{1.1}$. Since he throws the football down
    field, we take the positive root, so $x = 100 + 100\sqrt{1.1} \approx 204.9$ feet.

42. $P(x) = -0.001x^2 + 3x - 1800 = -0.001(x^2 - 3000x) - 1800$
$$= -0.001(x^2 - 3000x + 2,250,000) - 1800 + 2250$$
$$= -0.001(x - 1500)^2 + 450$$

The vendor's maximum profit occurs when he sells 1500 cans and realizes a profit of $450.

44. $C(t) = 0.06t - 0.0002t^2 = -0.0002(t^2 - 300t) = -0.0002(t^2 - 300t + 22,500) + 4.5$
$$= -0.0002(t - 150)^2 + 4.5.$$

The maximum concentration occurs after 150 minutes, and the maximum concentration is 4.5 mg/L.

46. (a) $f(x) = 1 + x - \sqrt{2}\,x^2$ is shown in the viewing rectangle on the right. The maximum value is $f(x) \approx 1.18$.

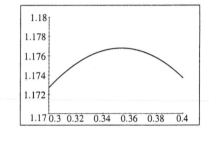

(b) $f(x) = 1 + x - \sqrt{2}\,x^2 = -\sqrt{2}\left[x^2 - \frac{\sqrt{2}}{2}x\right] + 1$
$$= -\sqrt{2}\left[x^2 - \frac{\sqrt{2}}{2}x + \left(\frac{\sqrt{2}}{4}\right)^2\right] + 1 + \frac{\sqrt{2}}{8}$$
$$= -\sqrt{2}\left(x - \frac{\sqrt{2}}{4}\right)^2 + \frac{8 + \sqrt{2}}{8}$$

Therefore, the exact minimum of $f(x)$ is $\frac{8+\sqrt{2}}{8}$.

48. In the viewing rectangle on the right, we see that $f(x) = 3 + x + x^2 - x^3$ has a local minimum and a local maximum. Smaller x and y ranges (shown in the viewing rectangles below) shows that $f(x)$ has a local maximum of ≈ 4.00 when $x \approx 1.00$ and a local minimum of ≈ 2.81 when $x \approx -0.33$.

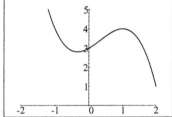

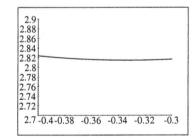

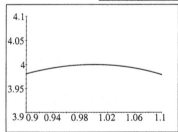

50. In the viewing rectangle on the right, we see that $g(x) = x^5 - 8x^3 + 20x$ has two local minimums and two local maximums. The local maximums are $g(x) \approx 13.02$ when $x = 1.04$ and $g(x) \approx -7.87$ when $x \approx -1.93$. Smaller x and y ranges (shown in the viewing rectangles below) shows that local minimums are $g(x) \approx -13.02$ when $x = -1.04$ and $g(x) \approx 7.87$ when $x \approx 1.93$. Notice that since $g(x)$ is odd, the local maximums and minimums are related.

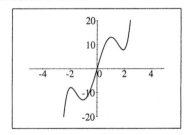

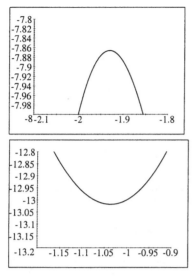

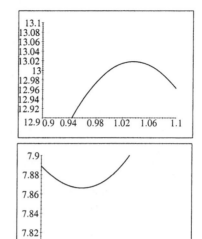

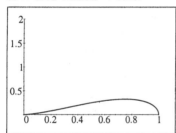

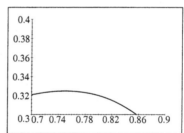

52. In the first viewing rectangle below, we see that $U(x) = x\sqrt{x - x^2}$ has only a local maximum.
     Smaller x and y ranges in the second viewing rectangle below show that $U(x)$ has a local maximum
     of ≈ 0.32 when $x \approx 0.75$.

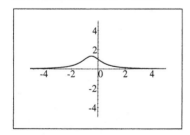

54. In the first viewing rectangle below, we see that $V(x) = \dfrac{1}{x^2 + x + 1}$ only has a local maximum.
     Smaller x and y ranges in the second viewing rectangle below show that $V(x)$ has a local maximum
     of ≈ 1.33 when $x \approx -0.50$.

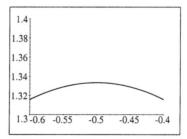

56. In the first viewing rectangle on the next page, we see the general location of the maximum of
     $N(s) = \dfrac{88s}{17 + 17\left(\frac{s}{20}\right)^2}$. In the second viewing rectangle we isolate the maximum, and from this
     graph we see that at the speed of 20 mi/h the largest number of cars that can use the highway safely
     is 52.

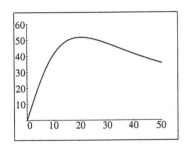   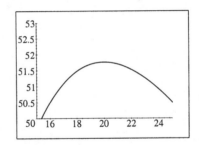

58.   In the first viewing rectangle below, we see the general location of the maximum of
      $v(r) = 3.2(1 - r)r^2$ is around $r = 0.7$ cm. In the second viewing rectangle, we isolate the
      maximum, and from this graph we see that at the maximum velocity is 0.47 when $r \approx 0.67$ cm.

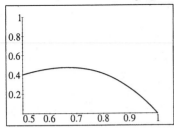   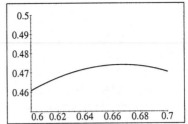

60.   Numerous answers are possible.

Exercises 4.7

2. $f(x) = x^3 + 2x^2$ has domain $(-\infty, \infty)$. $g(x) = 3x^2 - 1$ has domain $(-\infty, \infty)$. The intersection of the domains of f and g is $(-\infty, \infty)$.

    $(f + g)(x) = (x^3 + 2x^2) + (3x^2 - 1) = x^3 + 5x^2 - 1$, and the domain is $(-\infty, \infty)$.

    $(f - g)(x) = (x^3 + 2x^2) - (3x^2 - 1) = x^3 - x^2 + 1$, and the domain is $(-\infty, \infty)$.

    $(fg)(x) = (x^3 + 2x^2)(3x^2 - 1) = 3x^5 + 6x^4 - x^3 - 2x^2$, and the domain is $(-\infty, \infty)$.

    $\left(\frac{f}{g}\right)(x) = \frac{x^3 + 2x^2}{3x^2 - 1}$, $3x^2 - 1 \neq 0$ $\Leftrightarrow$ $x^2 \neq \frac{1}{3}$, and the domain is $\{\, x \mid x \neq \pm\frac{1}{\sqrt{3}} \,\}$.

4. $f(x) = \sqrt{9 - x^2}$ has domain $[-3, 3]$. $g(x) = \sqrt{x^2 - 1}$ has domain $(-\infty, -1] \cup [1, \infty)$. The intersection of the domains of f and g is $[-3, -1] \cup [1, 3]$.

    $(f + g)(x) = \sqrt{9 - x^2} + \sqrt{x^2 - 1}$, and the domain is $[-3, -1] \cup [1, 3]$.

    $(f - g)(x) = \sqrt{9 - x^2} - \sqrt{x^2 - 1}$, and the domain is $[-3, -1] \cup [1, 3]$.

    $(fg)(x) = \sqrt{9 - x^2} \cdot \sqrt{x^2 - 1} = \sqrt{-x^4 + 10x^2 - 9}$, and the domain is $[-3, -1] \cup [1, 3]$.

    $\left(\frac{f}{g}\right)(x) = \dfrac{\sqrt{9 - x^2}}{\sqrt{x^2 - 1}} = \sqrt{\dfrac{9 - x^2}{x^2 - 1}}$, and the domain is $[-3, -1) \cup (1, 3]$.

6. $f(x) = \frac{1}{x + 1}$ has domain $x \neq -1$. $g(x) = \frac{x}{x + 1}$ has domain $x \neq -1$. The intersection of the domains of f and g is $x \neq -1$, in interval notation, this is $(-\infty, -1) \cup (-1, \infty)$.

    $(f + g)(x) = \frac{1}{x + 1} + \frac{x}{x + 1} = \frac{x + 1}{x + 1} = 1$, and the domain is $(-\infty, -1) \cup (-1, \infty)$.

    $(f - g)(x) = \frac{1}{x + 1} - \frac{x}{x + 1} = \frac{1 - x}{x + 1}$, and the domain is $(-\infty, -1) \cup (-1, \infty)$.

    $(fg)(x) = \frac{1}{x + 1} \cdot \frac{x}{x + 1} = \frac{x}{(x + 1)^2}$, and the domain is $(-\infty, -1) \cup (-1, \infty)$.

    $\left(\frac{f}{g}\right)(x) = \dfrac{\frac{1}{x + 1}}{\frac{x}{x + 1}} = \dfrac{1}{x}$, so $x \neq 0$ as well. Thus the domain is $(-\infty, -1) \cup (-1, 0) \cup (0, \infty)$.

8. $g(x) = \sqrt{x + 1} + \frac{1}{x}$. The domain of $\sqrt{x + 1}$ is $[-1, \infty)$, and the domain of $\frac{1}{x}$ is $x \neq 0$. Since $x \neq 0$ is $(-\infty, 0) \cup (0, \infty)$, the domain is $[-1, \infty) \cap \{(-\infty, 0) \cup (0, \infty)\} = [-1, 0) \cup (0, \infty)$.

10. $k(x) = \dfrac{\sqrt{x + 3}}{x - 1}$. The domain of $\sqrt{x + 3}$ is $[-3, \infty)$, and the domain of $\frac{1}{x - 1}$ is $x \neq 1$. Since $x \neq 1$ is $(-\infty, 1) \cup (1, \infty)$, the domain is $[-3, \infty) \cap \{(-\infty, 1) \cup (1, \infty)\} = [-3, 1) \cup (1, \infty)$.

12.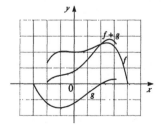

14. 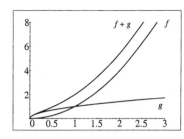 16.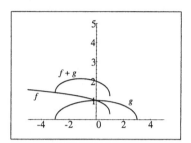

18. (a) $f(f(4)) = f(3(4) - 5) = f(7) = 3(7) - 5 = 16$

(b) $g(g(3)) = g(2 - (3)^2) = g(-7) = 2 - (-7)^2 = -47$

20. (a) $(f \circ f)(-1) = f(f(-1)) = f(3(-1) - 5) = f(-8) = 3(-8) - 5 = -29$

(b) $(g \circ g)(2) = g(g(2)) = g(2 - (2)^2) = g(-2) = 2 - (-2)^2 = -2$

22. (a) $(f \circ f)(x) = f(f(x)) = f(3x - 5) = 3(3x - 5) - 5 = 9x - 15 - 5 = 9x - 20$

(b) $(g \circ g)(x) = g(g(x)) = g(2 - x^2) = 2 - (2 - x^2)^2 = 2 - (4 - 4x^2 + x^4) = -x^4 + 4x^2 - 2$

24. $f(0) = 0$, so $g(f(0)) = g(0) = 3$.

26. $g(0) = 3$, so $(f \circ g)(0) = f(3) = 0$.

28. $f(4) = 2$, so $(f \circ f)(4) = f(2) = -2$.

30. $f(x) = 6x - 5$ has domain $(-\infty, \infty)$. $g(x) = \dfrac{x}{2}$ has domain $(-\infty, \infty)$.

$(f \circ g)(x) = f\left(\dfrac{x}{2}\right) = 6\left(\dfrac{x}{2}\right) - 5 = 3x - 5$, and the domain is $(-\infty, \infty)$.

$(g \circ f)(x) = g(6x - 5) = \dfrac{6x - 5}{2} = 3x - \dfrac{5}{2}$, and the domain is $(-\infty, \infty)$.

$(f \circ f)(x) = f(6x - 5) = 6(6x - 5) - 5 = 36x - 35$, and the domain is $(-\infty, \infty)$.

$(g \circ g)(x) = g\left(\dfrac{x}{2}\right) = \dfrac{\frac{x}{2}}{2} = \dfrac{x}{4}$, and the domain is $(-\infty, \infty)$.

32. $f(x) = x^3 + 2$ has domain $(-\infty, \infty)$. $g(x) = \sqrt[3]{x}$ has domain $(-\infty, \infty)$.

$(f \circ g)(x) = f(\sqrt[3]{x}) = (\sqrt[3]{x})^3 + 2 = x + 2$, and the domain is $(-\infty, \infty)$.

$(g \circ f)(x) = g(x^3 + 2) = \sqrt[3]{x^3 + 2}$ and the domain is $(-\infty, \infty)$.

$(f \circ f)(x) = f(x^3 + 2) = (x^3 + 2)^3 + 2 = x^9 + 6x^6 + 12x^3 + 8 + 2 = x^9 + 6x^6 + 12x^3 + 10$, and the domain is $(-\infty, \infty)$.

$(g \circ g)(x) = g(\sqrt[3]{x}) = \sqrt[3]{\sqrt[3]{x}} = (x^{1/3})^{1/3} = x^{1/9}$, and the domain is $(-\infty, \infty)$.

34. $f(x) = x^2$ has domain $(-\infty, \infty)$. $g(x) = \sqrt{x - 3}$ has domain $[3, \infty)$.

$(f \circ g)(x) = f\left(\sqrt{x - 3}\right) = \left(\sqrt{x - 3}\right)^2 = x - 3$, and the domain is $[3, \infty)$.

$(g \circ f)(x) = g(x^2) = \sqrt{x^2 - 3}$. For the domain we must have $x^2 \geq 3 \quad \Rightarrow \quad x \leq -\sqrt{3}$ or $x \geq \sqrt{3}$. Thus the domain is $(-\infty, -\sqrt{3}] \cup [\sqrt{3}, \infty)$.

$(f \circ f)(x) = f(x^2) = (x^2)^2 = x^4$, and the domain is $(-\infty, \infty)$.

$(g \circ g)(x) = g\left(\sqrt{x-3}\right) = \sqrt{\sqrt{x-3}-3}$. For the domain we must have $\sqrt{x-3} \geq 3$ $\Rightarrow$
$x - 3 \geq 9$ $\Rightarrow$ $x \geq 12$, so the domain is $[12, \infty)$.

36. $f(x) = x - 4$ has domain $(-\infty, \infty)$. $g(x) = |x+4|$ has domain $(-\infty, \infty)$.
$(f \circ g)(x) = f(|x+4|) = |x+4| - 4$, and the domain is $(-\infty, \infty)$.
$(g \circ f)(x) = g(x-4) = |(x-4)+4| = |x|$, and the domain is $(-\infty, \infty)$.
$(f \circ f)(x) = f(x-4) = (x-4) - 4 = x - 8$, and the domain is $(-\infty, \infty)$.
$(g \circ g)(x) = g(|x+4|) = ||x+4|+4| = |x+4| + 4$ ($|x+4|+4$ is always positive). The domain
is $(-\infty, \infty)$.

38. $f(x) = \dfrac{1}{\sqrt{x}}$ has domain $\{x \mid x > 0\}$; $g(x) = x^2 - 4x$ has domain $(-\infty, \infty)$.

$(f \circ g)(x) = f(x^2 - 4x) = \dfrac{1}{\sqrt{x^2 - 4x}}$. $(f \circ g)(x)$ is defined whenever $0 < x^2 - 4x = x(x-4)$.
The product of two numbers is positive either when both numbers are negative or when both
numbers are positive. So the domain of $f \circ g$ is $\{x \mid x < 0$ and $x < 4\} \cup \{x \mid x > 0$ and $x > 4\}$
which is $(-\infty, 0) \cup (4, \infty)$.

$(g \circ f)(x) = g\left(\dfrac{1}{\sqrt{x}}\right) = \left(\dfrac{1}{\sqrt{x}}\right)^2 - 4\left(\dfrac{1}{\sqrt{x}}\right) = \dfrac{1}{x} - \dfrac{4}{\sqrt{x}}$. $(g \circ f)(x)$ is defined whenever both
$f(x)$ and $g(f(x))$ are defined, that is, whenever $x > 0$. So the domain of $g \circ f$ is $(0, \infty)$.

$(f \circ f)(x) = f\left(\dfrac{1}{\sqrt{x}}\right) = \dfrac{1}{\sqrt{\dfrac{1}{\sqrt{x}}}} = x^{1/4}$. $(f \circ f)(x)$ is defined whenever both $f(x)$ and $f(f(x))$

are defined, that is, whenever $x > 0$. So the domain of $f \circ f$ is $(0, \infty)$.
$(g \circ g)(x) = g(x^2 - 4x) = (x^2 - 4x)^2 - 4(x^2 - 4x) = x^4 - 8x^3 + 16x^2 - 4x^2 + 16x$
$= x^4 - 8x^3 + 12x^2 + 16x$, and the domain is $(-\infty, \infty)$.

40. $f(x) = \dfrac{2}{x}$ has domain $\{x \mid x \neq 0\}$; $g(x) = \dfrac{x}{x+2}$ has domain $\{x \mid x \neq -2\}$.

$(f \circ g)(x) = f\left(\dfrac{x}{x+2}\right) = \dfrac{2}{\dfrac{x}{x+2}} = \dfrac{2x+4}{x}$. $(f \circ g)(x)$ is defined whenever both $g(x)$ and
$f(g(x))$ are defined; that is, whenever $x \neq 0$ and $x \neq -2$. So the domain is $\{x \mid x \neq 0, -2\}$.

$(g \circ f)(x) = g\left(\dfrac{2}{x}\right) = \dfrac{\dfrac{2}{x}}{\dfrac{2}{x}+2} = \dfrac{2}{2+2x} = \dfrac{1}{1+x}$. $(g \circ f)(x)$ is defined whenever both $f(x)$ and
$g(f(x))$ are defined; that is, whenever $x \neq 0$ and $x \neq -1$. So the domain is $\{x \mid x \neq 0, -1\}$.

$(f \circ f)(x) = f\left(\dfrac{2}{x}\right) = \dfrac{2}{\dfrac{2}{x}} = x$. $(f \circ f)(x)$ is defined whenever both $f(x)$ and $f(f(x))$ are

defined; that is, whenever $x \neq 0$. So the domain is $\{x \mid x \neq 0\}$.

$$(g \circ g)(x) = g\left(\frac{x}{x+2}\right) = \frac{\dfrac{x}{x+2}}{\dfrac{x}{x+2}+2} = \frac{x}{x+2(x+2)} = \frac{x}{3x+4}. \quad (g \circ g)(x) \text{ is defined whenever}$$

both $g(x)$ and $g(g(x))$ are defined; that is whenever $x \neq -2$ and $x \neq -\frac{4}{3}$. So the domain is $\{x \mid x \neq -2, -\frac{4}{3}\}$.

42. $(g \circ h)(x) = g(x^2 + 2) = (x^2 + 2)^3 = x^6 + 6x^4 + 12x^2 + 8.$

$$(f \circ g \circ h)(x) = f(x^6 + 6x^4 + 12x^2 + 8) = \frac{1}{x^6 + 6x^4 + 12x^2 + 8}.$$

44. $(g \circ h)(x) = g(\sqrt[3]{x}) = \dfrac{\sqrt[3]{x}}{\sqrt[3]{x}-1}.$ $(f \circ g \circ h)(x) = f\left(\dfrac{\sqrt[3]{x}}{\sqrt[3]{x}-1}\right) = \sqrt{\dfrac{\sqrt[3]{x}}{\sqrt[3]{x}-1}}$

46. $F(x) = \sqrt{x} + 1.$ If $f(x) = x + 1$ and $g(x) = \sqrt{x}$, then $F(x) = (f \circ g)(x).$

48. $G(x) = \dfrac{1}{x+3}.$ If $f(x) = \dfrac{1}{x}$ and $g(x) = x + 3$, then $G(x) = (f \circ g)(x).$

50. $H(x) = \sqrt{1 + \sqrt{x}}.$ If $f(x) = \sqrt{1+x}$ and $g(x) = \sqrt{x}$, then $H(x) = (f \circ g)(x).$

For Exercises 52 and 54 there are several possible solutions only one of which is shown.

52. $F(x) = \sqrt[3]{\sqrt{x} - 1}.$ If $g(x) = x - 1$ and $h(x) = \sqrt{x}$, then $(g \circ h)(x) = \sqrt{x} - 1$, and if $f(x) = \sqrt[3]{x}$, then $F(x) = (f \circ g \circ h)(x).$

54. $G(x) = \dfrac{2}{(3 + \sqrt{x})^2}.$ If $g(x) = 3 + x$ and $h(x) = \sqrt{x}$, then $(g \circ h)(x) = 3 + \sqrt{x}$, and if $f(x) = \dfrac{2}{x^2}$, then $G(x) = (f \circ g \circ h)(x).$

56. Let r be the radius of the spherical balloon in centimeters. Since the radius is increasing at a rate of 1 cm/s, the radius is $r = t$ after t seconds. Therefore, the volume of the balloon can be written as $V = \frac{4}{3}\pi r^3 = \frac{4}{3}\pi(t)^3 = \frac{4}{3}\pi t^3.$

58. $A(x) = 1.05x.$ $(A \circ A)(x) = A(A(x)) = A(1.05x) = 1.05(1.05x) = (1.05)^2 x.$
$(A \circ A \circ A)(x) = A(A \circ A(x)) = A((1.05)^2 x) = 1.05[(1.05)^2 x] = (1.05)^3 x.$
$(A \circ A \circ A \circ A)(x) = A(A \circ A \circ A(x)) = A((1.05)^3 x) = 1.05[(1.05)^3 x] = (1.05)^4 x.$ A represents the amount in the account after 1 year; $A \circ A$ represents the amount in the account after 2 years; $A \circ A \circ A$ represents the amount in the account after 3 years; and $A \circ A \circ A \circ A$ represents the amount in the account after 4 years. We can see that if we compose n copies of A, we get $(1.05)^n x.$

60. $g(x) = 2x + 1$ and $h(x) = 4x^2 + 4x + 7$

Method 1: Notice that $(2x + 1)^2 = 4x^2 + 4x + 1.$ We see that adding 6 to this quantity gives $(2x + 1)^2 + 6 = 4x^2 + 4x + 1 + 6 = 4x^2 + 4x + 7$, which is $h(x)$. So let $f(x) = x^2 + 6$, and we have $(f \circ g)(x) = (2x + 1)^2 + 6 = h(x).$

Method 2: Since $g(x)$ is linear and $h(x)$ is a second degree polynomial, $f(x)$ must be a second degree polynomial, that is, $f(x) = ax^2 + bx + c$ for some a, b, and c. Thus $f(g(x)) = f(2x + 1) = a(2x + 1)^2 + b(2x + 1) + c \quad \Leftrightarrow$

$4ax^2 + 4ax + a + 2bx + b + c = 4ax^2 + (4a + 2b)x + (a + b + c) = 4x^2 + 4x + 7$. Comparing this with $f(g(x))$, we have $4a = 4$ (the x^2 coefficients), $4a + 2b = 4$ (the x coefficients), and $a + b + c = 7$ (the constant terms) $\Leftrightarrow$ $a = 1$ and $2a + b = 2$ and $a + b + c = 7$ $\Leftrightarrow$ $a = 1$, $b = 0, c = 6$. Thus $f(x) = x^2 + 6$.

$\underline{f(x) = 3x + 5 \text{ and } h(x) = 3x^2 + 3x + 2}$

Note since $f(x)$ is linear and $h(x)$ is quadratic, $g(x)$ must also be quadratic. We can then use trial and error to find $g(x)$. Another method is the following: We wish to find g so that $(f \circ g)(x) = h(x)$. Thus $f(g(x)) = 3x^2 + 3x + 2$ $\Leftrightarrow$ $3(g(x)) + 5 = 3x^2 + 3x + 2$ $\Leftrightarrow$ $3(g(x)) = 3x^2 + 3x - 3$ $\Leftrightarrow$ $g(x) = x^2 + x - 1$.

Exercises 4.8

2. By the Horizontal Line Test, f is one-to-one.

4. By the Horizontal Line Test, f is not one-to-one.

6. By the Horizontal Line Test, f is one-to-one.

8. $f(x) = x^2 - 2x + 5 = (x^2 - 2x + 1) + 5 - 1 = (x-1)^2 + 4$. Thus, $f(0) = 5 = f(2)$, so f is not a one-to-one function. [Or use the Horizontal Line Test.]

10. $g(x) = |x|$. Since every number and its negative have the same absolute value, that is, $|-1| = 1 = |1|$, g is not a one-to-one function.

12. $h(x) = \sqrt[3]{x}$. If $x_1 \neq x_2$, then $\sqrt[3]{x_1} \neq \sqrt[3]{x_2}$. So f is a one-to-one function.

14. $f(x) = x^4 + 5, 0 \le x \le 2$. If $x_1 \neq x_2$, then $x_1^4 \neq x_2^4$ because two different <u>positive</u> numbers cannot have the same fourth power. Thus, $x_1^4 + 5 \neq x_2^4 + 5$. So f is a one-to-one function.

16. $f(x) = \dfrac{1}{x}$. If $x_1 \neq x_2$, then $\dfrac{1}{x_1} \neq \dfrac{1}{x_2}$. So f is a one-to-one function.

18. (a) $f(5) = 18$. Since f is one-to-one, $f^{-1}(18) = 5$.

    (b) $f^{-1}(4) = 2$. Since f is one-to-one, $f(2) = 4$.

20. To find $g^{-1}(5)$, we find the x value such that $g(x) = 5$; that is, we solve the equation
    $g(x) = x^2 + 4x = 5$. Now $x^2 + 4x = 5 \quad \Leftrightarrow \quad x^2 + 4x - 5 = 0 \quad \Leftrightarrow \quad (x-1)(x+5) = 0$
    $\Leftrightarrow \quad x = 1$ or $x = -5$. Since the domain of g is $[-2, \infty)$, $x = 1$ is the only value where $g(x) = 5$.
    Therefore, $g^{-1}(5) = 1$.

22. $f(g(x)) = f\left(\dfrac{x}{2}\right) = 2\left(\dfrac{x}{2}\right) = x$, for all x.

    $g(f(x)) = g(2x) = \dfrac{2x}{2} = x$, for all x. Thus f and g are inverses of each other.

24. $f(g(x)) = f(3 - 4x) = \dfrac{3 - (3 - 4x)}{4} = \dfrac{3 - 3 + 4x}{4} = x$, for all x.

    $g(f(x)) = g\left(\dfrac{3-x}{4}\right) = 3 - 4\left(\dfrac{3-x}{4}\right) = 3 - 3 + x = x$, for all x. Thus f and g are inverses of each other.

26. $f(g(x)) = f\left(\sqrt[5]{x}\right) = \left(\sqrt[5]{x}\right)^5 = x$, for all x.

    $g(f(x)) = g(x^5) = \sqrt[5]{x^5} = x$, for all x. Thus f and g are inverses of each other.

28. $f(g(x)) = f\left((x-1)^{1/3}\right) = \left((x-1)^{1/3}\right)^3 + 1 = x - 1 + 1 = x$, for all x.

    $g(f(x)) = g(x^3 + 1) = \left[(x-1)^{1/3}\right]^3 + 1 = x - 1 + 1 = x$, for all x. Thus f and g are inverses of each other.

30. $f(g(x)) = f\left(\sqrt{4 - x^2}\right) = \sqrt{4 - \left(\sqrt{4 - x^2}\right)^2} = \sqrt{4 - 4 + x^2} = \sqrt{x^2} = x$, for all $0 \le x \le 2$.
    (Note that the last equality is possible since $x \ge 0$.)

$g(f(x)) = g\left(\sqrt{4 - x^2}\right) = \sqrt{4 - \left(\sqrt{4 - x^2}\right)^2} = \sqrt{4 - 4 + x^2} = \sqrt{x^2} = x$, for all $0 \le x \le 2$.

(Again, the last equality is possible since $x \ge 0$.) Thus f and g are inverses of each other.

32. $f(x) = 6 - x.$ $y = 6 - x \;\Leftrightarrow\; x = 6 - y.$ So $f^{-1}(x) = 6 - x.$

34. $f(x) = 3 - 5x.$ $y = 3 - 5x \;\Leftrightarrow\; -5x = y - 3 \;\Leftrightarrow\; x = -\frac{1}{5}(y - 3) = \frac{1}{5}(3 - y).$ So $f^{-1}(x) = \frac{1}{5}(3 - x).$

36. In Exercise 15 we showed that $f(x) = \dfrac{1}{x^2}$ is not one-to-one. So $f(x)$ does not have an inverse.

38. $f(x) = \frac{x-2}{x+2}.$ $y = \frac{x-2}{x+2} \;\Leftrightarrow\; y(x + 2) = x - 2 \;\Leftrightarrow\; xy + 2y = x - 2 \;\Leftrightarrow$
$xy - x = -2 - 2y \;\Leftrightarrow\; x(y - 1) = -2(y + 1) \;\Leftrightarrow\; x = \dfrac{-2(y+1)}{y-1}.$ So
$f^{-1}(x) = \dfrac{-2(x+1)}{x-1}.$

40. $f(x) = 5 - 4x^3.$ $y = 5 - 4x^3 \;\Leftrightarrow\; 4x^3 = 5 - y \;\Leftrightarrow\; x^3 = \frac{1}{4}(5 - y) \;\Leftrightarrow$
$x = \sqrt[3]{\frac{1}{4}(5 - y)}.$ So $f^{-1}(x) = \sqrt[3]{\frac{1}{4}(5 - x)}.$

42. $f(x) = x^2 + x = \left(x^2 + x + \frac{1}{4}\right) - \frac{1}{4} = \left(x + \frac{1}{2}\right)^2 - \frac{1}{4},\ x \ge -\frac{1}{2}.$ $y = \left(x + \frac{1}{2}\right)^2 - \frac{1}{4} \;\Leftrightarrow$
$\left(x + \frac{1}{2}\right)^2 = y + \frac{1}{4} \;\Leftrightarrow\; x + \frac{1}{2} = \sqrt{y + \frac{1}{4}} \;\Leftrightarrow\; x = \sqrt{y + \frac{1}{4}} - \frac{1}{2},\ y \ge -\frac{1}{4}.$ So
$f^{-1}(x) = \sqrt{x + \frac{1}{4}} - \frac{1}{2},\ x \ge -\frac{1}{4}.$ (Note that $x \ge -\frac{1}{2}$, so that $x + \frac{1}{2} \ge 0$, and hence
$\left(x + \frac{1}{2}\right)^2 = y + \frac{1}{4} \;\Leftrightarrow\; x + \frac{1}{2} = \sqrt{y + \frac{1}{4}}.$ Also, since $x \ge -\frac{1}{2},\ y = \left(x + \frac{1}{2}\right)^2 - \frac{1}{4} \ge -\frac{1}{4}$ so that
$y + \frac{1}{4} \ge 0$, and hence $\sqrt{y + \frac{1}{4}}$ is defined.)

44. $f(x) = \sqrt{2x - 1}.$ $y = \sqrt{2x - 1} \;\Leftrightarrow\; 2x - 1 = y^2 \;\Leftrightarrow\; x = \frac{1}{2}(y^2 + 1).$ So
$f^{-1}(x) = \frac{1}{2}(x^2 + 1).$

46. $f(x) = (2 - x^3)^5.$ $y = (2 - x^3)^5 \;\Leftrightarrow\; 2 - x^3 = \sqrt[5]{y} \;\Leftrightarrow\; x^3 = 2 - \sqrt[5]{y} \;\Leftrightarrow$
$x = \sqrt[3]{2 - \sqrt[5]{y}}.$ So $f^{-1}(x) = \sqrt[3]{2 - \sqrt[5]{x}}.$

48. $f(x) = \sqrt{9 - x^2},\ 0 \le x \le 3.$ $y = \sqrt{9 - x^2} \;\Leftrightarrow\; y^2 = 9 - x^2 \;\Leftrightarrow\; x^2 = 9 - y^2 \;\Rightarrow$
$x = \sqrt{9 - y^2}$ (since we must have $x \ge 0$). So $f^{-1}(x) = \sqrt{9 - x^2},\ 0 \le x \le 3.$

50. $f(x) = 1 - x^3.$ $y = 1 - x^3 \;\Leftrightarrow\; x^3 = 1 - y \;\Leftrightarrow\; x = \sqrt[3]{1 - y}.$ So $f^{-1}(x) = \sqrt[3]{1 - x}.$

52. (a) $f(x) = 16 - x^2,\ x \ge 0$ (b)

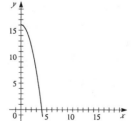

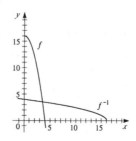

(c) $f(x) = 16 - x^2$, $x \geq 0$. $y = 16 - x^2$ $\Leftrightarrow$ $x^2 = 16 - y$ $\Leftrightarrow$ $x = \sqrt{16 - y}$. So
$f^{-1}(x) = \sqrt{16 - x}$, $x \leq 16$. (Note: $x \geq 0$ $\Rightarrow$ $f(x) = 16 - x^2 \leq 16$.)

54. (a) $f(x) = x^3 - 1$ (b)

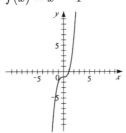 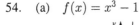 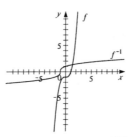

(c) $f(x) = x^3 - 1$ $\Leftrightarrow$ $y = x^3 - 1$ $\Leftrightarrow$ $x^3 = y + 1$ $\Leftrightarrow$ $x = \sqrt[3]{y + 1}$. So
$f^{-1}(x) = \sqrt[3]{x + 1}$.

56. $f(x) = x^3 + x$. Using a graphing device and the Horizontal Line Test, we see that f is a one-to-one function.

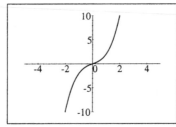

58. $f(x) = \sqrt{x^3 - 4x + 1}$. Using a graphing device and the Horizontal Line Test, we see that f is not a one-to-one function. For example, $f(0) = 1 = f(2)$.

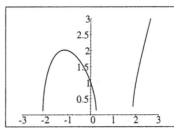

60. $f(x) = x \cdot |x|$. Using a graphing device and the Horizontal Line Test, we see that f is a one-to-one function.

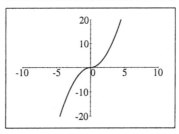

62. If we restrict the domain of $g(x)$ to $[1, \infty)$, then $y = (x - 1)^2$ $\Rightarrow$ $x - 1 = \sqrt{y}$ (since $x \geq 1$ we take the positive square root) $\Leftrightarrow$ $x = 1 + \sqrt{y}$. So $g^{-1}(x) = 1 + \sqrt{x}$.
If we restrict the domain of $g(x)$ to $(-\infty, 1]$, then $y = (x - 1)^2$ $\Rightarrow$ $x - 1 = -\sqrt{y}$ (since $x \leq 1$ we take the negative square root) $\Leftrightarrow$ $x = 1 - \sqrt{y}$. So $g^{-1}(x) = 1 - \sqrt{x}$.

64. $k(x) = |x - 3| = \begin{cases} -(x-3) & \text{if } x - 3 < 0 \quad \Leftrightarrow \quad x < 3 \\ x - 3 & \text{if } x - 3 \geq 0 \quad \Leftrightarrow \quad x \geq 3 \end{cases}$

If we restrict the domain of $k(x)$ to $[3, \infty)$, then $y = x - 3 \quad \Leftrightarrow \quad x = 3 + y$. So $k^{-1}(x) = 3 + x$.
If we restrict the domain of $k(x)$ to $(-\infty, 3]$, then $y = -(x - 3) \quad \Leftrightarrow \quad y = -x + 3 \quad \Leftrightarrow$
$x = 3 - y$. So $k^{-1}(x) = 3 - x$.

66.

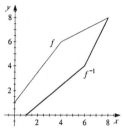

68. $f(x) = mx + b$. Notice that $f(x_1) = f(x_2) \quad \Leftrightarrow \quad mx_1 + b = mx_2 + b \quad \Leftrightarrow \quad mx_1 = mx_2$.
We can conclude that $x_1 = x_2$ if and only if $m \neq 0$. Therefore f is one-to-one if and only if $m \neq 0$.
If $m \neq 0$, $f(x) = mx + b \quad \Leftrightarrow \quad y = mx + b \quad \Leftrightarrow \quad mx = y - b \quad \Leftrightarrow \quad x = \dfrac{y - b}{m}$. So,
$f^{-1}(x) = \dfrac{x - b}{m}$.

70. $f(I(x)) = f(x)$; therefore $f \circ I = f$. $I(f(x)) = f(x)$; therefore $I \circ f = f$.
By definition, $f \circ f^{-1}(x) = x = I(x)$; therefore $f \circ f^{-1} = I$. Similarly, $f^{-1} \circ f(x) = x = I(x)$;
therefore $f^{-1} \circ f = I$.

Review Exercises for Chapter 4

2. $f(x) = 1 + \sqrt{x-1}$; $f(5) = 1 + \sqrt{5-1} = 3$; $f(9) = 1 + \sqrt{9-1} = 1 + \sqrt{8} = 1 + 2\sqrt{2}$;
    $f(a+1) = 1 + \sqrt{a+1-1} = 1 + \sqrt{a}$; $f(-x) = 1 + \sqrt{-x-1}$; $f(x^2) = 1 + \sqrt{x^2 - 1}$.
    $[f(x)]^2 = \left(1 + \sqrt{x-1}\right)^2 = 1 + 2\sqrt{x-1} + x - 1 = x + 2\sqrt{x-1}$.

4. By the Vertical Line Test, figures (b) and (c) are graphs of functions. By the Horizontal Line Test,
    figure (c) is the graph of a one-to-one function.

6. $F(t) = t^2 + 2t + 5 = (t^2 + 2t + 1) + 5 - 1 = (t+1)^2 + 4$. Therefore $F(t) \geq 4$ for all t. Since
    there are no restrictions on t, the domain of F is $(-\infty, \infty)$, and the range is $[4, \infty)$.

8. $f(x) = \dfrac{2x+1}{2x-1}$. Then $2x - 1 \neq 0 \quad \Leftrightarrow \quad x \neq \dfrac{1}{2}$. So the domain of f is $\{ x \mid x \neq \dfrac{1}{2} \}$.

10. $f(x) = 3x - \dfrac{2}{\sqrt{x+1}}$. The domain of f is the set of x where $x + 1 > 0 \quad \Leftrightarrow \quad x > -1$. So the
    domain is $(-1, \infty)$.

12. $g(x) = \dfrac{2x^2 + 5x + 3}{2x^2 - 5x - 3} = \dfrac{2x^2 + 5x + 3}{(2x+1)(x-3)}$. The domain of g is the set of all x where the
    denominator is not 0. So the domain is $\{x \mid 2x + 1 \neq 0 \text{ and } x - 3 \neq 0\} = \{x \mid x \neq -\frac{1}{2} \text{ and } x \neq 3 \}$.

14. $f(x) = \dfrac{\sqrt[3]{2x+1}}{\sqrt[3]{2x+2}}$. Since we have an odd root, the domain is the set of all x where the denominator
    is not 0. Now $\sqrt[3]{2x+2} \neq 0 \quad \Leftrightarrow \quad \sqrt[3]{2x} \neq -2 \quad \Leftrightarrow \quad 2x \neq -8 \quad \Leftrightarrow \quad x \neq -4$. Thus the
    domain of f is $\{x \mid x \neq -4\}$.

16. $f(x) = \frac{1}{3}(x - 5), \ 2 \leq x \leq 8$

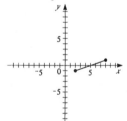

18. $g(t) = t^2 - 2t = (t-1)^2 - 1$

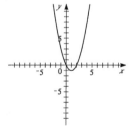

20. $f(x) = 3 - 8x - 2x^2 = -2(x-2)^2 + 11$

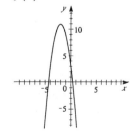

22. $y = -|x|$

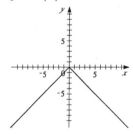

24. $y = \sqrt{x+3}$

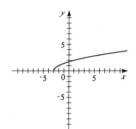

26. $H(x) = x^3 - 3x^2 = x^2(x-3)$

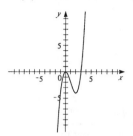

28. $G(x) = \dfrac{1}{(x-3)^2}$

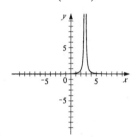

30. $f(x) = \begin{cases} 1 - 2x & \text{if } x \le 0 \\ 2x - 1 & \text{if } x > 0 \end{cases}$

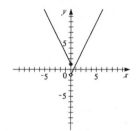

32. $f(x) = \begin{cases} -x & \text{if } x < 0 \\ x^2 & \text{if } 0 \le x < 2 \\ 1 & \text{if } x \ge 2 \end{cases}$

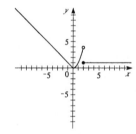

34. $f(x) = \sqrt{100 - x^3}$

   (a) $[-4, 4]$ by $[-4, 4]$

   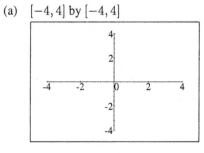

   (b) $[-10, 10]$ by $[-10, 10]$

   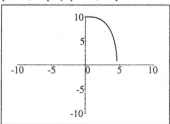

(c) $[-10, 10]$ by $[-10, 40]$ (d) $[-100, 100]$ by $[-100, 100]$

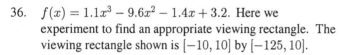

From the graphs, we see that the viewing rectangle in (c) produces the most appropriate graph of f.

36. $f(x) = 1.1x^3 - 9.6x^2 - 1.4x + 3.2$. Here we
     experiment to find an appropriate viewing rectangle. The
     viewing rectangle shown is $[-10, 10]$ by $[-125, 10]$.

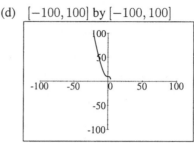

38. $y = |x(x + 2)(x + 4)|$. Here, the interesting parts of
     the function occur when $y = 0$. Thus we choose a
     viewing rectangle that includes the points $x = -4, -2$,
     and 0. So we choose the viewing rectangle $[-5, 5]$ by
     $[-1, 15]$.

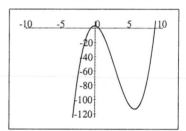

40. From the viewing rectangles, we see that the range of $f(x) = x^4 - x^3 + x^2 + 3x - 6$ is about
     $[-7.10, \infty)$.

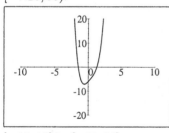

$[-10, 10]$ by $[-20, 20]$

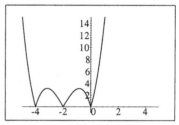

$[-3, 0]$ by $[-7.5, -7]$

42. Since z is inversely proportional to y, we have $z = \dfrac{k}{y}$. Substituting $z = 12$ when $y = 16$, we find

     $12 = \frac{k}{16}$ $\Leftrightarrow$ $k = 192$. Therefore $z = \dfrac{192}{y}$.

44. Let f be the frequency of the string and l be the length of the string. Since the frequency is inversely
     proportional to the length, we have $f = \dfrac{k}{l}$. Substituting $l = 12$ when $k = 440$, we find $440 = \dfrac{k}{12}$

$\Leftrightarrow$ $k = 5280$. Therefore $f = \dfrac{5280}{l}$. For $f = 660$, we must have $660 = \dfrac{5280}{l}$ $\Leftrightarrow$

$l = \frac{5280}{660} = 8$. So the string needs to be shortened to 8 inches.

46. Let r be the maximum range of the baseball and v be the velocity of the baseball. Since the maximum range is directly proportional to the square of the velocity, we have $r = lv^2$. Substituting $v = 60$ and $r = 242$, we find $242 = k(60)^2$ $\Leftrightarrow$ $k \approx 0.0672$. If $v = 70$, then we have a maximum range of $r = 0.0672(70)^2 = 329.4$ feet.

48. Average rate of change $= \dfrac{f(8) - f(4)}{8 - 4} = \dfrac{\left[\frac{1}{8-2}\right] - \left[\frac{1}{4-2}\right]}{4} = \dfrac{\frac{1}{6} - \frac{1}{2}}{4} \cdot \dfrac{6}{6} = \dfrac{1-3}{24} = -\dfrac{1}{12}.$

50. Average rate of change $= \dfrac{f(a+h) - f(a)}{(a+h) - a} = \dfrac{(a+h+1)^2 - (a+1)^2}{h}$

$= \dfrac{a^2 + 2ah + h^2 + 2a + 2h + 1 - a^2 - 2a - 1}{h} = \dfrac{2ah + h^2 + 2h}{h}$

$= \dfrac{h(2a + h + 2)}{h} = 2a + h + 2.$

52. $f(x) = |x^4 - 16|$ is graphed in the viewing rectangle $[-5, 5]$ by $[-5, 20]$. $f(x)$ is increasing on $[-2, 0]$ and $[2, \infty)$. It is decreasing on $(-\infty, -2]$ and $[0, 2]$.

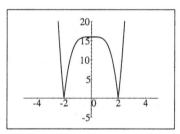

54. (a) $y = f(x - 2)$ (b) $y = -f(x)$

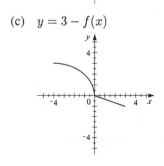

(c) $y = 3 - f(x)$ (d) $y = \frac{1}{2}f(x) - 1$

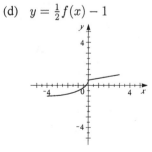

(e) $y = f^{-1}(x)$　　　　　　　　　　　(f) $y = f(-x)$

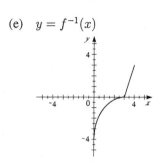　　　　　　　　　　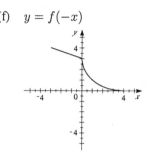

56. (a) $f(x)$ is odd;　(b) $g(x)$ is neither odd nor even;　(c) $h(x)$ is even.

58. $f(x) = -2x^2 + 12x + 12 = -2(x^2 - 6x) + 12 = -2(x^2 - 6x + 9) + 12 + 18$
$= -2(x - 3)^2 + 30$

60. $f(x) = 1 - x - x^2 = -(x^2 + x) + 1 = -\left(x^2 + x + \frac{1}{4}\right) + 1 + \frac{1}{4} = -\left(x + \frac{1}{2}\right)^2 + \frac{5}{4}$. So the
maximum value of f is $\frac{5}{4}$.

62. $P(x) = -1500 + 12x - 0.0004x^2 = -0.0004(x^2 - 30,000x) - 1500$
$= -0.0004(x^2 - 30,000x + 225,000,000) - 1500 + 90,000$
$= -0.0004(x - 15,000)^2 + 88,500$
The maximum profit occurs when $15,000$ units are sold, and the maximum profit is $\$88,500$.

64. $f(x) = x^{2/3}(6 - x)^{1/3}$. In the first viewing rectangle, $[-10, 10]$ by $[-10, 10]$, we see that $f(x)$ has a
local maximum and a local minimum. The local minimum is 0 at $x = 0$ (and is easily verified). In
the next viewing rectangle, $[3.95, 4.05]$ by $[3.16, 3.18]$, we isolate the local maximum value as
approximately 3.175 when $x \approx 4.00$.

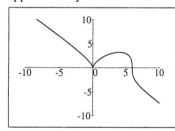　　　　　　　　　　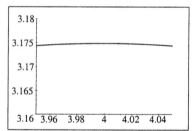

66. $f(x) = 1 + x^2$ and $g(x) = \sqrt{x - 1}$. (Remember that the proper domains must apply.)

(a) $(f \circ g)(x) = f\left(\sqrt{x - 1}\right) = 1 + \left(\sqrt{x - 1}\right)^2 = 1 + x - 1 = x$

(b) $(g \circ f)(x) = g(1 + x^2) = \sqrt{(1 + x^2) - 1} = \sqrt{x^2} = |x|$

(c) $(f \circ g)(2) = f(g(2)) = f\left(\sqrt{(2) - 1}\right) = f(1) = 1 + (1)^2 = 2.$

(d) $(f \circ f)(2) = f(f2)) = f(1 + (2)^2) = f(5) = 1 + (5)^2 = 26.$

(e) $(f \circ g \circ f)(x) = f((g \circ f)(x)) = f(|x|) = 1 + (|x|)^2 = 1 + x^2$. (Note $(g \circ f)(x) = |x|$ by
part (b).)

(f) $(g \circ f \circ g)(x) = g((f \circ g)(x)) = g(x) = \sqrt{x - 1}$. (Note $(f \circ g)(x) = x$ by part (a).)

68. $f(x) = \sqrt{x}$, has domain $\{\,x \mid x \geq 0\,\}$. $g(x) = \dfrac{2}{x-4}$, has domain $\{x \mid x \neq 4\}$.

$(f \circ g)(x) = f\left(\dfrac{2}{x-4}\right) = \sqrt{\dfrac{2}{x-4}}$. $(f \circ g)(x)$ is defined whenever both $g(x)$ and $f(g(x))$ are defined; that is, whenever $x \neq 4$ and $\dfrac{2}{x-4} \geq 0$. Now $\dfrac{2}{x-4} \geq 0 \quad \Leftrightarrow \quad x - 4 > 0 \quad \Leftrightarrow$ $x > 4$. So the domain of $f \circ g$ is $(4, \infty)$.

$(g \circ f)(x) = g(\sqrt{x}) = \dfrac{2}{\sqrt{x}-4}$. $(g \circ f)(x)$ is defined whenever both $f(x)$ and $g(f(x))$ are defined; that is, whenever $x \geq 0$ and $\sqrt{x} - 4 \neq 0$. Now $\sqrt{x} - 4 \neq 0 \quad \Leftrightarrow \quad x \neq 16$. So the domain of $g \circ f$ is $[0, 16) \cup (16, \infty)$.

$(f \circ f)(x) = f(\sqrt{x}) = \sqrt{\sqrt{x}} = x^{1/4}$. $(f \circ f)(x)$ is defined whenever both $f(x)$ and $f(f(x))$ are defined; that is, whenever $x \geq 0$. So the domain of $f \circ f$ is $[0, \infty)$.

$(g \circ g)(x) = g\left(\dfrac{2}{x-4}\right) = \dfrac{2}{\dfrac{2}{x-4} - 4} = \dfrac{2(x-4)}{2 - 4(x-4)} = \dfrac{x-4}{9 - 2x}$. $(g \circ g)(x)$ is defined whenever both $g(x)$ and $g(g(x))$ are defined; that is, whenever $x \neq 4$ and $9 - 2x \neq 0$. Now $9 - 2x \neq 0 \quad \Leftrightarrow$ $2x \neq 9 \quad \Leftrightarrow \quad x \neq \frac{9}{2}$. So the domain of $g \circ g$ is $\{x \mid x \neq \frac{9}{2}, 4\,\}$.

70. If $h(x) = \sqrt{x}$ and $g(x) = 1 + x$, then $(g \circ h)(x) = g(\sqrt{x}) = 1 + \sqrt{x}$. If $f(x) = \dfrac{1}{\sqrt{x}}$, then

$(f \circ g \circ h)(x) = f(1 + \sqrt{x}) = \dfrac{1}{\sqrt{1 + \sqrt{x}}} = T(x)$.

72. $g(x) = 2 - 2x + x^2 = (x^2 - 2x + 1) + 1 = (x-1)^2 + 1$. Since $g(0) = 2 = g(2)$, as is true for all pairs of numbers equidistant from 1, g is not a one-to-one function.

74. $r(x) = 2 + \sqrt{x + 3}$. If $x_1 \neq x_2$, then $x_1 + 3 \neq x_2 + 3$, so $\sqrt{x_1 + 3} \neq \sqrt{x_2 + 3}$ and $2 + \sqrt{x_1 + 3} \neq 2 + \sqrt{x_2 + 3}$. Thus r is one-to-one.

76. $q(x) = 3.3 + 1.6x + 2.5x^3$. Using a graphing device and the Horizontal Line Test, we see that q is a one-to-one function.

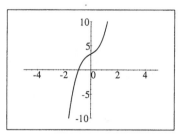

78. $f(x) = \dfrac{2x+1}{3}$. $y = \dfrac{2x+1}{3} \quad \Leftrightarrow \quad 2x + 1 = 3y \quad \Leftrightarrow \quad 2x = 3y - 1 \quad \Leftrightarrow \quad x = \frac{1}{2}(3y - 1)$. So $f^{-1}(x) = \frac{1}{2}(3x - 1)$.

80. $f(x) = 1 + \sqrt[5]{x - 2}$. $y = 1 + \sqrt[5]{x - 2} \quad \Leftrightarrow \quad y - 1 = \sqrt[5]{x - 2} \quad \Leftrightarrow \quad x - 2 = (y - 1)^5 \quad \Leftrightarrow$ $x = 2 + (y - 1)^5$. So $f^{-1}(x) = 2 + (x - 1)^5$.

82. $f(x) = 1 + \sqrt[4]{x}$

(a) If $x_1 \neq x_2$, then $\sqrt[4]{x_1} \neq \sqrt[4]{x_2}$, and so $1 + \sqrt[4]{x_1} \neq 1 + \sqrt[4]{x_2}$. Therefore, f is a one-to-one function.

(b) 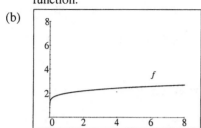   (c)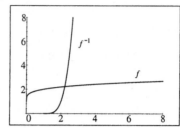

(d) $f(x) = 1 + \sqrt[4]{x}$. $y = 1 + \sqrt[4]{x}$ $\Leftrightarrow$ $\sqrt[4]{x} = y - 1$ $\Leftrightarrow$ $x = (y-1)^4$. So $f^{-1}(x) = (x-1)^4$, $x \geq 1$. Note that the domain of f is $[0, \infty)$, so $y = 1 + \sqrt[4]{x} \geq 1$. Hence, the domain of f^{-1} is $[1, \infty)$.

Focus on Modeling

2. Let w be the width of the poster. Then the length of the poster is $w + 10$. So the area of the poster is $A(w) = w(w + 10) = w^2 + 10w$.

4. Let r be the radius of the cylinder. Then the height of the cylinder is $4r$. Since for a cylinder $V = \pi r^2 h$, the volume of the cylinder is given by the function $V(r) = \pi r^2(4r) = 4\pi r^3$.

6. Let A be the area and y be the length of the other side. Then $A = xy = 16 \quad \Leftrightarrow \quad y = \dfrac{16}{x}$.

   Substituting into $P = 2x + 2y$ gives $P = 2x + 2 \cdot \dfrac{16}{x} = 2x + \dfrac{32}{x}$, where $x > 0$.

8. Let d represent the length of any side of a cube. Then the surface area is $A = 6d^2$, and the volume is $V = d^3 \quad \Leftrightarrow \quad d = \sqrt[3]{V}$. Substituting for d gives $A(V) = 6\left(\sqrt[3]{V}\right)^2 = 6V^{2/3}$, $V > 0$.

10. Let r be the radius of a circle. Then the area is $A = \pi r^2$, and the circumference is $C = 2\pi r \quad \Leftrightarrow \quad r = \dfrac{C}{2\pi}$. Substituting for r gives $A(C) = \pi\left(\dfrac{C}{2\pi}\right)^2 = \dfrac{C^2}{4\pi}$, $C > 0$.

12. By similar triangles, $\dfrac{5}{L} = \dfrac{12}{L + d} \quad \Leftrightarrow \quad 5(L + d) = 12L \quad \Leftrightarrow \quad 5d = 7L \quad \Leftrightarrow \quad L = \dfrac{5d}{7}$. The model is $L(d) = \frac{5}{7}d$.

14. Let n be one of the numbers. Then the other number is $60 - n$, so the product is given by the function $f(n) = n(60 - n) = 60n - n^2$.

16. Let l be the length of the shorter leg of the right triangle. Then the length of the other triangle is $2l$. Since it is a right triangle, the length of the hypotenuse is $\sqrt{l^2 + (2l)^2} = \sqrt{5l^2} = \sqrt{5}\,l$ (since $l \geq 0$). Thus the perimeter of the triangle is $P(l) = l + 2l + \sqrt{5}\,l = (3 + \sqrt{5})l$.

18. Using the formula for the volume of a cone, $V = \frac{1}{3}\pi r^2 h$, we substitute $V = 100$ and solve for h. Thus $100 = \frac{1}{3}\pi r^2 h \quad \Leftrightarrow \quad h(r) = \dfrac{300}{\pi r^2}$.

20. Let the positive numbers be x and y. Since their sum is 100, we have $x + y = 100 \quad \Leftrightarrow \quad y = 100 - x$. We wish to minimize the sum of squares, which is $S = x^2 + y^2 = x^2 + (100 - x)^2$. So $S(x) = x^2 + (100 - x)^2 = x^2 + 10000 - 200x + x^2 = 2x^2 - 200x + 10000 = 2(x^2 - 100x) + 10000 = 2(x^2 - 100x + 2500) + 10000 - 5000 = 2(x - 50)^2 + 5000$. Thus the minimum sum of squares occurs when $x = 50$. Then $y = 100 - 50 = 50$. Therefore both numbers are 50.

22. Let w and l be the width and the length of the rectangle in feet. We want all rectangles with perimeter equal to 20, so we have $2w + 2l = 20 \quad \Leftrightarrow \quad l = 10 - w$. The area of a rectangle is given by $A(w) = l \cdot w = (10 - w)w = 10w - w^2 = -(w^2 - 10w) = -(w^2 - 10w + 25) + 25 = -(w - 5)^2 + 25$. So the area is maximized when $w = 5$, and hence the largest rectangle is a square where the dimension of each side is 5 feet.

24. Let w be the width of the rectangular area (in feet) and l be the length of the field (in feet). Since the farmer has 750 feet of fencing, we must have $5w + 2l = 750 \quad \Leftrightarrow \quad 2l = 750 - 5w \quad \Leftrightarrow \quad l = \frac{5}{2}(150 - w)$. The area of the four pens is $A(w) = l \cdot w = \frac{5}{2}w(150 - w) = -\frac{5}{2}(w^2 - 150w)$

$= -\frac{5}{2}(w^2 - 150w + 75^2) + \left(\frac{5}{2}\right) \cdot 75^2 = -\frac{5}{2}(w - 75)^2 + 14062.5$. Therefore, the largest possible area of the four pens is 14,062.5 square feet.

26. Let x be the length of wire in cm that is bent into a square. So $10 - x$ is the length of wire in cm that is bent into the second square. The width of each square is $\frac{x}{4}$ and $\frac{10 - x}{4}$, and the area of each

square is $\left(\frac{x}{4}\right)^2 = \frac{x^2}{16}$ and $\left(\frac{10 - x}{4}\right)^2 = \frac{100 - 20x + x^2}{16}$. Thus the sum of the areas is

$A(x) = \frac{x^2}{16} + \frac{100 - 20x + x^2}{16} = \frac{100 - 20x + 2x^2}{16} = \frac{1}{8}x^2 - \frac{5}{4}x + \frac{25}{4}$

$= \frac{1}{8}(x^2 - 10x) + \frac{25}{4} = \frac{1}{8}(x^2 - 10x + 25) + \frac{25}{4} - \frac{25}{8} = \frac{1}{8}(x - 5)^2 + \frac{25}{8}$.

So the minimum area is $\frac{25}{8}$ cm^2 when each piece is 5 cm long.

28. Let x be the number of one dollar increases in the price of a necklace. So the selling price will be $10 + x$ dollars, and the number of necklaces sold will be $20 - 2x$. The revenue from the sales will be $(10 + x)(20 - 2x)$, and the cost will be $6(20 - 2x)$. The profits will be
$P(x) = (10 + x)(20 - 2x) - 6(20 - 2x) = (4 + x)(20 - 2x) = 80 + 12x - 2x^2$
$= -2(x^2 - 6x) + 80 = -2(x^2 - 6x + 9) + 80 + 18 = -2(x - 3)^2 + 98$. Thus the profit would be maximized at \$98 when $x = 3$. So he should set the selling price at $10 + x = \$13$.

30. The height of the box is x, the width of the box is $12 - 2x$, and the length of the box is $20 - 2x$. Therefore, the volume of the box is $V(x) = x(12 - 2x)(20 - 2x) = 4x^3 - 64x^2 + 240x$, $0 < x < 6$. Doesn't answer the question $x \approx 2.6$ max vol. fulls $2 < x < 3$

32. Let A, B, C, D be the vertices of the rectangle such that its base AB is on the x-axis, and its other two vertices, C and D, are above the x-axis and lying on the parabola $y = 8 - x^2$. Let C have the coordinates (x, y), $x > 0$, by symmetry, the coordinates of D must be $(-x, y)$. See the graph on the left. So the width of the rectangle is $2x$, and the length is $y = 8 - x^2$. Thus the area of the rectangle is $A(x) = length \cdot width = 2x(8 - x^2)$ $= 16x - 2x^3$. The graphs below show that the area is maximized when $x \approx 1.63$. Hence the maximum area occurs when the width is 3.27 and the length is 5.33.

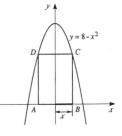

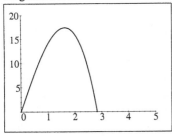
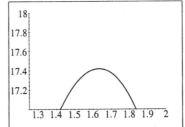

34. Let t_1 represent the time, in hours, spent walking, and let t_2 represent the time spent rowing. Since the distance walked is x and the walking speed is 5 mi/h, the time spent walking is $t_1 = \frac{1}{5}x$. By the Pythagorean Theorem, the distance rowed is $d = \sqrt{2^2 + (7 - x)^2} = \sqrt{x^2 - 14x + 53}$, and so the time spent rowing is $t_2 = \frac{1}{2} \cdot \sqrt{x^2 - 14x + 53}$. Thus the total time is
$T = \frac{1}{2}\sqrt{x^2 - 14x + 53} + \frac{1}{5}x$. Using Zoom, we see that T is minimized when $x \approx 6.13$. He should land at a point 6.13 miles from point B.

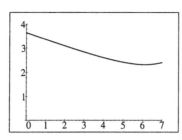

36. (a) Using the Pythagorean Theorem, we have that the height of the upper triangles is $\sqrt{25 - x^2}$ and the height of the lower triangles is $\sqrt{144 - x^2}$. So the area of the each of the upper triangles is $\frac{1}{2}x\sqrt{25 - x^2}$, and the area of the each of the lower triangles is $\frac{1}{2}x\sqrt{144 - x^2}$. Since there are two upper triangles and two lower triangles, we get that the total area is

$$A(x) = 2 \cdot \left[\frac{1}{2}x\sqrt{25 - x^2}\right] + 2 \cdot \left[\frac{1}{2}x\sqrt{144 - x^2}\right] = x\left(\sqrt{25 - x^2} + \sqrt{144 - x^2}\right).$$

(b) The function $y = A(x) = x\left(\sqrt{25 - x^2} + \sqrt{144 - x^2}\right)$ is shown in the first viewing rectangle below. In the second viewing rectangle, we isolate the maximum, and we see that the area of the kite is maximized when $x \approx 4.615$. So the length of the horizontal crosspiece must be $2 \cdot 4.615 = 9.23$. The length of the vertical crosspiece is $\sqrt{5^2 - (4.615)^2} + \sqrt{12^2 - (4.615)^2} \approx 13.00$.

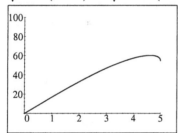
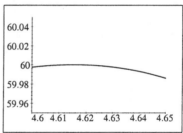

Chapter Five
Exercises 5.1

2. $P(x) = (x-2)^3$

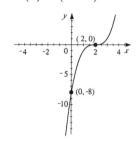

4. $P(x) = -2(x-1)^3$

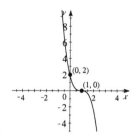

6. $P(x) = 3x^5 - 9$

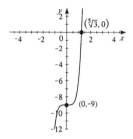

8. $P(x) = 3x^4 - 27$

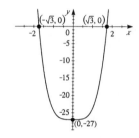

10. $P(x) = (x-1)(x+1)(x-2)$

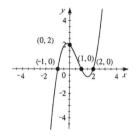

12. $P(x) = (2x-1)(x+1)(x+3)$

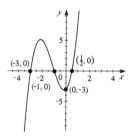

14. $P(x) = \frac{1}{5}x(x-5)^2$

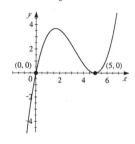

16. $P(x) = \frac{1}{4}(x+1)^3(x-3)$

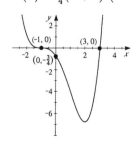

18. $P(x) = (x-1)^2(x+2)^3$

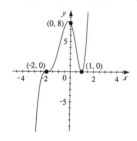

20. $P(x) = (x^2 - 2x - 3)^2 = (x-3)^2(x+1)^2$

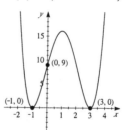

22. $P(x) = x^3 + 2x^2 - 8x$
       $= x(x-2)(x+4)$

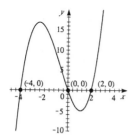

24. $P(x) = -2x^3 - x^2 + x = -x(2x^2 + x - 1)$
       $= -x(2x-1)(x+1)$

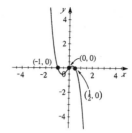

26. $P(x) = x^5 - 9x^3$
       $= x^3(x+3)(x-3)$

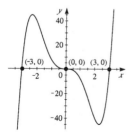

28. $P(x) = x^3 + 3x^2 - 4x - 12$
       $= (x+3)(x-2)(x+2)$

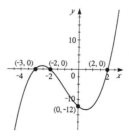

30. $P(x) = \frac{1}{8}(2x^4 + 3x^3 - 16x - 24)^2$
       $= \frac{1}{8}(x-2)^2(2x+3)^2(x^2 + 2x + 4)^2$

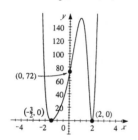

32. $P(x) = x^4 - 2x^3 + 8x - 16$
       $= (x+2)(x-2)(x^2 - 2x + 4)$

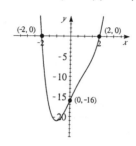

34. $P(x) = x^6 - 2x^3 + 1 = (x^3 - 1)^2 = (x - 1)^2(x^2 + x + 1)^2$

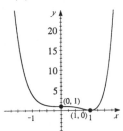

36. I   38. II   40. IV

42. $P(x) = -\frac{1}{8}x^3 + \frac{1}{4}x^2 + 12x$; $Q(x) = -\frac{1}{8}x^3$

Since P has odd degree and negative leading coefficient, it has the following end behavior:

$y \to -\infty$ as $x \to \infty$ and $y \to \infty$ as $x \to -\infty$.

On the large viewing rectangle, the graphs of P and Q look almost the same.

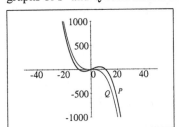

On the small viewing rectangle, the graphs of P and Q look very different and seem to have different end behavior.

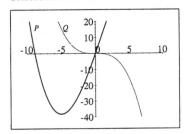

44. $P(x) = -x^5 + 2x^2 + x$; $Q(x) = -x^5$

Since P has odd degree and negative leading coefficient, it has the following end behavior:

$y \to -\infty$ as $x \to \infty$ and $y \to \infty$ as $x \to -\infty$.

On the large viewing rectangle, the graphs of P and Q look almost the same.

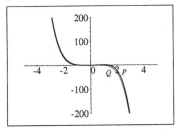

On the small viewing rectangle, the graphs of P and Q look very different.

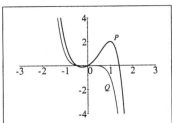

46. $P(x) = 2x^2 - x^{12}$; $Q(x) = -x^{12}$

Since P has even degree and negative leading coefficient, it has the following end behavior:

$y \to -\infty$ as $x \to \infty$ and $y \to -\infty$ as $x \to -\infty$.

On the large viewing rectangle, the graphs of P and Q look almost the same.

On the small viewing rectangle, the graphs of P and Q look very different.

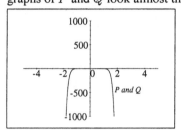

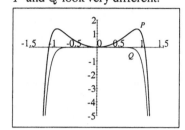

48. $y = x^3 - 3x^2$, $[-2, 5]$ by $[-10, 10]$

Local minimum at $(2, -4)$.

Local maximum at $(0, 0)$.

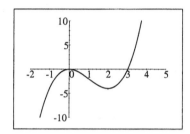

50. $y = 2x^3 - 3x^2 - 12x - 32$, $[-5, 5]$

by $[-60, 30]$

Local minimum at $(2, -52)$.

Local maximum at $(-1, -25)$.

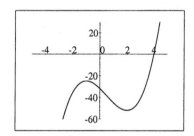

52. $y = x^4 - 18x^2 + 32$, $[-5, 5]$ by $[-100, 100]$

Local minima at $(-3, -49)$ and $(3, -49)$.

Local maximum at $(0, 32)$.

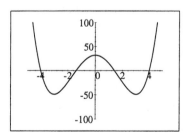

54. $y = x^5 - 5x^2 + 6, [-3, 3]$ by $[-5, 10]$
     Local maximum at $(0, 6)$.
     Local minimum at $(1.26, 1.24)$.

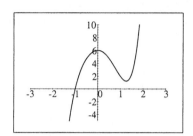

56. $y = x^3 + 12x$ has no local extremum.

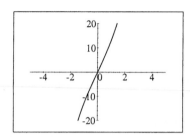

58. $y = 6x^3 + 3x + 1$ has no local extremum.

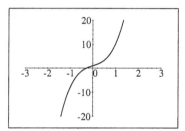

60. $y = 1.2x^5 + 3.75x^4 - 7x^3 - 15x^2 + 18x$
     Two local maxima occur at $(0.50, 4.65)$ and
     $(-2.97, 12.10)$, and two local minima occur
     at $(-1.40, -27.44)$ and $(1.40, -2.54)$.

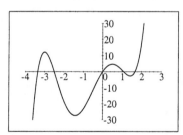

62. $y = (x^2 - 2)^3$ has one local minimum at
     $(0, -8)$.

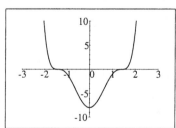

64. $y = \frac{1}{3}x^7 - 17x^2 + 7$.
One local maximum at $(0, 7)$ and one
local minimum at $(1.71, -28.46)$.

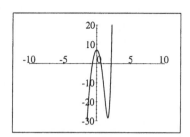

66. $P(x) = (x - c)^4$
Increasing the value of c shifts the graph
to the right.

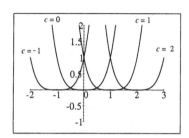

68. $P(x) = x^3 + cx$
Increasing the value of c makes the "bumps"
in the graph flatter.

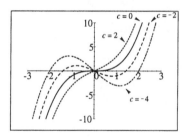

70. $P(x) = x^c$.
The larger c gets, the flatter the graph is
near the origin, and the steeper it is away
from the origin.

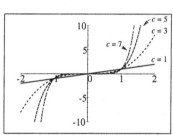

72. Graph 1 belongs to $y = x^4$. Graph 2 belongs to $y = x^2$. Graph 3 belongs to $y = x^6$. Graph 4
belongs to $y = x^3$. Graph 5 belongs to $y = x^5$.

74. (a) The length of the bottom is $40 - 2x$, the width of the bottom is $20 - 2x$, and the height is x, so
the volume of the box is $V = x(20 - 2x)(40 - 2x) = 4x^3 - 120x^2 + 800x$.

(b) Since the height and width must be positive, we must have $x > 0$ and $20 - 2x > 0$, and so the
domain of V is $0 < x < 10$.

148   Exercises 5.1

(c) Using the domain from part (b), we graph
V in the viewing rectangle $[0, 10]$ by
$[0, 1600]$. The maximum volume is
$V \approx 1539.6$ when $x = 4.23$.

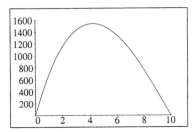

76. $P(x) = 8x + 0.3x^2 - 0.0013x^3 - 372$

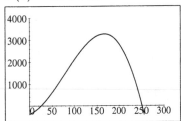

(a) For the firm to break even, $P(x) = 0$. From the
graph, we see that $P(x) = 0$ when $x \approx 25.2$. Of
course, the firm cannot produce fractions of a
blender, so the manufacturer must produce at least
26 blenders a year.

(b) No, the profit does not increase indefinitely. The
largest profit is approximately $3276.22, which
occurs when the firm produces 166 blenders per
year.

78. (a) $P(x) = (x - 1)(x - 3)(x - 4)$.

Local maximum at $(1.8, 2.1)$.

Local minimum at $(3.6, -0.6)$.

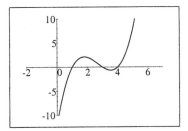

(b) Since $Q(x) = P(x) + 5$, each point on
the graph of Q has y-coordinate 5 units
more than the corresponding point on the
graph of P. Thus Q has:

Local maximum: $(1.8, 7.1)$

Local minimum: $(3.5, 4.4)$

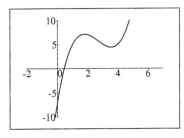

(c) Since $P(a) = P(b) = 0$, and $P(x) > 0$ for $a < x < b$ (see the table below), the graph of P
must first rise and then fall on the interval (a, b), and so P must have at least one local
maximum between a and b. Using similar reasoning, the fact that $P(b) = P(c) = 0$ and
$P(x) < 0$ for $b < x < c$ shows that P must have at least one local minimum between b and c.
Thus P has at least two local extrema.

Interval	$(-\infty, a)$	(a, b)	(b, c)	(c, ∞)
Sign of $x - a$	$-$	$+$	$+$	$+$
Sign of $x - b$	$-$	$-$	$+$	$+$
Sign of $x - c$	$-$	$-$	$-$	$+$
Sign of $(x - a)(x - b)(x - c)$	$-$	$+$	$-$	$+$

(d) $Q(x) = (x - a)(x - b)(x - c) + d$, where $a < b < c$. Since the graph of Q is obtained by shifting the graph of $P(x) = (x - a)(x - b)(x - c)$ vertically by d units, it follows that Q has the same number of local extrema as P, which was found to be 2 in part (c).

80. The graph of $y = x^{100}$ would be close to the x-axis until just before $x = 1$ and would then pass through the points $(1, 1)$ and $(-1, 1)$. The graph of $y = x^{101}$ behaves similarly except that the y-values are negative for negative values of x.

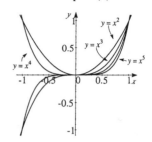

82. No, it is impossible. The end behavior of a third degree polynomial is the same as that of $y = kx^3$, and for this function, the values of y go off in opposite directions as $x \to \infty$ and $x \to -\infty$. But for a function with just one extremum, the values of y would head off in the same direction (either both up or both down) on either side of the extremum. An nth degree polynomial can have $n - 1$ extrema or $n - 3$ extrema or $n - 5$ extrema, and so on (decreasing by 2). An example of a polynomial that has six local extrema must be of degree 7 or higher. For example, $P(x) = (x - 1)(x - 2)(x - 3)(x - 4)(x - 5)(x - 6)(x - 7)$ has six local extrema.

Exercises 5.2

2.

$$
\begin{array}{r}
x^2 \ \ + x \\
x - 2 \overline{\smash{\big)}\, x^3 \ - x^2 - 2x + 6} \\
\underline{x^3 - 2x^2} \\
x^2 - 2x \\
\underline{x^2 - 2x} \\
0 + 6
\end{array}
$$

Thus the quotient is $x^2 + x$, and the remainder is 6.

4.

$$
\begin{array}{r}
\tfrac{1}{3}x^2 \ + \tfrac{1}{3}x \ + \tfrac{2}{3} \\
3x + 6 \overline{\smash{\big)}\, x^3 + 3x^2 + 4x + 3} \\
\underline{x^3 + 2x^2} \\
x^2 + 4x \\
\underline{x^2 + 2x} \\
2x + 3 \\
\underline{2x + 4} \\
-1
\end{array}
$$

Thus the quotient is $\tfrac{1}{3}x^2 + \tfrac{1}{3}x + \tfrac{2}{3}$, and the remainder is -1.

6.

$$
\begin{array}{r}
3x^2 \ - 8x \ - 1 \\
x^2 + x + 3 \overline{\smash{\big)}\, 3x^4 - 5x^3 + 0x^2 - 20x - 5} \\
\underline{3x^4 + 3x^3 + 9x^2} \\
-8x^3 - 9x^2 - 20x \\
\underline{-8x^3 - 8x^2 - 24x} \\
-x^2 \ + 4x - 5 \\
\underline{-x^2 \ - x - 3} \\
5x - 2
\end{array}
$$

Thus the quotient is $3x^2 - 8x - 1$, and the remainder is $5x - 2$.

8.

$$
\begin{array}{r}
3 \\
3x^2 - 7x \overline{\smash{\big)}\, 9x^2 \ - x + 5} \\
\underline{9x^2 - 21x} \\
20x + 5
\end{array}
$$

Thus the quotient is 3, and the remainder is $20x + 5$.

10.

$$
\begin{array}{r}
\tfrac{1}{2}x^3 \ - x^2 \ - \tfrac{5}{2}x \ - \tfrac{7}{4} \\
4x^2 - 6x + 8 \overline{\smash{\big)}\, 2x^5 - 7x^4 + 0x^3 + 0x^2 + 0x - 13} \\
\underline{2x^5 - 3x^4 + 4x^3} \\
-4x^4 - 4x^3 + 0x^2 \\
\underline{-4x^4 + 6x^3 - 8x^2} \\
-10x^3 + 8x^2 + 0x \\
\underline{-10x^3 + 15x^2 - 20x} \\
-7x^2 + 20x - 13 \\
\underline{-7x^2 + \tfrac{21}{2}x - 14} \\
\tfrac{19}{2}x + 1
\end{array}
$$

Thus the quotient is $\tfrac{1}{2}x^3 - x^2 - \tfrac{5}{2}x - \tfrac{7}{4}$, and the remainder is $\tfrac{19}{2}x + 1$.

12. The synthetic division table for this problem takes the following form.

$$
\begin{array}{r|rrr}
1 & 1 & -5 & 4 \\
  &   & 1 & -4 \\
\hline
  & 1 & -4 & 0
\end{array}
$$

Thus the quotient is $x - 4$, and the remainder is 0.

14. The synthetic division table for this problem takes the following form.

$$
\begin{array}{r|rrr}
-5 & 4 & 0 & -3 \\
   &   & -20 & 100 \\
\hline
   & 4 & -20 & 97
\end{array}
$$

Thus the quotient is $4x - 20$, and the remainder is 97.

16. The synthetic division table for this problem takes the following form.

$$
\begin{array}{r|rrrr}
5 & 3 & -12 & -9 & 1 \\
  &   & 15 & 15 & 30 \\
\hline
  & 3 & 3   & 6 & 31
\end{array}
$$

Thus the quotient is $3x^2 + 3x + 6$, and the remainder is 31.

18. The synthetic division table for this problem takes the following form.

$$
\begin{array}{r|rrrrr}
2 & 1 & -1 & 1 & -1 & 2 \\
  &   & 2 & 2 & 6 & 10 \\
\hline
  & 1 & 1 & 3 & 5 & 12
\end{array}
$$

Thus the quotient is $x^3 + x^2 + 3x + 5$, and the remainder is 12.

20. The synthetic division table for this problem takes the following form.

$$
\begin{array}{r|rrrr}
3 & 1 & -9 & 27 & -27 \\
  &   & 3 & -18 & 27 \\
\hline
  & 1 & -6 & 9 & 0
\end{array}
$$

Thus the quotient is $x^2 - 6x + 9$, and the remainder is 0.

22. The synthetic division table for this problem takes the following form.

$$
\begin{array}{r|rrrrr}
-\frac{2}{3} & 6 & 10 & 5 & 1 & 1 \\
             &   & -4 & -4 & -\frac{2}{3} & -\frac{2}{9} \\
\hline
             & 6 & 6 & 1 & \frac{1}{3} & \frac{7}{9}
\end{array}
$$

Thus the quotient is $6x^3 + 6x^2 + x + \frac{1}{3}$, and the remainder is $\frac{7}{9}$.

24. The synthetic division table for this problem takes the following form.

$$
\begin{array}{r|rrrrr}
-2 & 1 & 0 & 0 & 0 & -16 \\
   &   & -2 & 4 & -8 & 16 \\
\hline
   & 1 & -2 & 4 & -8 & 0
\end{array}
$$

Thus the quotient is $x^3 - 2x^2 + 4x - 8$, and the remainder is 0.

26. $P(x) = 2x^2 + 9x + 1, c = \frac{1}{2}$

$$
\begin{array}{r|rrr}
\frac{1}{2} & 2 & 9 & 1 \\
            &   & 1 & 5 \\
\hline
            & 2 & 10 & 6
\end{array}
$$

Therefore, by the Remainder Theorem, $P\left(\frac{1}{2}\right) = 6$.

28. $P(x) = x^3 - x^2 + x + 5, c = -1$

$$
\begin{array}{r|rrrr}
-1 & 1 & -1 & 1 & 5 \\
   &   & -1 & 2 & -3 \\
\hline
   & 1 & -2 & 3 & 2
\end{array}
$$

Therefore, by the Remainder Theorem, $P(-1) = 2$.

30. $P(x) = 2x^3 - 21x^2 + 9x - 200, c = 11$

$$
\begin{array}{r|rrrr}
11 & 2 & -21 & 9 & -200 \\
   &   & 22 & 11 & 220 \\
\hline
   & 2 & 1   & 20 & 20
\end{array}
$$

Therefore, by the Remainder Theorem, $P(11) = 20$.

32. $P(x) = 6x^5 + 10x^3 + x + 1, c = -2$

$$
\begin{array}{r|rrrrrr}
-2 & 6 & 0 & 10 & 0 & 1 & 1 \\
   &   & -12 & 24 & -68 & 136 & -274 \\
\hline
   & 6 & -12 & 34 & -68 & 137 & -273
\end{array}
$$

Therefore, by the Remainder Theorem, $P(-2) = -273$.

34. $P(x) = -2x^6 + 7x^5 + 40x^4 - 7x^2 + 10x + 112, c = -3$

$$
\begin{array}{r|rrrrrrr}
-3 & -2 & 7 & 40 & 0 & -7 & 10 & 112 \\
   &   & 6 & -39 & -3 & 9 & -6 & -12 \\
\hline
   & -2 & 13 & 1 & -3 & 2 & 4 & 100
\end{array}
$$

Therefore, by the Remainder Theorem, $P(-3) = 100$.

36. $P(x) = x^3 - x + 1, c = \frac{1}{4}$

$$
\begin{array}{r|rrrr}
\frac{1}{4} & 1 & 0 & -1 & 1 \\
            &   & \frac{1}{4} & \frac{1}{16} & -\frac{15}{64} \\
\hline
            & 1 & \frac{1}{4} & -\frac{15}{16} & \frac{49}{64}
\end{array}
$$
  Therefore, by the Remainder Theorem, $P\left(\frac{1}{4}\right) = \frac{49}{64}$.

38.   (a) $P(x) = 6x^7 - 40x^6 + 16x^5 - 200x^4 - 60x^3 - 69x^2 + 13x - 139, c = 7$

$$
\begin{array}{r|rrrrrrrr}
7 & 6 & -40 & 16 & -200 & -60 & -69 & 13 & -139 \\
  &   & 42 & 14 & 210 & 70 & 70 & 7 & 140 \\
\hline
  & 6 & 2 & 30 & 10 & 10 & 1 & 20 & 1
\end{array}
$$

Therefore, by the Remainder Theorem, $P(7) = 1$.

(b) $P(7) = 6(7)^7 - 40(7)^6 + 16(7)^5 - 200(7)^4 - 60(7)^3 - 69(7)^2 + 13(7) - 139$
$$= 6(823543) - 40(117649) + 16(16807) - 200(2401) - 60(343)$$
$$- 69(49) + 13(7) - 139$$
$$= 1,$$
which agrees with the value obtained by synthetic division, but requires more work.

40. $P(x) = x^3 + 2x^2 - 3x - 10, c = 2$

$$
\begin{array}{r|rrrr}
2 & 1 & 2 & -3 & -10 \\
  &   & 2 & 8 & 10 \\
\hline
  & 1 & 4 & 5 & 0
\end{array}
$$
  Since the remainder is 0, $x - 2$ is a factor.

42. $P(x) = x^4 + 3x^3 - 16x^2 - 27x + 63, c = 3, -3$

$$
\begin{array}{r|rrrrr}
3 & 1 & 3 & -16 & -27 & 63 \\
  &   & 3 & 18 & 6 & -63 \\
\hline
  & 1 & 6 & 2 & -21 & 0
\end{array}
$$
  Since the remainder is 0, $x - 3$ is a factor.

We next show that $x + 3$ is also a factor by using synthetic division on the quotient of the above synthetic division, $x^3 + 6x^2 - 2x - 21$.

$$
\begin{array}{r|rrrr}
-3 & 1 & 6 & 2 & -21 \\
   &   & -3 & -9 & 21 \\
\hline
   & 1 & 3 & -7 & 0
\end{array}
$$
  Since the remainder is 0, $x + 3$ is a factor.

44. $P(x) = 3x^4 - x^3 - 21x^2 - 11x + 6, c = \frac{1}{3}, -2$

$$
\begin{array}{r|rrrrr}
\frac{1}{3} & 3 & -1 & -21 & -11 & 6 \\
            &   & 1 & 0 & -7 & -6 \\
\hline
            & 3 & 0 & -21 & -18 & 0
\end{array}
$$
  Since the remainder is 0, it follows that $\frac{1}{3}$ is a zero.

Thus $P(x) = \left(x - \frac{1}{3}\right)(3x^3 - 21x - 18)$. Next, we use synthetic division on the quotient.

$$
\begin{array}{r|rrrr}
-2 & 3 & 0 & -21 & -18 \\
   &   & -6 & 12 & 18 \\
\hline
   & 3 & -6 & -9 & 0
\end{array}
$$ Since the remainder is 0, it follows that 2 is a zero.

So $P(x) = \left(x - \frac{1}{3}\right)(x + 2)(3x^2 - 6x - 9) = 3\left(x - \frac{1}{3}\right)(x + 2)(x^2 - 2x - 3)$
$= 3\left(x - \frac{1}{3}\right)(x + 2)(x - 3)(x + 1)$.
Hence, the zeros are $\frac{1}{3}$, -2, -1, and 3.

46. Since the zeros are $x = -2$, $x = 0$, $x = 2$, and $x = 4$, the factors are $x + 2$, x, $x - 2$, and $x - 4$. Thus $P(x) = c(x + 2)x(x - 2)(x - 4)$. If we let $c = 1$, then $P(x) = x^4 - 4x^3 - 4x^2 + 16x$.

48. Since the zeros are $x = -2$, $x = -1$, $x = 0$, $x = 1$, and $x = 2$, the factors are $x + 2$, $x + 1$, x, $x - 1$, and $x - 2$. Thus $P(x) = c(x + 2)(x + 1)x(x - 1)(x - 2)$. If we let $c = 1$, then $P(x) = x^5 - 5x^3 + 4x$.

50. Since the zeros of the polynomial are 1, -1, 2, and $\frac{1}{2}$, it follows that
$P(x) = C(x - 1)(x + 1)(x - 2)\left(x - \frac{1}{2}\right) = C(x^2 - 1)\left(x^2 - \frac{5}{2}x + 1\right)$. To ensure integer coefficients, we choose C to be any nonzero multiple of 2. When $C = 2$, we have
$P(x) = 2(x^2 - 1)\left(x^2 - \frac{5}{2}x + 1\right) = (x^2 - 1)(2x^2 - 5x + 2) = 2x^4 - 5x^3 + 5x - 2$. (Note: This is just one of many polynomials with the desired zeros and integer coefficients. We can choose C to be any even integer.)

52. $R(x) = x^5 - 2x^4 + 3x^3 - 2x^2 + 3x + 4 = (x^4 - 2x^3 + 3x^2 - 2x + 3)x + 4$
$= ((x^3 - 2x^2 + 3x - 2)x + 3)x + 4$
$= (((x^2 - 2x + 3)x - 2)x + 3)x + 4$
$= ((((x - 2)x + 3)x - 2)x + 3)x + 4$

So to calculate $R(3)$, we start with 3, then:

    subtract 2; multiply by 3;

    add 3; multiply by 3;

    subtract 2; multiply by 3;

    add 3; multiply by 3; and

    add 4; to get 157.

Exercises 5.3

2. $Q(x) = x^4 - 3x^3 - 6x + 20$ has possible rational zeros $\pm 1, \pm 2, \pm 4, \pm 5, \pm 10, \pm 20$.

4. $S(x) = 6x^4 - x^2 + 2x + 12$ has possible rational zeros $\pm 1, \pm 2, \pm 3, \pm 4, \pm 6, \pm 12, \pm \frac{1}{2}, \pm \frac{3}{2}, \pm \frac{1}{3},$
$\pm \frac{2}{3}, \pm \frac{4}{3}, \pm \frac{1}{6}$.

6. $P(x) = x^3 - 7x^2 + 14x - 8$. The possible rational zeros are $\pm 1, \pm 2, \pm 4, \pm 8$. $P(x)$ has 3
variations in sign and hence 1 or 3 positive real zeros. $P(-x) = -x^3 - 7x^2 - 14x - 8$ has 0
variations in sign and hence no negative real zeros.

$$\begin{array}{r|rrrr}
1 & 1 & -7 & 14 & -8 \\
  &   & 1 & -6 & 8 \\
\hline
  & 1 & -6 & 8 & 0
\end{array} \quad \Rightarrow \quad x = 1 \text{ is a zero.}$$

So $P(x) = x^3 - 7x^2 + 14x - 8 = (x - 1)(x^2 - 6x + 8) = (x - 1)(x - 2)(x - 4)$. Therefore, the
zeros are $x = 1, 2, 4$.

8. $P(x) = x^3 + 4x^2 - 3x - 18$. The possible rational zeros are $\pm 1, \pm 2, \pm 3, \pm 6, \pm 9, \pm 18$. $P(x)$ has
1 variation in sign and hence 1 positive real zero. $P(-x) = -x^3 + 4x^2 + 3x - 18$ has 2 variations
in sign and hence 0 or 2 negative real zeros.

$$\begin{array}{r|rrrr}
1 & 1 & 4 & -3 & -18 \\
  &   & 1 & 5 & 2 \\
\hline
  & 1 & 5 & 2 & -16
\end{array} \qquad\qquad
\begin{array}{r|rrrr}
2 & 1 & 4 & -3 & -18 \\
  &   & 2 & 12 & 18 \\
\hline
  & 1 & 6 & 9 & 0
\end{array} \quad \Rightarrow \quad x = 2 \text{ is a zero.}$$

$P(x) = x^3 + 4x^2 - 3x - 18 = (x - 2)(x^2 + 6x + 9) = (x - 2)(x + 3)^2$. Therefore, the zeros are
$x = -3, 2$.

10. $P(x) = x^3 - x^2 - 8x + 12$. The possible rational zeros are $\pm 1, \pm 2, \pm 3, \pm 4, \pm 6, \pm 12$. $P(x)$ has 2
variations in sign and hence 0 or 2 positive real zeros. $P(-x) = -x^3 - x^2 + 8x + 12$ has 1
variation in sign and hence 1 negative real zero.

$$\begin{array}{r|rrrr}
1 & 1 & -1 & -8 & 12 \\
  &   & 1 & 0 & -8 \\
\hline
  & 1 & 0 & -8 & 4
\end{array} \qquad\qquad
\begin{array}{r|rrrr}
2 & 1 & -1 & -8 & 12 \\
  &   & 2 & 2 & -12 \\
\hline
  & 1 & 1 & -6 & 0
\end{array} \quad \Rightarrow \quad x = 2 \text{ is a zero.}$$

$P(x) = x^3 - x^2 - 8x + 12 = (x - 2)(x^2 + x - 6) = (x - 2)(x + 3)(x - 2)$. Therefore, the zeros
are $x = -3, 2$.

12. $P(x) = x^3 - 4x^2 - 7x + 10$. The possible rational zeros are $\pm 1, \pm 2, \pm 5, \pm 10$. $P(x)$ has 2
variations in sign and hence 0 or 2 positive real zeros. $P(-x) = -x^3 - 4x^2 + 7x + 10$ has 1
variation in sign and hence 1 negative real zero.

$$\begin{array}{r|rrrr}
1 & 1 & -4 & -7 & 10 \\
  &   & 1 & -3 & -10 \\
\hline
  & 1 & -3 & -10 & 0
\end{array} \quad \Rightarrow \quad x = 1 \text{ is a zero.}$$

So $P(x) = x^3 - 4x^2 - 7x + 10 = (x - 1)(x^2 - 3x - 10) = (x - 1)(x - 5)(x + 2)$. Therefore,
the zeros are $x = -2, 1, 5$.

14. $P(x) = x^3 - 2x^2 - 2x - 3$. The possible rational zeros are $\pm 1, \pm 3$. $P(x)$ has 1 variation in sign
and hence 1 positive real zero. $P(-x) = -x^3 - 2x^2 + 2x - 3$ has 2 variations in sign and hence 0
or 2 negative real zeros.

$$\begin{array}{r|rrrr}1 & 1 & -2 & -2 & -3 \\ & & 1 & -1 & -3 \\ \hline & 1 & -1 & -3 & -6\end{array} \qquad \begin{array}{r|rrrr}3 & 1 & -2 & -2 & -3 \\ & & 3 & 3 & 3 \\ \hline & 1 & 1 & 1 & 0\end{array} \Rightarrow \quad x = 3 \text{ is a zero.}$$

So $P(x) = x^3 - 2x^2 - 2x - 3 = (x - 3)(x^2 + x + 1)$. Now, $Q(x) = x^2 + x + 1$ has no real zeros, since the discriminant is $b^2 - 4ac = (1)^2 - 4(1)(1) = -3 < 0$. Thus, the only real zero is $x = 3$.

16. $P(x) = x^4 - 2x^3 - 3x^2 + 8x - 4$. Using synthetic division, we see that $(x - 1)$ is a factor of $P(x)$:

$$\begin{array}{r|rrrrr}1 & 1 & -2 & -3 & 8 & -4 \\ & & 1 & -1 & -4 & 4 \\ \hline & 1 & -1 & -4 & 4 & 0\end{array} \Rightarrow \quad x = 1 \text{ is a zero.}$$

We continue by factoring the quotient, and we see that $(x - 1)$ is again a factor:

$$\begin{array}{r|rrrr}1 & 1 & -1 & -4 & 4 \\ & & 1 & 0 & -4 \\ \hline & 1 & 0 & -4 & 0\end{array} \Rightarrow \quad x = 1 \text{ is a zero.}$$

$P(x) = x^4 - 2x^3 - 3x^2 + 8x - 4 = (x - 1)(x - 1)(x^2 - 4) = (x - 1)^2(x - 2)(x + 2)$.
Therefore, the zeros are $x = 1, \pm 2$.

18. $P(x) = x^4 - x^3 - 23x^2 - 3x + 90$. The possible rational zeros are ± 1, ± 2, ± 3, ± 5, ± 6, ± 9, ± 10, ± 15, ± 18, ± 30, ± 45, ± 90. Since $P(x)$ has 2 variations in sign, P has 0 or 2 positive real zeros. Since $P(-x) = x^4 + x^3 - 23x^2 + 3x + 90$ has 2 variations in sign, P has 0 or 2 negative real zeros.

$$\begin{array}{r|rrrrr}1 & 1 & -1 & -23 & -3 & 90 \\ & & 1 & 0 & -23 & -26 \\ \hline & 1 & 0 & -23 & -26 & 64\end{array}$$

$$\begin{array}{r|rrrrr}2 & 1 & -1 & -23 & -3 & 90 \\ & & 2 & 2 & -42 & -90 \\ \hline & 1 & 1 & -21 & -45 & 0\end{array} \Rightarrow \quad x = 2 \text{ is a zero.}$$

$P(x) = (x - 2)(x^3 + x^2 - 21x - 45)$. Continuing with the quotient we have:

$$\begin{array}{r|rrrr}3 & 1 & 1 & -21 & -45 \\ & & 3 & 12 & -27 \\ \hline & 1 & 4 & -9 & -72\end{array} \qquad \begin{array}{r|rrrr}5 & 1 & 1 & -21 & -45 \\ & & 5 & 30 & 45 \\ \hline & 1 & 6 & 9 & 0\end{array} \Rightarrow \quad x = 5 \text{ is a zero.}$$

$P(x) = (x - 2)(x - 5)(x^2 + 6x + 9) = (x - 2)(x - 5)(x + 3)^2$. Therefore, the zeros are $x = -3, 2, 5$.

20. $P(x) = x^4 - x^3 - 5x^2 + 3x + 6$. The possible rational zeros are ± 1, ± 2, ± 3, ± 6. Since $P(x)$ has 2 variations in sign, P has 0 or 2 positive real zeros. Since $P(-x) = x^4 + x^3 - 5x^2 - 3x + 6$ has 2 variations in sign, P has 0 or 2 negative real zeros.

$$\begin{array}{r|rrrrr}1 & 1 & -1 & -5 & 3 & 6 \\ & & 1 & 0 & -5 & -2 \\ \hline & 1 & 0 & -5 & -2 & 4\end{array} \qquad \begin{array}{r|rrrrr}2 & 1 & -1 & -5 & 3 & 6 \\ & & 2 & 2 & -6 & -6 \\ \hline & 1 & 1 & -3 & -3 & 0\end{array} \Rightarrow \quad x = 2 \text{ is a zero.}$$

$P(x) = (x - 2)(x^3 + x^2 - 3x - 3)$. Continuing with the quotient we have:

$$\begin{array}{r|rrrr}3 & 1 & 1 & -3 & -3 \\ & & 3 & 12 & 27 \\ \hline & 1 & 4 & 9 & 24\end{array} \Rightarrow \quad x = 3 \text{ is an upper bound, thus we try negative zeros.}$$

$$\begin{array}{r|rrrr} -1 & 1 & 1 & -3 & -3 \\ & & -1 & 0 & 3 \\ \hline & 1 & 0 & -3 & 0 \end{array} \quad \Rightarrow \quad x = -1 \text{ is a zero.}$$

$P(x) = (x-2)(x+1)(x^2-3)$. Therefore, the rational zeros are $x = -1, 2$.

22. $P(x) = 2x^3 + 7x^2 + 4x - 4$. The possible rational zeros are $\pm 1, \pm 2, \pm 4, \pm \frac{1}{2}$. Since $P(x)$ has 1 variation in sign, P has 1 positive real zero. Since $P(-x) = -2x^3 + 7x^2 - 4x - 4$ has 2 variations in sign, P has 0 or 2 negative real zeros.

$$\begin{array}{r|rrrr} 1 & 2 & 7 & 4 & -4 \\ & & 2 & 9 & 13 \\ \hline & 2 & 9 & 13 & 9 \end{array} \Rightarrow x = 1 \text{ is an upper bound.} \qquad \begin{array}{r|rrrr} \frac{1}{2} & 2 & 7 & 4 & -4 \\ & & 1 & 4 & 4 \\ \hline & 2 & 8 & 8 & 0 \end{array} \Rightarrow x = \frac{1}{2} \text{ is a zero.}$$

$P(x) = \left(x - \frac{1}{2}\right)(2x^2 + 8x + 8) = 2\left(x - \frac{1}{2}\right)(x^2 + 4x + 4) = 2\left(x - \frac{1}{2}\right)(x+2)^2$. Therefore, the zeros are $x = -2, \frac{1}{2}$.

24. We use factoring by grouping: $P(x) = 2x^3 - 3x^2 - 2x + 3 = 2x(x^2 - 1) - 3(x^2 - 1)$
$= (x^2 - 1)(2x - 3) = (x - 1)(x + 1)(2x - 3)$. Therefore, the zeros are $x = \frac{3}{2}, \pm 1$.

26. $P(x) = 8x^3 + 10x^2 - x - 3$. The possible rational zeros are $\pm 1, \pm 3, \pm \frac{1}{2}, \pm \frac{3}{2}, \pm \frac{1}{4}, \pm \frac{3}{4}, \pm \frac{1}{8}, \pm \frac{3}{8}$. Since $P(x)$ has 1 variation in sign, P has 1 positive real zero. Since $P(-x) = -8x^3 + 10x^2 + x - 3$ has 2 variations in sign, P has 0 or 2 negative real zeros.

$$\begin{array}{r|rrrr} 1 & 8 & 10 & -1 & -3 \\ & & 8 & 18 & 17 \\ \hline & 8 & 18 & 17 & 14 \end{array} \Rightarrow x = 1 \text{ is an upper bound, thus we try fractions.}$$

$$\begin{array}{r|rrrr} \frac{1}{2} & 8 & 10 & -1 & -3 \\ & & 4 & 7 & 3 \\ \hline & 8 & 14 & 6 & 0 \end{array} \Rightarrow x = \frac{1}{2} \text{ is a zero.}$$

$P(x) = 8x^3 + 10x^2 - x - 3 = \left(x - \frac{1}{2}\right)(8x^2 + 14x + 6) = 2\left(x - \frac{1}{2}\right)(4x^2 + 7x + 3)$
$= (2x - 1)(x + 1)(4x + 3) = 0$. Therefore, the zeros are $x = -1, -\frac{3}{4}, \frac{1}{2}$.

28. $P(x) = 6x^4 - 7x^3 - 12x^2 + 3x + 2$. The possible rational zeros are $\pm 1, \pm 2, \pm \frac{1}{2}, \pm \frac{1}{3}, \pm \frac{2}{3}, \pm \frac{1}{6}$. Since $P(x)$ has 2 variations in sign, P has 0 or 2 positive real zeros. Since $P(-x) = 6x^4 + 7x^3 - 12x^2 - 3x + 2$ has 2 variations in sign, P has 0 or 2 negative real zeros.

$$\begin{array}{r|rrrrr} 1 & 6 & -7 & -12 & 3 & 2 \\ & & 6 & -1 & -13 & -10 \\ \hline & 6 & -1 & -13 & -10 & -8 \end{array} \qquad \begin{array}{r|rrrrr} 2 & 6 & -7 & -12 & 3 & 2 \\ & & 12 & 10 & -4 & -2 \\ \hline & 6 & 5 & -2 & -1 & 0 \end{array} \Rightarrow x = 2 \text{ is a zero.}$$

$P(x) = 6x^4 - 7x^3 - 12x^2 + 3x + 2 = (x - 2)(6x^3 + 5x^2 - 2x - 1)$. Continuing by factoring the quotient, we first note that the possible rational zeros are $-1, \pm \frac{1}{2}, \pm \frac{1}{3}, \pm \frac{1}{6}$. We have:

$$\begin{array}{r|rrrr} \frac{1}{2} & 6 & 5 & -2 & -1 \\ & & 3 & 4 & 1 \\ \hline & 6 & 8 & 2 & 0 \end{array} \Rightarrow x = \frac{1}{2} \text{ is a zero.}$$

$P(x) = (x - 2)\left(x - \frac{1}{2}\right)(6x^2 + 8x + 2) = 2(x - 2)\left(x - \frac{1}{2}\right)(3x^2 + 4x + 1)$
$= (x - 2)\left(x - \frac{1}{2}\right)(x + 1)(3x + 1)$. Therefore, the zeros are $x = -1, -\frac{1}{3}, \frac{1}{2}, 2$.

30. $P(x) = x^5 - 4x^4 - 3x^3 + 22x^2 - 4x - 24$ has possible rational zeros $\pm 1, \pm 2, \pm 3, \pm 4, \pm 6, \pm 8,$ $\pm 12, \pm 24$. Since $P(x)$ has 3 variations in sign, there are 1 or 3 positive real zeros. Since $P(-x) = -x^5 - 4x^4 + 3x^3 + 22x^2 + 4x - 24$ has 2 variations in sign, there are 0 or 2 negative real zeros.

$$
\begin{array}{r|rrrrrr}
1 & 1 & -4 & -3 & 22 & -4 & -24 \\
  &   & 1 & -3 & -6 & 16 & 12 \\
\hline
  & 1 & -3 & -6 & 16 & 12 & -12
\end{array}
$$

$$
\begin{array}{r|rrrrrr}
2 & 1 & -4 & -3 & 22 & -4 & -24 \\
  &   & 2 & -4 & -14 & 16 & 24 \\
\hline
  & 1 & -2 & -7 & 8 & 12 & 0
\end{array} \Rightarrow \quad x = 2 \text{ is a zero.}
$$

$P(x) = (x - 2)(x^4 - 2x^3 - 7x^2 + 8x + 12)$

$$
\begin{array}{r|rrrrr}
2 & 1 & -2 & -7 & 8 & 12 \\
  &   & 2 & 0 & -14 & -12 \\
\hline
  & 1 & 0 & -7 & -6 & 0
\end{array} \Rightarrow \quad x = 2 \text{ is a zero again.}
$$

$P(x) = (x - 2)^2(x^3 - 7x - 6)$

$$
\begin{array}{r|rrrr}
2 & 1 & 0 & -7 & -6 \\
  &   & 2 & 4 & -6 \\
\hline
  & 1 & 2 & -3 & -12
\end{array}
\qquad
\begin{array}{r|rrrr}
3 & 1 & 0 & -7 & -6 \\
  &   & 3 & 9 & 6 \\
\hline
  & 1 & 3 & 2 & 0
\end{array} \Rightarrow \quad x = 3 \text{ is a zero.}
$$

$P(x) = (x - 2)^2(x - 3)(x^2 + 3x + 2) = (x - 2)^2(x - 3)(x + 1)(x + 2) = 0$. Therefore, the zeros are $x = -1, \pm 2, 3$.

32. $P(x) = 2x^6 - 3x^5 - 13x^4 + 29x^3 - 27x^2 + 32x - 12$ has possible rational zeros $\pm 1, \pm 2, \pm 3, \pm 4,$ $\pm 6, \pm 12, \pm \frac{1}{2}, \pm \frac{3}{2}$. Since $P(x)$ has 5 variations in sign, there are 1 or 3 or 5 positive real zeros. Since $P(-x) = 2x^6 + 3x^5 - 13x^4 - 29x^3 + 27x^2 - 32x - 12$ has 3 variations in sign, there are 1 or 3 negative real zeros.

$$
\begin{array}{r|rrrrrrr}
1 & 2 & -3 & -13 & 29 & -27 & 32 & -12 \\
  &   & 2 & -1 & -14 & 15 & -12 & 20 \\
\hline
  & 2 & -1 & -14 & 15 & -12 & 20 & 8
\end{array}
$$

$$
\begin{array}{r|rrrrrrr}
2 & 2 & -3 & -13 & 29 & -27 & 32 & -12 \\
  &   & 4 & 2 & -22 & 14 & -26 & 12 \\
\hline
  & 2 & 1 & -11 & 7 & -13 & 6 & 0
\end{array} \Rightarrow \quad x = 2 \text{ is a zero.}
$$

$P(x) = (x - 2)(2x^5 + x^4 - 11x^3 + 7x^2 - 13x + 6)$. We continue with the quotient:

$$
\begin{array}{r|rrrrrr}
2 & 2 & 1 & -11 & 7 & -13 & 6 \\
  &   & 4 & 10 & -2 & 10 & -6 \\
\hline
  & 2 & 5 & -1 & 5 & -3 & 0
\end{array} \Rightarrow \quad x = 2 \text{ is a zero again.}
$$

$P(x) = (x - 2)^2(2x^4 + 5x^3 - x^2 + 5x - 3)$. We continue with the quotient, first noting 2 is no longer a possible rational solution:

$$
\begin{array}{r|rrrrr}
3 & 2 & 5 & -1 & 5 & -3 \\
  &   & 6 & 22 & 42 & 94 \\
\hline
  & 2 & 11 & 21 & 47 & 91
\end{array} \Rightarrow x = 3 \text{ is an upper bound.}
$$

We know that there is at least 1 more positive zero.

$$\frac{1}{2} \,\big|\, \begin{array}{ccccc} 2 & 5 & -1 & 5 & -3 \\ & 1 & 2 & 1 & 3 \\ \hline 2 & 6 & 2 & 6 & 0 \end{array} \quad \Rightarrow x = \tfrac{1}{2} \text{ is a zero.}$$

$P(x) = (x-2)^2(x-\tfrac{1}{2})(2x^3 + 6x^2 + 2x + 6)$.

We can factor $2x^3 + 6x^2 + 2x + 6$ by grouping; $2x^3 + 6x^2 + 2x + 6 = (2x^3 + 6x^2) + (2x + 6)$
$= (2x + 6)(x^2 + 1)$. So $P(x) = 2(x-2)^2(x-\tfrac{1}{2})(x+3)(x^2 + 1)$. Since $x^2 + 1$ has no real zeros, the zeros of P are $x = -3, 2, \tfrac{1}{2}$.

34. $P(x) = x^3 - 5x^2 + 2x + 12$. The possible rational zeros are $\pm 1, \pm 2, \pm 3, \pm 4, \pm 6, \pm 12$. $P(x)$ has 2 variations in sign and hence 0 or 2 positive real zeros. $P(-x) = -x^3 - 5x^2 - 2x + 12$ has 1 variation in sign and hence 1 negative real zero.

$$1 \,\big|\, \begin{array}{cccc} 1 & -5 & 2 & 12 \\ & 1 & -4 & -2 \\ \hline 1 & -4 & -2 & 10 \end{array} \qquad\qquad 2 \,\big|\, \begin{array}{cccc} 1 & -5 & 2 & 12 \\ & 2 & -6 & -8 \\ \hline 1 & -3 & -4 & 4 \end{array}$$

$$3 \,\big|\, \begin{array}{cccc} 1 & -5 & 2 & 12 \\ & 3 & -6 & -12 \\ \hline 1 & -2 & -4 & 0 \end{array} \quad \Rightarrow x = 3 \text{ is a zero.}$$

So $P(x) = (x-3)(x^2 - 2x - 4)$. Using the quadratic formula on the second factor, we have:

$$x = \frac{-(-2) \pm \sqrt{(-2)^2 - 4(1)(-4)}}{2(1)} = \frac{2 \pm \sqrt{20}}{2} = \frac{2 \pm 4\sqrt{5}}{2} = 1 \pm 2\sqrt{5}. \text{ Therefore, the zeros}$$

are $x = 3, 1 \pm 2\sqrt{5}$.

36. $P(x) = x^4 + 2x^3 - 2x^2 - 3x + 2$. The possible rational zeros are $\pm 1, \pm 2$. $P(x)$ has 2 variations in sign and hence 0 or 2 positive real zeros. $P(-x) = x^4 - 2x^3 - 2x^2 + 3x + 2$ has 2 variations in sign and hence 0 or 2 negative real zeros.

$$1 \,\big|\, \begin{array}{ccccc} 1 & 2 & -2 & -3 & 2 \\ & 1 & 3 & 1 & -2 \\ \hline 1 & 3 & 1 & -2 & 0 \end{array} \quad \Rightarrow x = 1 \text{ is a zero.}$$

$P(x) = (x-1)(x^3 + 3x^2 + x - 2)$. Continuing with the quotient:

$$1 \,\big|\, \begin{array}{cccc} 1 & 3 & 1 & -2 \\ & 1 & 4 & 5 \\ \hline 1 & 4 & 5 & 3 \end{array} \quad \Rightarrow x = 1 \text{ is an upper bound.}$$

$$-1 \,\big|\, \begin{array}{cccc} 1 & 3 & 1 & -2 \\ & -1 & -2 & 1 \\ \hline 1 & 2 & -1 & -1 \end{array} \qquad\qquad -2 \,\big|\, \begin{array}{cccc} 1 & 3 & 1 & -2 \\ & -2 & -2 & 2 \\ \hline 1 & 1 & -1 & 0 \end{array} \quad \Rightarrow x = -2 \text{ is a zero.}$$

So $P(x) = (x-1)(x+2)(x^2 + x - 1)$. Using the quadratic formula on the third factor, we have:

$$x = \frac{-1 \pm \sqrt{1^2 - 4(1)(-1)}}{2(1)} = \frac{1 \pm \sqrt{5}}{2}. \text{ Therefore, the zeros are } x = 1, -2, \frac{1 \pm \sqrt{5}}{2}.$$

38. $P(x) = x^5 - 4x^4 - x^3 + 10x^2 + 2x - 4$. The possible rational zeros are $\pm 1, \pm 2, \pm 4$. $P(x)$ has 3 variations in sign and hence 1 or 3 positive real zeros. $P(-x) = -x^5 - 4x^4 + x^3 + 10x^2 - 2x - 4$ has 2 variations in sign and hence 0 or 2 negative real zeros.

$$
\begin{array}{r|rrrrr}
1 & 1 & -4 & -1 & 10 & 2 & -4 \\
  &   & 1 & -3 & -4 & 6 & 8 \\
\hline
  & 1 & -3 & -4 & 6 & 8 & 4
\end{array}
\qquad
\begin{array}{r|rrrrr}
2 & 1 & -4 & -1 & 10 & 2 & -4 \\
  &   & 2 & -4 & -10 & 0 & 4 \\
\hline
  & 1 & -2 & -5 & 0 & 2 & 0 \quad \Rightarrow \quad x = 2 \text{ is a zero.}
\end{array}
$$

So $P(x) = (x-2)(x^4 - 2x^3 - 5x^2 + 2)$. Since the constant term of the second factor is 2, ± 4 are no longer possible zeros. Continuing by factoring the quotient, we have:

$$
\begin{array}{r|rrrr}
2 & 1 & -2 & -5 & 0 & 2 \\
  &   & 2 & 0 & -10 & -20 \\
\hline
  & 1 & 0 & -5 & -10 & 18
\end{array}
\qquad
\begin{array}{r|rrrr}
-1 & 1 & -2 & -5 & 0 & 2 \\
   &   & -1 & 3 & 2 & -2 \\
\hline
   & 1 & -3 & -2 & 2 & 0 \quad \Rightarrow \quad x = -1 \text{ is a zero.}
\end{array}
$$

So $P(x) = (x-2)(x+1)(x^3 - 3x^2 - 2x - 2)$. Continuing by factoring the quotient, we have:

$$
\begin{array}{r|rrr}
-1 & 1 & -3 & -2 & 2 \\
   &   & -1 & 4 & -2 \\
\hline
   & 1 & -4 & 2 & 0 \quad \Rightarrow \quad x = -1 \text{ is a zero again.}
\end{array}
$$

So $P(x) = (x-2)(x+1)^2(x^2 - 4x + 2)$. Using the quadratic formula on the second factor, we have: $x = \dfrac{-(-4) \pm \sqrt{(-4)^2 - 4(1)(2)}}{2(1)} = \dfrac{4 \pm \sqrt{8}}{2} = \dfrac{4 \pm 2\sqrt{2}}{2} = 2 \pm \sqrt{2}$. Therefore, the zeros are $x = -1, 2, 2 \pm \sqrt{2}$.

40. $P(x) = 3x^3 - 5x^2 - 8x - 2$. The possible rational zeros are $\pm 1, \pm 2, \pm\frac{1}{3}, \pm\frac{2}{3}$. $P(x)$ has 1 variation in sign and hence 1 positive real zero. $P(-x) = -3x^3 - 5x^2 + 8x - 2$ has 2 variations in sign and hence 0 or 2 negative real zeros.

$$
\begin{array}{r|rrr}
1 & 3 & -5 & -8 & -2 \\
  &   & 3 & -2 & -10 \\
\hline
  & 3 & -2 & -10 & -12
\end{array}
\qquad
\begin{array}{r|rrr}
2 & 3 & -5 & -8 & -2 \\
  &   & 6 & 2 & -12 \\
\hline
  & 3 & 1 & -6 & -14
\end{array}
$$

$$
\begin{array}{r|rrr}
\frac{1}{3} & 3 & -5 & -8 & -2 \\
  &   & 1 & -\frac{4}{3} & -\frac{28}{9} \\
\hline
  & 3 & -4 & -\frac{28}{3} & -\frac{46}{9}
\end{array}
\qquad
\begin{array}{r|rrr}
\frac{2}{3} & 3 & -5 & -8 & -2 \\
  &   & 2 & -2 & -\frac{20}{3} \\
\hline
  & 3 & -3 & -10 & -\frac{26}{3}
\end{array}
$$

Thus we have tried all the positive rational zeros, so we try the negative zeros.

$$
\begin{array}{r|rrr}
-1 & 3 & -5 & -8 & -2 \\
   &   & -3 & 8 & 0 \\
\hline
   & 3 & -8 & 0 & -2
\end{array}
\qquad
\begin{array}{r|rrr}
-2 & 3 & -5 & -8 & -2 \\
   &   & -6 & 22 & -28 \\
\hline
   & 3 & -11 & 14 & -30
\end{array}
$$

$$
\begin{array}{r|rrr}
-\frac{1}{3} & 3 & -5 & -8 & -2 \\
   &   & -1 & 2 & 2 \\
\hline
   & 3 & -6 & -6 & 0 \quad \Rightarrow \quad x = -\frac{1}{3} \text{ is a zero.}
\end{array}
$$

So $P(x) = \left(x + \frac{1}{3}\right)(3x^2 - 6x - 6) = 3\left(x + \frac{1}{3}\right)(x^2 - 2x - 2)$. Using the quadratic formula on the second factor, we have: $x = \dfrac{-(-2) \pm \sqrt{(-2)^2 - 4(1)(-2)}}{2(1)} = \dfrac{2 \pm \sqrt{12}}{2} = \dfrac{2 \pm 2\sqrt{3}}{2} = 1 \pm \sqrt{3}$. Therefore, the zeros are $x = -\frac{1}{3}, 1 \pm \sqrt{3}$.

42. $P(x) = 4x^5 - 18x^4 - 6x^3 + 91x^2 - 60x + 9$. The possible rational zeros are $\pm 1, \pm 3, \pm 9, \pm\frac{1}{2}, \pm\frac{3}{2}, \pm\frac{9}{2}, \pm\frac{1}{4}, \pm\frac{3}{4}, \pm\frac{9}{4}$. $P(x)$ has 4 variations in sign and hence 0 or 2 or 4 positive real zeros. $P(-x) = -4x^5 - 18x^4 + 6x^3 + 91x^2 + 60x + 9$ has 1 variation in sign and hence 1 negative real zero.

$$
\begin{array}{r|rrrrrr}
1 & 4 & -18 & -6 & 91 & -60 & 9 \\
  &   & 4 & -14 & -20 & 71 & 1 \\
\hline
  & 4 & -14 & -20 & 71 & 11 & 20
\end{array}
$$

$$
\begin{array}{r|rrrrrr}
3 & 4 & -18 & -6 & 91 & -60 & 9 \\
  &   & 12 & -18 & -72 & 57 & 9 \\
\hline
  & 4 & -6 & -24 & 19 & -3 & 0 \quad \Rightarrow \quad x = 3 \text{ is a zero.}
\end{array}
$$

So $P(x) = (x - 3)(4x^4 - 6x^3 - 24x^2 + 19x - 3)$. Continuing by factoring the quotient, we have:

$$
\begin{array}{r|rrrrr}
3 & 4 & -6 & -24 & 19 & -3 \\
  &   & 12 & 18 & -18 & 3 \\
\hline
  & 4 & 6 & -6 & 1 & 0 \quad \Rightarrow \quad x = 3 \text{ is a zero again.}
\end{array}
$$

So $P(x) = (x - 3)^2(4x^3 + 6x^2 - 6x + 1)$. Continuing by factoring the quotient, we have:

$$
\begin{array}{r|rrrr}
3 & 4 & 6 & -6 & 1 \\
  &   & 12 & 54 & 144 \\
\hline
  & 4 & 18 & 48 & 1445 \quad \Rightarrow \quad x = 3 \text{ is an upper bound.}
\end{array}
$$

$$
\begin{array}{r|rrrr}
\frac{1}{2} & 4 & 6 & -6 & 1 \\
  &   & 2 & 4 & -1 \\
\hline
  & 4 & 8 & -2 & 0 \quad \Rightarrow \quad x = \frac{1}{2} \text{ is a zero.}
\end{array}
$$

So $P(x) = (x - 3)^2\left(x - \frac{1}{2}\right)(4x^2 + 8x - 2) = 2(x - 3)^2\left(x - \frac{1}{2}\right)(2x^2 + 4x - 1)$. Using the quadratic formula on the second factor, we have:

$$x = \frac{-4 \pm \sqrt{4^2 - 4(2)(-1)}}{2(2)} = \frac{-4 \pm \sqrt{8}}{4} = \frac{-4 \pm 2\sqrt{2}}{4} = \frac{-2 \pm \sqrt{2}}{2}.$$ Therefore, the zeros are $x = \frac{1}{2}, 3, \frac{-2 \pm \sqrt{2}}{2}$.

44. (a) $P(x) = -x^3 - 2x^2 + 5x + 6$ has possible rational zeros $\pm 1, \pm 2, \pm 3, \pm 6$.

$$
\begin{array}{r|rrrr}
1 & -1 & -2 & 5 & 6 \\
  &   & -1 & -3 & 2 \\
\hline
  & -1 & -3 & 2 & 8
\end{array}
\qquad
\begin{array}{r|rrrr}
2 & -1 & -2 & 5 & 6 \\
  &   & -2 & -8 & -6 \\
\hline
  & -1 & -4 & -3 & 0 \quad \Rightarrow \quad x = 2 \text{ is a zero.}
\end{array}
$$

So $P(x) = (x - 2)(-x^2 - 4x - 3) = -(x - 2)(x^2 + 4x + 3) = -(x - 2)(x + 1)(x + 3)$. The real zeros of P are $2, -1, -3$.

(b)

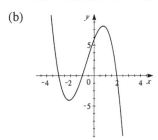

46. (a) $P(x) = 3x^3 + 17x^2 + 21x - 9$ has possible rational zeros $\pm 1, \pm 3, \pm 9, \pm \frac{1}{3}, \pm \frac{2}{3}$.

$$
\begin{array}{r|rrrr}
1 & 3 & 17 & 21 & -9 \\
  &   & 3 & 20 & 41 \\
\hline
  & 3 & 20 & 41 & 32 \quad \Rightarrow x = 1 \text{ is an upper bound.}
\end{array}
$$

$$\frac{1}{3} \begin{array}{|rrrr} 3 & 17 & 21 & -9 \\ & 1 & 6 & 9 \\ \hline 3 & 18 & 27 & 0 \end{array} \Rightarrow x = \frac{1}{3} \text{ is a zero.}$$

So $P(x) = \left(x - \frac{1}{3}\right)(3x^2 + 18x + 27) = 3\left(x - \frac{1}{3}\right)(x^2 + 6x + 9) = 3\left(x - \frac{1}{3}\right)(x + 3)^2$. The real zeros of P are $-3, \frac{1}{3}$.

(b)

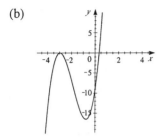

48. (a) $P(x) = -x^4 + 10x^2 + 8x - 8$ has possible rational zeros $\pm 1, \pm 2, \pm 4, \pm 8$.

$$1 \begin{array}{|rrrrr} -1 & 0 & 10 & 8 & -8 \\ & -1 & -1 & 9 & 17 \\ \hline -1 & -1 & 9 & 17 & 9 \end{array} \qquad 2 \begin{array}{|rrrrr} -1 & 0 & 10 & 8 & -8 \\ & -2 & -4 & 12 & 40 \\ \hline -1 & -2 & 6 & 20 & 32 \end{array}$$

$$4 \begin{array}{|rrrrr} -1 & 0 & 10 & 8 & -8 \\ & -4 & -16 & -24 & -64 \\ \hline -1 & -4 & -6 & -16 & -72 \end{array} \Rightarrow x = 4 \text{ is an upper bound.}$$

$$-1 \begin{array}{|rrrrr} -1 & 0 & 10 & 8 & -8 \\ & 1 & -1 & -9 & 1 \\ \hline -1 & 1 & 9 & -1 & -7 \end{array}$$

$$-2 \begin{array}{|rrrrr} -1 & 0 & 10 & 8 & -8 \\ & 2 & -4 & -12 & 8 \\ \hline -1 & 2 & 6 & -4 & 0 \end{array} \Rightarrow x = -2 \text{ is a zero.}$$

So $P(x) = (x + 2)(-x^3 + 2x^2 + 6x - 4)$. Continuing, we have:

$$-2 \begin{array}{|rrrr} -1 & 2 & 6 & -4 \\ & 2 & -8 & 4 \\ \hline -1 & 4 & -2 & 0 \end{array} \Rightarrow x = -2 \text{ is a zero again.}$$

$P(x) = (x + 2)^2(-x^2 + 4x - 2)$. Using the quadratic formula on the second factor, we have

$$x = \frac{-4 \pm \sqrt{4^2 - 4(-1)(-2)}}{2(-1)} = \frac{-4 \pm \sqrt{8}}{-2} = \frac{-4 \pm 2\sqrt{2}}{-2} = 2 \pm \sqrt{2}. \text{ So the real zeros of } P$$

are $-2, 2 \pm \sqrt{2}$.

(b)

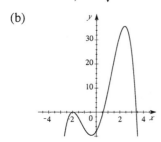

50. (a) $P(x) = x^5 - x^4 - 6x^3 + 14x^2 - 11x + 3$ has possible rational zeros $\pm 1, \pm 3$.

$$
\begin{array}{r|rrrrrr}
1 & 1 & -1 & -6 & 14 & -11 & 3 \\
  &   & 1 & 0 & -6 & 8   & -3 \\
\hline
  & 1 & 0 & -6 & 8 & -3 & 0
\end{array}
\quad \Rightarrow \quad x = 1 \text{ is a zero.}
$$

So $P(x) = (x - 1)(x^4 - 6x^2 + 8x - 3)$:

$$
\begin{array}{r|rrrrr}
1 & 1 & 0 & -6 & 8 & -3 \\
  &   & 1 & 1 & -5 & 3 \\
\hline
  & 1 & 1 & -5 & 3 & 0
\end{array}
\quad \Rightarrow \quad x = 1 \text{ is a zero again.}
$$

So $P(x) = (x - 1)^2(x^3 + x^2 - 5x + 3)$:

$$
\begin{array}{r|rrrr}
1 & 1 & 1 & -5 & 3 \\
  &   & 1 & 2 & -3 \\
\hline
  & 1 & 2 & -3 & 0
\end{array}
\quad \Rightarrow \quad x = 1 \text{ is a zero again.}
$$

So $P(x) = (x - 1)^3(x^2 + 2x - 3) = (x - 1)^4(x + 3)$, and the real zeros of P are 1 and -3.

(b)

52. $P(x) = 2x^3 - x^2 + 4x - 7$. Since $P(x)$ has 3 variations in signs, P has 3 or 1 positive real zeros. Since $P(-x) = -2x^3 - x^2 - 4x - 7$ has no variations in sign, there are no negative real zeros. Thus, P has 1 or 3 real zeros.

54. $P(x) = x^4 + x^3 + x^2 + x + 12$. Since $P(x)$ has no variations in sign, P has no positive real zeros. Since $P(-x) = x^4 - x^3 + x^2 - x + 12$ has 4 variations in sign, P has 4, 2, or 0 negative real zeros. Therefore, $P(x)$ has 0, 2, or 4 real zeros.

56. $P(x) = x^8 - x^5 + x^4 - x^3 + x^2 - x + 1$. Since $P(x)$ has 6 variations in sign, the polynomial has 6, 4, 2, or 0 positive real zeros. Since $P(-x)$ has no variations in sign, the polynomial has no negative real zeros. Therefore, P has 6, 4, 2, or 0 real zeros.

58. $P(x) = x^4 - 2x^3 - 9x^2 + 2x + 8$; $a = -3, b = 5$

$$
\begin{array}{r|rrrrr}
-3 & 1 & -2 & -9 & 2   & 8 \\
   &   & -3 & 15 & -18 & 48 \\
\hline
   & 1 & -5 & 6   & -16 & 56
\end{array}
\quad \text{Alternating signs} \quad \Rightarrow \quad \text{lower bound.}
$$

$$
\begin{array}{r|rrrrr}
5 & 1 & -2 & -9 & 2 & 8 \\
  &   & 5 & 15 & 30 & 160 \\
\hline
  & 1 & 3 & 6 & 32 & 168
\end{array}
\quad \text{All non-negative} \quad \Rightarrow \quad \text{upper bound.}
$$

Therefore $a = -3, b = 5$ are lower and upper bounds, respectively.

60. $P(x) = 3x^4 - 17x^3 + 24x^2 - 9x + 1; a = 0, b = 6$

$$\begin{array}{r|rrrrr} 0 & 3 & -17 & 24 & -9 & 1 \\ & & 0 & 0 & 0 & 0 \\ \hline & 3 & -17 & 24 & -9 & 1 \end{array}$$ Alternating signs $\Rightarrow$ lower bound.

$$\begin{array}{r|rrrrr} 6 & 3 & -17 & 24 & -9 & 1 \\ & & 18 & 6 & 180 & 1026 \\ \hline & 3 & 1 & 30 & 171 & 1027 \end{array}$$ All non-negative $\Rightarrow$ upper bound.

Therefore $a = 0$, $b = 6$ are lower and upper bounds, respectively. Note, since $P(x)$ alternates in sign, by Descartes' Rule of Signs, 0 is automatically a lower bound.

There are many possible solutions to Exercises 62 and 64 since we only asked to find 'an upper bound' and 'a lower bound'.

62. $P(x) = 2x^3 - 3x^2 - 8x + 12$ and using the Upper and Lower Bounds Theorem:

$$\begin{array}{r|rrrr} -2 & 2 & -3 & -8 & 12 \\ & & -4 & 14 & -12 \\ \hline & 2 & -7 & 6 & 0 \end{array}$$ Alternating signs $\Rightarrow$ $x = -2$ is a lower bound (and a zero).

$$\begin{array}{r|rrrr} 3 & 2 & -3 & -8 & 12 \\ & & 6 & 9 & 3 \\ \hline & 2 & 3 & 1 & 15 \end{array}$$ All non-negative $\Rightarrow$ $x = 3$ is an upper bound.

64. Set $P(x) = x^5 - x^4 + 1$.

$$\begin{array}{r|rrrrrr} 1 & 1 & -1 & 0 & 0 & 0 & 1 \\ & & 1 & 0 & 0 & 0 & 0 \\ \hline & 1 & 0 & 0 & 0 & 0 & 1 \end{array}$$ All non-negative $\Rightarrow$ $x = 1$ is an upper bound.

$$\begin{array}{r|rrrrrr} -1 & 1 & -1 & 0 & 0 & 0 & 1 \\ & & -1 & 2 & -2 & 2 & -2 \\ \hline & 1 & -2 & 2 & -2 & 2 & -1 \end{array}$$ Alternating signs $\Rightarrow$ $x = -1$ is a lower bound.

66. $P(x) = 2x^4 + 15x^3 + 31x^2 + 20x + 4$. The possible rational zeros are $\pm 1, \pm 2, \pm 4, \pm\frac{1}{2}$. Since all of the coefficients are positive, there are no positive zeros. Since $P(-x) = 2x^4 - 15x^3 + 31x^2 - 20x + 4$ has 4 variations in sign, there are 0, 2, or 4 negative real zeros.

$$\begin{array}{r|rrrrr} -1 & 2 & 15 & 31 & 20 & 4 \\ & & -2 & -13 & -18 & -2 \\ \hline & 2 & 13 & 18 & 2 & 2 \end{array}$$

$$\begin{array}{r|rrrrr} -2 & 2 & 15 & 31 & 20 & 4 \\ & & -4 & -22 & -18 & -4 \\ \hline & 2 & 11 & 9 & 2 & 0 \end{array}$$ $\Rightarrow$ $x = -2$ is a zero, and
$$P(x) = (x + 2)(2x^3 + 11x^2 + 9x + 2).$$

$$\begin{array}{r|rrrr} -2 & 2 & 11 & 9 & 2 \\ & & -4 & -14 & 10 \\ \hline & 2 & 7 & -5 & 12 \end{array}$$ $$\begin{array}{r|rrrr} -4 & 2 & 11 & 9 & 2 \\ & & -8 & -12 & 12 \\ \hline & 2 & 3 & -3 & 14 \end{array}$$

$$\begin{array}{r|rrrr} -\frac{1}{2} & 2 & 11 & 9 & 2 \\ & & -1 & -5 & -2 \\ \hline & 2 & 10 & 4 & 0 \end{array}$$ $x = -\frac{1}{2}$ is a zero, $P(x) = (x + 2)(2x + 1)(x^2 + 5x + 2)$.

Now, if $x^2 + 5x + 2 = 0$, then $x = \dfrac{-5 \pm \sqrt{25 - 4(1)(2)}}{2} = \dfrac{-5 \pm \sqrt{17}}{2}$. Thus, the zeros are -2, $-\frac{1}{2}$, and $\frac{-5 \pm \sqrt{17}}{2}$.

68. $P(x) = 6x^4 - 7x^3 - 8x^2 + 5x = x(6x^3 - 7x^2 - 8x + 5)$. So $x = 0$ is a zero. Continuing with the quotient, $Q(x) = 6x^3 - 7x^2 - 8x + 5$. The possible rational zeros are ± 1, ± 5, $\pm \frac{1}{2}$, $\pm \frac{5}{2}$, $\pm \frac{1}{3}$, $\pm \frac{5}{3}$, $\pm \frac{1}{6}$, $\pm \frac{5}{6}$. Since $Q(x)$ has 2 variations in sign, there are 0 or 2 positive real zeros. Since $Q(-x) = 6x^4 + 7x^3 - 8x^2 - 5x$ has 1 variation in sign, there is 1 negative real zero.

$$
\begin{array}{r|rrrr}
1 & 6 & -7 & -8 & 5 \\
  &   & 6 & -1 & -9 \\
\hline
  & 6 & -1 & -9 & -4
\end{array}
$$

$$
\begin{array}{r|rrrr}
5 & 6 & -7 & -8 & 5 \\
  &   & 30 & 115 & 535 \\
\hline
  & 6 & 23 & 107 & 540
\end{array}
\qquad \text{All positive} \quad \Rightarrow \quad \text{upper bound.}
$$

$$
\begin{array}{r|rrrr}
\frac{1}{2} & 6 & -7 & -8 & 5 \\
  &   & 3 & -2 & -5 \\
\hline
  & 6 & -4 & -10 & 0
\end{array}
\qquad \Rightarrow \quad x = \tfrac{1}{2} \text{ is a zero.}
$$

$P(x) = x(2x - 1)(3x^2 - 2x - 5) = x(2x - 1)(3x - 5)(x + 1)$. Therefore, the zeros are 0, -1, $\frac{1}{2}$ and $\frac{5}{3}$.

70. $P(x) = 8x^5 - 14x^4 - 22x^3 + 57x^2 - 35x + 6$. The possible rational zeros are ± 1, ± 2, ± 3, ± 6, $\pm \frac{1}{2}$, $\pm \frac{3}{2}$, $\pm \frac{1}{4}$, $\pm \frac{3}{4}$, $\pm \frac{1}{8}$, $\pm \frac{3}{8}$. Since $P(x)$ has 4 variations in sign, there are 0, 2, or 4 positive real zeros. Since $P(-x) = -8x^5 - 14x^4 + 22x^3 + 57x^2 + 35x + 6$ has 1 variation in sign, there is 1 negative real zero.

$$
\begin{array}{r|rrrrrr}
-1 & 8 & -14 & -22 & 57 & -35 & 6 \\
   &   & -8 & 22 & 0 & -57 & 92 \\
\hline
   & 8 & -22 & 0 & 57 & -92 & 98
\end{array}
$$

$$
\begin{array}{r|rrrrrr}
-2 & 8 & -14 & -22 & 57 & -35 & 6 \\
   &   & -16 & 60 & -76 & 38 & -6 \\
\hline
   & 8 & -30 & 38 & -19 & 3 & 0
\end{array}
\qquad \Rightarrow \quad x = -2 \text{ is a zero.}
$$

$P(x) = (x + 2)(8x^4 - 30x^3 + 38x^2 - 19x + 3)$. All the other real zeros are positive.

$$
\begin{array}{r|rrrrr}
1 & 8 & -30 & 38 & -19 & 3 \\
  &   & 8 & -22 & 16 & -3 \\
\hline
  & 8 & -22 & 16 & -3 & 0
\end{array}
\qquad \Rightarrow \quad x = 1 \text{ is a zero.}
$$

$P(x) = (x + 2)(x - 1)(8x^3 - 22x^2 + 16x - 3)$.

$$
\begin{array}{r|rrrr}
1 & 8 & -22 & 16 & -3 \\
  &   & 8 & -14 & 2 \\
\hline
  & 8 & -14 & 2 & -1
\end{array}
\qquad\qquad
\begin{array}{r|rrrr}
\frac{1}{2} & 8 & -22 & 16 & -3 \\
  &   & 4 & -9 & \frac{7}{2} \\
\hline
  & 8 & -18 & 7 & \frac{1}{2}
\end{array}
$$

Since $f\left(\frac{1}{2}\right) > 0 > f(1)$, there must be a zero between $\frac{1}{2}$ and 1. We try $\frac{3}{4}$:

$$
\begin{array}{r|rrrr}
\frac{3}{4} & 8 & -22 & 16 & -3 \\
  &   & 6 & -12 & 3 \\
\hline
  & 8 & -16 & 4 & 0
\end{array}
\qquad \Rightarrow \quad x = \tfrac{3}{4} \text{ is a zero.}
$$

$P(x) = (x+2)(x-1)(4x-3)(2x^2 - 4x + 1)$. Now, $2x^2 - 4x + 1 = 0$ when $x = \frac{4 \pm \sqrt{16 - 4(2)(1)}}{2(2)} = \frac{2 \pm \sqrt{2}}{2}$. Thus, the zeros are 1, $\frac{3}{4}$, -2, and $\frac{2 \pm \sqrt{2}}{2}$.

72. $P(x) = 2x^4 - x^3 + x + 2$. The only possible rational zeros of $P(x)$ are ± 1, ± 2, $\pm \frac{1}{2}$.

$$
\begin{array}{r|rrrrr}
\tfrac{1}{2} & 2 & -1 & 0 & 1 & 2 \\
& & 1 & 0 & 0 & \tfrac{1}{2} \\
\hline
& 2 & 0 & 0 & 1 & \tfrac{5}{2}
\end{array}
$$
All nonnegative　$\Rightarrow$　$x = \frac{1}{2}$ is an upper bound.

$$
\begin{array}{r|rrrrr}
-1 & 2 & -1 & 0 & 1 & 2 \\
& & -2 & 3 & -3 & 2 \\
\hline
& 2 & -3 & 3 & -2 & 4
\end{array}
$$
Alternating signs　$\Rightarrow$　$x = -1$ is a lower bound.

$$
\begin{array}{r|rrrrr}
-\tfrac{1}{2} & 2 & -1 & 0 & 1 & 2 \\
& & -1 & 1 & -\tfrac{1}{2} & -\tfrac{1}{4} \\
\hline
& 2 & -2 & 1 & \tfrac{1}{2} & \tfrac{7}{4}
\end{array}
$$

Therefore, there are no rational zeros.

74. $P(x) = x^{50} - 5x^{25} + x^2 - 1$. The only possible rational zeros of $P(x)$ are ± 1. Since $P(1) = (1)^{50} - 5(1)^{25} + (1)^2 - 1 = -4$ and $P(-1) = (-1)^{50} - 5(-1)^{25} + (-1)^2 - 1 = 6$, $P(x)$ does not have a rational zero.

76. $x^4 - 5x^2 + 4 = 0$, $[-4, 4]$ by $[-30, 30]$.

The possible rational solutions are ± 1, ± 2, ± 4.

By observing the graph of the equation, the solutions of the given equation are $x = \pm 1$, ± 2.

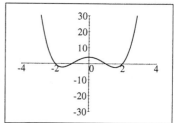

78. $3x^3 + 8x^2 + 5x + 2 = 0$; $[-3, 3]$ by $[-10, 10]$

The possible rational solutions are ± 1, ± 2, $\pm \frac{1}{3}$, $\pm \frac{2}{3}$.

By observing the graph of the equation, the only solution of the given equation is $x = -2$.

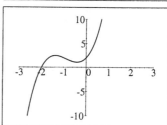

80. $2x^3 - 8x^2 + 9x - 9 = 0$. Possible rational solutions are ± 1, ± 3, ± 9, $\pm \frac{1}{2}$, $\pm \frac{3}{2}$, $\pm \frac{9}{2}$.

$$
\begin{array}{r|rrrr}
1 & 2 & -8 & 9 & -9 \\
& & 2 & -6 & 3 \\
\hline
& 2 & -6 & 3 & -6
\end{array}
\qquad
\begin{array}{r|rrrr}
3 & 2 & -8 & 9 & -9 \\
& & 6 & -6 & 9 \\
\hline
& 2 & -2 & 3 & 0
\end{array}
\quad \Rightarrow \quad x = 3 \text{ is a zero.}
$$

$2x^3 - 8x^2 + 9x - 9 = (x - 3)(2x^2 - 2x + 3)$. Since the quotient is a quadratic expression, we can use the quadratic formula to locate the other possible solutions: $x = \frac{2 \pm \sqrt{2^2 - 4(2)(3)}}{2(2)}$, which are not real solutions. You can also use a graphing device to see that $2x^2 - 2x + 3 = 0$ has no solution. So the only solution is $x = 3$.

82. $x^5 + 2x^4 + 0.96x^3 + 5x^2 + 10x + 4.8 = 0$. Since all the coefficients are positive, there is no positive solution. So $x = 0$ is an upper bound.

$$
\begin{array}{r|rrrrrr}
-2 & 1 & 2 & 0.96 & 5 & 10 & 4.8 \\
   &   & -2 & 0 & -1.92 & -6.16 & -7.68 \\
\hline
   & 1 & 0 & 0.96 & 3.08 & 3.84 & -2.88
\end{array}
$$

$$
\begin{array}{r|rrrrrr}
-3 & 1 & 2 & 0.96 & 5 & 10 & 4.8 \\
   &   & -3 & 3 & -11.88 & 20.64 & -91.92 \\
\hline
   & 1 & -1 & 3.96 & -6.88 & 30.64 & -87.12
\end{array}
$$

$\Rightarrow \quad x = -3$ is a lower bound.

Therefore, we graph the function in the viewing rectangle $[-3, 0]$ by $[-10, 5]$ and see that there are three possible solutions.

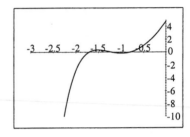

Viewing rectangle: $[-1.75, -1.7]$ by $[-0.1, 0.1]$. Solution $x \approx -1.71$.

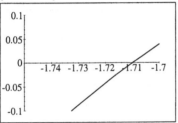

Viewing rectangle: $[-1.25, -1.15]$ by $[-0.1, 0.1]$. Solution $x \approx -1.20$.

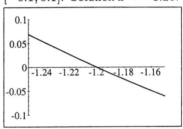

Viewing rectangle: $[-0.85, -0.75]$ by $[-0.1, 0.1]$. Solution $x \approx -0.80$.

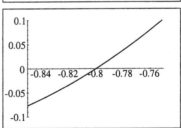

So the solutions are $x \approx -1.71, -1.20, -0.80$.

84. Given that x is the length of a side of the rectangle, we have that the length of the diagonal is $x + 10$, and the length of the other side of the rectangle is $\sqrt{(x + 10)^2 - x^2}$. Hence
$x\sqrt{(x + 10)^2 - x^2} = 5000 \quad \Rightarrow \quad x^2(20x + 100) = 25{,}000{,}000 \quad \Leftrightarrow$
$2x^3 + 10x^2 - 2{,}500{,}000 = 0 \quad \Leftrightarrow \quad x^3 + 5x^2 - 1{,}250{,}000 = 0$. The first viewing rectangle, $[0, 120]$ by $[-1, 500]$, shows there is one solution. The second viewing rectangle, $[106, 106.1]$ by $[-0.1, 0.1]$, shows the solution is $x = 106.08$. Therefore, the dimensions of the rectangle are 47 ft by 106 ft.

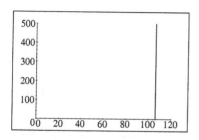
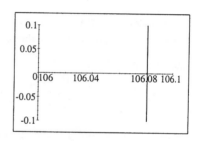

86. The volume of the box is $V = 1500 = x(20 - 2x)(40 - 2x) = 4x^3 - 120x^2 + 800x$ $\Leftrightarrow$ $4x^3 - 120x^2 + 800x - 1500 = 4(x^3 - 30x^2 + 200x - 375) = 0$. Clearly, we must have $20 - 2x > 0$, and so $0 < x < 10$.

$$
\begin{array}{r|rrrr}
5 & 1 & -30 & 200 & -375 \\
  &   & 5 & -125 & 375 \\
\hline
  & 1 & -25 & 75 & 0
\end{array}
\qquad \Rightarrow \qquad x = 5 \text{ is a zero.}
$$

$x^3 - 30x^2 + 200x - 375 = (x - 5)(x^2 - 25x + 75) = 0$. Using the quadratic equation, we find the other zeros: $x = \frac{25 \pm \sqrt{625 - 4(1)(75)}}{2} = \frac{25 \pm \sqrt{325}}{2} = \frac{25 \pm 5\sqrt{13}}{2}$. Since $\frac{25 + 5\sqrt{13}}{2} > 10$, the two answers are: $x = \text{height} = 5$ cm, width $= 20 - 2(5) = 10$ cm, and length $= 40 - 2(5) = 30$ cm; and $x = \frac{25 - 5\sqrt{13}}{2}$, width $= 20 - (25 - 5\sqrt{13}) = 5\sqrt{13} - 5$ cm, and length $= 40 - (25 - 5\sqrt{13}) = 15 + 5\sqrt{13}$ cm.

88. (a) Let x be the length, in ft, of each side of the base and let h be the height. The volume of the box is $V = 2\sqrt{2} = hx^2$, and so $hx^2 = 2\sqrt{2}$. The length of the diagonal on the base is $\sqrt{x^2 + x^2} = \sqrt{2x^2}$, and hence the length of the diagonal between opposite corners is $\sqrt{2x^2 + h^2} = x + 1$. Squaring both sides of the equation, we have $2x^2 + h^2 = x^2 + 2x + 1$ $\Leftrightarrow$ $h^2 = -x^2 + 2x + 1$ $\Leftrightarrow$ $h = \sqrt{-x^2 + 2x + 1}$. Therefore, $2\sqrt{2} = hx^2 = \left(\sqrt{-x^2 + 2x + 1}\right)x^2$ $\Leftrightarrow$ $(-x^2 + 2x + 1)x^4 = 8$ $\Leftrightarrow$ $x^6 - 2x^5 - x^4 + 8 = 0$.

(b) We graph $y = x^6 - 2x^5 - x^4 + 8$ in the viewing rectangle $[0, 5]$ by $[-10, 10]$, and we see that there are two solutions. In the second viewing rectangle, $[1.4, 1.5]$ by $[-1, 1]$, shows the solution $x \approx 1.45$. The third viewing rectangle, $[2.25, 2.35]$ by $[-1, 1]$, shows the solution $x \approx 2.31$.

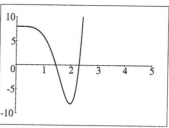

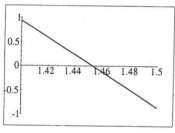
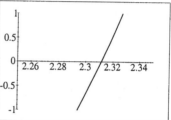

If $x =$ width $=$ length $= 1.45$ ft, then height $= \sqrt{-x^2 + 2x + 1} = 1.34$ ft, and if
$x =$ width $=$ length $= 2.31$ ft, then height $= \sqrt{-x^2 + 2x + 1} = 0.53$ ft.

90. (a) Since $z > b$, we have $z - b > 0$. Since all the coefficients of $Q(x)$ are nonnegative, and since $z > 0$, we have $Q(z) > 0$ (being a sum of positive terms). Thus, $P(z) = (z - b) \cdot Q(z) + r > 0$, since P the sum of a positive number and a nonnegative number.

    (b) In part (a), we showed that if b satisfies the conditions of the first part of the Upper and Lower Bounds Theorem and $z > b$, then $P(z) > 0$. This means that no real zero of P can be larger than b, so b is an upper bound for the real zeros.

92. $P(x) = x^5 - x^4 - x^3 - 5x^2 - 12x - 6$ has possible rational zeros $\pm 1, \pm 2, \pm 3, \pm 6$. Since $P(x)$ has 1 variation in sign, there is 1 positive real zero. Since $P(-x) = -x^5 - x^4 + x^3 - 5x^2 + 12x - 6$ has 4 variations in sign, there are 0, 2, or 4 negative real zeros.

$$
\begin{array}{r|rrrrrr}
1 & 1 & -1 & -1 & -5 & -12 & -6 \\
  &   & 1 & 0 & -1 & -6 & -18 \\
\hline
  & 1 & 0 & -1 & -6 & -18 & -24
\end{array}
\qquad
\begin{array}{r|rrrrrr}
2 & 1 & -1 & -1 & -5 & -12 & -6 \\
  &   & 2 & 2 & 2 & -6 & -36 \\
\hline
  & 1 & 1 & 1 & -3 & -18 & -42
\end{array}
$$

$$
\begin{array}{r|rrrrrr}
3 & 1 & -1 & -1 & -5 & -12 & -6 \\
  &   & 3 & 6 & 15 & 30 & 54 \\
\hline
  & 1 & 2 & 5 & 10 & 18 & 48
\end{array}
\quad \Rightarrow \quad 3 \text{ is an upper bound.}
$$

$$
\begin{array}{r|rrrrrr}
-1 & 1 & -1 & -1 & -5 & -12 & -6 \\
   &   & -1 & 2 & -1 & 6 & 6 \\
\hline
   & 1 & -2 & 1 & -6 & -6 & 0
\end{array}
\quad \Rightarrow \quad x = -1 \text{ is a zero.}
$$

$P(x) = (x + 1)(x^4 - 2x^3 + x^2 - 6x - 6)$, continuing with the quotient we have

$$
\begin{array}{r|rrrrr}
-1 & 1 & -2 & 1 & -6 & -6 \\
   &   & -1 & 3 & -4 & 10 \\
\hline
   & 1 & -3 & 4 & -10 & 4
\end{array}
\quad \Rightarrow \quad -1 \text{ is a lower bound.}
$$

Therefore, there is 1 rational zero, namely -1. Since there are 1, 3 or 5 real zeros, and we found 1 rational zero, there must be 0, 2 or 4 irrational zeros. However, since 1 zero must be positive, there cannot be 0 irrational zeros. Therefore, there is exactly 1 rational zero and 2 or 4 irrational zeros.

94. (a) Substituting $X - \frac{a}{3}$ for x we have

$$
\begin{aligned}
x^3 + ax^2 + bx + c &= \left(X - \tfrac{a}{3}\right)^3 + a\left(X - \tfrac{a}{3}\right)^2 + b\left(X - \tfrac{a}{3}\right) + c \\
&= X^3 - aX^2 + \tfrac{a^2}{3}X + \tfrac{a^3}{27} + a\left(X^2 - \tfrac{2a}{3}X + \tfrac{a^2}{9}\right) + bX - \tfrac{ab}{3} + c \\
&= X^3 - aX^2 + \tfrac{a^2}{3}X + \tfrac{a^3}{27} + aX^2 - \tfrac{2a^2}{3}X + \tfrac{a^3}{9} + bX - \tfrac{ab}{3} + c \\
&= X^3 + (-a + a)X^2 + \left(-\tfrac{a^2}{3} - \tfrac{2a^2}{3} + b\right)X + \left(\tfrac{a^3}{27} + \tfrac{a^3}{9} - \tfrac{ab}{3} + c\right) \\
&= X^3 + (b - a^2)X + \left(\tfrac{4a^3}{27} - \tfrac{ab}{3} + c\right).
\end{aligned}
$$

    (b) $x^3 + 6x^2 + 9x + 4 = 0$. Setting $a = 6$, $b = 9$, and $c = 4$, we have:
$X^3 + (9 - 6^2)X + (32 - 18 + 4) = X^3 - 27X + 18$.

Exercises 5.4

2. $P(x) = 4x^2 + 25 = (2x - 5i)(2x + 5i)$. The zeros of P are $\frac{5}{2}i$ and $-\frac{5}{2}i$, both multiplicity 1.

4. $Q(x) = x^2 - 8x + 17$. Using the quadratic formula, we have
$$x = \frac{8 \pm \sqrt{(-8)^2 - 4(17)}}{2} = \frac{8 \pm \sqrt{-4}}{2} = \frac{8 \pm 2i}{2} = 4 \pm i.$$ The zeros of Q are $4 + i$ and $4 - i$, both multiplicity 1.

6. $P(x) = x^3 + x^2 + x = x(x^2 + x + 1)$. Using the quadratic formula, we have
$$x = \frac{-(1) \pm \sqrt{(1)^2 - 4(1)(1)}}{2(1)} = \frac{1 \pm \sqrt{-3}}{2} = \frac{1}{2} \pm i\frac{\sqrt{3}}{2}.$$ The zeros of P are 0, $\frac{1}{2} + i\frac{\sqrt{3}}{2}$, and $\frac{1}{2} - i\frac{\sqrt{3}}{2}$, all multiplicity 1.

8. $Q(x) = x^4 - 625 = (x^2 - 25)(x^2 + 25) = (x - 5)(x + 5)(x^2 + 25)$
$= (x - 5)(x + 5)(x - 5i)(x + 5i)$. The zeros of Q are 5, -5, $5i$, and $5i$, all multiplicity 1.

10. $P(x) = x^3 - 64 = (x - 4)(x^2 + 4x + 16)$. Using the quadratic formula, we have
$$x = \frac{-4 \pm \sqrt{16 - 4(1)(16)}}{2} = \frac{-4 \pm \sqrt{-48}}{2} = \frac{-4 \pm 4\sqrt{3}\,i}{2} = -2 \pm 2\sqrt{3}\,i.$$ The zeros of P are 4, $-2 + 2\sqrt{3}\,i$, and $-2 - 2\sqrt{3}\,i$, all multiplicity 1.

12. $P(x) = x^6 - 729 = (x^3 - 27)(x^3 + 27) = (x - 3)(x^2 + 3x + 9)(x + 3)(x^2 - 3x + 9)$. Using the quadratic formula on $x^2 + 3x + 9$ we have $x = \dfrac{-3 \pm \sqrt{9 - 4(1)(9)}}{2} = \dfrac{-3 \pm \sqrt{-27}}{2}$
$= -\frac{3}{2} \pm \frac{\sqrt{-27}}{2}$. Using the quadratic formula on $x^2 - 3x + 9$ we have
$$x = \frac{3 \pm \sqrt{9 - 4(1)(9)}}{2} = \frac{3 \pm \sqrt{-27}}{2} = \frac{3}{2} \pm \frac{\sqrt{-27}}{2} = \frac{3}{2} \pm \frac{3\sqrt{3}}{2}i.$$ The zeros of P are 3, -3,
$-\frac{3}{2} + \frac{3\sqrt{3}}{2}i$, $-\frac{3}{2} - \frac{3\sqrt{3}}{2}i$, $\frac{3}{2} + \frac{3\sqrt{3}}{2}i$, and $\frac{3}{2} - \frac{3\sqrt{3}}{2}i$, all multiplicity 1.

14. $Q(x) = x^4 + 10x^2 + 25 = (x^2 + 5)^2 (x - i\sqrt{5})^2(x + i\sqrt{5})^2$. The zeros of Q are $i\sqrt{5}$ and $-i\sqrt{5}$, both multiplicity 2.

16. $P(x) = x^5 + 7x^3 = x^3(x^2 + 7) = x^3(x - i\sqrt{7})(x + i\sqrt{7})$. The zeros of P are 0 (multiplicity 3), $i\sqrt{7}$ and $-i\sqrt{7}$, both multiplicity 1.

18. $P(x) = x^6 + 16x^3 + 64 = (x^3 + 8)^2 = (x + 2)^2(x^2 - 2x + 4)^2$. Using the quadratic formula, on $x^2 - 2x + 4$ we have $x = \frac{-(-2) \pm \sqrt{(-2)^2 - 4(1)(4)}}{2} = \frac{2 \pm \sqrt{-12}}{2} = \frac{2 \pm 2i\sqrt{3}}{2} = 1 \pm i\sqrt{3}$. The zeros of P are -2, $1 + i\sqrt{3}$, and $1 - i\sqrt{3}$, all multiplicity 2.

20. Since $1 + i\sqrt{2}$ and $1 - i\sqrt{2}$ are conjugates, the factorization of the polynomial must be $P(x) = c(x - [1 + i\sqrt{2}])(x - [1 - i\sqrt{2}]) = c(x^2 - 2x + 5)$. If we let $c = 1$, we get $P(x) = x^2 - 2x + 5$.

22. Since i is a zero, by the Conjugate Roots Theorem, $-i$ is also a zero. So the factorization of the polynomial must be $Q(x) = b(x + 0)(x - i)(x + i) = bx(x^2 + 1) = b(x^3 + x)$. If we let $b = 1$, we get $Q(x) = x^3 + x$.

24. Since $1 + i$ is a zero, by the Conjugate Roots Theorem, $1 - i$ is also a zero. So the factorization of the polynomial must be $Q(x) = a(x + 3)(x - [1 + i])(x - [1 - i]) = a(x + 3)(x^2 - 2x + 2)$
$= a(x^3 + x^2 - 4x + 6)$. If we let $a = 1$, we get $Q(x) = x^3 + x^2 - 4x + 6$.

26. Since $S(x)$ has zeros $2i$ and $3i$, by the Conjugate Roots Theorem, the other zeros of $S(x)$ are $-2i$ and $-3i$. So a factorization of $S(x)$ is
$$S(x) = C(x - 2i)(x + 2i)(x - 3i)(x + 3i) = C(x^2 - 4i^2)(x^2 - 9i^2) = C(x^2 + 4)(x^2 + 9)$$
$$= C(x^4 + 13x^2 + 36). \text{ If we let } C = 1, \text{ we get } S(x) = x^4 + 13x^2 + 36.$$

28. Since $U(x)$ has zeros $\frac{1}{2}$, -1 (with multiplicity two), and $-i$, by the Conjugate Roots Theorem, the other zero is i. So a factorization of $U(x)$ is
$$U(x) = c(x - \tfrac{1}{2})(x + 1)^2(x + i)(x - i) = \tfrac{1}{2}c(2x - 1)(x^2 + 2x + 1)(x^2 + 1)$$
$$= \tfrac{1}{2}c(2x^5 + 3x^4 + 2x^3 + 2x^2 - 1). \text{ Since the leading coefficient is 4, we have } 4 = \tfrac{1}{2}c(2) = c.$$
Thus we have $U(x) = \tfrac{1}{2}(4)(2x^5 + 3x^4 + 2x^3 + 2x^2 - 1) = 4x^5 + 6x^4 + 4x^3 + 4x^2 - 2.$

30. $P(x) = x^3 - 7x^2 + 17x - 15$. We start by trying the possible rational factors of the polynomial:

$$
\begin{array}{r|rrrr}
1 & 1 & -7 & 17 & -15 \\
  &   & 1 & -6 & 11 \\
\hline
  & 1 & -6 & 11 & -4
\end{array}
\qquad
\begin{array}{r|rrrr}
3 & 1 & -7 & 17 & -15 \\
  &   & 3 & -12 & 15 \\
\hline
  & 1 & -4 & 5 & 0
\end{array}
\Rightarrow \quad x = 3 \text{ is a zero.}
$$

So $P(x) = (x - 3)(x^2 - 4x + 5)$. Using the quadratic formula on the second factor, we have
$$x = \frac{4 \pm \sqrt{16 - 4(1)(5)}}{2} = \frac{4 \pm \sqrt{-4}}{2} = \frac{4 \pm 2i}{2} = 2 \pm i. \text{ Thus the zeros are } 3, \, 2 \pm i.$$

32. $P(x) = x^3 + 7x^2 + 18x + 18$ has possible rational zeros $\pm 1, \pm 2, \pm 3, \pm 6, \pm 9, \pm 18$. Since all of the coefficients are positive, there are no positive real zeros.

$$
\begin{array}{r|rrrr}
-1 & 1 & 7 & 18 & 18 \\
   &   & -1 & -6 & -12 \\
\hline
   & 1 & 6 & 12 & 6
\end{array}
\qquad
\begin{array}{r|rrrr}
-2 & 1 & 7 & 18 & 18 \\
   &   & -2 & -10 & -16 \\
\hline
   & 1 & 5 & 8 & 2
\end{array}
$$

$$
\begin{array}{r|rrrr}
-3 & 1 & 7 & 18 & 18 \\
   &   & -3 & -12 & -18 \\
\hline
   & 1 & 4 & 6 & 0
\end{array}
\Rightarrow \quad x = -3 \text{ is a zero.}
$$

So $P(x) = (x - 3)(x^2 + 4x + 6)$. Using the quadratic formula on the second factor, we have
$$x = \frac{-4 \pm \sqrt{16 - 4(1)(6)}}{2} = \frac{-4 \pm \sqrt{-8}}{2} = \frac{-4 \pm 2\sqrt{2}i}{2} = -2 \pm \sqrt{2}i. \text{ Thus the zeros are } -3,$$
$-2 \pm \sqrt{2}i.$

34. $P(x) = x^3 - x - 6$ has possible zeros $\pm 1, \pm 2, \pm 3$.

$$
\begin{array}{r|rrrr}
1 & 1 & 0 & -1 & -6 \\
  &   & 1 & 1 & 0 \\
\hline
  & 1 & 1 & 0 & -6
\end{array}
\qquad
\begin{array}{r|rrrr}
2 & 1 & 0 & -1 & -6 \\
  &   & 2 & 4 & 6 \\
\hline
  & 1 & 2 & 3 & 0
\end{array}
\Rightarrow \quad x = 2 \text{ is a zero.}
$$

$P(x) = (x - 2)(x^2 + 2x + 3)$. Now $x^2 + 2x + 3$ has zeros $x = \dfrac{-2 \pm \sqrt{4 - 4(1)(3)}}{2}$
$$= \frac{-2 \pm 2i\sqrt{2}}{2} = -1 \pm i\sqrt{2}. \text{ Thus the zeros are } 2, \, -1 \pm i\sqrt{2}.$$

36. Using synthetic division, we see that $(x - 3)$ is a factor of the polynomial:

$$
\begin{array}{r|rrrr}
1 & 2 & -8 & 9 & -9 \\
  &   & 2 & -6 & 3 \\
\hline
  & 2 & -6 & 3 & -6
\end{array}
\qquad
\begin{array}{r|rrrr}
3 & 2 & -8 & 9 & -9 \\
  &   & 6 & -6 & 9 \\
\hline
  & 2 & -2 & 3 & 0
\end{array}
\Rightarrow \quad x = 3 \text{ is a zero.}
$$

So $P(x) = 2x^3 - 8x^2 + 9x - 9 = (x - 3)(2x^2 - 2x + 3)$. Using the quadratic formula, we find

the other two solutions: $x = \dfrac{2 \pm \sqrt{4 - 4(3)(2)}}{2(2)} = \dfrac{2 \pm \sqrt{-20}}{4} = \dfrac{1}{2} \pm \dfrac{\sqrt{5}}{2}\, i$. Thus the zeros are

$3, \frac{1}{2} \pm \frac{\sqrt{5}}{2}\, i$.

38. $P(x) = x^4 - 2x^3 - 2x^2 - 2x - 3$ has possible zeros $\pm 1, \pm 3$.

$$
\begin{array}{r|rrrrr}
1 & 1 & -2 & -2 & -2 & -3 \\
  &   & 1 & -1 & -3 & -5 \\
\hline
  & 1 & -1 & -3 & -5 & -8
\end{array}
\qquad
\begin{array}{r|rrrrr}
3 & 1 & -2 & -2 & -2 & -3 \\
  &   & 3 & 3 & 3 & 3 \\
\hline
  & 1 & 1 & 1 & 1 & 0
\end{array}
\;\Rightarrow\; x = 3 \text{ is a zero.}
$$

$P(x) = (x - 3)(x^3 + x^2 + x + 1)$. If we factor the second factor by grouping, we get
$x^3 + x^2 + x + 1 = x^2(x + 1) + 1(x + 1) = (x + 1)(x^2 + 1)$. So we have
$P(x) = (x - 3)(x + 1)(x^2 + 1) = (x - 3)(x + 1)(x - i)(x + i)$. Thus the zeros are $3, -1, i$, and
$-i$.

40. $P(x) = x^5 + x^3 + 8x^2 + 8 = x^3(x^2 + 1) + 8(x^2 + 1) = (x^2 + 1)(x^3 + 8)$
$= (x^2 + 1)(x + 2)(x^2 - 2x + 4)$ (factoring a sum of cubes). So $x = -2$, or $x^2 + 1 = 0$. If

$x^2 + 1 = 0$, then $x^2 = -1 \;\Rightarrow\; x = \pm i$. If $x^2 - 2x + 4 = 0$, then $x = \dfrac{2 \pm \sqrt{4 - 4(1)(4)}}{2}$

$= 1 \pm \dfrac{\sqrt{-12}}{2} = 1 \pm \sqrt{3}\, i$. Thus, the zeros are $-2, \pm i, 1 \pm \sqrt{3}\, i$.

42. $P(x) = x^4 - x^2 + 2x + 2$ has possible rational zeros $\pm 1, \pm 2$.

$$
\begin{array}{r|rrrrr}
1 & 1 & 0 & -1 & 2 & 2 \\
  &   & 1 & 1 & 0 & 2 \\
\hline
  & 1 & 1 & 0 & 2 & 4
\end{array}
\;\text{1 is an upper bound.}
\qquad
\begin{array}{r|rrrrr}
-1 & 1 & 0 & -1 & 2 & 2 \\
   &   & -1 & 1 & 0 & -2 \\
\hline
   & 1 & -1 & 0 & 2 & 0
\end{array}
$$

$$
\begin{array}{r|rrrr}
-1 & 1 & -1 & 0 & 2 \\
   &   & -1 & 2 & -2 \\
\hline
   & 1 & -2 & 2 & 0
\end{array}
$$

$P(x) = (x + 1)^2(x^2 - 2x + 2)$. Using the quadratic formula on $x^2 - 2x + 2$, we have
$x = \frac{2 \pm \sqrt{4 - 8}}{2} = \frac{2 \pm 2i}{2} = 1 \pm i$. Thus, the zeros of $P(x)$ are $-1, 1 \pm i$.

44. $P(x) = x^5 - 2x^4 + 2x^3 - 4x^2 + x - 2$ has possible rational zeros $\pm 1, \pm 2$.

$$
\begin{array}{r|rrrrrr}
1 & 1 & -2 & 2 & -4 & 1 & -2 \\
  &   & 1 & -1 & 1 & -3 & -2 \\
\hline
  & 1 & -1 & 1 & -3 & -2 & -4
\end{array}
\qquad
\begin{array}{r|rrrrrr}
2 & 1 & -2 & 2 & -4 & 1 & -2 \\
  &   & 2 & 0 & 4 & 0 & 2 \\
\hline
  & 1 & 0 & 2 & 0 & 1 & 0
\end{array}
\;\Rightarrow\; x = 2 \text{ is a zero.}
$$

$P(x) = (x - 1)(x^4 + 2x^2 + 1) = (x - 1)(x^2 + 1)^2 = (x - 1)(x - i)^2(x + i)^2$. Thus, the zeros of
$P(x)$ are $1, \pm i$.

46. (a) $P(x) = x^3 - 2x - 4$

$$
\begin{array}{r|rrrr}
1 & 1 & 0 & -2 & -4 \\
  &   & 1 & 1 & -1 \\
\hline
  & 1 & 1 & -1 & -5
\end{array}
\qquad
\begin{array}{r|rrrr}
2 & 1 & 0 & -2 & -4 \\
  &   & 2 & 4 & 4 \\
\hline
  & 1 & 2 & 2 & 0
\end{array}
$$

$P(x) = x^3 - 2x - 4 = (x - 2)(x^2 + 2x + 2)$.

(b) $P(x) = (x - 2)(x + 1 - i)(x + 1 + i)$.

48. (a) $P(x) = x^4 + 8x^2 + 16 = (x^2 + 4)^2$.

(b) $P(x) = (x - 2i)^2(x + 2i)^2$.

50.   (a) $P(x) = x^5 - 16x = x(x^4 - 16) = x(x^2 - 4)(x^2 + 4) = x(x - 2)(x + 2)(x^2 + 4)$.

      (b) $P(x) = x(x - 2)(x + 2)(x - 2i)(x + 2i)$.

52.   (a) $2x - 4i = 1 \quad \Leftrightarrow \quad 2x = 1 + 4i \quad \Leftrightarrow \quad x = \frac{1}{2} + 2i$.

      (b) $x^2 - ix = 0 \quad \Leftrightarrow \quad x(x - i) = 0 \quad \Leftrightarrow \quad x = 0, i$.

      (c) $x^2 + 2ix - 1 = 0 \quad \Leftrightarrow \quad (x + i)^2 = 0 \quad \Leftrightarrow \quad x = -i$.

      (d) $ix^2 - 2x + i = 0$. Using the quadratic equation we get $x = \dfrac{2 \pm \sqrt{(-2)^2 - 4(i)(i)}}{2i}$

$$= \frac{2 \pm \sqrt{8}}{2i} = \frac{1 \pm \sqrt{2}}{i} = (1 \pm \sqrt{2})(-i) = (-1 \pm \sqrt{2})i.$$

54.   (a) Since i and $1 + i$ are zeros, $-i$ and $1 - i$ are also zeros. So
          $P(x) = C(x - i)(x + i)(x - [1 + i])(x - [1 - i]) = C(x^2 + 1)(x^2 - 2x + 2)$
          $= C(x^4 - 2x^3 + 2x^2 + x^2 - 2x + 2) = C(x^4 - 2x^3 + 3x^2 - 2x + 2)$. Since $C = 1$, the
          polynomial is $P(x) = x^4 - 2x^3 + 3x^2 - 2x + 2$.

      (b) Since i and $1 + i$ are zeros, $P(x) = C(x - i)(x - [i + 1]) = C(x^2 - xi - x - xi - 1 + i)$
          $= C[x^2 - (1 + 2i)x - 1 + i]$. Since $C = 1$, the polynomial is
          $P(x) = x^2 - (1 + 2i)x - 1 + i$.

56. $x^4 - 1 = 0 \quad \Leftrightarrow \quad (x^2 - 1)(x^2 + 1) = 0 \quad \Leftrightarrow \quad (x - 1)(x + 1)(x + i)(x - i) = 0 \quad \Leftrightarrow$
      $x = \pm 1, \pm i$. So there are four fourth zeros of 1, two that are real and two that are complex.
      Consider $P(x) = x^n - 1$, where n is even. P has one change in sign so P has exactly one real
      positive zero, namely $x = 1$. Since $P(-x) = P(x)$, P also has exactly one real negative zero,
      namely $x = -1$. Thus P must have $n - 2$ complex zeros. As a result, $x^n = 1$ has two real nth
      zeros and $n - 2$ complex zeros.

      $x^3 - 1 = 0 \quad \Leftrightarrow \quad (x - 1)(x^2 + x + 1) = 0 \quad \Leftrightarrow \quad x = 1, \frac{-1 \pm \sqrt{3}i}{2}$. So there is one real cube zero
      of unity and two complex zeros. Now consider $Q(x) = x^k - 1$, where k is odd. Since Q has one
      change in sign, Q has exactly one real positive zero, namely $x = 1$. But $Q(-x) = -x^k - 1$ has no
      changes in sign, so there are no negative real zeros. As a result, $x^k = 1$ has one real kth zero and
      $k - 1$ complex zeros.

Exercises 5.5

2. $s(x) = \dfrac{2x}{3x+5}$. When $x = 0$, we have $s(0) = 0$, so the y-intercept is 0. The numerator is zero when $2x = 0$ or $x = 0$, so the x-intercept is 0.

4. $r(x) = \dfrac{2}{x^2 + 3x - 4}$. When $x = 0$, we have $r(0) = \frac{2}{-4} = -\frac{1}{2}$, so the y-intercept is $-\frac{1}{2}$. The numerator is never zero, so there is no x-intercept.

6. $r(x) = \dfrac{x^3 + 8}{x^2 + 4}$. When $x = 0$, we have $r(0) = \frac{8}{4} = 2$, so the y-intercept is 2. The x-intercept occurs when $x^3 + 8 = 0 \iff (x + 2)(x^2 - 2x + 4) = 0 \iff x = -2$ or $x = 1 \pm i\sqrt{3}$, which has only one real solution, so the x-intercept is -2.

8. From the graph, the x-intercept is 0, the y-intercept is 0, the horizontal asymptote is $y = 0$, and the vertical asymptotes are $x = -1$ and $x = 2$.

10. $s(x) = \dfrac{3x + 3}{x - 3} = \dfrac{3 + \dfrac{3}{x}}{1 - \dfrac{3}{x}} \to 3$ as $x \to \pm\infty$. The horizontal asymptote is $y = 3$. There is a vertical asymptote when $x - 3 = 0 \iff x = 3$, so the vertical asymptote is $x = 3$.

12. $r(x) = \dfrac{2x - 4}{x^2 + 2x + 1} = \dfrac{\dfrac{2}{x} - \dfrac{4}{x^2}}{1 + \dfrac{2}{x} + \dfrac{1}{x^2}} \to 0$ as $x \to \pm\infty$. Thus, the horizontal asymptote is $y = 0$.

Also, $y = \dfrac{2(x - 2)}{(x + 1)^2}$ so there is a vertical asymptote when $x + 1 = 0 \iff x = -1$, so the vertical asymptote is $x = -1$.

14. $t(x) = \dfrac{(x - 1)(x - 2)}{(x - 3)(x - 4)} = \dfrac{x^2 - 3x + 2}{x^2 - 7x + 12} = \dfrac{1 - \dfrac{3}{x} + \dfrac{2}{x^2}}{1 - \dfrac{7}{x} + \dfrac{12}{x^2}} \to 1$ as $x \to \pm\infty$, so the horizontal asymptote is $y = 1$. Also, vertical asymptotes occur when $(x - 3)(x - 4) = 0 \Rightarrow x = 3, 4$, so the two vertical asymptotes are $x = 3$ and $x = 4$.

16. $s(x) = \dfrac{3x^2}{x^2 + 2x + 5} = \dfrac{3}{1 + \dfrac{2}{x} + \dfrac{5}{x^2}} \to 3$ as $x \to \pm\infty$, so the horizontal asymptote is $y = 3$.

Also, vertical asymptotes occur when $x^2 + 2x + 5 = 0 \Rightarrow x = \dfrac{-2 \pm \sqrt{4 - 20}}{2} = -1 \pm 2i$. Since there are no real zeros, there are no vertical asymptotes.

18. $r(x) = \dfrac{x^3 + 3x^2}{x^2 - 4} = \dfrac{x^2(x + 3)}{(x - 2)(x + 2)}$. Because the degree of the numerator is greater than the degree of the denominator, the function has no horizontal asymptotes. Two vertical asymptotes occur at $x = 2$ and $x = -2$. By using long division, we see that $r(x) = x + 3 + \dfrac{4x + 12}{x^2 - 4}$ so $y = x + 3$ is a slant asymptote.

20. $r(x) = \dfrac{9}{x+3}$. When $x = 0$ we have $y = 3$, so the y-intercept is 3.
Since the numerator can never equal zero, there is no x-intercept.
The vertical asymptote is $x = -3$, and because the degree of the
denominator is greater than the degree of the numerator, the
horizontal asymptote is $y = 0$.

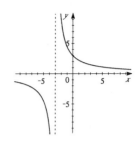

22. $r(x) = \dfrac{x+9}{x-3}$. When $x = 0$, $y = \dfrac{0+9}{0-3} = -3$, so the y-intercept
is -3. When $y = 0$, $x + 9 = 0 \Leftrightarrow x = -9$, so the x-intercept is
-9. Since $y = \dfrac{x+9}{x-3} = \dfrac{1+\frac{9}{x}}{1-\frac{3}{x}} \to 1$ as $x \to \pm\infty$, $y = 1$ is the
horizontal asymptote. The vertical asymptote occurs when $x - 3 = 0$
$\Leftrightarrow x = 3$, so $x = 3$ is the vertical asymptote.

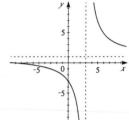

24. $r(x) = \dfrac{2x+6}{-6x+3} = \dfrac{2(x+3)}{-3(2x-1)}$. When $x = 0$, we have $y = 2$, so
the y-intercept is 2. When $y = 0$, we have $x + 3 = 0 \Leftrightarrow x = -3$,
so the x-intercept is -3. A vertical asymptote occurs when
$2x - 1 = 0 \Leftrightarrow x = \frac{1}{2}$. Because the degree of the denominator
and the numerator are the same, the horizontal asymptote is
$y = \frac{2}{-6} = -\frac{1}{3}$.

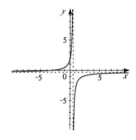

26. $s(x) = \dfrac{1-2x}{2x+3}$. When $x = 0$, $y = \frac{1}{3}$, so the graph passes through
the origin. A vertical asymptote occurs when $2x + 3 = 0 \Leftrightarrow$
$x = -\frac{3}{2}$, and because the degree of the denominator and the
numerator are the same, the horizontal asymptote is $y = -1$.

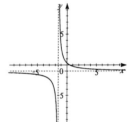

28. $r(x) = \dfrac{x-2}{(x+1)^2}$. When $x = 0$, we have $y = -2$, so the y-intercept
is -2. When $y = 0$, we have $x - 2 = 0 \Leftrightarrow x = 2$., so the
x-intercept is 2. A vertical asymptote occurs when $x = -1$, and
because the degree of the denominator is greater than the degree
of the numerator, the horizontal asymptote is $y = 0$.

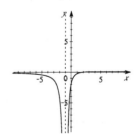

30. $s(x) = \dfrac{x+2}{(x+3)(x-1)}$. When $x = 0$, $y = \dfrac{2}{-3}$, so the y-intercept

is $-\frac{2}{3}$. A vertical asymptote occurs when $(x+3)(x-1) = 0$

$\Leftrightarrow \quad x = -3$ and $x = 1$. Because the degree of the denominator is

greater than the degree of the numerator, the horizontal asymptote

is $y = 0$.

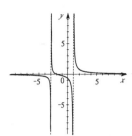

32. $s(x) = \dfrac{2x-4}{x^2+x-2} = \dfrac{2(x-2)}{(x-1)(x+2)}$. When $x = 0$, $y = 2$, so the

y-intercept is 2. A vertical asymptote occurs when $(x-1)(x+2) = 0$

$\Leftrightarrow \quad x = 1$ and $x = -2$. Because the degree of the denominator is

greater than the degree of the numerator, the horizontal asymptote

is $y = 0$.

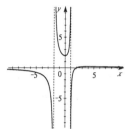

34. $t(x) = \dfrac{x-2}{x^2-4x} = \dfrac{x-2}{x(x-4)}$. Since $x = 0$ is not in the domain of

$t(x)$, there is no y-intercept. A vertical asymptote occurs when

$x(x-4) = 0 \quad \Leftrightarrow \quad x = 0$ and $x = 4$. Because the degree of the

denominator is greater than the degree of the numerator, the

horizontal asymptote is $y = 0$.

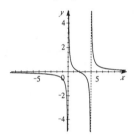

36. $r(x) = \dfrac{2x(x+4)}{(x-1)(x-2)}$. When $x = 0$, we have $y = 0$, so the graph

passes through the origin. Also, when $y = 0$, we have $2x(x+4) = 0$

$\Leftrightarrow \quad x = 0, -4$, so the x-intercepts are 0 and -4. There are two

vertical asymptotes at $x = 1$ and $x = 2$. Because the degree of the

denominator and numerator are the same, the horizontal asymptote

is $y = \frac{2}{1} = 2$.

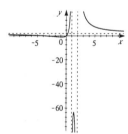

38. $r(x) = \dfrac{4x^2}{x^2-2x-3} = \dfrac{4x^2}{(x-3)(x+1)}$. When $x = 0$, we have $y = 0$,

so the graph passes through the origin. Vertical asymptotes occur at

$x = -1$, and $x = 3$. Because the degree of the denominator and

numerator are the same, the horizontal asymptote is $y = \frac{4}{1} = 4$.

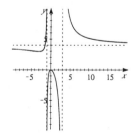

40. $r(x) = \dfrac{2x^2 + 2x - 4}{x^2 + x} = \dfrac{2(x+2)(x-1)}{x(x+1)}$. Vertical asymptotes

occur at $x = 0$ and $x = -1$. Since x cannot equal zero, there is no
y-intercept. When $y = 0$, we have $x = -2$ or 1, so the x-intercepts
are -2 and 1. Because the degree of the denominator and numerator
are the same, the horizontal asymptote is $y = \frac{2}{1} = 2$.

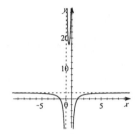

42. $r(x) = \dfrac{x^2 + 3x}{x^2 - x - 6} = \dfrac{x(x+3)}{(x-3)(x+2)}$. When $x = 0$, we have $y = 0$,

so the graph passes through the origin. When $y = 0$, we have $x = 0$
or -3, so the x-intercepts are 0 and -3. Vertical asymptotes occur
at $x = -2$ and $x = 3$. Because the degree of the denominator and
numerator are the same, the horizontal asymptote is $y = \frac{1}{1} = 1$.

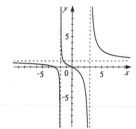

44. $r(x) = \dfrac{5x^2 + 5}{x^2 + 4x + 4} = \dfrac{5(x^2 + 1)}{(x+2)^2}$. When $x = 0$, we have $y = \frac{5}{4}$,

so the y-intercept is $\frac{5}{4}$. Since $x^2 + 1 > 0$ for all real x, y never equals
zero, and there are no x-intercepts. The vertical asymptote is $x = -2$.
Because the degree of the denominator and numerator are the same,
the horizontal asymptote occurs at $y = \frac{5}{1} = 5$.

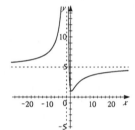

46. $r(x) = \dfrac{x^3 - x^2}{x^3 - 3x - 2} = \dfrac{x^2(x-1)}{x^3 - 3x - 2}$. When $x = 0$, we have $y = 0$,

so the y-intercept is 0. When $y = 0$, we have $x^2(x-1) = 0$, so the
x-intercepts are 0 and 1. Vertical asymptotes occur when
$x^3 - 3x - 2 = 0$. Since $x^3 - 3x - 2 = 0$ when $x = 2$, we can factor
$(x-2)(x+1)^2 = 0$, so the vertical asymptotes occur at $x = 2$ and
$x = -1$. Because the degree of the denominator and numerator are
the same, the horizontal asymptote is $y = \frac{1}{1} = 1$.

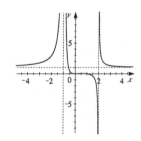

48. $r(x) = \dfrac{x^2 + 2x}{x - 1} = \dfrac{x(x+2)}{x - 1}$. When $x = 0$, we have $y = 0$, so

the graph passes through the origin. Also, when $y = 0$, we have
$x = 0$ or -2, so the x-intercepts are -2 and 0. The vertical
asymptote is $x = 1$. There is no horizontal asymptote, and the
line $y = x + 3$ is a slant asymptote because by long division,

we have $y = x + 3 + \dfrac{2}{x - 1}$.

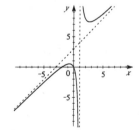

50. $r(x) = \dfrac{3x - x^2}{2x - 2} = \dfrac{x(3 - x)}{2(x - 1)}$. When $x = 0$, we have $y = 0$, so the

graph passes through the origin. Also, when $y = 0$, we have
$x = 0$ or $x = 3$, so the x-intercepts are 0 and 3. The vertical
asymptote is $x = 1$. There is no horizontal asymptote, and the line
$y = -\frac{1}{2}x + 1$ is a slant asymptote because by long division we

have $y = -\frac{1}{2}x + 1 + \dfrac{1}{x - 1}$.

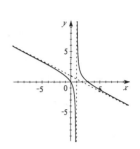

52. $r(x) = \dfrac{x^3 + 4}{2x^2 + x - 1} = \dfrac{x^3 + 4}{(2x - 1)(x + 1)}$. When $x = 0$, we have $y = \frac{0 + 4}{0 + 0 - 1} = -4$, so the

y-intercept is -4. Since $x^3 + 4 = 0 \Rightarrow x = -\sqrt[3]{4}$, the x-intercept
is $x = -\sqrt[3]{4}$. There are vertical asymptotes where $(2x - 1)(x + 1) = 0$
$\Rightarrow \quad x = \frac{1}{2}$ or $x = -1$. Since the degree of the numerator is greater
than the degree of the denominator, there is no horizontal asymptote.

By long division, we have $y = \frac{1}{2}x - \frac{1}{4} + \dfrac{\frac{3}{4}x + \frac{15}{4}}{2x^2 - x - 1}$,

so the line $y = \frac{1}{2}x - \frac{1}{4}$ is a slant asymptote.

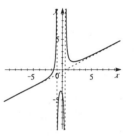

54. $r(x) = \dfrac{2x^3 + 2x}{x^2 - 1} = \dfrac{2x(x^2 + 1)}{(x - 1)(x + 1)}$. When $x = 0$, we have $y = 0$,

so the graph passes through the origin. Also, note that $x^2 + 1 > 0$,
for all real x, so the only x-intercept is 0. There are two vertical
asymptotes at $x = -1$ and $x = 1$. There is no horizontal
asymptote, and the line $y = 2x$ is a slant asymptote because

by long division, we have $y = 2x + \dfrac{4x}{x^2 - 1}$.

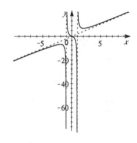

56. $f(x) = \dfrac{-x^3 + 6x^2 - 5}{x^2 - 2x}$, $g(x) = -x + 4$. The vertical asymptotes are $x = 0$ and $x = 2$.

$[-8, 8]$ by $[-20, 20]$ Graph of f.

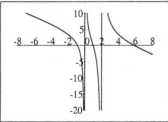

$[-20, 20]$ by $[-20, 20]$ Graph of f and g.

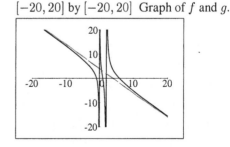

58. $f(x) = \dfrac{-x^4 + 2x^3 - 2x}{(x-1)^2}$, $g(x) = 1 - x^2$. The vertical asymptote is $x = 1$.

$[-4, 4]$ by $[-10, 2]$ Graph of f.

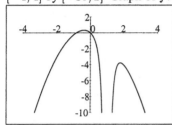

$[-4, 4]$ by $[-10, 2]$ Graph of f and g.

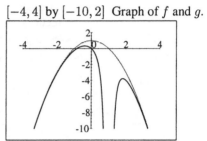

60. $f(x) = \dfrac{x^4 - 3x^3 + x^2 - 3x + 3}{x^2 - 3x}$

Vertical asymptote: $x = 0$, $x = 3$

x-intercept: 0.82

y-intercept: none

The local minima are $(-0.80, 2.63)$ and $(3.38, 14.76)$. The local maximum is $(2.56, 4.88)$.

$$
\begin{array}{r}
x^2 \qquad\qquad\; +1 \\
x^2 - 3x \overline{)\,x^4 - 3x^3 + x^2 - 3x + 3} \\
\underline{x^4 - 3x^3} \qquad\qquad\qquad \\
0x^3 + x^2 - 3x \\
\underline{x^2 - 3x} \\
3
\end{array}
$$

By using long division, we see that $f(x) = x^2 + 1 + \dfrac{3}{x^2 - 3x}$. From the second graph, we see that the end behavior of $f(x)$ is the same as the end behavior of $g(x) = x^2 + 1$.

$[-6, 6]$ by $[-25, 25]$ Graph of f.

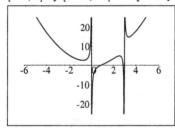

$[-8, 8]$ by $[-65, 65]$ Graph of f and g.

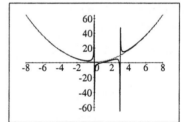

62. $f(x) = \dfrac{x^4}{x^2 - 2}$

Vertical asymptote: $x = -1.41$, $x = 1.41$

x-intercept: 0

y-intercept: 0

The local maximum is $(0, 0)$. The local minima are $(-2, 8)$ and $(2, 8)$.

$$
\begin{array}{r}
x^2 \qquad\qquad\quad +2 \\
x^2 - 2 \overline{)\,x^4 + 0x^3 + 0x^2 + 0x + 0} \\
\underline{x^4 \qquad\quad -2x^2} \qquad\quad \\
2x^2 \\
\underline{2x^2 \qquad -4} \\
4
\end{array}
$$

By using long division, we see that $f(x) = x^2 + 2 + \dfrac{4}{x^2 - 2}$. From the second graph, we see that the end behavior of $f(x)$ is the same as the end behavior of $g(x) = x^2 + 2$.

[−5, 5] by [−10, 20] Graph of $f(x)$.

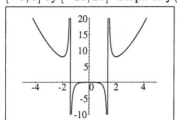

[−8, 8] by [−10, 75] Graph of $f(x)$ and $g(x)$.

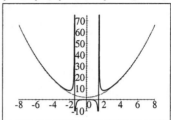

64. $r(x) = \dfrac{4 + x^2 - x^4}{x^2 - 1} = \dfrac{-x^4 + x^2 + 4}{(x-1)(x+1)}$

Vertical asymptote: $x = -1.41$, $x = 1.41$

x-intercept: -1.6, 1.6

y-intercept: -1

The local maximum is $(0, -0.4)$. No local minima.

Thus $y = -x^2 + \dfrac{6}{x^2 - 1}$. From the graph we see that the end behavior of $f(x)$ is like the end behavior of $g(x) = -x^2$.

$$\begin{array}{r} -x^2 \\ x^2 - 1 \overline{) -x^4 + 0x^3 + x^2 + 0x + 4} \\ \underline{-x^4 + x^2 } \\ 0 + 4 \end{array}$$

[−10, 10] by [−20, 20] Graph of f.

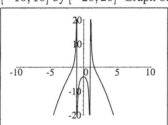

[−10, 10] by [−20, 20] Graph of f and g.

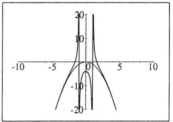

66. (a)

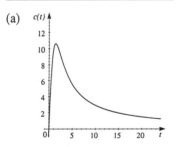

(b) $c(t) = \dfrac{30t}{t^2 + 2}$. Since the degree of the denominator is larger than the degree of the numerator, $c(t) \to 0$ as $t \to \infty$.

68. Substituting for R and g, we have
$$h(v) = \frac{(6.4 \times 10^6) v^2}{2(9.8)(6.4 \times 10^6) - v^2}.$$ The vertical asymptote is $v \approx 11,000$, and it represents the escape velocity from the earth's gravitational pull: $11,000$ m/s ≈ 1900 mi/h.

[0, 20000] by [0, 20000000]

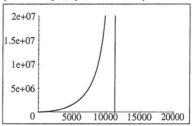

70. (a)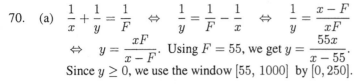

$\Leftrightarrow \quad y = \dfrac{xF}{x - F}$. Using $F = 55$, we get $y = \dfrac{55x}{x - 55}$.

Since $y \geq 0$, we use the window $[55, 1000]$ by $[0, 250]$.

(b) y approaches 55 millimeters.

(c) y approaches ∞.

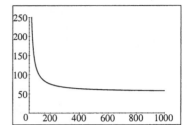

72. $r(x) = \dfrac{x^6 + 10}{x^4 + 8x^2 + 15}$ has no x-intercept since the numerator has no real roots. Likewise, $r(x)$ has no vertical asymptotes, since the denominator has no real roots. Since the degree of the numerator is two greater than the degree of the denominator, $r(x)$ has no horizontal or slant asymptotes.

Review Exercises for Chapter 5

2. $P(x) = 32 - 2x^4 = -2(x^4 - 16)$

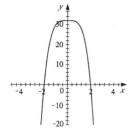

4. $P(x) = x^3 - 5x^2 - 6x = x(x-6)(x+1)$

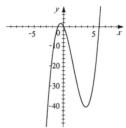

6. $P(x) = x^4 - 9x^2 = x^2(x-3)(x+3)$

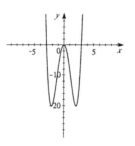

8. $P(x) = x^4 - 8x^2 + 16$

   x-intercepts: $-2, 2$

   y-intercept: 16

   Local maximum is $(0, 16)$.

   Local minima are $(-2, 0)$ and $(2, 0)$.

   $y \to \infty$ as $x \to \pm\infty$

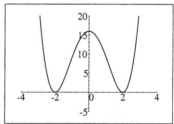

10. $P(x) = 3x^5 + x^4 - 4x$

    x-intercepts: $-1.17, 0$, and 1

    y-intercept: 0

    Local maximum is $(-0.8, 2.63)$.

    Local minimum is $(0.66, -2.08)$.

    $y \to -\infty$ as $x \to -\infty$ and

    $y \to \infty$ as $x \to \infty$

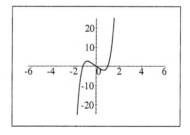

12. $\dfrac{x^4 + 30x + 12}{x + 3}$

$$
\begin{array}{r|rrrrr}
-3 & 1 & 0 & 0 & 30 & 12 \\
   &   & -3 & 9 & -27 & -9 \\
\hline
   & 1 & -3 & 9 & 3 & 3
\end{array}
$$

Using synthetic division, we see that $Q(x) = x^3 - 3x^2 + 9x + 3$ and $R(x) = 3$.

14.

$$
\begin{array}{r}
x^3 - 5x^2 + 19x \quad - 68 \\
x^2 + 2x - 6 \overline{)\, x^5 - 3x^4 + 3x^3 + 0x^2 + 20x \quad - 6} \\
\underline{x^5 + 2x^4 - 6x^3} \\
-5x^4 + 9x^3 + 0x^2 \\
\underline{-5x^4 - 10x^3 + 30x^2} \\
19x^3 - 30x^2 + 20x \\
\underline{19x^3 + 38x^2 - 114x} \\
-68x^2 + 134x \quad - 6 \\
\underline{-68x^2 - 136x + 408} \\
270x - 414
\end{array}
$$

Therefore, $Q(x) = x^3 - 5x^2 + 19x - 68$, and $R(x) = 270x - 414$.

16. $\dfrac{3}{2}$ $\bigg|$

$$
\begin{array}{rrrr}
2 & -1 & 0 & -5 \\
 & 3 & 3 & \frac{9}{2} \\
\hline
2 & 2 & 3 & -\frac{1}{2}
\end{array}
$$

Therefore, $Q(x) = 2x^2 + 2x + 3$, and $R(x) = -\frac{1}{2}$.

18. -1 $\bigg|$

$$
\begin{array}{rrrrr}
1 & 0 & -3 & 0 & 1 \\
 & -1 & 1 & 2 & -2 \\
\hline
1 & -1 & -2 & 2 & -1
\end{array}
$$

Therefore, $Q(x) = x^3 - x^2 - 2x + 2$, and $R(x) = -1$.

20. $Q(x) = x^4 + 4x^3 + 7x^2 + 10x + 15$; find $Q(-3)$

$$
\begin{array}{rrrrr}
-3 \,\big| & 1 & 4 & 7 & 10 & 15 \\
 & & -3 & -3 & -12 & 6 \\
\hline
 & 1 & 1 & 4 & -2 & 21
\end{array}
$$

By the Remainder Theorem, we have $Q(-3) = 21$.

22. $x + 4$ is a factor of $P(x) = x^5 + 4x^4 - 7x^3 - 23x^2 + 23x + 12$ if $P(-4) = 0$.

$$
\begin{array}{rrrrrr}
-4 \,\big| & 1 & 4 & -7 & -23 & 23 & 12 \\
 & & -4 & 0 & 28 & -20 & -12 \\
\hline
 & 1 & 0 & -7 & 5 & 3 & 0
\end{array}
$$

Since $P(-4) = 0$, $x + 4$ is a factor of the polynomial.

24.   Let $P(x) = x^{101} - x^4 + 2$. The remainder from dividing $P(x)$ by $x + 1$ is
$P(-1) = (-1)^{101} - (-1)^4 + 2 = 0$.

26. $6x^4 + 3x^3 + x^2 + 3x + 4 = 0$ has possible rational zeros $\pm 1, \pm 2, \pm 4, \pm\frac{1}{2}, \pm\frac{1}{3}, \pm\frac{2}{3}, \pm\frac{4}{3}, \pm\frac{1}{6}$. Since
$P(x)$ has no variations in sign, there are no positive real zeros. Since
$P(-x) = 6x^4 - 3x^3 + x^2 - 3x + 4$ has 4 variations in sign, there are 0, 2, or 4 negative real zeros.

28.   Since the zeros are $\pm 3i$ and 4 (which is a double zero), a factorization is
$P(x) = C(x-4)^2(x-3i)(x+3i) = C(x^2 - 8x + 16)(x^2 + 9) =$
$C(x^4 - 8x^3 + 25x^2 - 72x + 144)$. Since all of the coefficients are integers, we can choose $C = 1$,
so $P(x) = x^4 - 8x^3 + 25x^2 - 72x + 144$.

30. $P(x) = 3x^4 + 5x^2 + 2 = (3x^2 + 2)(x^2 + 1)$. Since $3x^2 + 2 = 0$ and $x^2 + 1 = 0$ have no real
zeros, it follows that $3x^4 + 5x^2 + 2$ has no real zeros.

32. $P(x) = 2x^3 + 5x^2 - 6x - 9$ has possible rational zeros $\pm 1, \pm 3, \pm 9, \pm\frac{1}{2}, \pm\frac{3}{2}, \pm\frac{9}{2}$. Since there is one variation in sign, there is a positive real zero.

$$
\begin{array}{r|rrrr}
1 & 2 & 5 & -6 & -9 \\
  &   & 2 & 7 & 1 \\
\hline
  & 2 & 7 & 1 & -8
\end{array}
$$

$$
\begin{array}{r|rrrr}
3 & 2 & 5 & -6 & -9 \\
  &   & 6 & 33 & 81 \\
\hline
  & 2 & 11 & 27 & 72
\end{array}
\Rightarrow \quad x = 3 \text{ is an upper bound, and there is a zero between 1 and 3.}
$$

$$
\begin{array}{r|rrrr}
\frac{3}{2} & 2 & 5 & -6 & -9 \\
  &   & 3 & 12 & 9 \\
\hline
  & 2 & 8 & 6 & 0
\end{array}
\Rightarrow \quad x = \frac{3}{2} \text{ is a zero.}
$$

So $P(x) = 2x^3 + 5x^2 - 6x - 9 = (2x - 3)(x^2 + 4x + 3) = (2x - 3)(x + 3)(x + 1)$. Therefore, the zeros are $-3, -1$ and $\frac{3}{2}$.

34. $P(x) = x^4 + 7x^3 + 9x^2 - 17x - 20$ has possible rational zeros $\pm 1, \pm 2, \pm 4, \pm 5, \pm 10, \pm 20$.

$$
\begin{array}{r|rrrrr}
1 & 1 & 7 & 9 & -17 & -20 \\
  &   & 1 & 8 & 17 & 0 \\
\hline
  & 1 & 8 & 17 & 0 & -20
\end{array}
$$

$$
\begin{array}{r|rrrrr}
2 & 1 & 7 & 9 & -17 & -20 \\
  &   & 2 & 18 & 54 & 74 \\
\hline
  & 1 & 9 & 27 & 37 & 54
\end{array}
\Rightarrow \quad x = 2 \text{ is an upper bound.}
$$

$$
\begin{array}{r|rrrrr}
-1 & 1 & 7 & 9 & -17 & -20 \\
   &   & -1 & -6 & -3 & 20 \\
\hline
   & 1 & 6 & 3 & -20 & 0
\end{array}
\Rightarrow \quad x = -1 \text{ is a zero.}
$$

So $P(x) = x^4 + 7x^3 + 9x^2 - 17x - 20 = (x + 1)(x^3 + 6x^2 + 3x - 20)$. Continuing with the quotient, we have

$$
\begin{array}{r|rrrr}
-1 & 1 & 6 & 3 & -20 \\
   &   & -1 & -5 & 2 \\
\hline
   & 1 & 5 & -2 & -18
\end{array}
\qquad
\begin{array}{r|rrrr}
-2 & 1 & 6 & 3 & -20 \\
   &   & -2 & -8 & 10 \\
\hline
   & 1 & 4 & -5 & -10
\end{array}
$$

$$
\begin{array}{r|rrrr}
-4 & 1 & 6 & 3 & -20 \\
   &   & -4 & -8 & 20 \\
\hline
   & 1 & 2 & -5 & 0
\end{array}
\Rightarrow \quad x = -4 \text{ is a zero.}
$$

So $P(x) = x^4 + 7x^3 + 9x^2 - 17x - 20 = (x + 1)(x + 4)(x^2 + 2x - 5)$. Now using the quadratic formula on $x^2 + 2x - 5$ we have: $x = \dfrac{-2 \pm \sqrt{4 - 4(1)(-5)}}{2} = \dfrac{-2 \pm 2\sqrt{6}}{2} = -1 \pm \sqrt{6}$. Thus, the zeros are $-4, -1$ and $-1 \pm \sqrt{6}$.

36. $P(x) = x^4 - 81 = (x^2 - 9)(x^2 + 9) = (x - 3)(x + 3)(x^2 + 9) = (x - 3)(x + 3)(x - 3i)(x + 3i)$. Thus, the zeros are $\pm 3, \pm 3i$.

38. $P(x) = 18x^3 + 3x^2 - 4x - 1$ has possible rational zeros $\pm 1, \pm\frac{1}{2}, \pm\frac{1}{3}, \pm\frac{1}{6}, \pm\frac{1}{9}, \pm\frac{1}{18}$.

$$
\begin{array}{r|rrrr}
1 & 18 & 3 & -4 & -1 \\
  &   & 18 & 21 & 17 \\
\hline
  & 18 & 21 & 17 & 16
\end{array}
\Rightarrow \quad x = 1 \text{ is an upper bound.}
$$

$$\frac{1}{2} \begin{array}{|rrrr} 18 & 3 & -4 & -1 \\ & 9 & 6 & 1 \\ \hline 18 & 12 & 2 & 0 \end{array} \quad \Rightarrow \quad x = \tfrac{1}{2} \text{ is a zero.}$$

So $P(x) = 18x^3 + 3x^2 - 4x - 1 = (2x - 1)(9x^2 + 6x + 1) = (2x - 1)(3x + 1)^2$. Thus the zeros are $\tfrac{1}{2}$ and $-\tfrac{1}{3}$ (multiplicity 2).

40. $P(x) = x^4 + 15x^2 + 54 = (x^2 + 9)(x^2 + 6)$. If $x^2 = -9$, then $x = \pm 3i$. If $x^2 = -6$, then $x = \pm\sqrt{6}\,i$. Therefore, the zeros are $\pm 3i$ and $\pm\sqrt{6}\,i$.

42. Let $P(x) = x^3 + x^2 - 14x - 24$. The solutions to $P(x) = 0$ are $x = -3, -2$ and 4.

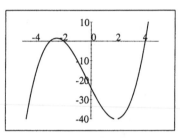

44. $x^5 = x + 3 \quad \Leftrightarrow \quad x^5 - x - 3 = 0$. The only real solution is 1.34. We graph $P(x) = x^5 - x - 3$.

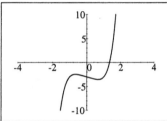

46. $r(x) = \dfrac{1}{(x + 2)^2}$. When $x = 0$, we have $r(0) = \dfrac{1}{2^2} = \dfrac{1}{4}$, so the y-intercept is $\tfrac{1}{4}$. Since the numerator is 1, y never equals zero and there are no x-intercepts. A vertical asymptote occurs when $x = -2$. The horizontal asymptote is $y = 0$ because the degree of the denominator is greater than the degree of the numerator.

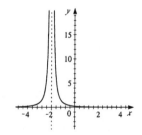

48. $r(x) = \dfrac{2x^2 - 6x - 7}{x - 4}$. When $x = 0$, we have $r(0) = \dfrac{-7}{-4} = \dfrac{7}{4}$, so the y-intercept is $y = \tfrac{7}{4}$. We use the quadratic formula to find the x-intercepts: $x = \dfrac{-(-6) \pm \sqrt{(-6)^2 - 4(2)(-7)}}{2(2)} = \dfrac{6 \pm \sqrt{92}}{4}$

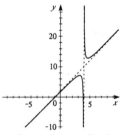

$= \dfrac{3 \pm \sqrt{23}}{2}$. Thus the x-intercepts are $x \approx 3.9$ and $x \approx -0.9$. The vertical asymptote is $x = 4$. Because the degree of the numerator is greater than the degree of the denominator, there is no horizontal asymptote. By long division, we have $r(x) = 2x + 2 + \dfrac{1}{x - 4}$, so the slant asymptote is $r(x) = 2x + 2$.

50. $r(x) = \dfrac{x^3 + 27}{x + 4}$. When $x = 0$, we have $r(0) = \frac{27}{4}$, so the y-intercept

is $y = \frac{27}{4}$. When $y = 0$, we have $x^3 + 27 = 0$ $\Leftrightarrow$ $x^3 = -27$

$\Rightarrow$ $x = -3$. Thus the x-intercept is $x = -3$. The vertical

asymptote is $x = -4$. Because the degree of the numerator is

greater than the degree of the denominator, there is no horizontal

asymptote. By long division, we have $r(x) = x^2 - 4x + 16 - \dfrac{37}{x + 4}$.

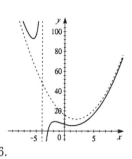

So the end behavior of y is like the end behavior of $g(x) = x^2 - 4x - 16$.

52. $r(x) = \dfrac{2x - 7}{x^2 + 9}$. From the graph we see that

x-intercept: 3.5

y-intercept: -0.78

Vertical asymptote: none

Horizontal asymptote: $y = 0$

Local minimum is $(-1.11, -0.90)$.

Local maximum is $(8.11, 0.12)$.

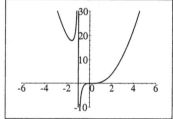

54. $r(x) = \dfrac{2x^3 - x^2}{x + 1}$. From the graph we see that

x-intercepts: $0, \frac{1}{2}$

y-intercept: 0

Vertical asymptote: $x = -1$

Local minimum is $(0.425, -3.599)$.

Local maxima are $(-1.57, 17.90)$ and $(0.32, -0.03)$.

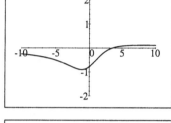

By using long division, we see that $r(x) = 2x^2 - 3x + 3 - \dfrac{3}{x + 1}$. So the end behavior of r is the

same as the end behavior of $g(x) = 2x^2 - 3x + 3$.

Focus on Problem Solving

2. No, the network is not traversable since it has
    4 vertices with odd order

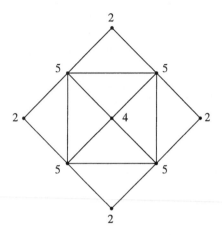

4. Since there are exactly two vertices of
    odd order, the network is traversable.
    Any path that traverses this network must
    start at one odd vertex and end at the
    other. For example, we may choose the
    path shown.

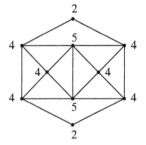
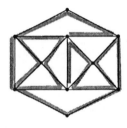

6. Imagine that on the same day that the monk makes the uphill trip, a twin monk makes the downhill
    trip. The two monks will meet at a certain point on the path. That point is exactly where the first
    monk will be at the same time the next day.

8. (a) $P_2(x) = (x - a)(x - b) = x^2 - (a + b)x + ab.$
        $P_3(x) = (x - a)(x - b)(x - c) = x^3 - (a + b + c)x^2 + (ab + ac + bc)x - abc$

    (b) $P_4(x) = (x - a)(x - b)(x - c)(x - d)$
        $$= x^4 - (a + b + c + d)x^3 + (ab + ac + ad + bc + bd + cd)x^2$$
        $$- (abc + abd + acd + bcd)x + abcd$$
        $P_5(x) = (x - a)(x - b)(x - c)(x - d)(x - e)$
        $$= x^5 - (a + b + c + d + e)x^4$$
        $$+ (ab + ac + ad + ae + bc + bd + be + cd + ce + de)x^3$$
        $$- (abc + abd + abe + acd + ace + ade + bcd + bce + bde + cde)x^2$$
        $$+ (abcd + abce + abde + acde + bcde)x - abcde$$

    (c) Let $a_1, a_2, \ldots, a_n$ be the zeros of the polynomial. When
        $P_n(x) = (x - a_1)(x - a_2) \cdots (x - a_n)$ is expanded, the coefficient of x^{n-1} is
        $-(a_1 + a_2 + \cdots + a_n)$ and the constant coefficient is $(-1)^n \cdot a_1 \cdot a_2 \cdots a_n$.

    (d) The sum of the zeros is the negative of the coefficient of x^5, and this is $-(-7) = 7$. The
        product of the coefficients is $(-1)^6$ times the constant term, and this is $(-1)^6 \cdot 17 = 17$.

10. $x = 2 - \sqrt[3]{2} \quad \Leftrightarrow \quad x - 2 = -\sqrt[3]{2} \quad \Leftrightarrow \quad (x-2)^3 = -2 \quad \Leftrightarrow \quad x^3 - 6x^2 + 12x - 8 = -2$
$\Leftrightarrow \quad x^3 - 6x^2 + 12x - 6 = 0$. Thus the polynomial is $P(x) = x^3 - 6x^2 + 12x - 6$. Since the graph of $P(x) = (x-2)^3 + 2$ is just the graph of $y = x^3$ shifted 2 units up and 2 units to the right, $P(x)$ has one real zero, and there are no others.

12. Since $\sqrt[3]{1729} \approx 12.0023$, we start with $n = 12$ and find the other perfect cube.

n	$1729 - n^3$
12	$1729 - (12)^3 = 1$
11	$1729 - (11)^3 = 398$
10	$1729 - (10)^3 = 729$

Since 1 and 729 are perfect cubes, the two representations we seek are $1^3 + 12^3 = 1729$ and $9^3 + 10^3 = 1729$.

14. $f(x) = |x^2 - 1| - |x^2 - 4|$.
Case (i): If $x \le -2$, then $f(x) = x^2 - 1 - (x^2 - 4) = 3$.
Case (ii): If $-2 < x \le -1$, then
$f(x) = x^2 - 1 + x^2 - 4 = 2x^2 - 5$.
Case (iii): If $-1 < x \le 1$, then $f(x) = -(x^2 - 1) + x^2 - 4 = -3$.
Case (iv): If $1 < x \le 2$, then $f(x) = x^2 - 1 + x^2 - 4 = 2x^2 - 5$.
Case (v): If $x > 2$, then $f(x) = x^2 - 1 - (x^2 - 4) = 3$.

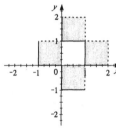

16. $[\![x]\!]^2 + [\![y]\!]^2 = 1$.
Since $[\![x]\!]^2$ and $[\![y]\!]^2$ are positive integers or 0, there are only 4 cases:
Case (i): $[\![x]\!] = 1$, $[\![y]\!] = 0 \quad \Rightarrow \quad 1 \le x < 2$ and $0 \le y < 1$
Case (ii): $[\![x]\!] = -1$, $[\![y]\!] = 0 \quad \Rightarrow \quad -1 \le x < 0$ and $0 \le y < 1$
Case (iii): $[\![x]\!] = 0$, $[\![y]\!] = 1 \quad \Rightarrow \quad 0 \le x < 1$ and $1 \le y < 2$
Case (iv): $[\![x]\!] = 0$, $[\![y]\!] = -1 \quad \Rightarrow \quad 0 \le x < 1$ and $-1 \le y < 0$

18. $x^3 = 1 \quad \Leftrightarrow \quad x^3 - 1 = 0 \quad \Leftrightarrow \quad (x-1)(x^2 + x + 1) = 0$. Since ω is one of the imaginary roots, we have $\omega^2 + \omega + 1 = 0$. Thus
$$(1 - \omega + \omega^2)(1 + \omega - \omega^2) = 1 + \omega - \omega^2 - \omega - \omega^2 + \omega^3 + \omega^2 + \omega^3$$
$$= 1 - \omega^2 + 2\omega^3 - \omega^4$$
$$= 1 - \omega^2 + 2 - \omega \text{ (since } \omega^3 = 1)$$
$$= 4 - (1 + \omega + \omega^2)$$
$$= 4.$$

Chapter Six
Exercises 6.1

2. $g(x) = 8^x$

x	y
-2	$\frac{1}{64}$
-1	$\frac{1}{8}$
0	1
1	8
2	64

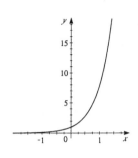

4. $h(x) = (0.8)^x$

x	y
-4	4.44140625
-2	1.5625
0	1
2	0.64
4	0.4096

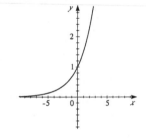

6. $h(x) = (1.1)^x$

x	y
-5	0.620921323
-1	$0.\overline{90}$
0	1
5	1.61051
10	2.59374246

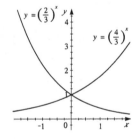

8. $f(x) = \left(\frac{3}{2}\right)^x$

x	y
-2	$\frac{4}{9}$
-1	$\frac{2}{3}$
0	1
1	1.5
2	2.25

10. $y = \left(\frac{2}{3}\right)^x$ and $y = \left(\frac{4}{3}\right)^x$.

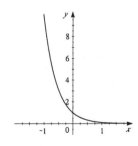

12. From the graph, $f(-1) = a^{-1} = \frac{1}{5}$, so $a = 5$. Thus $f(x) = 5^x$.

14. From the graph, $f(-3) = a^{-3} = 8$, so $a = \frac{1}{2}$. Thus $f(x) = \left(\frac{1}{2}\right)^x$.

16. V   **18.** VI   **20.** IV

22. $f(x) = 10^{-x}$

The graph of f is obtained by reflecting the graph of $y = 10^x$ about the y-axis.

Domain: $(-\infty, \infty)$

Range: $(0, \infty)$

Asymptote: $y = 0$

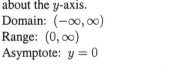

24. $g(x) = 2^{x-3}$

The graph of g is obtained by shifting the graph of $y = 2^x$
to the right 3 units.
Domain: $(-\infty, \infty)$
Range: $(0, \infty)$
Asymptote: $y = 0$

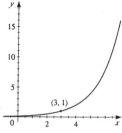

26. $h(x) = 6 - 3^x$

The graph of h is obtained by reflecting the graph of $y = 3^x$
about the x-axis and shifting upward 6 units.
Domain: $(-\infty, \infty)$
Range: $(-\infty, 6)$
Asymptote: $y = 6$

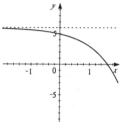

28. $f(x) = -\left(\frac{1}{5}\right)^x$

Note that $f(x) = -\left(\frac{1}{5}\right)^x = -5^{-x}$. So the graph of f is
obtained by reflecting the graph of $y = 5^x$ about the y-axis and
about the x-axis.
Domain: $(-\infty, \infty)$
Range: $(-\infty, 0)$
Asymptote: $y = 0$

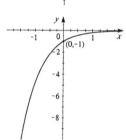

30. $f(x) = 10^{-x} - 4$

The graph of f is obtained by reflecting the graph of $y = 10^x$
about the y-axis and shifting downward 4 units.
Domain: $(-\infty, \infty)$
Range: $(-4, \infty)$
Asymptote: $y = -4$

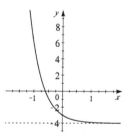

32. $y = 1 + 2^{x+1}$

The graph of $y = 1 + 2^{x+1}$ is obtained by shifting the graph
of $y = 2^x$ to the left 1 unit and then upward 1 unit.
Domain: $(-\infty, \infty)$
Range: $(1, \infty)$
Asymptote: $y = 1$

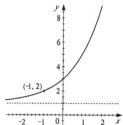

34. $f(x) = 1 - 2^{-x}$

The graph of f is obtained by reflecting the graph of $y = 2^x$ about the y-axis, reflecting about the x-axis, and then shifting upward 1 unit.

Domain: $(-\infty, \infty)$

Range: $(1, \infty)$

Asymptote: $y = 1$

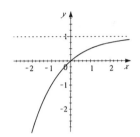

36. $y = 2^{-|x|}$

Note that $y = \begin{cases} 2^{-x} & x \geq 0 \\ 2^x & x < 0. \end{cases}$

The graph of $y = 2^{-|x|}$ is obtained by reflecting the part of the graph of $y = 2^x$ for $x < 0$ about the y-axis, thus giving the portion of the graph for $x \geq 0$.

Domain: $(-\infty, \infty)$

Range: $(0, 1]$

Asymptote: $y = 0$

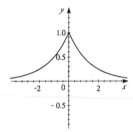

38. Using the points $(-1, 15)$ and $(0, 5)$ we have $f(0) = Ca^0 = 5 \quad \Leftrightarrow \quad C = 5$. Then $f(-1) = 5a^{-1} = 15 \quad \Leftrightarrow \quad a^{-1} = 3 \quad \Leftrightarrow \quad a = \frac{1}{3}$. Thus $f(x) = 5\left(\frac{1}{3}\right)^x$.

40. (a)

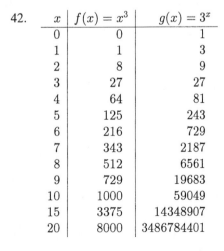

(b) $f(x) = 9^{x/2} = (3^2)^{x/2} = 3^{2 \cdot x/2} = 3^x = g(x)$. So $f(x) = g(x)$, and the graphs are the same.

42.

x	$f(x) = x^3$	$g(x) = 3^x$
0	0	1
1	1	3
2	8	9
3	27	27
4	64	81
5	125	243
6	216	729
7	343	2187
8	512	6561
9	729	19683
10	1000	59049
15	3375	14348907
20	8000	3486784401

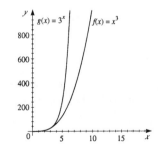

44. (a)   (i) $[-4, 4]$ by $[0, 20]$ (ii) $[0, 10]$ by $[0, 5000]$

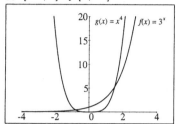   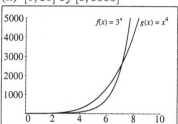

(iii) $[0, 20]$ by $[0, 10^5]$ (b)   From the graphs in parts (i) and (ii), we
see that the solutions of $3^x = x^4$ are
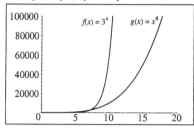 $x \approx -0.80$, $x \approx 1.52$ and $x \approx 7.17$.

46.
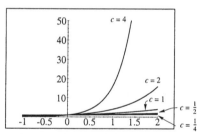

The larger the value of c, the more rapidly the
graph of $f(x) = 2^{cx}$ increases. In general,
$f(x) = 2^{cx} = (2^c)^x$; so, for example,
$f(x) = 2^{2x} = (2^2)^x = 4^x$.

48. $y = \dfrac{2^x}{x}$

Vertical Asymptote: $x = 0$

Horizontal Asymptote: $y = 0$, left side only.

As $x \to -\infty$, $y \to 0$, and as $x \to \infty$,
$y \to \infty$.

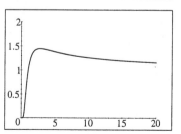

50. $g(x) = \sqrt[x]{x}$. $g(x)$ is only defined for $x > 0$.
The graph of $g(x)$ is shown in the viewing
rectangle $[0, 20]$ by $[0, 2]$. From the graph, we
see that there is a local maximum ≈ 1.44
when $x \approx 2.72$.

$(-\infty, -1.44]$ and increasing on
$[-1.44, \infty)$.

52. $y = x2^x$

(a)   From the graph, we see that the function
$f(x) = x\,2^x$ is decreasing on

(b) From the graph, we see that the range is
approximately $[-0.53, \infty)$.

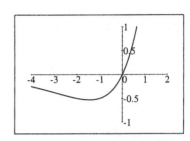

54. Since $f(40) = 2^{40} = 1099511627776$, it would take a sheet of paper 4 inches by 1099511627776 inches. Since there are 12 inches in every foot and 5,280 feet in ever mile, 1099511627776 inches ≈ 1.74 million miles. So the dimensions of the sheet of paper required are 4 inches by about 1.74 million miles.

Exercises 6.2

2. $g(x) = 2e^{-0.5x}$

x	$g(x) = 2e^{-0.5x}$
-4	14.7761
-3	8.96338
-2	5.43656
-1	3.29744
0	2
1	1.21306
2	0.735759
3	0.44626
4	0.270671

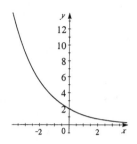

4. $y = 1 - e^x$

The graph of $y = 1 - e^x$ is obtained by reflecting the graph of $y = e^x$ about the x-axis and then shifting upward 1 unit.

Domain: $(-\infty, \infty)$

Range: $(-\infty, 1)$

Asymptote: $y = 1$

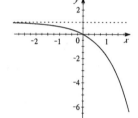

6. $y = -e^{-x}$

The graph of $y = -e^{-x}$ is obtained by reflecting the graph of $y = e^x$ about the y-axis and then about the x-axis.

Domain: $(-\infty, \infty)$

Range: $(-\infty, 0)$

Asymptote: $y = 0$

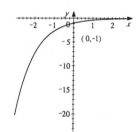

8. $y = e^{x-3} + 4$

The graph of $y = e^{x-3} + 4$ is obtained by shifting the graph of $y = e^x$ to the right 3 units, and then upward 4 units.

Domain: $(-\infty, \infty)$

Range: $(4, \infty)$

Asymptote: $y = 4$

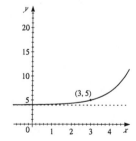

10. $P = 4,000$, $r = 0.16$, and $n = 4$. So $A(t) = 4000\left(1 + \frac{0.16}{4}\right)^{4t} = 4000 \cdot 1.04^{4t}$.

(a) $A(4) = 4000 \cdot (1.04)^{16} \approx 7491.92$, and so the amount due is $7,491.92.

(b) $A(6) = 4000 \cdot (1.04)^{24} \approx 10,253.22$, and so the amount due is $10,253.22.

(c) $A(8) = 4000 \cdot (1.04)^{32} \approx 14,032.23$, and so the amount due is $14,032.23.

12. $P = 4000$, $n = 4$, and $t = 5$. Then $A(5) = 4000\left(1 + \dfrac{r}{4}\right)^{4(5)}$, and so $A(5) = 4000\left(1 + \dfrac{r}{4}\right)^{20}$.

   (a) If $r = 0.06$, $A(5) = 4000\left(1 + \dfrac{0.06}{4}\right)^{20} = 4000 \cdot (1.015)^{20} \approx \$5{,}387.42$.

   (b) If $r = 0.065$, $A(5) = 4000\left(1 + \dfrac{0.065}{4}\right)^{20} = 4000 \cdot (1.01625)^{20} \approx \$5{,}521.68$.

   (c) If $r = 0.07$, $A(5) = 4000\left(1 + \dfrac{0.07}{4}\right)^{20} = 4000 \cdot (1.0175)^{20} \approx \$5{,}659.11$.

   (d) If $r = 0.08$, $A(5) = 4000\left(1 + \dfrac{0.08}{4}\right)^{20} = 4000 \cdot (1.02)^{20} \approx \$5{,}943.79$.

14. We find the effective rate for $P = 1$ and $t = 1$.

   (i) If $r = 0.0925$ and $n = 2$, then $A(2) = \left(1 + \dfrac{0.0925}{2}\right)^2 = (1.04625)^2 \approx 1.0946$.

   (ii) If $r = 0.09$ and interest is compounded continuously, then $A(1) = e^{0.09} \approx 1.0942$.

   Since the effective rate in (i) is greater than the effective rate in (ii), we can see that the account paying $9\frac{1}{4}\%$ per year compounded semiannually is the better investment.

16. We must solve for P in the equation $100000 = P\left(1 + \dfrac{0.08}{12}\right)^{12(5)} = P(1.00667)^{60}$ $\Leftrightarrow$
    $100000 = 1.4898P$ $\Leftrightarrow$ $P = \$67{,}121.04$.

18. $n(t) = 54\,e^{0.12t}$

   (a) The relative growth rate is 12%.

   (b) $n(0) = 54\,e^0 = 54$. Thus the initial rat population was 54 million.

   (c) $t = 2000 - 1990 = 10$;
   $n(10) = 54\,e^{0.12(10)} = 54\,e^{1.2} \approx 179.29$.
   Thus the rat population is expected to be about 179 million in the year 2000.

   (d)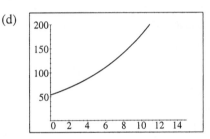

20. $n(t) = n_0\,e^{rt}$; $n_0 = 421{,}000$, $r = 0.05$, so $n(t) = 421{,}000\,e^{0.05t}$.

   (a) $t = 2000 - 1988 = 12$; $n(12) = 421{,}000\,e^{0.05(12)} = 421{,}000\,e^{0.60} \approx 767{,}112$. Thus the projected population of the city in the year 2000 is about 767,000.

   (b) $t = 2030 - 1988 = 42$; $n(42) = 421{,}000\,e^{0.05(42)} = 421{,}000\,e^{2.1} \approx 3{,}437{,}957$. Thus the projected population of the city in the year 2030 is about 3,438,000.

22. (a) $n(t) = n_0\,e^{rt}$; $n_0 = 680{,}000$, $r = 0.12$. So $n(t) = 680{,}000\,e^{0.12t}$.

   (b) $t = 2000 - 1992 = 8$; $n(8) = 680{,}000\,e^{0.12(8)} = 680{,}000\,e^{0.96} \approx 1{,}775{,}954$. Thus the population of the city will be about 1,776,000 in the year 2000.

24. $r = 0.80$, $n(t) = n_0\,e^{0.80t}$.

   (a) We have $n(3) = n_0\,e^{0.80(3)} = 21500$ $\Leftrightarrow$ $n_0 \cdot 11.023 = 21500$ $\Leftrightarrow$ $n_0 \approx 1950$.

   (b) $n(5) = 1950\,e^{0.80(5)} \approx 106{,}466$. Thus the number of bacteria after 5 hours is about 106,500.

26. $m(t) = 13\,e^{-0.015t}$

   (a) $m(0) = 13$ g.

   (b) $m(45) = 13\,e^{-0.015(45)} = 13\,e^{-0.675} = 6.619$ g. Thus the mass of the radioactive substance after 45 days is about 7 g.

28. $v(t) = 80(1 - e^{-0.2t})$

   (a) $v(0) = 80(1 - e^0) = 80(1 - 1) = 0.$

   (b) $v(5) = 80(1 - e^{-0.2(5)}) \approx 80(0.632) = 50.57$ ft/s. So the velocity after 5 s is about 51 ft/s.
       $v(10) = 80(1 - e^{-0.2(10)}) \approx 80(0.865) = 69.2$ ft/s. So the velocity after 10 s is about 69 ft/s.

   (c)

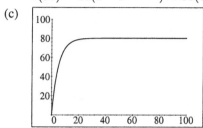

   (d) The terminal velocity is 80 ft/s.

30. (a) $A(t) = 5000\left(1 + \frac{0.09}{2}\right)^{2t} = 5000(1.045)^{2t} = 5000(1.092025)^t.$

     (b)

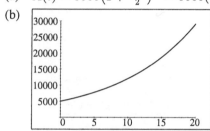

   (c) $A(t) = 25000$ when $t \approx 18.28.$

32. $n(t) = \dfrac{5600}{0.5 + 27.5\,e^{-0.044t}}$

   (a) $n(0) = \frac{5600}{28} = 200.$

   (b)

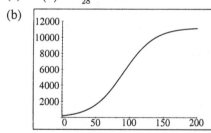
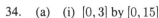

   (c) From the graph, we see that $n(t)$ approaches about 11,200 as t gets large.

34. (a) (i) $[0, 3]$ by $[0, 15]$ (ii) $[0, 6]$ by $[0, 120]$

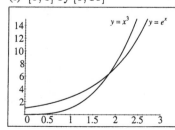
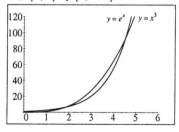

(iii) $[0, 20]$ by $[0, 10000]$

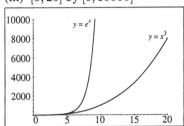

(b) The two solutions are $x \approx 1.86$ and $x \approx 4.54$

36.

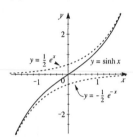

38. $\sinh(-x) = \dfrac{e^{-x} - e^{-(-x)}}{2} = \dfrac{e^{-x} - e^{x}}{2} = -\dfrac{-e^{-x} + e^{x}}{2} = -\dfrac{e^{x} - e^{-x}}{2} = -\sinh(x).$

40. $\sinh(x)\cosh(y) + \cosh(x)\sinh(y) = \dfrac{e^{x} - e^{-x}}{2} \cdot \dfrac{e^{y} + e^{-y}}{2} + \dfrac{e^{x} + e^{-x}}{2} \cdot \dfrac{e^{y} - e^{-y}}{2}$

$= \dfrac{e^{x+y} + e^{x-y} - e^{y-x} - e^{-(x+y)}}{4} + \dfrac{e^{x+y} - e^{x-y} + e^{y-x} - e^{-(x+y)}}{4}$

$= \dfrac{e^{x+y} - e^{-(x+y)}}{2} = \sinh(x+y).$

42.

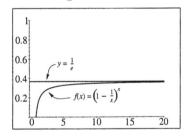

From the graph, we see that

$f(x) = \left(1 - \dfrac{1}{x}\right)^{x}$ approaches $\dfrac{1}{e}$ as x get

large.

44. $y = \dfrac{e^{x}}{x}$

Vertical asymptote: $x = 0$

Horizontal asymptote: $y = 0$

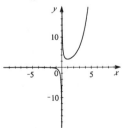

46. $f(x) = e^x + e^{-3x}$

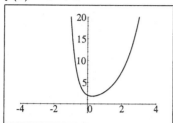

The graph of $f(x)$ is shown in the viewing rectangle $[-4, 4]$ by $[0, 20]$. From the graph, we see that there is a local minimum ≈ 1.75 when $x \approx 0.27$.

Exercises 6.3

2. (a) $10^{-1} = 0.1$ (b) $8^3 = 512$

4. (a) $3^4 = 81$ (b) $8^{2/3} = 4$

6. (a) $e^2 = x + 1$ (b) $e^4 = x - 1$

8. (a) $\log_{10} 10000 = 4$ (b) $\log_{81} 9 = \frac{1}{2}$

10. (a) $\log_8 \frac{1}{8} = -1$ (b) $\log_{10} n = m$

12. (a) $\ln 0.5 = x + 1$ (b) $\ln t = 0.5x$

14. (a) $\log_3 3 = 1$ (b) $\log_3 1 = \log_3 3^0 = 0$
    (c) $\log_3 3^2 = 2$

16. (a) $\log_2 32 = \log_2 2^5 = 5$ (b) $\log_8 8^{17} = 17$
    (c) $\log_6 1 = \log_6 6^0 = 0$

18. (a) $\log_5 125 = \log_5 5^3 = 3$ (b) $\log_{49} 7 = \log_{49} 49^{1/2} = \frac{1}{2}$
    (c) $\log_9 \sqrt{3} = \log_9 3^{1/2} = \log_9 \left(9^{1/2}\right)^{1/2} = \log_9 9^{1/4} = \frac{1}{4}$

20. (a) $e^{\ln \pi} = \pi$ (b) $10^{\log 5} = 5$
    (c) $10^{\log 87} = 87$

22. (a) $\log_4 \sqrt{2} = \log_4 2^{1/2} = \log_4 \left(4^{1/2}\right)^{1/2} = \log_4 4^{1/4} = \frac{1}{4}$
    (b) $\log_4 \left(\frac{1}{2}\right) = \log_4 2^{-1} = \log_4 \left(4^{1/2}\right)^{-1} = \log_4 4^{-1/2} = -\frac{1}{2}$
    (c) $\log_4 8 = \; = \log_4 2^3 = \log_4 \left(4^{1/2}\right)^3 = \log_4 4^{3/2} = \frac{3}{2}$

24. (a) $\log_5 x = 4 \quad \Leftrightarrow \quad x = 5^4 = 625$ (b) $x = \log_{10}(0.1) = \log_{10} 10^{-1} = -1$

26. (a) $\log_x 1000 = 3 \quad \Leftrightarrow \quad x^3 = 1000 \quad \Leftrightarrow \quad x = 10$
    (b) $\log_x 25 = 2 \quad \Leftrightarrow \quad x^2 = 25 \quad \Leftrightarrow \quad x = 5$

28. (a) $\log_x 6 = \frac{1}{2} \quad \Leftrightarrow \quad x^{1/2} = 6 \quad \Leftrightarrow \quad x = 36$
    (b) $\log_x 3 = \frac{1}{3} \quad \Leftrightarrow \quad x^{1/3} = 3 \quad \Leftrightarrow \quad x = 27$

30. (a) $\log 50 \approx 1.6990$ (b) $\log \sqrt{2} \approx 0.1505$
    (c) $\log\left(3\sqrt{2}\right) \approx 0.6276$

32. (a) $\ln 27 \approx 3.2958$ (b) $\ln 7.39 \approx 2.0001$
    (c) $\ln 54.6 \approx 4.0000$

34. Since the point $\left(\frac{1}{2}, -1\right)$ is on the graph, we have $-1 = \log_a \left(\frac{1}{2}\right) \quad \Leftrightarrow \quad a^{-1} = \frac{1}{2} \quad \Leftrightarrow \quad a = 2$.
    Thus the function is $y = \log_2 x$.

36. Since the point $(9, 2)$ is on the graph, we have $2 = \log_a 9 \quad \Leftrightarrow \quad a^2 = 9 \quad \Leftrightarrow \quad a = 3$. Thus the
    function is $y = \log_3 x$.

38. V   40. IV   42. I

44.   The graph of $y = \log_3 x$ is obtained from the graph of $y = 3^x$
      by reflecting it about the line $y = x$.

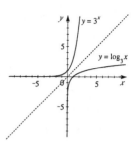

46. $f(x) = -\log_{10} x$
      The graph of f is obtained from the graph of $y = \log_{10} x$ by
      reflecting it about the x-axis.
      Domain: $(0, \infty)$
      Range: $(-\infty, \infty)$
      Vertical asymptote: $x = 0$

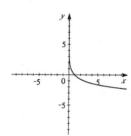

48. $g(x) = \ln(x + 2)$
      The graph of g is obtained from the graph of $y = \ln x$ by
      shifting it to the left 2 units.
      Domain: $(-2, \infty)$
      Range: $(-\infty, \infty)$
      Vertical asymptote: $x = -2$

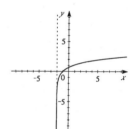

50. $y = \log_3(x - 1) - 2$
      The graph of $y = \log_3(x - 1) - 2$ is obtained from the graph
      of $y = \log_3 x$ by shifting it to the right 1 unit and then
      downward 2 units.
      Domain: $(1, \infty)$
      Range: $(-\infty, \infty)$
      Vertical asymptote: $x = 1$

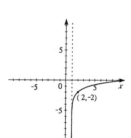

52. $y = 1 + \ln(-x)$
      The graph of $y = 1 + \ln(-x)$ is obtained from the graph of
      $y = \ln x$ by reflecting it about the y-axis and then shifting it
      upward 1 unit.
      Domain: $(-\infty, 0)$
      Range: $(-\infty, \infty)$
      Vertical asymptote: $x = 0$

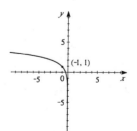

54. $y = \ln|x|$

Note that $y = \begin{cases} \ln x & x > 0 \\ \ln(-x) & x < 0 \end{cases}$.

The graph of $y = \ln|x|$ is obtained by reflecting the graph of
$y = \ln x$ about the x-axis.
Domain: $(-\infty, 0) \cup (0, \infty)$
Range: $(-\infty, \infty)$
Vertical asymptote: $x = 0$

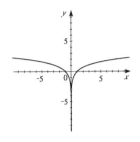

56. $f(x) = \log_2(10 - 3x)$. Then we must have $10 - 3x > 0$ $\Leftrightarrow$ $10 > 3x$ $\Leftrightarrow$ $\frac{10}{3} > x$, and so
the domain is $\left(-\infty, \frac{10}{3}\right)$.

58. $g(x) = \ln(x - x^2)$. Then we must have $x - x^2 > 0$ $\Leftrightarrow$ $x(1 - x) > 0$. Using the methods from
Chapter 3 with the endpoints 0 and 1, we have

Interval	$(-\infty, 0)$	$(0, 1)$	$(1, \infty)$
Sign of x	$-$	$+$	$+$
Sign of $1 - x$	$+$	$+$	$-$
Sign of $x(1 - x)$	$-$	$+$	$-$

Thus the domain is $(0, 1)$.

60. $h(x) = \sqrt{x - 2} - \log_5(10 - x)$. Then we must have $x - 2 \geq 0$ and $10 - x > 0$ $\Leftrightarrow$ $x \geq 2$ and
$10 > x$ $\Leftrightarrow$ $2 \leq x < 10$. So the domain is $[2, 10)$.

62. $y = \ln(x^2 - x) = \ln(x(x - 1))$
Domain: $(-\infty, 0) \cup (1, \infty)$
Vertical asymptotes: $x = 0$ and $x = 1$
No local extrema.

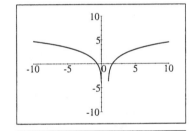

64. $y = x(\ln x)^2$
Domain: $(0, \infty)$
Vertical asymptote: none
Local minimum $y = 0$ at $x = 1$
Local maximum $y \approx 0.54$ at $x \approx 0.14$

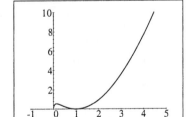

66. $y = x \log_{10}(x + 10)$
Domain: $(-10, \infty)$
Vertical asymptote: $x = -10$
Local minimum $y \approx -3.62$ at $x \approx -5.87$

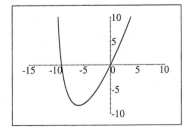

68. (a)

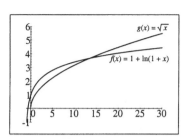

(b) From the graph, we see that the solution to the equation $\sqrt{x} = 1 + \ln(1 + x)$ is $x \approx 13.50$.

70. (a)

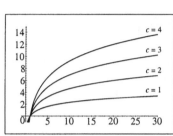

(b) As c increases, the graph of $f(x) = c\log(x)$ stretches vertically by a factor of c.

72. (a) $f(x) = \ln(\ln(\ln x))$. We must have $\ln(\ln x) > 0$ $\Leftrightarrow$ $\ln x > 1$ $\Leftrightarrow$ $x > e$. So the domain of f is (e, ∞).

(b) $y = \ln(\ln(\ln x))$ $\Leftrightarrow$ $e^y = \ln(\ln x)$ $\Leftrightarrow$ $e^{e^y} = \ln x$ $\Leftrightarrow$ $e^{e^{e^y}} = x$. Thus the inverse function is $f^{-1}(x) = e^{e^{e^x}}$.

74. (a) Since 2 feet = 24 inches, the height of the graph is $2^{24} = 1677216$ inches. Now, since there are 12 inches per foot and 5280 feet per mile, there are $12(5280) = 63360$ inches per mile. So the height of the graph is $\frac{1677216}{63360} \approx 264.8$, or about 265 miles.

(b) Since $\log_2(2^{24}) = 24$, we must be about 2^{24} inches ≈ 265 miles to the right of the origin before the height of the graph of $y = \log_2 x$ reaches 24 inches or 2 feet.

76. Notice that $\log_a x$ is increasing for $a > 1$. So we have $\log_4 17 > \log_4 16 = \log_4 4^2 = 2$. Also, we have $\log_5 24 < \log_5 25 = \log_5 5^2 = 2$. Thus, $\log_5 24 < 2 < \log_4 17$.

Exercises 6.4

2. $\log_5\left(\dfrac{x}{2}\right) = \log_5 x - \log_5 2$

4. $\ln(\pi x) = \ln \pi + \ln x$

6. $\log_6 \sqrt[4]{17} = \frac{1}{4}\log_6 17$

8. $\log_2(xy)^{10} = 10\log_2(xy) = 10(\log_2 x + \log_2 y)$

10. $\log_a\left(\dfrac{x^2}{yz^3}\right) = \log_a x^2 - \log_a(yz^3) = 2\log_a x - (\log_a y + 3\log_a z)$

12. $\ln\sqrt[3]{3r^2 s} = \frac{1}{3}\ln(3r^2 s) = \frac{1}{3}[\ln(3s) + 2\ln r] = \frac{1}{3}(\ln 3 + \ln s + 2\ln r)$

14. $\log\dfrac{a^2}{b^4\sqrt{c}} = \log a^2 - \log(b^4\sqrt{c}) = 2\log a - \left(4\log b + \dfrac{1}{2}\log c\right)$

16. $\log_5\sqrt{\dfrac{x-1}{x+1}} = \dfrac{1}{2}\log_5\left(\dfrac{x-1}{x+1}\right) = \dfrac{1}{2}\left[\log_5(x-1) - \log_5(x+1)\right]$

18. $\ln\dfrac{3x^2}{(x+1)^{10}} = \ln(3x^2) - \ln(x+1)^{10} = \ln 3 + 2\ln x - 10\ln(x+1)$

20. $\log\dfrac{x}{\sqrt[3]{1-x}} = \log x - \log\sqrt[3]{1-x} = \log x - \dfrac{1}{3}\log(1-x)$

22. $\log\sqrt{x\sqrt{y\sqrt{z}}} = \dfrac{1}{2}\log\left(x\sqrt{y\sqrt{z}}\right) = \dfrac{1}{2}\left(\log x + \log\sqrt{y\sqrt{z}}\right) = \dfrac{1}{2}\left[\log x + \dfrac{1}{2}\log\left(y\sqrt{z}\right)\right]$

     $= \dfrac{1}{2}\left[\log x + \dfrac{1}{2}\left(\log y + \dfrac{1}{2}\log z\right)\right] = \dfrac{1}{2}\log x + \dfrac{1}{4}\log y + \dfrac{1}{8}\log z$

24. $\log\dfrac{10^x}{x(x^2+1)(x^4+2)} = \log 10^x - \log[x(x^2+1)(x^4+2)]$

     $= x - [\log x + \log(x^2+1) + \log(x^4+2)]$

26. $\log_2 112 - \log_2 7 = \log_2\dfrac{112}{7} = \log_2 16 = \log_2 2^4 = 4$

28. $\log\sqrt{0.1} = \log 0.1^{1/2} = \frac{1}{2}\log 0.1 = \frac{1}{2}\log 10^{-1} = -\frac{1}{2}$

30. $\log_{12} 9 + \log_{12} 16 = \log_{12}(9\cdot 16) = \log_{12} 144 = \log_{12} 12^2 = 2$

32. $e^{3\ln 5} = (e^{\ln 5})^3 = 5^3 = 125$

34. $\log_2 8^{33} = \log_2(2^3)^{33} = \log_2 2^{99} = 99$

36. $\log 12 + \frac{1}{2}\log 7 - \log 2 = \log\left(12\sqrt{7}\right) - \log 2 = \log\dfrac{12\sqrt{7}}{2} = \log\left(6\sqrt{7}\right)$

38. $\log_5(x^2-1) - \log_5(x-1) = \log_5\dfrac{x^2-1}{x-1} = \log_5\dfrac{(x-1)(x+1)}{x-1} = \log_5(x+1)$

40. $\ln(a+b) + \ln(a-b) - 2\ln c = \ln[(a+b)(a-b)] - \ln(c^2) = \ln\dfrac{a^2 - b^2}{c^2}$

42. $2\left[\log_5 x + 2\log_5 y - 3\log_5 z\right] = 2\log_5\dfrac{xy^2}{z^3} = \log_5\left(\dfrac{xy^2}{z^3}\right)^2 = \log_5\dfrac{x^2 y^4}{z^6}$

44. $\log_a b + c\log_a d - r\log_a s = \log_a(bd^c) - \log_a s^r = \log_a\dfrac{bd^c}{s^r}$

46. $\log_5 2 = \dfrac{\log 2}{\log 5} \approx 0.430677$

48. $\log_6 92 = \dfrac{\log 92}{\log 6} \approx 2.523658$

50. $\log_6 532 = \dfrac{\log 532}{\log 6} \approx 3.\overline{5}03061$

52. $\log_{12} 2.5 = \dfrac{\log 2.5}{\log 12} \approx 0.368743$

54.

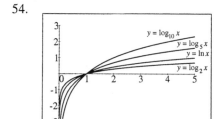

Note that $\log_c x = \left(\frac{1}{\ln c}\right)\ln x$ (by the change of base formula). So the graph of $y = \log_c x$ is obtained from the graph of $y = \ln x$ by either shrinking or stretching vertically by a factor of $\dfrac{1}{\ln c}$ depending on whether $\ln c > 1$ or $\ln c < 1$ (respectively).

56. $(\log_2 5)(\log_5 7) = \dfrac{\log 5}{\log 2} \cdot \dfrac{\log 7}{\log 5} = \dfrac{\log 7}{\log 2} = \log_2 7$

58. (a) False; $\log\left(\dfrac{x}{y}\right) = \log x - \log y \neq \dfrac{\log x}{\log y}$

(b) False; $\log_2 x - \log_2 y = \log_2\left(\dfrac{x}{y}\right) \neq \log_2(x - y)$

(c) True; the equation is an identity: $\log_5\dfrac{a}{b^2} = \log_5 a - \log_5 b^2 = \log_5 a - 2\log_5 b$.

(d) True; the equation is an identity: $\log 2^z = z\log 2$.

(e) False; $\log P + \log Q = \log(PQ) \neq (\log P)(\log Q)$.

(f) False; $\log a - \log b = \log\left(\dfrac{a}{b}\right) \neq \dfrac{\log a}{\log b}$.

(g) False; $x\log_2 7 = \log_2 7^x \neq (\log_2 7)^x$.

(h) True; the equation is an identity. $\log_a a^a = a\log_a a = a \cdot 1 = a$.

(i) False; $\log(x - y) \neq \dfrac{\log x}{\log y}$. For example, $0 = \log(3 - 2) \neq \dfrac{\log 3}{\log 2}$.

(j) True; the equation is an identity: $-\ln\left(\frac{1}{A}\right) = -\ln A^{-1} = -1(-\ln A) = \ln A$.

60. Let $f(x) = x^2$. Then $f(2x) = (2x)^2 = 4x^2 = 4f(x)$. Now the graph of $f(2x)$ is the same as the graph of f shrunk horizontally by a factor of $\frac{1}{2}$, whereas the graph of $4f(x)$ is the same as the graph of $f(x)$ stretched vertically by a factor of 4.

Let $g(x) = e^x$. Then $g(x + 2) = e^{x+2} = e^2 e^x = e^2 g(x)$. This shows that a horizontal shift of 2 units to the right is the same as a vertical stretch by a factor of e^2.

Let $h(x) = \ln x$. Then $h(2x) = \ln 2x = \ln 2 + \ln x = \ln 2 + h(x)$. This shows that a horizontal shrinking by a factor of $\frac{1}{2}$ is the same as a vertical shift by an amount $\ln 2$ upward.

Exercises 6.5

2. $10^{-x} = 2 \quad \Leftrightarrow \quad \log 10^{-x} = \log 2 \quad \Leftrightarrow \quad -x = \log 2 \quad \Leftrightarrow \quad x = -\log 2 \approx -0.3010$

4. $3^{2x-1} = 5 \quad \Leftrightarrow \quad \log 3^{2x-1} = \log 5 \quad \Leftrightarrow \quad (2x-1)\log 3 = \log 5 \quad \Leftrightarrow \quad 2x - 1 = \frac{\log 5}{\log 3} \quad \Leftrightarrow$

    $2x = 1 + \frac{\log 5}{\log 3} \quad \Leftrightarrow \quad x = \frac{1}{2}\left(1 + \frac{\log 5}{\log 3}\right) \approx 1.2325$

6. $2\,e^{12x} = 17 \quad \Leftrightarrow \quad e^{12x} = \frac{17}{2} \quad \Leftrightarrow \quad 12x = \ln\left(\frac{17}{2}\right) \quad \Leftrightarrow \quad x = \frac{1}{12}\left[\ln\left(\frac{17}{2}\right)\right] \approx 0.1783$

8. $4(1 + 10^{5x}) = 9 \quad \Leftrightarrow \quad 1 + 10^{5x} = \frac{9}{4} \quad \Leftrightarrow \quad 10^{5x} = \frac{5}{4} \quad \Leftrightarrow \quad 5x = \log\left(\frac{5}{4}\right) \quad \Leftrightarrow$

    $x = \frac{1}{5}[\log 5 - \log 4] \approx 0.0194.$

10. $2^{3x} = 34 \quad \Leftrightarrow \quad \log 2^{3x} = \log 34 \quad \Leftrightarrow \quad 3x \log 2 = \log 34 \quad \Leftrightarrow \quad x = \frac{\log 34}{3\log 2} \approx 1.6958$

12. $3^{x/14} = 0.1 \quad \Leftrightarrow \quad \log 3^{x/14} = \log 0.1 \quad \Leftrightarrow \quad \left(\frac{x}{14}\right)\log 3 = \log 0.1 \quad \Leftrightarrow$

    $x = \frac{14 \log 0.1}{\log 3} \approx -29.3426$

14. $e^{3-5x} = 16 \quad \Leftrightarrow \quad 3 - 5x = \ln 16 \quad \Leftrightarrow \quad -5x = \ln 16 - 3 \quad \Leftrightarrow \quad x = -\frac{1}{5}(\ln 16 - 3) \approx 0.0455$

16. $\left(\frac{1}{4}\right)^x = 75 \quad \Leftrightarrow \quad 4^{-x} = 75 \quad \Leftrightarrow \quad \log 4^{-x} = \log 75 \quad \Leftrightarrow \quad (-x)(\log 4) = \log 75 \quad \Leftrightarrow$

    $-x = \frac{\log 75}{\log 4} \quad \Leftrightarrow \quad x = -\frac{\log 75}{\log 4} \approx -3.1144$

18. $10^{1-x} = 6^x \quad \Leftrightarrow \quad \log 10^{1-x} = \log 6^x \quad \Leftrightarrow \quad 1 - x = x(\log 6) \quad \Leftrightarrow \quad 1 = x(\log 6) + x \quad \Leftrightarrow$

    $1 = x(\log 6 + 1) \quad \Leftrightarrow \quad x = \frac{1}{\log 6 + 1} \approx 0.5624$

20. $7^{x/2} = 5^{1-x} \quad \Leftrightarrow \quad \log 7^{x/2} = \log 5^{1-x} \quad \Leftrightarrow \quad \left(\frac{x}{2}\right)\log 7 = (1-x)\log 5 \quad \Leftrightarrow$

    $\left(\frac{x}{2}\right)\log 7 = \log 5 - x\log 5 \quad \Leftrightarrow \quad \left(\frac{x}{2}\right)\log 7 + x\log 5 = \log 5 \quad \Leftrightarrow \quad x\left(\frac{1}{2}\log 7 + \log 5\right) = \log 5$

    $\Leftrightarrow \quad x = \frac{\log 5}{\frac{1}{2}\log 7 + \log 5} \approx 0.6232$

22. $\frac{10}{1 + e^{-x}} = 2 \quad \Leftrightarrow \quad 10 = 2 + 2e^{-x} \quad \Leftrightarrow \quad 8 = 2e^{-x} \quad \Leftrightarrow \quad 4 = e^{-x} \quad \Leftrightarrow \quad \ln 4 = -x \quad \Leftrightarrow$

    $x = -\ln 4 \approx -1.3863$

24. $(1.00625)^{12t} = 2 \quad \Leftrightarrow \quad \log 1.00625^{12t} = \log 2 \quad \Leftrightarrow \quad 12t \log 1.00625 = \log 2 \quad \Leftrightarrow$

    $t = \frac{\log 2}{12 \log 1.00625} \approx 9.2708$

26. $x^2 10^x - x 10^x = 2(10^x) \quad \Leftrightarrow \quad x^2 10^x - x 10^x - 2(10^x) = 0 \quad \Leftrightarrow \quad 10^x(x^2 - x - 2) = 0 \quad \Rightarrow$

    $10^x = 0$ (never) or $x^2 - x - 2 = 0$. If $x^2 - x - 2 = 0$, then $(x-2)(x+1) = 0 \quad \Rightarrow \quad x = 2, -1$.

    So the only solutions are $x = 2, -1$.

28. $x^2 e^x + x e^x - e^x = 0 \quad \Leftrightarrow \quad e^x(x^2 + x - 1) = 0 \quad \Rightarrow \quad e^x = 0$ (impossible) or $x^2 + x - 1 = 0$.

    If $x^2 + x - 1 = 0$, then $x = \frac{-1 \pm \sqrt{5}}{2}$. So the solutions are $x = \frac{-1 \pm \sqrt{5}}{2}$.

30. $e^{2x} - e^x - 6 = 0 \quad \Leftrightarrow \quad (e^x - 3)(e^x + 2) = 0 \quad \Rightarrow \quad e^x + 2 = 0$ (impossible) or $e^x - 3 = 0$. If

    $e^x - 3 = 0$, then $e^x = 3 \quad \Leftrightarrow \quad x = \ln 3 \approx 1.0986$. So the only solution is $x \approx 1.0986$.

32. $e^x - 12e^{-x} - 1 = 0 \quad \Leftrightarrow \quad e^x - 1 - 12e^{-x} = 0 \quad \Leftrightarrow \quad e^x(e^x - 1 - 12e^{-x}) = 0 \cdot e^x \quad \Leftrightarrow$

    $e^{2x} - e^x - 12 = 0 \quad \Leftrightarrow \quad (e^x - 4)(e^x + 3) = 0 \quad \Rightarrow \quad e^x + 3 = 0$ (impossible) or $e^x - 4 = 0$.

    If $e^x - 4 = 0$, then $e^x = 4 \quad \Leftrightarrow \quad x = \ln 4 \approx 1.3863$. So the only solution is $x \approx 1.3863$.

34. $\ln(2 + x) = 1 \quad \Leftrightarrow \quad 2 + x = e^1 \quad \Leftrightarrow \quad x = e - 2 \approx 0.7183$

36. $\log(x - 4) = 3 \quad \Leftrightarrow \quad x - 4 = 10^3 = 1000 \quad \Leftrightarrow \quad x = 1004$

38. $\log_3(2 - x) = 3 \quad \Leftrightarrow \quad 2 - x = 3^3 = 27 \quad \Leftrightarrow \quad -x = 25 \quad \Leftrightarrow \quad x = -25$

40. $\log_2(x^2 - x - 2) = 2 \quad \Leftrightarrow \quad x^2 - x - 2 = 2^2 = 4 \quad \Leftrightarrow \quad x^2 - x - 6 = 0 \quad \Leftrightarrow$
     $(x - 3)(x + 2) = 0 \quad \Leftrightarrow \quad x = 3$ or $x = -2$. Thus the solutions are $x = 3$ and $x = -2$.

42. $2\log x = \log 2 + \log(3x - 4) \quad \Leftrightarrow \quad \log(x^2) = \log(6x - 8) \quad \Leftrightarrow \quad x^2 = 6x - 8 \quad \Leftrightarrow$
     $x^2 - 6x + 8 = 0 \quad \Leftrightarrow \quad (x - 4)(x - 2) = 0 \quad \Leftrightarrow \quad x = 4$ or $x = 2$. Thus the solutions are $x = 4$
     and $x = 2$.

44. $\log_5 x + \log_5(x + 1) = \log_5 20 \quad \Leftrightarrow \quad \log_5(x^2 + x) = \log_5 20 \quad \Leftrightarrow \quad x^2 + x = 20 \quad \Leftrightarrow$
     $x^2 + x - 20 = 0 \quad \Leftrightarrow \quad (x + 5)(x - 4) = 0 \quad \Leftrightarrow \quad x = -5$ or $x = 4$. Since $\log_5(-5)$ is
     undefined, the only solution is $x = 4$.

46. $\log x + \log(x - 3) = 1 \quad \Leftrightarrow \quad \log[x(x - 3)] = 1 \quad \Leftrightarrow \quad x^2 - 3x = 10 \quad \Leftrightarrow \quad x^2 - 3x - 10 = 0$
     $\Leftrightarrow \quad (x + 2)(x - 5) = 0 \quad \Leftrightarrow \quad x = -2$ or $x = 5$. Since $\log(-2)$ is undefined, the only solution
     is $x = 5$.

48. $\ln(x - 1) + \ln(x + 2) = 1 \quad \Leftrightarrow \quad \ln[(x - 1)(x + 2)] = 1 \quad \Leftrightarrow \quad x^2 + x - 2 = e \quad \Leftrightarrow$
     $x^2 + x - (2 + e) = 0 \quad \Rightarrow \quad x = \frac{-1 \pm \sqrt{1 + 4(2 + e)}}{2} = \frac{-1 \pm \sqrt{9 + 4e}}{2}$. Since $x - 1 < 0$ when
     $x = \frac{-1 - \sqrt{9 + 4e}}{2}$, the only solution is $x = \frac{-1 + \sqrt{9 + 4e}}{2} \approx 1.7290$

50. $(\log x)^3 = 3\log x \quad \Leftrightarrow \quad (\log x)^3 - 3\log x = 0 \quad \Leftrightarrow \quad (\log x)((\log x)^2 - 3) \quad \Leftrightarrow \quad (\log x) = 0$
     or $(\log x)^2 - 3 = 0$. Now $\log x = 0 \quad \Leftrightarrow \quad x = 1$. Also $(\log x)^2 - 3 = 0 \quad \Leftrightarrow \quad (\log x)^2 = 3$
     $\Leftrightarrow \quad \log x = \pm \sqrt{3} \quad \Leftrightarrow \quad x = 10^{\pm \sqrt{3}}$, so $x = 10^{\sqrt{3}} \approx 53.9574$ or $x = 10^{-\sqrt{3}} \approx 0.0185$. Thus
     the solutions to the equation are $x = 1$, $x = 10^{\sqrt{3}} \approx 53.9574$ and $x = 10^{-\sqrt{3}} \approx 0.0185$.

52. $\log_2(\log_3 x) = 4 \quad \Leftrightarrow \quad \log_3 x = 2^4 = 16 \quad \Leftrightarrow \quad x = 3^{16} = 43046721$

54. We want to solve for t in the equation $80(e^{-0.2t} - 1) = -70$ (when motion is downwards, the
     velocity is negative). Then $80(e^{-0.2t} - 1) = -70 \quad \Leftrightarrow \quad e^{-0.2t} - 1 = -\frac{7}{8} \quad \Leftrightarrow \quad e^{-0.2t} = \frac{1}{8} \quad \Leftrightarrow$
     $-0.2t = \ln\left(\frac{1}{8}\right) \quad \Leftrightarrow \quad t = \frac{\ln\left(\frac{1}{8}\right)}{-0.2} \approx 10.4$ seconds. Thus the velocity is 70 ft/sec after about 10
     seconds.

56. (a) $P = M - Ce^{-kt} \quad \Leftrightarrow \quad Ce^{-kt} = M - P \quad \Leftrightarrow \quad e^{-kt} = \frac{M - P}{C} \quad \Leftrightarrow \quad -kt = \ln\left(\frac{M - P}{C}\right)$
          $\Leftrightarrow \quad t = -\frac{1}{k}\ln\left(\frac{M - P}{C}\right)$.

     (b) $P(t) = 20 - 14e^{-0.024t}$. Substituting $M = 20$, $C = 14$, $k = 0.024$, and $P = 12$ into
          $t = -\frac{1}{k}\ln\left(\frac{M - P}{C}\right)$, we have $t = -\frac{1}{0.024}\ln\left(\frac{20 - 12}{14}\right) \approx 23.32$. So it takes about 23 months.

     (c)
     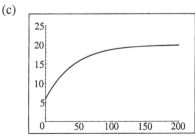

58. $\log x = x^2 - 2$ $\Leftrightarrow$ $\log x - x^2 + 2 = 0$. Let
     $f(x) = \log x - x^2 + 2$. We need to solve the equation
     $f(x) = 0$. From the graph of f, we get $x \approx 0.01$ or $x \approx 1.47$.

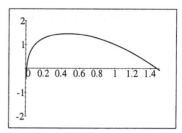

60. $x = \ln(4 - x^2)$ $\Leftrightarrow$ $x - \ln(4 - x^2) = 0$. Let
     $f(x) = x - \ln(4 - x^2)$. We need to solve the equation
     $f(x) = 0$. From the graph of f, we get $x \approx -1.96$ or $x \approx 1.06$.

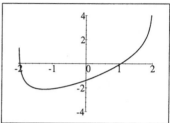

62. $2^{-x} = x - 1$ $\Leftrightarrow$ $2^{-x} - x + 1 = 0$. Let
     $f(x) = 2^{-x} - x + 1$. We need to solve the equation $f(x) = 0$.
     From the graph of f, we get $x \approx 1.38$.

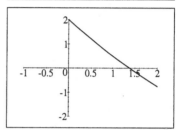

64. $e^{x^2} - 2 = x^3 - x$ $\Leftrightarrow$ $e^{x^2} - 2 - x^3 + x = 0$. Let
     $f(x) = e^{x^2} - 2 - x^3 + x$. We need to solve the equation
     $f(x) = 0$. From the graph of f, we get $x \approx -0.89$ or $x \approx 0.71$.

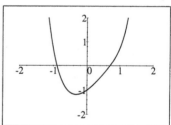

66. $3 \le \log_2 x \le 4$ $\Leftrightarrow$ $2^3 \le x \le 2^4$ $\Leftrightarrow$ $8 \le x \le 16$.

68. $x^2 e^x - 2 e^x < 0$ $\Leftrightarrow$ $e^x(x^2 - 2) < 0$ $\Leftrightarrow$ $e^x(x - \sqrt{2})(x + \sqrt{2}) < 0$. We use the methods
     of Chapter 3 with the endpoints $-\sqrt{2}$ and $\sqrt{2}$ and note that $e^x > 0$ for all x. We have

Interval	$(-\infty, -\sqrt{2})$	$(-\sqrt{2}, \sqrt{2})$	$(\sqrt{2}, \infty)$
Sign of e^x	$+$	$+$	$+$
Sign of $(x - \sqrt{2})$	$-$	$-$	$+$
Sign of $(x + \sqrt{2})$	$-$	$+$	$+$
Sign of $e^x(x - \sqrt{2})(x + \sqrt{2})$	$+$	$-$	$+$

Thus $-\sqrt{2} < x < \sqrt{2}$.

70. Using the Change of Base Formula, we have $\log_4 x = \frac{\log_2 x}{\log_2 4} = \frac{1}{2}\log_2 x$, and $\log_8 x = \frac{\log_2 x}{\log_2 8} = \frac{1}{3}\log_2 x$.
     So $\log_2 x + \log_4 x + \log_8 x = 11 \quad\Leftrightarrow\quad \log_2 x + \frac{1}{2}\log_2 x + \frac{1}{3}\log_2 x = 11 \quad\Leftrightarrow\quad \frac{11}{6}\log_2 x = 11$
     $\Leftrightarrow \quad \log_2 x = 6 \quad\Leftrightarrow\quad x = 2^6 = 64$.

72. Since $9^1 = 9$, $9^2 = 81$, and $9^3 = 729$, the solution of $9^x = 20$ must be between 1 and 2 (because 20 is between 9 and 81), whereas the solution to $9^x = 100$ must be between 2 and 3 (because 100 is between 81 and 729).

Exercises 6.6

2. (a) $A(2) = 6500\,e^{0.06(2)} \approx \$7328.73$

   (b) $8000 = 6500\,e^{0.06t} \quad \Leftrightarrow \quad \frac{16}{13} = e^{0.06t} \quad \Leftrightarrow \quad \ln\!\left(\frac{16}{13}\right) = 0.06t \quad \Leftrightarrow \quad t = \frac{1}{0.06}\ln\!\left(\frac{16}{13}\right) \approx 3.46$.
   So the investment doubles in about $3\frac{1}{2}$ years.

4. $5000 = 4000\!\left(1 + \frac{0.0975}{2}\right)^{2t} \quad \Leftrightarrow \quad 1.25 = (1.04875)^{2t} \quad \Leftrightarrow$

   $\log 1.25 = 2t \log 1.04875 \quad \Leftrightarrow \quad t = \frac{\log 1.25}{2 \log 1.04875} \approx 2.344$. So it takes about $2\frac{1}{3}$ years to save $\$5000$.

6. $1435.77 = 1000\!\left(1 + \frac{r}{2}\right)^{2(4)} \quad \Leftrightarrow \quad 1.43577 = \left(1 + \frac{r}{2}\right)^{8} \quad \Leftrightarrow \quad 1 + \frac{r}{2} = \sqrt[8]{1.43577} \quad \Leftrightarrow$

   $\frac{r}{2} = \sqrt[8]{1.43577} - 1 \quad \Leftrightarrow \quad r = 2\left(\sqrt[8]{1.43577} - 1\right) \approx 0.0925$. Thus the rate was about 9.25%.

8. $r_{\text{APR}} = e^{r} - 1$. Here $r = 0.05.5$ so $r\text{APR} = e^{0.055} - 1 \approx 1.0565 - 1 = 0.565$. So the annual percentage yield is about 5.65%.

10. (a) The relative growth rate is $0.012 = 1.2\%$.
    (d)

    (b) $n(5) = 12\,e^{0.012(5)} = 12\,e^{0.06} \approx 12.74$ million fish.

    (c) $30 = 12\,e^{0.012t} \quad \Leftrightarrow \quad 2.5 = e^{0.012t} \quad \Leftrightarrow$
    $0.012t = \ln 2.5 \quad \Leftrightarrow \quad t = \frac{\ln 2.5}{0.012} \approx 76.36$.
    Thus the fish population reaches 30 million after about 76 years.

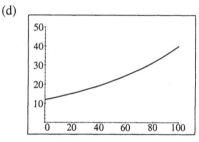

12. (a) $n(t) = n_0 e^{rt}$ with $n_0 = 85$ and $r = 0.18$. Thus $n(t) = 85\,e^{0.18t}$.

    (b) $n(3) = 85\,e^{0.18(3)} \approx 146$ frogs.

    (c) $600 = 85\,e^{0.18t} \quad \Leftrightarrow \quad \frac{120}{17} = e^{0.18t} \quad \Leftrightarrow \quad 0.18t = \ln\!\left(\frac{120}{17}\right) \quad \Leftrightarrow \quad t = \frac{1}{0.18}\ln\!\left(\frac{120}{17}\right) \approx 10.86$.
    So the population will reach 600 frogs in about 11 years.

14. (a) Since the population grows exponentially, the population is represented by $n(t) = n_0\,e^{rt}$, with $n_0 = 1500$ and $n(30) = 3000$. Solving for r, we have $3000 = 1500\,e^{30r} \quad \Leftrightarrow \quad 2 = e^{30r}$
    $\Leftrightarrow \quad 30r = \ln 2 \quad \Leftrightarrow \quad r = \frac{\ln 2}{30} \approx 0.023$. Thus $n(t) = 1500\,e^{0.023t}$.

    (b) Since 2 hours is 120 minutes, the number of bacteria in 2 hours is
    $n(120) = 1500\,e^{0.023(120)} \approx 24000$.

    (c) We need to solve $4000 = 1500\,e^{0.023t}$ for t. So $4000 = 1500\,e^{0.023t} \quad \Leftrightarrow \quad \frac{8}{3} = e^{0.023t} \quad \Leftrightarrow$
    $0.023t = \ln \frac{8}{3} \quad \Leftrightarrow \quad t = \frac{\ln(8/3)}{0.023} \approx 42.6$. Thus the bacteria population will reach 4000 in about 43 minutes.

16. (a) Using $n(t) = n_0\,e^{rt}$ with $n(2) = 400$ and $n(6) = 25{,}600$, we have $n_0\,e^{2r} = 400$ and
    $n_0\,e^{6r} = 25600$. Dividing the second equation by the first gives $\dfrac{n_0\,e^{6r}}{n_0\,e^{2r}} = \dfrac{25600}{400} = 64 \quad \Leftrightarrow$
    $e^{4r} = 64 \quad \Leftrightarrow \quad 4r = \ln 64 \quad \Leftrightarrow \quad r = \frac{1}{4}\ln 64 \approx 1.04$. Thus the relative rate of growth is about 104%.

(b) Since $r = \frac{1}{4}\ln 64 = \frac{1}{2}\ln 8$, we have from part (a) $n(t) = n_0\, e^{\left(\frac{1}{2}\ln 8\right)t}$. Since $n(2) = 400$, we have $400 = n_0\, e^{\ln 8}$ $\Leftrightarrow$ $n_0 = \frac{400}{e^{\ln 8}} = \frac{400}{8} = 50$. So the initial size of the culture was 50.

(c) Substituting $n_0 = 50$ and $r = 1.04$, we have $n(t) = n_0\, e^{rt} = 50\, e^{1.04t}$.

(d) $n(4.5) = 50e^{1.04(4.5)} = 50e^{4.68} \approx 5388.5$, so the size after 4.5 hours is approximately 5400.

(e) $n(t) = 50000 = 50e^{1.04t}$ $\Leftrightarrow$ $e^{1.04t} = 1000$ $\Leftrightarrow$ $1.04t = \ln 1000$ $\Leftrightarrow$

$t = \frac{\ln 1000}{1.04} \approx 6.64$. Hence the population will reach 50,000 after roughly $6\frac{2}{3}$ hours.

18. (a) Calculating dates relative to 1950 gives $n_0 = 10{,}586{,}223$ and $n(30) = 23{,}668{,}562$. Then $n(30) = 10586223e^{30r} = 23668562$ $\Leftrightarrow$ $e^{30r} = \frac{23668562}{10586223} \approx 2.2358$ $\Leftrightarrow$ $30r = \ln 2.2358$ $\Leftrightarrow$ $r = \frac{1}{30}\ln 2.2358 \approx 0.0268$. Thus $n(t) = 10586223\, e^{0.0268\,t}$.

(b) $2(10586223) = 10586223\, e^{0.0268\,t}$ $\Leftrightarrow$ $2 = e^{0.0268\,t}$ $\Leftrightarrow$ $\ln 2 = 0.0268\,t$ $\Leftrightarrow$ $t = \frac{\ln 2}{0.0268} \approx 25.86$. So the population doubles in about 26 years.

(c) $t = 2000 - 1950 = 50$; $n(50) \approx 10586223\, e^{0.0268(50)} \approx 40{,}429{,}246$ and so the population in the year 2000 will be approximately 40,429,000.

20. From the formula for radioactive decay, we have $m(t) = m_0\, e^{-rt}$, where $r = \frac{\ln 2}{h}$.

(a) We have $m_0 = 22$ and $h = 1600$, so $r = \frac{\ln 2}{1600} \approx 0.000433$ and the amount after t years is given by $m(t) = 22\, e^{-0.000433t}$.

(b) $m(4000) = 22\, e^{-0.000433(4000)} \approx 3.89$, so the amount after 4000 years is about 4 mg.

(c) We have to solve for t in the equation $18 = 22\, e^{-0.000433t}$. This gives $18 = 22\, e^{-0.000433t}$

$\Leftrightarrow$ $\frac{9}{11} = e^{-0.000433t}$ $\Leftrightarrow$ $-0.000433t = \ln\left(\frac{9}{11}\right)$ $\Leftrightarrow$ $t = \frac{\ln\left(\frac{9}{11}\right)}{-0.000433} \approx 463.4$, so it takes about 463 years.

22. (a) $m(60) = 40\, e^{-0.0277(60)} \approx 7.59$, so the mass remaining after 60 days is about 8 g.

(b) $10 = 40\, e^{-0.0277t}$ $\Leftrightarrow$ $0.25 = e^{-0.0277t}$ $\Leftrightarrow$ $\ln 0.25 = -0.0277t$ $\Leftrightarrow$ $t = -\frac{\ln 0.25}{0.0277} \approx 50.05$, so it takes about 50 days.

(c) We need to solve for t in the equation $20 = 40\, e^{-0.0277t}$. We have $20 = 40\, e^{-0.0277t}$ $\Leftrightarrow$

$e^{-0.277t} = \frac{1}{2}$ $\Leftrightarrow$ $-0.0277t = \ln\frac{1}{2}$ $\Leftrightarrow$ $t = \frac{\ln\frac{1}{2}}{-0.0277} \approx 25.02$. Thus the half-life of thorium-234 is about 25 days.

24. From the formula for radioactive decay, we have $m(t) = m_0\, e^{-rt}$, where $r = \frac{\ln 2}{h}$. Since $h = 30$, we have $r = \frac{\ln 2}{30} \approx 0.0231$ and $m(t) = m_0 e^{-0.0231t}$. In this exercise we have to solve for t in the equation $0.05\, m_0 = m_0 e^{-0.0231t}$ $\Leftrightarrow$ $e^{-0.0231t} = 0.05$ $\Leftrightarrow$ $-0.0231t = \ln 0.05$ $\Leftrightarrow$ $t = \frac{\ln 0.05}{-0.0231} \approx 129.7$. So it will take about 130 s.

26. From the formula for radioactive decay, we have $m(t) = m_0\, e^{-rt}$, where $r = \frac{\ln 2}{h}$. In other words, $m(t) = m_0\, e^{-\frac{\ln 2}{h}\,t}$.

(a) Using $m(3) = 0.58\, m_0$, we have to solve for h in the equation $0.58\, m_0 = m(3) = m_0\, e^{-\frac{\ln 2}{h}3}$.

Then $0.58\, m_0 = m_0\, e^{-\frac{3\ln 2}{h}}$ $\Leftrightarrow$ $e^{-\frac{3\ln 2}{h}} = 0.58$ $\Leftrightarrow$ $-\frac{3\ln 2}{h} = \ln 0.58$ $\Leftrightarrow$

$h = -\frac{3\ln 2}{\ln 0.58} \approx 3.82$ days. Thus the half-life of Radon-222 is about 3.82 days.

(b) Here we have to solve for t in the equation $0.2\, m_0 = m_0\, e^{-\frac{\ln 2}{3.82}t}$. So we have

$0.2\, m_0 = m_0\, e^{-\frac{\ln 2}{3.82}t}$ $\Leftrightarrow$ $0.2 = e^{-\frac{\ln 2}{3.82}t}$ $\Leftrightarrow$ $-\frac{\ln 2}{3.82}t = \ln 0.2$ $\Leftrightarrow$

$t = -\frac{3.82 \ln 0.2}{\ln 2} \approx 8.87$. So it takes roughly 9 days for a sample of Radon-222 to decay to 20% of its original mass.

28. From the formula for radioactive decay, we have $m(t) = m_0\,e^{-rt}$ where $r = \frac{\ln 2}{h}$. Since $h = 5730$, $r = \frac{\ln 2}{5730} \approx 0.000121$ and $m(t) = m_0\,e^{-0.000121\,t}$. We need to solve for t in the equation
$0.59\,m_0 = m_0\,e^{-0.000121\,t} \quad \Leftrightarrow \quad e^{-0.000121\,t} = 0.59 \quad \Leftrightarrow \quad -0.000121\,t = \ln 0.59 \quad \Leftrightarrow$
$t = \frac{\ln 0.59}{-0.000121} \approx 4360.6$. So it will take about 4360 years.

30. (a) We use Newton's Law of Cooling: $T(t) = T_s + D_0\,e^{-kt}$ with $k = 0.1947$, $T_s = 60$, and $D_0 = 98.6 - 60 = 38.6$. So $T(t) = 60 + 38.6\,e^{-0.1947t}$.

     (b) Solve $T(t) = 72$. So $72 = 60 + 38.6\,e^{-0.1947t} \quad \Leftrightarrow \quad 38.6\,e^{-0.1947t} = 12 \quad \Leftrightarrow$
     $e^{-0.1947t} = \frac{12}{38.6} \quad \Leftrightarrow \quad -0.1947\,t = \ln\left(\frac{12}{38.6}\right) \quad \Leftrightarrow \quad t = -\frac{1}{0.1947}\ln\left(\frac{12}{38.6}\right) \approx 6.00$, and the time of death was about 6 hours ago.

32. We use Newton's Law of Cooling: $T(t) = T_s + D_0\,e^{-kt}$, with $T_s = 20$ and $D_0 = 100 - 20 = 80$. So $T(t) = 20 + 80\,e^{-kt}$. Since $T(15) = 75$, we have $20 + 80\,e^{-15k} = 75 \quad \Leftrightarrow$
$80\,e^{-15k} = 55 \quad \Leftrightarrow \quad e^{-15k} = \frac{11}{16} \quad \Leftrightarrow \quad -15k = \ln\left(\frac{11}{16}\right)$
$\Leftrightarrow \quad k = -\frac{1}{15}\ln\left(\frac{11}{16}\right)$. Thus $T(25) = 20 + 80$
$e^{(25/15)\cdot\ln(11/16)} \approx 62.8$, and so the temperature after another 10 min is 63°C. The function $T(t) = 20 + 80\,e^{(1/15)\cdot\ln(11/16)t}$ is shown in the viewing rectangle $[0, 30]$ by $[50, 100]$.

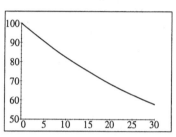

34. $\text{pH} = -\log\,[\text{H}^+] = -\log(3.1 \times 10^{-8}) \approx 7.5$ and the substance is basic.

36. (a) $\text{pH} = -\log\,[\text{H}^+] = 4.6 \quad \Leftrightarrow \quad [\text{H}^+] = 10^{-4.6}\ \text{M} \approx 2.5 \times 10^{-5}\ \text{M}$

     (b) $\text{pH} = -\log\,[\text{H}^+] = 7.3 \quad \Leftrightarrow \quad [\text{H}^+] = 10^{-7.3}\ \text{M} \approx 5.0 \times 10^{-8}\ \text{M}$

38. $2.8 \le \text{pH} \le 3.8 \quad \Leftrightarrow \quad -2.8 \ge -\text{pH} \ge -3.8 \quad \Leftrightarrow \quad 10^{-2.8} \ge 10^{-\text{pH}} \ge 10^{-3.8} \quad \Leftrightarrow$
$1.58 \times 10^{-3} \ge [\text{H}^+] \ge 1.58 \times 10^{-4}$. The range of $[\text{H}^+]$ is 1.58×10^{-4} to 1.58×10^{-3}.

40. Let the subscript SF represent the San Francisco earthquake and J the Japan earthquake. Then we have $M_{\text{SF}} = \log\left(\frac{I_{\text{SF}}}{S}\right) = 8.3 \quad \Leftrightarrow \quad I_{\text{SF}} = S \cdot 10^{8.3}$ and $M_{\text{J}} = \log\left(\frac{I_{\text{J}}}{S}\right) = 4.9 \quad \Leftrightarrow \quad I_{\text{J}} = S \cdot 10^{4.9}$. So $\frac{I_{\text{SF}}}{I_{\text{J}}} = \frac{10^{8.3}}{10^{4.9}} = 10^{3.4} \approx 2511.9$, and so the San Francisco earthquake was 2500 times more intense than the Japan earthquake.

42. Let the subscript N represent the Northridge, California earthquake and K the Kobe, Japan earthquake. Then $M_{\text{N}} = \log\left(\frac{I_{\text{N}}}{S}\right) = 6.8 \quad \Leftrightarrow \quad I_{\text{N}} = S \cdot 10^{6.8}$ and $M_{\text{K}} = \log\left(\frac{I_{\text{K}}}{S}\right) = 7.2 \quad \Leftrightarrow$
$I_{\text{K}} = S \cdot 10^{7.2}$. So $\frac{I_{\text{K}}}{I_{\text{N}}} = \frac{10^{7.2}}{10^{6.8}} = 10^{0.4} \approx 2.51$, and so the Kobe, Japan earthquake was 2.5 times more intense than the Northridge, California earthquake.

44. $\beta = 10\log\left(\frac{I}{I_0}\right) = 10\log\left(\frac{2.0 \times 10^{-5}}{1.0 \times 10^{-12}}\right) = 10\log(2 \times 10^7) = 10(\log 2 + \log 10^7) = 10(\log 2 + 7)$
≈ 73. Therefore the intensity level was 73 dB.

46. Let the subscripts PM represent the power mower and RC the rock concert. Then
$106 = 10\log\left(\frac{I_{\text{PM}}}{10^{-12}}\right) \quad \Leftrightarrow \quad \log(I_{\text{PM}} \cdot 10^{12}) = 10.6 \quad \Leftrightarrow \quad I_{\text{PM}} \cdot 10^{12} = 10^{10.6}$. Also
$120 = 10\log\left(\frac{I_{\text{RC}}}{10^{-12}}\right) \quad \Leftrightarrow \quad \log(I_{\text{RC}} \cdot 10^{12}) = 12.0 \quad \Leftrightarrow \quad I_{\text{RC}} \cdot 10^{12} = 10^{12.0}$. So
$\frac{I_{\text{RC}}}{I_{\text{PM}}} = \frac{10^{12}}{10^{10.6}} = 10^{1.4} \approx 25.12$, and so the ratio of intensity is roughly 25.

Review Exercises for Chapter 6

2. $g(x) = 3^{x-2}$.
   Domain: $(-\infty, \infty)$
   Range: $(0, \infty)$
   Asymptote: $y = 0$.

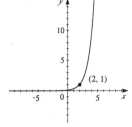

4. $y = 1 + 5^{-x}$.
   Domain: $(-\infty, \infty)$
   Range: $(1, \infty)$
   Asymptote: $y = 1$.

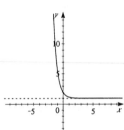

6. $g(x) = \log(-x)$.
   Domain: $(-\infty, 0)$
   Range: $(-\infty, \infty)$
   Asymptote: $x = 0$.

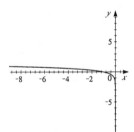

8. $y = 3 + \log_5(x + 4)$.
   Domain: $(-4, \infty)$
   Range: $(-\infty, \infty)$
   Asymptote: $x = -4$.

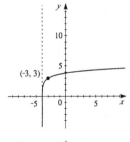

10. $G(x) = \frac{1}{2} e^{x-1}$.
    Domain: $(-\infty, \infty)$
    Range: $(0, \infty)$
    Asymptote: $y = 0$.

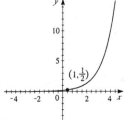

12. $y = \ln(x^2)$.
Domain: $\{x \mid x \neq 0\} = (-\infty, 0) \cup (0, \infty)$
Range: $(-\infty, \infty)$
Asymptote: $x = 0$.

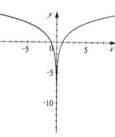

14. $g(x) = \ln(2 + x - x^2)$. We must have $2 + x - x^2 > 0$ (since $\ln y$ is defined only for $y > 0$)
$\Leftrightarrow \quad x^2 - x - 2 < 0 \quad \Leftrightarrow \quad (x - 2)(x + 1) < 0$. The endpoints of the intervals are 2 and -1.

Interval	$(-\infty, -1)$	$(-1, 2)$	$(2, \infty)$
Sign of $x - 2$	$-$	$-$	$+$
Sign of $x + 1$	$-$	$+$	$+$
Sign of $(x - 2)(x + 1)$	$+$	$-$	$+$

Thus the domain is $(-1, 2)$.

16. $\log_6 37 = x \quad \Leftrightarrow \quad 6^x = 37$

18. $\ln c = 17 \quad \Leftrightarrow \quad e^{17} = c$

20. $49^{-1/2} = \frac{1}{7} \quad \Leftrightarrow \quad \log_{49} \frac{1}{7} = -\frac{1}{2}$

22. $e^k = m \quad \Leftrightarrow \quad \ln m = k$

24. $\log_8 1 = \log_8(8^0) = 0$

26. $\log 0.000001 = \log 10^{-6} = -6$

28. $\log_4 8 = \log_4(4^{3/2}) = \frac{3}{2}$

30. $2^{\log_2 13} = 13$

32. $e^{2\ln 7} = (e^{\ln 7})^2 = 7^2 = 49$

34. $\log_3 \sqrt{243} = \log_3(3^{5/2}) = \frac{5}{2}$

36. $\log_5 250 - \log_5 2 = \log_5 \frac{250}{2} = \log_5 125 = \log_5 5^3 = 3$

38. $\log_{10}(\log_{10} 10^{100}) = \log_{10} 100 = \log_{10} 10^2 = 2$

40. $\log_2\left(x\sqrt{x^2 + 1}\right) = \log_2 x + \log_2 \sqrt{x^2 + 1} = \log_2 x + \frac{1}{2}\log_2(x^2 + 1)$

42. $\log\left(\dfrac{4x^3}{y^2(x-1)^5}\right) = \log(4x^3) - \log[y^2(x-1)^5] = \log 4 + 3\log x - [2\log y + 5\log(x-1)]$

44. $\ln\left(\dfrac{\sqrt[3]{x^4 + 12}}{(x+16)\sqrt{x-3}}\right) = \frac{1}{3}\ln(x^4 + 12) - [\ln(x+16) + \frac{1}{2}\ln(x-3)]$

46. $\log x + \log(x^2 y) + 3\log y = \log(x \cdot x^2 y \cdot y^3) = \log(x^3 y^4)$

48. $\log_5 2 + \log_5(x+1) - \frac{1}{3}\log_5(3x+7) = \log_5[2(x+1)] - \log_5(3x+7)^{1/3} = \log_5\left(\dfrac{2(x+1)}{\sqrt[3]{3x+7}}\right)$

50. $\frac{1}{2}[\ln(x-4) + 5\ln(x^2+4x)] = \frac{1}{2}\ln[(x-4)(x^2+4x)^5] = \ln\sqrt{(x-4)(x^2+4x)^5}$

52. $2^{3x-5} = 7 \quad\Leftrightarrow\quad \log 2^{3x-5} = \log 7 \quad\Leftrightarrow\quad 3x - 5 = \frac{\log 7}{\log 2} \quad\Leftrightarrow\quad x = \frac{1}{3}\left(5 + \frac{\log 7}{\log 2}\right) \approx 2.60$

54. $\ln(2x-3) = 14 \quad\Leftrightarrow\quad e^{\ln(2x-3)} = e^{14} \quad\Leftrightarrow\quad 2x - 3 = e^{14} \quad\Leftrightarrow\quad x = \frac{1}{2}(3 + e^{14}) \approx 601303.64$

56. $2^{1-x} = 3^{2x+5} \quad\Leftrightarrow\quad \log 2^{1-x} = \log 3^{2x+5} \quad\Leftrightarrow\quad (1-x)\log 2 = (2x+5)\log 3 \quad\Leftrightarrow$

$x(2\log 3 + \log 2) = \log 2 - 5\log 3 \quad\Leftrightarrow\quad x = \frac{\log 2 - 5\log 3}{\log 2 + 2\log 3} = \frac{\log\frac{2}{3^5}}{\log(2\cdot 9)} \approx -1.66$

58. $\log_8(x+5) - \log_8(x-2) = 1 \quad\Leftrightarrow\quad \log_8\left(\frac{x+5}{x-2}\right) = 1 \quad\Leftrightarrow\quad \frac{x+5}{x-2} = 8^1 = 8 \quad\Leftrightarrow$

$x + 5 = 8x - 16 \quad\Leftrightarrow\quad 7x = 21 \quad\Leftrightarrow\quad x = 3$

60. $2^{3^x} = 5 \quad\Leftrightarrow\quad \log 2^{3^x} = \log 5 \quad\Leftrightarrow\quad 3^x\log 2 = \log 5 \quad\Leftrightarrow\quad 3^x = \frac{\log 5}{\log 2} \quad\Leftrightarrow$

$\log 3^x = \log\left(\frac{\log 5}{\log 2}\right) \quad\Leftrightarrow\quad x\log 3 = \log\left(\frac{\log 5}{\log 2}\right) \quad\Leftrightarrow\quad x = \frac{1}{\log 3}\cdot\log\left(\frac{\log 5}{\log 2}\right) \approx 0.77$

62. $2^{3x-5} = 7 \quad\Leftrightarrow\quad (3x-5)\log 2 = \log 7 \quad\Leftrightarrow\quad x = \frac{1}{3}\left(5 + \frac{\log 7}{\log 2}\right) \approx 2.602452$

64. $e^{-15k} = 10000 \quad\Leftrightarrow\quad -15k = \ln 10000 \quad\Leftrightarrow\quad k = -\frac{1}{15}\ln 10000 \approx -0.614023$

66. $y = 2x^2 - \ln x.$
Vertical Asymptote: $x = 0$
Horizontal Asymptote: none
Local minimum ≈ 1.19 at $x \approx 0.5$

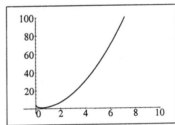

68. $y = 10^x - 5^x.$
Vertical Asymptote: none
Horizontal Asymptote: $y = 0$
Local minimum ≈ -0.13 at $x \approx -0.5$

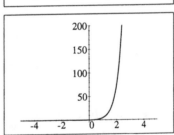

70. $4 - x^2 = e^{-2x}.$
From the graphs, we see that the solutions are
$x \approx -0.64$ and $x \approx 2.$

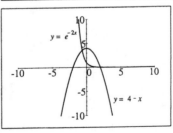

72. $e^x < 4x^2 \quad \Leftrightarrow \quad e^x - 4x^2 < 0.$

We graph the function $f(x) = e^x - 4x^2$, and we see
that the graph lies below the x-axis for
$(-\infty, -0.41) \cup (0.71, 4.31)$.

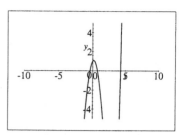

74. The line has x-intercept at $x = e^0 = 1$. When $x = e^a$, $y = \ln e^a = a$. Therefore, using the point-
slope equation, we have $y - 0 = \dfrac{a - 0}{e^a - 1}(x - 1) \quad \Leftrightarrow \quad y = \dfrac{a}{e^a - 1}(x - 1)$.

76. $0.2 \le \log x < 2 \quad \Leftrightarrow \quad 10^{0.2} \le x < 10^2 \quad \Leftrightarrow \quad \sqrt[5]{10} \le x < 100$.

78. $f(x) = 2^{3^x}$. Then $y = 2^{3^x} \quad \Leftrightarrow \quad \log_2 y = 3^x \quad \Leftrightarrow \quad \log_3(\log_2 y) = x$, and so the inverse function
is $f^{-1}(x) = \log_3(\log_2 x)$. Since $\log_3 y$ is defined only when $y > 0$, we have $\log_2 x > 0 \quad \Leftrightarrow$
$x > 1$. Therefore the domain is $(1, \infty)$, and the range is $(-\infty, \infty)$.

80. $P = 5000$, $r = 0.085$, and $n = 2$.

(a) For $t = 1.5$, $A = 5000\left(1 + \frac{0.085}{2}\right)^{2(1.5)} = 5000 \cdot 1.0425^3 \approx \$5664.98$.

(b) We want to find t such that $A = 7000$. Then $A = 5000 \cdot 1.0425^{2t} = 7000 \quad \Leftrightarrow$
$1.0425^{2t} = \frac{7000}{5000} = \frac{7}{5} \quad \Leftrightarrow \quad 2t = \dfrac{\log\left(\frac{7}{5}\right)}{\log 1.0425} \quad \Leftrightarrow \quad t = \dfrac{\log\left(\frac{7}{5}\right)}{2 \log 1.0425} \approx 4.04$, and so the
investment will amount to \$7000 after approximately 4 years.

82. Using the model $n(t) = n_0 \, e^{rt}$, with $n_0 = 10000$ and $n(1) = 25000$, we have
$25000 = n(1) = 10000 e^{r \cdot 1} \quad \Leftrightarrow \quad e^r = \frac{5}{2} \quad \Leftrightarrow \quad r = \ln \frac{5}{2} \approx 0.916$. So $n(t) = 10000 e^{0.916\,t}$.

(a) Here we must solve the equation $n(t) = 20000$ for t. So $n(t) = 10000 e^{0.916\,t} = 20000 \quad \Leftrightarrow$
$e^{0.916\,t} = 2 \quad \Leftrightarrow \quad 0.916t = \ln 2 \quad \Leftrightarrow \quad t = \frac{\ln 2}{0.916} \approx 0.756$. Thus the doubling period is about
45 minutes.

(b) $n(3) = 10000 e^{0.916 \cdot 3} \approx 156250$, so the population after 3 hours is about 156,250.

84. From the formula for radioactive decay, we have $m(t) = m_0 \, e^{-rt}$, where $r = \frac{\ln 2}{h}$. So
$m(t) = m_0 \, e^{-\frac{\ln 2}{h}t}$.

(a) Using $m(8) = 0.33 \, m_0$, we solve for h. We have $0.33 \, m_0 = m(8) = m_0 \, e^{-\frac{8\ln 2}{h}} \quad \Leftrightarrow$
$0.33 = e^{-\frac{8\ln 2}{h}} \quad \Leftrightarrow \quad -\frac{8\ln 2}{h} = \ln 0.33 \quad \Leftrightarrow \quad h = -\frac{8\ln 2}{\ln 0.33} \approx 5.002$. So the half-life of this
element is roughly 5 days.

(b) $m(12) = m_0 \, e^{-\frac{\ln 2}{5} \cdot 12} \approx 0.19 \, m_0$, so about 19% of the original mass remains.

86. From the formula for radioactive decay, we have $m(t) = m_0 \, e^{-rt}$, where $r = \frac{\ln 2}{h}$. Since $h = 4$, we
have $r = \frac{\ln 2}{4} \approx 0.173$ and $m(t) = m_0 \, e^{-0.173t}$.

(a) Using $m(20) = 0.375$, we solve for m_0. We have $0.375 = m(20) = m_0 \, e^{-0.173 \cdot 20} \quad \Leftrightarrow$
$0.03125 m_0 = 0.375 \quad \Leftrightarrow \quad m_0 = \frac{0.375}{0.03125} \approx 12$. So the initial mass of the sample was about
12 g.

(b) $m(t) = 12 \, e^{-0.173t}$.

(c) $m(3) = 12 \, e^{-0.173 \cdot 3} \approx 7.135$. So there are about 7 g remaining after 3 days.

(d) Here we solve $m(t) = 0.15$ for t: $0.15 = 12\,e^{-0.173t}$ $\Leftrightarrow$ $0.0125 = e^{-0.173t}$ $\Leftrightarrow$
    $-0.173t = \ln 0.0125$ $\Leftrightarrow$ $t = \dfrac{\ln 0.0125}{-0.173} \approx 25.3$. So it will take about 25 days until only
    15% of the substance remains.

88. We use Newton's Law of Cooling: $T(t) = T_s + D_0\,e^{-kt}$ with $k = 0.0341$, $T_s = 60$ and
    $D_0 = 190 - 60 = 130$. So $90 = T(t) = 60 + 130\,e^{-0.0341t}$ $\Leftrightarrow$ $90 = 60 + 130\,e^{-0.0341t}$ $\Leftrightarrow$
    $130\,e^{-0.0341t} = 30$ $\Leftrightarrow$ $e^{-0.0341t} = \frac{3}{13}$ $\Leftrightarrow$ $-0.0341\,t = \ln\left(\frac{3}{13}\right)$ $\Leftrightarrow$ $t = \dfrac{-\ln(3/13)}{0.0341} \approx 43.0$,
    so the engine cools to 90°F in about 43 minutes.

90. $\text{pH} = 1.9 = -\log\,[\text{H}^+]$. Then $[\text{H}^+] = 10^{-1.9} \approx 1.26 \times 10^{-2}$ M.

92. Let the subscript JH represent the jackhammer and W the whispering: $\beta_{\text{JH}} = 132 = 10\log\left(\frac{I_{\text{JH}}}{I_0}\right)$
    $\Leftrightarrow$ $\log\left(\frac{I_{\text{JH}}}{I_0}\right) = 13.2$ $\Leftrightarrow$ $\frac{I_{\text{JH}}}{I_0} = 10^{13.2}$. Similarly $\frac{I_{\text{W}}}{I_0} = 10^{2.8}$. So
    $\frac{I_{\text{JH}}}{I_{\text{W}}} = \dfrac{10^{13.2}}{10^{2.8}} = 10^{10.4} \approx 2.51 \times 10^{10}$, and so the ratio of intensities is 2.51×10^{10}.

Focus on Modeling

2. (a)

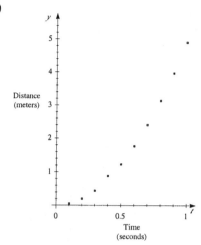

(b) We let t represent the time (in seconds) and y the distance fallen (in meters). Using a calculator, we obtain the power model: $y = 4.9622t^{2.0027}$.

(c) When $t = 3$ the model predicts that $y = 44.792$ m.

4. (a)

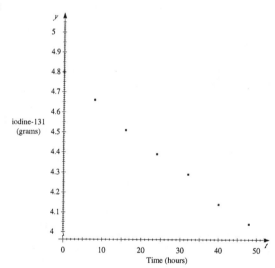

(b) Let t be the time (in hours) and y be amount of iodine-131 (in grams). Using a calculator, we obtain the exponential model $y = ab^t$, where $a = 4.79246$ and $b = 0.99642$.

(c) To find the half-life of iodine-131, we must find the time when the sample has decayed to half its original mass. Setting $y = 2.40$ g, we get $2.40 = 4.79246 \cdot (0.99642)^t$ $\Leftrightarrow$

$\ln 2.40 = \ln 4.79246 + t \ln 0.99642$ $\Leftrightarrow$ $t = \dfrac{\ln 2.40 - \ln 4.79246}{\ln 0.99642} \approx 192.8$ h.

6. Let x be the reduction in emissions (in percent), and y be the cost (in dollars). First we make a scatter plot of the data. A linear model does not appear appropriate, so we try an exponential model. Using a calculator, we get the model $y = ab^x$, where $a = 2.414$ and $b = 1.05452$. This model is graphed on the scatter plot.

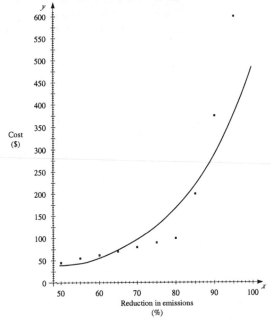

Chapter Seven
Exercises 7.1

2. $330° = 330° \cdot \frac{\pi}{180}$ rad $= \frac{11\pi}{6}$ rad ≈ 5.759 rad

4. $-30° = -30° \cdot \frac{\pi}{180}$ rad $= \frac{-\pi}{6}$ rad ≈ -0.524 rad

6. $-80° = -80° \cdot \frac{\pi}{180}$ rad $= \frac{-4\pi}{9}$ rad ≈ -1.396 rad

8. $-150° = -150° \cdot \frac{\pi}{180}$ rad $= \frac{-5\pi}{6}$ rad ≈ -2.618 rad

10. $\frac{3\pi}{4} = \frac{3\pi}{4} \cdot \frac{180°}{\pi} = 135°$

12. $\frac{5\pi}{6} = \frac{5\pi}{6} \cdot \frac{180°}{\pi} = 150°$

14. $1.5 = 1.5 \cdot \frac{180°}{\pi} = \frac{270°}{\pi} \approx 85.9°$

16. $-\frac{\pi}{12} = -\frac{\pi}{12} \cdot \frac{180°}{\pi} = -15°$

18. $\frac{\pi}{18} \times \frac{180°}{\pi \, \text{rad}} = 10°$

20. $135°$ is coterminal with: $135° + 360° = 495°$, $135° + 720° = 855°$, $135° - 360° = -225°$, $135° - 720° = -585°$.

22. $\frac{11\pi}{6}$ is coterminal with: $\frac{11\pi}{6} + 2\pi = \frac{23\pi}{6}$, $\frac{11\pi}{6} + 4\pi = \frac{35\pi}{6}$, $\frac{11\pi}{6} - 2\pi = -\frac{\pi}{6}$, $\frac{11\pi}{6} - 4\pi = -\frac{13\pi}{6}$.

24. $-50°$ is coterminal with: $-50° + 360° = 310°$, $-50° + 720° = 670°$, $-50° - 360° = -410°$, $-50° - 720° = -770°$.

26. Since $330° - (-30°) = 360°$, the angles are coterminal.

28. Since $\frac{32\pi}{3} - \frac{11\pi}{3} = \frac{21\pi}{3} = 7\pi$ is not a multiple of 2π, the angles are not coterminal.

30. Since $340° - 50° = 290°$ is not a multiple of $360°$, the angles are not coterminal.

32. Since $361° - 1° = 360°$, the angles $361°$ and $1°$ are coterminal.

34. Since $-100° - 260° = -360°$ is a multiple of $360°$, the angles $-100°$ and $260°$ are coterminal.

36. Since $1270° - 190° = 1080° = 3 \cdot 360°$ is a multiple of $360°$, the angles $1270°$ and $190°$ are coterminal.

38. Since $-\frac{7\pi}{3} - \frac{5\pi}{3} = 4\pi$ is a multiple of 2π, the angles $-\frac{7\pi}{3}$ and $\frac{5\pi}{3}$ are coterminal.

40. Since $10 - 2\pi \approx 3.717$, the angles 10 and $10 - 2\pi$ are coterminal.

42. Since $\frac{51\pi}{2} - \frac{3\pi}{2} = 24\pi = 12 \cdot 2\pi$, the angles $\frac{51\pi}{2}$ and $\frac{3\pi}{2}$ are coterminal.

44. $\theta = \frac{s}{r} = \frac{10}{5} = 2$ rad $= 2 \cdot \frac{180°}{\pi} \approx 114.6°$

46. Using the formula $s = \theta r$, the length of the arc is $s = 45° \cdot \frac{\pi}{180°} \cdot 10 = \frac{5\pi}{2} \approx 7.85$ m

48. Solving for θ we have $\theta = \frac{s}{r}$, the measure of the central angle is $\theta = \frac{6}{5} = 1.2$ rad $= 1.2 \cdot \frac{180°}{\pi} \approx 68.8°$.

50. Solving for r we have $r = \dfrac{s}{\theta}$, so the radius of the circle is $r = \dfrac{3}{25° \cdot \frac{\pi}{180°}} = 3 \cdot \dfrac{36}{5\pi} \approx 6.88$ ft.

52. Since the diameter is 30 in, we have $r = 15$ in. In one revolution, the arc length (distance traveled) is $s = \theta r = 2\pi \cdot 15 = 30\pi$ in. The total distance traveled is 1 mi $\cdot$ 5280 ft/mi $\cdot$ 12 in/ft $= 63{,}360$ in $= 63{,}360$ in $\cdot \frac{1 \text{ rev}}{30\pi \text{ in}} \approx 672.27$ rev. Therefore the car wheel will make approximately 672 revolutions.

54. $\theta = 35° - 30° = 5° = 5° \cdot \frac{\pi}{180°}$ rad $= \frac{\pi}{36}$ rad. Then using the formula $s = \theta r$, the length of the arc is $s = \frac{\pi}{36} \cdot 3960 = 110\pi \approx 345.575$. So the distance between the two cities is roughly 346 mi.

56. Since the sun is so far away we can assume that the rays of the sun are parallel when striking the earth, thus the angle formed at the center of the earth is also $\theta = 7.2°$. So $r = \frac{s}{\theta} = \dfrac{500}{7.2° \cdot \frac{\pi}{180°}}$
     $= \frac{180 \cdot 500}{7.2\pi} \approx 3980$ mi, and the circumference is $c = 2\pi r = \frac{2\pi \cdot 180 \cdot 500}{7.2\pi} = 25{,}000$ mi.

58. (a) $A = \frac{1}{2}r^2\theta = \frac{1}{2} \cdot 8^2 \cdot 80° \cdot \frac{\pi}{180°} = 32 \cdot \frac{4\pi}{9} = \frac{128\pi}{9} \approx 35.45$

     (b) $A = \frac{1}{2}r^2\theta = \frac{1}{2} \cdot 10^2 \cdot 0.5 = 25$

60. $\theta = 60° = 60° \cdot \frac{\pi}{180°} = \frac{\pi}{3}$ rad. Then $A = \frac{1}{2}r^2\theta = \frac{1}{2} \cdot 3^2 \cdot \frac{\pi}{3} = \frac{3\pi}{2} \approx 4.7$ mi^2

62. $r = 24$ mi, $A = 288$ mi^2. Then $\theta = \frac{2A}{r^2} = \frac{2 \cdot 288}{24^2} = 1$ rad $\approx 57.3°$

64. Referring to the figure, we have
     $AC = 3 + 1 = 4$, $BC = 1 + 2 = 3$, and
     $AB = 2 + 3 = 5$. Since
     $AB^2 = AC^2 + BC^2$, then by the Pythagorean
     Theorem, the triangle is a right triangle.
     Therefore $\theta = \frac{\pi}{2}$, and
     $A = \frac{1}{2}r^2\theta = \frac{1}{2} \cdot 1^2 \cdot \frac{\pi}{2} = \frac{\pi}{4}$ ft^2.

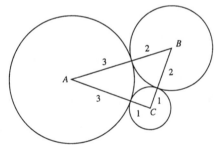

66. There is 5 hours and 45 minutes between 1:00 pm and 6:45 pm. Since 45 minutes is 0.75 of an hour, the minute hand moves through $5.75 \times 2\pi = 11.5\pi \approx 36.128$ rad. The hour hand moves through $5.75 \times \frac{1}{12} \times 2\pi = \frac{23}{24}\pi \approx 3.011$ rad.

Exercises 7.2

2. $\sin\theta = \frac{7}{25}$, $\cos\theta = \frac{24}{25}$, $\tan\theta = \frac{7}{24}$, $\csc\theta = \frac{25}{7}$, $\sec\theta = \frac{25}{24}$, $\cot\theta = \frac{24}{7}$

4. The hypotenuse is obtained by the Pythagorean Theorem: $\sqrt{8^2 + 15^2} = \sqrt{289} = 17$. Then
    $\sin\theta = \frac{15}{17}$, $\cos\theta = \frac{8}{17}$, $\tan\theta = \frac{15}{8}$, $\csc\theta = \frac{17}{15}$, $\sec\theta = \frac{17}{8}$, $\cot\theta = \frac{8}{15}$

6. $b = \sqrt{7^2 - 3^2} = \sqrt{40} = 2\sqrt{10}$
    (a) $\sin\alpha = \cos\beta = \frac{3}{7}$
    (b) $\tan\alpha = \cot\beta = \frac{3}{2\sqrt{10}}$
    (c) $\sec\alpha = \csc\beta = \frac{7}{2\sqrt{10}}$

8. Since $\sin 45° = \dfrac{12}{x}$, we have $x = \dfrac{12}{\sin 45°} = \dfrac{12}{\frac{1}{\sqrt{2}}} = 12\sqrt{2}$.

10. Since $\tan 30° = \dfrac{4}{x}$, we have $x = \dfrac{4}{\tan 30°} = \dfrac{4}{\frac{1}{\sqrt{3}}} = 4\sqrt{3}$.

12. Since $\sin 53° = \dfrac{25}{x}$, we have $x = \dfrac{25}{\sin 53°} \approx 31.30339$.

14. $\dfrac{x}{4} = \tan\theta \quad\Leftrightarrow\quad x = 4\tan\theta$, and $\dfrac{4}{y} = \cos\theta \quad\Leftrightarrow\quad y = \dfrac{4}{\cos\theta} = 4\sec\theta$

16. $\cos\theta = \frac{2}{7}$. The third side is $y = \sqrt{7^2 - 2^2} = \sqrt{45} = 3\sqrt{5}$. The other five ratios
    are $\sin\theta = \frac{3\sqrt{5}}{7}$, $\tan\theta = \frac{3\sqrt{5}}{2}$, $\csc\theta = \frac{7}{3\sqrt{5}}$, $\sec\theta = \frac{7}{2}$, and $\cot\theta = \frac{2}{3\sqrt{5}}$.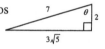

18. $\tan\theta = \sqrt{3}$. The third side is $r = \sqrt{1^2 + 3} = 2$. The other five
    ratios are $\sin\theta = \frac{\sqrt{3}}{2}$, $\cos\theta = \frac{1}{2}$, $\csc\theta = \frac{2}{\sqrt{3}}$, $\sec\theta = 2$, and
    $\cot\theta = \frac{1}{\sqrt{3}}$.

20. $\csc\theta = \frac{13}{12}$. The third side is $x = \sqrt{13^2 - 12^2} = 5$. The other five ratios are
    $\sin\theta = \frac{12}{13}$, $\cos\theta = \frac{5}{13}$, $\tan\theta = \frac{12}{5}$, $\sec\theta = \frac{13}{5}$, and $\cot\theta = \frac{5}{12}$.

22. $\sin 30° \csc 30° = \sin 30° \cdot \frac{1}{\sin 30°} = 1$

24. $(\sin 60°)^2 + (\cos 60°)^2 = \left(\frac{\sqrt{3}}{2}\right)^2 + \left(\frac{1}{2}\right)^2 = \frac{3}{4} + \frac{1}{4} = 1$

26. $\left(\sin\frac{\pi}{3}\cos\frac{\pi}{4} - \sin\frac{\pi}{4}\cos\frac{\pi}{3}\right)^2 = \left(\frac{\sqrt{3}}{2} \cdot \frac{1}{\sqrt{2}} - \frac{1}{\sqrt{2}} \cdot \frac{1}{2}\right)^2 = \left[\frac{1}{2\sqrt{2}}\left(\sqrt{3} - 1\right)\right]^2$
    $= \frac{1}{8}(\sqrt{3} - 1)^2 = \frac{1}{8}(3 - 2\sqrt{3} + 1) = \frac{1}{8}(4 - 2\sqrt{3}) = \frac{1}{4}(2 - \sqrt{3})$

28. The other leg $= 100\tan 75° = 26.79$,
    hypotenuse $= \frac{100}{\sin 75°} = 103.52$, and the
    other angle $= 90° - 75° = 15°$

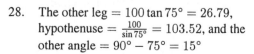
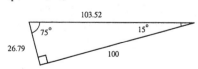

30. The adjacent leg $= 1000 \cos 68° = 374.61$,
     opposite leg $= 1000 \sin 68° = 927.18$, and the
     other angle $= 90° - 68° = 22°$

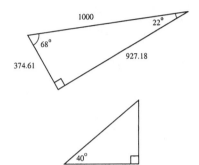

32. $\sin 40° \approx 0.64$, $\cos 40° \approx 0.77$,
     $\tan 40° \approx \frac{0.64}{0.77} \approx 0.83$, $\csc 40° \approx 1.56$,
     $\sec 40° \approx 1.39$, $\cot 40° \approx 1.20$.

34. (a) Let r be the distance, in feet, between the plane and the Gateway Arch. Therefore,
          $\sin 22° = \frac{35,000}{r}$ $\Leftrightarrow$ $r = \frac{35,000}{\sin 22°} \approx 93,431$ ft.

     (b) Let x be the distance, also in feet, between a point on the ground directly below the plane and
          the Gateway Arch. Then $\tan 22° = \dfrac{35,000}{x}$ $\Leftrightarrow$ $x = \dfrac{35,000}{\tan 22°} \approx 86,628$ ft.

36. Let x be the distance, in feet, of the ship from the base of the lighthouse. Then $\tan 23° = \dfrac{200}{x}$ $\Leftrightarrow$
     $x = \dfrac{200}{\tan 23°} \approx 471$ ft.

38. Let θ represent the angle of elevation of the ladder. Let h represent the height, in feet, that the
     ladder reaches on the building. Then $\cos \theta = \frac{6}{20} = 0.3$ $\Leftrightarrow$ $\theta = \cos^{-1} 0.3 \approx 1.266$ rad $\approx 72.5°$.
     By the Pythagorean Theorem $h^2 + 6^2 = 20^2$ $\Leftrightarrow$ $h = \sqrt{400 - 36} = \sqrt{364} \approx 19$ ft.

40. Let h be the height, in feet, of the communication tower. Then $\sin 65° = \dfrac{h}{600}$ $\Leftrightarrow$ $h = 600 \cdot \sin$
     $65° \approx 544$ ft.

42. From triangle ABC we get $\tan 50° = \dfrac{|AC|}{58.2}$ $\Leftrightarrow$ $|AC| = 58.2 \cdot \tan 50° \approx 69.36$ m. Then
     $\tan 76.3° = \dfrac{|CD|}{|AC|}$ $\Leftrightarrow$ $|CD| = |AC| \cdot \tan 76.3° \approx 69.36 \cdot \tan 76.3° \approx 285$ m.

44. Let d_1 be the distance, in feet, between a point directly below the plane and
     one car, and d_2 be the distance, in feet, between the same point and the
     other car. Then $\tan 52° = \dfrac{5150}{d_1}$ $\Leftrightarrow$ $d_1 = \dfrac{5150}{\tan 52°} \approx 4023.62$ ft,
     and $\tan 35° = \dfrac{5150}{d_2}$ $\Leftrightarrow$ $d_2 = \dfrac{5150}{\tan 35°} \approx 7354.96$ ft. So the
     distance between the two cars is about $d_1 + d_2 \approx 4023.62 + 7354.96 \approx 11,379$ ft.

46. Let x be the distance, in feet, between a point directly below the balloon and the first mile post. Let
     h be the height, in feet, of the balloon. Then $\tan 22° = \dfrac{h}{x}$ and $\tan 20° = \dfrac{h}{x + 5280}$. So
     $h = x \tan 22° = (x + 5280) \tan 20°$ $\Leftrightarrow$ $x = \dfrac{5280 \cdot \tan 20°}{\tan 22° - \tan 20°} \approx 47,977$ mi. Therefore
     $h \approx 47,976.9 \cdot \tan 22° \approx 19.384 \approx 3.7$ mi.

48. (a) Solution #1: Let x be the base of the smaller triangle, as shown in the figure on the right. We see that $x + d = h \cdot \cot\alpha$ and $x = h \cdot \cot\beta$. Therefore, $h \cdot \cot\alpha - d = h \cdot \cot\beta$ $\Leftrightarrow$ $h \cdot \cot\alpha - h \cdot \cot\beta = d$ $\Leftrightarrow$ $h(\cot\alpha - \cot\beta) = d$ $\Leftrightarrow$

$$h = \frac{d}{\cot\alpha - \cot\beta} = \frac{d}{\dfrac{1}{\tan\alpha} - \dfrac{1}{\tan\beta}} = \frac{d}{\dfrac{\tan\beta - \tan\alpha}{\tan\alpha \cdot \tan\beta}} = d \cdot \frac{\tan\alpha \cdot \tan\beta}{\tan\beta - \tan\alpha}$$

Solution #2: From the figure, we see that $\tan\alpha = \dfrac{h}{x + d}$ and $\tan\beta = \dfrac{h}{x}$.

Solving each of these equations for x, we find that

$$x = \frac{h}{\tan\beta} \text{ and } x = \frac{h}{\tan\alpha} - d, \text{ so } \frac{h}{\tan\beta} = \frac{h}{\tan\alpha} - d$$

$$\Rightarrow \quad \frac{h}{\tan\beta} - \frac{h}{\tan\alpha} = -d \quad \Rightarrow$$

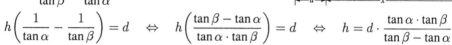

$$h\left(\frac{1}{\tan\alpha} - \frac{1}{\tan\beta}\right) = d \quad \Leftrightarrow \quad h\left(\frac{\tan\beta - \tan\alpha}{\tan\alpha \cdot \tan\beta}\right) = d \quad \Leftrightarrow \quad h = d \cdot \frac{\tan\alpha \cdot \tan\beta}{\tan\beta - \tan\alpha}$$

To complete this part of the exercise we show that

$$h = d \cdot \frac{\tan\alpha \cdot \tan\beta}{\tan\beta - \tan\alpha} = d \cdot \frac{\tan\alpha \cdot \tan\beta}{\tan\beta - \tan\alpha} \cdot \frac{\dfrac{1}{\tan\alpha \cdot \tan\beta}}{\dfrac{1}{\tan\alpha \cdot \tan\beta}} = \frac{d}{\dfrac{1}{\tan\alpha} - \dfrac{1}{\tan\beta}} = \frac{d}{\cot\alpha - \cot\beta}$$

(b) $h = d \cdot \dfrac{\tan\alpha \cdot \tan\beta}{\tan\beta - \tan\alpha} = (800) \cdot \dfrac{\tan 25° \cdot \tan 29°}{\tan 29° - \tan 25°} \approx 2350$ ft.

50. (a) $s = r\theta \quad \Leftrightarrow \quad \theta = \dfrac{s}{r} = \dfrac{6155}{3960} \approx 1.5543$ rad $\approx 89.05°$

(b) Let d represent the distance, in miles, from the center of the earth to the moon. Since $\cos\theta = \dfrac{3960}{d}$, we have $d = \dfrac{3960}{\cos\theta} \approx \dfrac{3960}{\cos 89.05°} \approx 239{,}961.5$. So the distance AC is $239{,}961.5 - 3960 \approx 236{,}000$ mi.

52. Let d represent the distance, in miles, from the earth to Alpha Centauri. Since $\sin 0.000211° = \dfrac{93{,}000{,}000}{d}$, we have $d = \dfrac{93{,}000{,}000}{\sin 0.000211°} \approx 25{,}253{,}590{,}022{,}410$. So the distance from the earth to Alpha Centauri is about 2.53×10^{13} mi.

54. Let d be the length of the base of the $60°$ triangle. Then $\tan 60° = \dfrac{85}{d} \quad \Leftrightarrow$ $d = \dfrac{85}{\tan 60°} \approx 49.075$, and so $\tan 30° = \dfrac{85}{d + x} \quad \Leftrightarrow \quad d + x = \dfrac{85}{\tan 30°} \quad \Leftrightarrow$ $x = \dfrac{85}{\tan 30°} - d \approx 98.1$.

56. Let h be the hypotenuse of the top triangle. Then $\sin 30° = \dfrac{5}{h} \quad \Leftrightarrow \quad h = \dfrac{5}{\sin 30°} = 10$, and so $\tan 60° = \dfrac{h}{x} \quad \Leftrightarrow \quad x = \dfrac{h}{\tan 60°} = \dfrac{10}{\tan 60°} \approx 5.8$.

58. If two triangles are similar, then their corresponding angles are equal and their corresponding sides are proportional. That is, if triangle ABC is similar to triangle $A'B'C'$ then

length $AB = r \cdot$ length $A'B$; length $AC = r \cdot$ length $A'B'$; length $BC = r \cdot$ length $B'C'$. Thus the factor r cancels in any trigonometric ratio.

Exercises 7.3

2. (a) 290°: reference angle is $360° - 290° = 70°$.

   (b) 750°: reference angle is $750° - 720° = 30°$.

   (c) 570°: reference angle is $570° - 360° - 180° = 30°$.

4. (a) $\frac{3\pi}{5}$: reference angle is $\pi - \frac{3\pi}{5} = \frac{2\pi}{5}$.

   (b) $\frac{7\pi}{6}$: reference angle is $\frac{7\pi}{6} - \pi = \frac{\pi}{6}$.

   (c) $-\frac{2\pi}{3}$: reference angle is $\pi - \frac{2\pi}{3} = \frac{\pi}{3}$.

6. (a) $\frac{23\pi}{11}$: reference angle is $\frac{23\pi}{11} - 2\pi = \frac{\pi}{11}$.

   (b) $\frac{23}{11}$: reference angle is $\pi - \frac{23}{11} \approx 1.05$.

   (c) $\frac{17\pi}{7}$: reference angle is $\frac{17\pi}{7} - 2\pi = \frac{3\pi}{7}$.

8. $\cos 225° = -\cos 45° = -\frac{1}{\sqrt{2}} = -\frac{\sqrt{2}}{2}$

10. $\tan 330° = -\tan 30° = -\frac{1}{\sqrt{3}} = -\frac{\sqrt{3}}{3}$

12. $\sec(-60°) = \sec 60° = \dfrac{1}{\cos 60°} = 2$

14. $\cot 210° = \cot 30° = \dfrac{1}{\tan 30°} = \sqrt{3}$

16. $\sec 120° = -\sec 60° = -\dfrac{1}{\cos 60°} = -2$

18. $\cos 660° = \cos 60° = \frac{1}{2}$

20. $\sin\left(\frac{5\pi}{3}\right) = -\sin\left(\frac{\pi}{3}\right) = -\frac{\sqrt{3}}{2}$

22. $\cos\left(\frac{7\pi}{3}\right) = \cos\left(\frac{\pi}{3}\right) = \frac{1}{2}$

24. $\tan\left(\frac{5\pi}{6}\right) = -\tan\left(\frac{\pi}{6}\right) = -\frac{1}{\sqrt{3}} = -\frac{\sqrt{3}}{3}$

26. $\csc\left(\frac{5\pi}{4}\right) = -\csc\left(\frac{\pi}{4}\right) = -\frac{1}{\sin\left(\frac{\pi}{4}\right)} = -\sqrt{2}$

28. $\cos\left(\frac{7\pi}{4}\right) = \cos\left(\frac{\pi}{4}\right) = \frac{1}{\sqrt{2}} = \frac{\sqrt{2}}{2}$

30. $\sin\left(\frac{11\pi}{6}\right) = -\sin\left(\frac{\pi}{6}\right) = -\frac{1}{2}$

32. Since both $\tan\theta$ and $\sin\theta$ are negative, θ is in quadrant IV.

34. Since $\csc\theta > 0 \quad\Rightarrow\quad \sin\theta > 0$ and $\cos\theta < 0$, θ is in quadrant II.

36. $\cot\theta = \dfrac{\cos\theta}{\sin\theta} = \dfrac{-\sqrt{1 - \sin^2\theta}}{\sin\theta}$ ($\cos\theta < 0$ in quadrant II)

38. $\sec\theta = \dfrac{1}{\cos\theta} = \dfrac{1}{\sqrt{1 - \sin^2\theta}}$ (all trigonometric functions are positive in quadrant I)

40. $\csc^2\theta = 1 + \cot^2\theta \quad\Leftrightarrow\quad \csc\theta = -\sqrt{1 + \cot^2\theta}$ ($\csc\theta < 0$ in quadrant III)

42. $\cos\theta = -\frac{7}{12}$. Since θ is in quadrant III, $y = -\sqrt{12^2 - 7^2} = -\sqrt{95}$, and so $\sin\theta = -\frac{\sqrt{95}}{12}$, $\tan\theta = \frac{\sqrt{95}}{7}$, $\csc\theta = -\frac{12}{\sqrt{95}}$, $\sec\theta = -\frac{12}{7}$, $\cot\theta = \frac{7}{\sqrt{95}}$.

44. $\sec\theta = 5$. Then $\cos\theta = \frac{1}{5}$ and $y = -\sqrt{5^2 - 1^2} = -2\sqrt{6}$. So $\sin\theta = -\frac{2\sqrt{6}}{5}$, $\cos\theta = \frac{1}{5}$, $\tan\theta = -2\sqrt{6}$, $\csc\theta = -\frac{5}{2\sqrt{6}}$, $\cot\theta = -\frac{1}{2\sqrt{6}}$.

46. $\cot\theta = \frac{1}{4}$. Then $\tan\theta = 4$ and $r = \sqrt{4^2 + 1^2} = \sqrt{17}$. So $\sin\theta = -\frac{4}{\sqrt{17}}$, $\cos\theta = -\frac{1}{\sqrt{17}}$, $\tan\theta = 4$, $\csc\theta = -\frac{\sqrt{17}}{4}$, $\sec\theta = -\sqrt{17}$.

48. $\tan\theta = -4$. Then $r = \sqrt{4^2 + 1^2} = \sqrt{17}$, and so $\sin\theta = \frac{4}{\sqrt{17}}$, $\cos\theta = -\frac{1}{\sqrt{17}}$, $\csc\theta = \frac{\sqrt{17}}{4}$, $\sec\theta = -\sqrt{17}$, $\cot\theta = -\frac{1}{4}$.

50. $a = 7$, $b = 9$, and $\theta = 72°$. Then $\mathcal{A} = \frac{1}{2}ab\sin\theta = \frac{1}{2} \cdot 7 \cdot 9 \cdot \sin 72° = \frac{63}{2}\sin 72° \approx 30.0$

52. Since the triangle is equilateral, $\theta = 60°$, and $a = b = 10$. Substituting we get $\mathcal{A} = \frac{1}{2}ab\sin\theta = \frac{1}{2} \cdot 10 \cdot 10 \cdot \sin 60° = 50 \cdot \sin 60° \approx 43.3$.

54. For the sector defined by the two sides, $A_1 = \frac{1}{2}r^2\theta = \frac{1}{2} \cdot 2^2 \cdot 120 \cdot \frac{\pi}{180} = \frac{4\pi}{3}$. For the triangle defined by the two sides, $A_2 = \frac{1}{2}ab\sin\theta = \frac{1}{2} \cdot 2 \cdot 2 \cdot \sin 120° = 2 \cdot \sin 60° = \sqrt{3}$. Thus the area of the region is $A_1 - A_2 = \frac{4\pi}{3} - \sqrt{3} \approx 2.46$.

56. $\sin^2\theta + \cos^2\theta = 1 \quad \Leftrightarrow \quad (\sin^2\theta + \cos^2\theta) \cdot \frac{1}{\sin^2\theta} = 1 \cdot \frac{1}{\sin^2\theta} \quad \Leftrightarrow \quad 1 + \cot^2\theta = \csc^2\theta$

58. $\cos\theta = \dfrac{\text{adj}}{\text{hyp}} = \dfrac{|OP|}{|OR|} = \dfrac{|OP|}{1} = |OP|$.

Since QS is tangent to the circle at R, $\triangle ORQ$ is a right triangle. Then $\tan\theta = \dfrac{\text{opp}}{\text{adj}} = \dfrac{|RQ|}{|OR|} = |RQ|$ and $\sec\theta = \dfrac{\text{hyp}}{\text{adj}} = \dfrac{|OQ|}{|OR|} = |OQ|$.

Since $\angle SOQ$ is a right angle $\triangle SOQ$ is a right triangle and $\angle OSR = \theta$. Then $\csc\theta = \dfrac{\text{hyp}}{\text{opp}} = \dfrac{|OS|}{|OR|} = |OS|$ and $\cot\theta = \dfrac{\text{adj}}{\text{opp}} = \dfrac{|SR|}{|OR|} = |SR|$.

Summarizing we have $\sin\theta = |PR|$, $\cos\theta = |OP|$, $\tan\theta = |RQ|$, $\sec\theta = |OQ|$, $\csc\theta = |OS|$ and $\cot\theta = |SR|$.

Exercises 7.4

2. $\sin\theta = \dfrac{50\cdot\sin 67°}{70} \approx 0.658.$ Then $\theta \approx \sin^{-1}0.658 \approx 41.1°$

4. $\angle C = 180° - 98.4° - 24.6° = 57°.$ $x = \dfrac{420\cdot\sin 57°}{\sin 98.4°} \approx 356.1$

6. $\angle C = 180° - 102° - 28° = 50°.$ $x = \dfrac{80\cdot\sin 50°}{\sin 102°} \approx 62.7$

8. $\angle B = 180° - 30° - 100° = 50°.$ Then $c = \dfrac{2\cdot\sin 100°}{\sin 50°} \approx 2.57$ and $a = \dfrac{2\cdot\sin 30°}{\sin 50°} \approx 1.31.$

10. $\angle C = 180° - 110° - 23° = 47°.$ Then $a = \dfrac{50\cdot\sin 23°}{\sin 47°} \approx 26.7,$

and $b = \dfrac{50\cdot\sin 110°}{\sin 47°} \approx 64.2.$

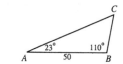

12. $\angle C = 180° - 95° - 22° = 63°.$ Then $b = \dfrac{420\cdot\sin 95°}{\sin 22°} \approx 1116.9,$

and $c = \dfrac{420\cdot\sin 63°}{\sin 22°} \approx 999.0.$

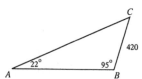

14. $\angle A = 180° - 100° - 10° = 70°.$ Then $a = \dfrac{115\cdot\sin 70°}{\sin 100°} \approx 109.7,$

and $b = \dfrac{115\cdot\sin 10°}{\sin 100°} \approx 20.3.$

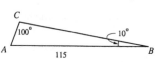

16. $\sin C = \dfrac{40\cdot\sin 37°}{30} \approx 0.802$ $\Leftrightarrow$ $\angle C_1 \approx \sin^{-1}0.822 \approx 53.4°$ or
$\angle C_2 \approx 180° - 53.4° \approx 126.6°.$

If $\underline{\angle C_1 \approx 53.4°}$, then $\angle B_1 \approx 180° - 37° - 53.4° = 89.6°$ and $b_1 = \dfrac{30\cdot\sin 89.6°}{\sin 37°} \approx 49.8.$

If $\underline{\angle C_2 \approx 126.6°}$, then $\angle B_2 \approx 180° - 37° - 126.6° = 16.4°$ and $b_2 = \dfrac{30\cdot\sin 16.4°}{\sin 37°} \approx 14.1.$

Thus the two triangles are: $\angle B_1 \approx 89.6°$, $\angle C_1 \approx 53.4°$, and $b_1 \approx 49.8$; or $\angle B_2 \approx 16.4°$, $\angle C_2 \approx 126.6°$, and $b_2 \approx 14.1.$

18. $\sin B = \dfrac{45\cdot\sin 38°}{42} \approx 0.660$ $\Leftrightarrow$ $\angle B_1 \approx \sin^{-1}0.660 \approx 41.3°$ or
$\angle B_2 \approx 180° - 41.3° \approx 138.7°.$

If $\underline{\angle B_1 \approx 41.3°}$, then $\angle A_1 \approx 180° - 38° - 41.3° = 100.7°$ and $a_1 = \dfrac{42\cdot\sin 100.7°}{\sin 38°} \approx 67.$

If $\underline{\angle B_2 \approx 138.7°}$, then $\angle A_2 \approx 180° - 38° - 138.7° = 3.3°$ and $a_2 = \dfrac{42\cdot\sin 3.3°}{\sin 38°} \approx 3.9.$

Thus the two triangles are: $\angle A_1 \approx 100.7°$, $\angle B_1 \approx 41.3°$, and $a_1 \approx 67$; or $\angle A_2 \approx 3.3°$, $\angle B_2 \approx 138.7°$, and $a_2 \approx 3.9.$

20. $\sin B = \dfrac{100 \cdot \sin 30°}{75} = \dfrac{2}{3} \quad \Leftrightarrow \quad \angle B_1 \approx \sin^{-1}\dfrac{2}{3} \approx 41.8°$ or $\angle B_2 \approx 180° - 41.8° \approx 138.2°$.

If $\angle B_1 \approx 41.8°$, then $\angle C_1 \approx 180° - 30° - 41.8° = 108.2°$ and $c_1 = \dfrac{75 \cdot \sin 108.2°}{\sin 30°} \approx 142.5$.

If $\angle B_2 \approx 138.2°$, then $\angle A_2 \approx 180° - 30° - 138.2° = 11.8°$ and $c_2 = \dfrac{75 \cdot \sin 11.8°}{\sin 30°} \approx 30,7$.

Thus the two triangles are: $\angle B_1 \approx 41.8°$, $\angle C_1 \approx 108.2°$, and $c_1 \approx 142.5$; or $\angle B_2 \approx 138.2°$, $\angle C_2 \approx 11.8°$, and $c_2 \approx 30.7$.

22. $\sin B = \dfrac{80 \cdot \sin 135°}{100} \approx 0.566 \quad \Leftrightarrow \quad \angle B_1 \approx \sin^{-1} 0.566 \approx 34.4°$ or

$\angle B_2 \approx 180° - 34.4° = 145.6°$.

If $\angle B_1 \approx 34.4°$, then $\angle C \approx 180° - 135° - 34.4° = 10.6°$ and $c = \dfrac{100 \cdot \sin 10.6°}{\sin 135°} \approx 25.9$.

If $\angle B_2 \approx 180° - 34.4° = 145.6°$, then $\angle A + \angle B_2 = 135° + 145.6° > 180°$, so there is no such triangle.

Thus, the only triangle is: $\angle B \approx 34.4°$, $\angle C \approx 10.6°$, and $c \approx 25.9$.

24. (a) Let x be the distance from the plane to point A. Then $\dfrac{x}{AB} = \dfrac{\sin 48°}{\sin(180° - 32° - 48°)}$

$= \dfrac{\sin 48°}{\sin 100°} \quad \Leftrightarrow \quad x = 5 \cdot \dfrac{\sin 48°}{\sin 100°} \approx 3.77$ mi.

(b) Let h be the height of the plane. Then $\sin 32° = \dfrac{h}{x} \quad \Rightarrow \quad h = (3.77) \sin 32° \approx 2.00$ mi.

26. Assuming that the tree is growing perpendicular to flat ground and not the hillside, then the angle subtended by the top of the tree and the sun's rays is $\angle A = 180° - 90° - 52° = 38°$. Thus the height of the tree is $h = \dfrac{215 \cdot \sin 30°}{\sin 38°} \approx 175$ ft.

28. $\sin \angle ABC = \dfrac{312 \cdot \sin 48.6°}{527} \approx 0.444 \quad \Leftrightarrow \quad \angle ABC \approx \sin^{-1} 0.444 \approx 26.4°$, and so $\angle BCA \approx 180° - 48.6° - 26.4° = 105°$. Then the distance between A and B is $|AB| = \dfrac{527 \cdot \sin 105°}{\sin 48.6°} \approx 678.5$ ft.

30. Call the balloon's position R. Then in $\triangle PQR$, we see that $\angle P = 62° - 32° = 30°$, and $\angle Q = 180° - 71° + 32° = 141°$. Therefore, $\angle R = 180° - 30° - 141° = 9°$. So by the Law of Sines, $\dfrac{QR}{\sin 30°} = \dfrac{PQ}{\sin 9°} \quad \Leftrightarrow \quad QR = 60 \cdot \dfrac{\sin 30°}{\sin 9°} \approx 192$ m.

32. (a) From $\triangle ABC$ and the Law of Sines we get $\dfrac{\sin 30°}{20} = \dfrac{\sin B}{28} \quad \Leftrightarrow$

$\sin B = \dfrac{28 \cdot \sin 30°}{20} = 0.7$, so $\angle B \approx \sin^{-1} 0.7 \approx 44.427°$. Since $\triangle BCD$ is isosceles, $\angle B = \angle BDC \approx 44.427°$. Thus, $\angle BCD = 180° - 2\angle B \approx 91.146° \approx 91.1°$.

(b) From $\triangle ABC$ we get $\angle BCA = 180° - \angle A - \angle B \approx 180° - 30° - 44.427° = 105.573°$. Hence $\angle DCA = \angle BCA - \angle BCD \approx 105.573° - 91.146° = 14.4°$.

34. By the formula of Section 7.3, the area of $\triangle ABC$ is $\mathcal{A} = \frac{1}{2}ab\sin C$. Since we are given a and the 3 angles, we need to find b in terms of these. By the Law of Sines $\dfrac{\sin B}{b} = \dfrac{\sin A}{a}$ $\Leftrightarrow$ $b = \dfrac{a\sin B}{\sin A}$. Thus, $\mathcal{A} = \dfrac{1}{2}ab\sin C = \dfrac{1}{2}a \cdot \left(\dfrac{a\sin B}{\sin A}\right) \cdot \sin C = \dfrac{a^2\sin B\sin C}{2\sin A}$.

Exercises 7.5

2. $x^2 = 10^2 + 16^2 - 2 \cdot 10 \cdot 16 \cdot \cos 98° = 100 + 256 - 320 \cos 98° \approx 400.535$ and so
   $x \approx \sqrt{400.535} \approx 20$.

4. $154.6^2 = 60.1^2 + 122.5^2 - 2 \cdot 60.1 \cdot 122.5 \cdot \cos \theta$. Then $\cos \theta = \dfrac{154.6^2 - 60.1^2 - 122.5^2}{-2 \cdot 60.1 \cdot 122.5}$
   $\approx -0.359 \quad \Leftrightarrow \quad \theta \approx \cos^{-1}(-0.359) \approx 111°$.

6. $20^2 = 10^2 + 12^2 - 2 \cdot 10 \cdot 12 \cdot \cos \theta$. Then $\cos \theta = \dfrac{20^2 - 10^2 - 12^2}{-2 \cdot 10 \cdot 12} = \dfrac{156}{-240} = -0.65 \quad \Leftrightarrow$
   $\theta \approx \cos^{-1}(-0.65) \approx 130.54°$.

8. $12^2 = 40^2 + 44^2 - 2 \cdot 40 \cdot 44 \cdot \cos B \quad \Leftrightarrow \quad \cos B = \dfrac{12^2 - 40^2 - 44^2}{-2 \cdot 40 \cdot 44} \approx 0.964 \quad \Leftrightarrow$
   $\angle B \approx \cos^{-1} 0.964 \approx 15°$. Then $\sin A = \dfrac{40 \cdot \sin 15.5°}{12} \approx 0.891 \quad \Leftrightarrow \quad \angle A \approx \sin^{-1} 0.891 \approx 63°$,
   and so $\angle C \approx 180° - 15° - 63° = 102°$.

10. $a^2 = 60^2 + 30^2 - 2 \cdot 60 \cdot 30 \cdot \cos 70° = 3600 + 900 - 3600 \cos 70° \approx 3268.73$
    $\Leftrightarrow \quad a = \sqrt{3268.73} \approx 57.2$. Then $\sin C \approx \dfrac{30 \cdot \sin 70°}{57.2} \approx 0.493 \quad \Leftrightarrow$
    $\angle C \approx \sin^{-1} 0.493 \approx 29.5°$, and $\quad \angle B \approx 180° - 70° - 29.5° = 80.5°$.

12. $10^2 = 12^2 + 16^2 - 2 \cdot 12 \cdot 16 \cdot \cos A \quad \Leftrightarrow \quad \cos A = \dfrac{10^2 - 12^2 - 16^2}{-2 \cdot 12 \cdot 16} = 0.78125 \quad \Leftrightarrow$
    $\angle A \approx \cos^{-1} 0.78125 \approx 38.6°$. Then $\sin B \approx \dfrac{12 \cdot \sin 38.6°}{10} \approx 0.749 \quad \Leftrightarrow$
    $\angle B \approx \sin^{-1} 0.749 \approx 48.5°$, and so $\angle C \approx 180° - 38.6° - 48.5° = 92.9°$.

14. $\sin A = \dfrac{65 \cdot \sin 52°}{50} \approx 1.024$. Since $|\sin \theta| \leq 1$ for all θ, there is no such $\angle A$, and hence there is
    no such triangle.

16. $\angle A = 180° - 61° - 83° = 36°$. Then $b = \dfrac{73.5 \cdot \sin 61°}{\sin 36°} \approx 109.4$ and $c = \dfrac{73.5 \cdot \sin 83°}{\sin 36°} \approx 124.1$.

18. $x^2 = 10° + 18° - 2 \cdot 10 \cdot 18 \cdot \cos 40° = 100 + 324 - 360 \cos 40° \approx 148.224$ and so
    $x \approx \sqrt{148.224} \approx 12.2$.

20. $4^2 = 10^2 + 11^2 - 2 \cdot 10 \cdot 11 \cdot \cos \theta$. Then $\cos \theta = \dfrac{4^2 - 10^2 - 11^2}{-2 \cdot 10 \cdot 11} = \dfrac{-205}{-220} \approx 0.932 \quad \Leftrightarrow$
    $\theta \approx \cos^{-1} 0.932 \approx 21.3°$.

22. $\sin \theta = \dfrac{10 \cdot \sin 40°}{8} \approx 0.803 \quad \Leftrightarrow \quad \theta \approx \sin^{-1} 0.803 \approx 53.5°$ or $\theta \approx 180° - 53.5° \approx 126.5°$.

24. $\angle A = 180° - 98° - 25° = 57°$. Then $x = \dfrac{1000 \cdot \sin 98°}{\sin 57°} \approx 1180.8$.

26. Suppose $ABCD$ is a parallelogram with $AB = DC = 5$,
     $AD = BC = 3$, and $\angle A = 50°$ (see figure to the right).
     Since opposite angles are equal in a parallelogram, it
     follows that $\angle C = 50°$, and $\angle B + \angle D = 360° - 100°$
     $= 260°$. Thus, $\angle B = \angle D = \frac{260°}{2} = 130°$. By the Law of
     Cosines, $AC^2 = 3^2 + 5^2 - 2(3)(5) \cdot \cos 130°$ $\Rightarrow$
     $AC = \sqrt{9 + 25 - 30 \cdot \cos 130°} \approx 7.3$ Similarly, $BD = \sqrt{3^2 + 5^2 - 2(3)(5) \cdot \cos 50°} \approx 3.8$.

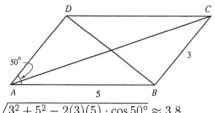

28. Let x be the car's distance from its original position. Since the car
     travels at a constant speed of 40 miles per hour, it must have traveled
     40 miles east, and then 20 miles northeast (which is 45° east of "due
     north"). From the diagram on the right, we see that: $\angle \beta = 135°$ so
     $x = \sqrt{20^2 + 40^2 - 2(20)(40) \cdot \cos 135°} = 10\sqrt{4 + 16 - 16 \cdot \cos 135°} \approx 56.0$ mi.

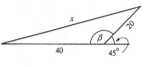

30. Let d be the distance between the two boats in miles. After one hour, the boats have traveled
     distances of 30 miles and 26 miles. Also, the angle subtended by their directions is
     $180° - 50° - 70° = 60°$. Then $d^2 = 30^2 + 26^2 - 2 \cdot 30 \cdot 26 \cdot \cos 60° = 796$ $\Leftrightarrow$
     $d \approx \sqrt{796} \approx 28.2$. Thus the distance between the two boats is about 28 miles.

32. Let θ be the angle formed by the cables. The two tugboats and the barge form a triangle: the
     side opposite θ has a length of 120 ft. and the other two sides have lengths of 212 and 230 ft.
     Therefore, $120^2 = 212^2 + 230^2 - 2(212)(230) \cdot \cos \theta$ $\Leftrightarrow$ $\cos \theta = \dfrac{212^2 + 230^2 - 120^2}{2(212)(230)}$ $\Rightarrow$
     $\cos \theta = 0.8557$ $\Rightarrow$ $\theta \approx \cos^{-1} 0.8557 \approx 31°$.

34. Let x be the length of the wire, and let θ be the angle opposite x as
     shown in the figure on the right. Since the mountain is inclined 32°,
     we must have $\theta = 180° - (90° - 32°) = 122°$. Thus,
     $x = \sqrt{55^2 + 125^2 - 2(55)(125) \cdot \cos 122°} \approx 161$ ft.

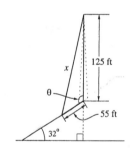

36. Let the woman be at point A, the first landmark (at 62°) be at point B, and the other landmark be at
     point C. We want to find the length BC. Now, $\cos 62° = \dfrac{1150}{AB}$ $\Leftrightarrow$ $AB = \dfrac{1150}{\cos 62°} \approx 2450$.
     Similarly, $\cos 54° = \dfrac{1150}{AC}$ $\Leftrightarrow$ $AC = \dfrac{1150}{\cos 54°} \approx 1956$. Therefore, by the Law of Cosines,
     $BC^2 = AB^2 + AC^2 - 2(AB)(AC) \cdot \cos 43°$ $\Rightarrow$
     $BC = \sqrt{2450^2 + 1956^2 - 2(2450)(1956) \cdot \cos 43°}$ $\Rightarrow$ $BC \approx 1679$. Thus, the two landmarks
     are roughly 1679 feet apart.

38. In any $\triangle ABC$, the Law of Cosines gives $a^2 = b^2 + c^2 - 2bc \cdot \cos A$, $b^2 = a^2 + c^2 - 2ac \cdot \cos B$,
     and $c^2 = a^2 + b^2 - 2ab \cdot \cos C$. Adding the second and third equations gives:

$$b^2 = a^2 + c^2 - 2ac \cdot \cos B$$
$$+ \quad c^2 = a^2 + b^2 - 2ab \cdot \cos C$$

     $\overline{b^2 + c^2 = 2a^2 + b^2 + c^2 - 2a(c \cos B + b \cos C)}$ $\Leftrightarrow$ $2a^2 - 2a(c \cos B + b \cos C) = 0$ $\Leftrightarrow$

$2a(a - c\cos B + b\cos C) = 0$. Since $a \neq 0$ we must have $a - (c\cos B + b\cos C) = 0 \quad \Leftrightarrow$
$a = b\cos C + c\cos B$. The other laws follow from the symmetry of a, b, and c.

40. By Heron's formula, $\mathcal{A} = \sqrt{s(s-a)(s-b)(s-c)}$, where $s = \frac{1}{2}(a+b+c) = \frac{1}{2}(12 + 18 + 24)$
$= 27$. Thus, $\mathcal{A} = \sqrt{27(15)(9)(3)} = \sqrt{10935} \approx 104.6 \text{ m}^2$.

42. Consider the triangle with sides of length 5 and 6 and contained angle $100°$. By the Law of Cosines,
$c^2 = a^2 + b^2 - 2ab \cdot \cos C = 5^2 + 6^2 - 2(5)(6) \cdot \cos 100° \approx 71.419 \quad \Rightarrow \quad c \approx 8.45$. Using
Heron's formula for the second triangle, we have $s = \frac{8+7+8.45}{2} \approx 11.73$, and so
$\mathcal{A} = \sqrt{11.73(11.73 - 8)(11.73 - 7)(11.73 - 8.45)} \approx 26.00$. Since the area of the quadrilateral
is the sum of the areas of the two triangles, we have:
$\mathcal{A} = \frac{1}{2}(5)(6)\sin 100° + 26.00 \approx 14.77 + 26.00 = 40.77 \text{ units}^2$.

Review Exercises for Chapter 7

2. (a) $24° = 24 \cdot \frac{\pi}{180} = \frac{2\pi}{15} \approx 0.42$ rad   (b) $-330° = -330 \cdot \frac{\pi}{180} = -\frac{11\pi}{6} \approx -5.76$ rad

   (c) $750° = 750 \cdot \frac{\pi}{180} = \frac{25\pi}{6} \approx 13.09$ rad   (d) $5° = 5 \cdot \frac{\pi}{180} = \frac{\pi}{36} \approx 0.87$ rad

4. (a) 8 rad $= 8 \cdot \frac{180}{\pi} = \frac{1440}{\pi} \approx 458.37°$ (b) $-\frac{5}{2}$ rad $= -\frac{5}{2} \cdot \frac{180}{\pi} = \frac{450}{\pi} \approx 143.24°$

   (c) $\frac{11\pi}{6}$ rad $= \frac{11\pi}{6} \cdot \frac{180}{\pi} = 330°$ (d) $\frac{3\pi}{5}$ rad $= \frac{3\pi}{5} \cdot \frac{180}{\pi} = 108°$

6. $s = 7$ ft, $r = 5$ ft. Then $\theta = \dfrac{s}{r} = \dfrac{7}{5} = 1.4$ rad $\approx 80.2°$

8. Since the diameter is 28 in, $r = 14$ in. In one revolution, the arc length (distance traveled) is
   $s = \theta r = 2\pi \cdot 14 = 28\pi$ in. The total distance traveled is 60 mi/h $\cdot$ 0.5 h $= 30$ mi.
   $= 30$ mi $\cdot$ 5280 ft/mi $\cdot$ 12 in/ft $= 1{,}900{,}800$ in. The number of revolution is
   $1{,}900{,}800$ in $\cdot \dfrac{1 \text{ rev}}{28\pi \text{ in}} \approx 21608.7$ rev. Therefore the car wheel will make approximately 21609
   revolutions.

10. $r = 5$ m, $\theta = 2$ rad. Then $A = \frac{1}{2}r^2\theta = \frac{1}{2} \cdot 5^2 \cdot 2 = 25$ m^2.

12. $A = 125$ ft^2, $r = 25$ ft. Then $\theta = \dfrac{2A}{r^2} = \dfrac{2 \cdot 125}{25^2} = \dfrac{250}{625} = 0.4$ rad $\approx 22.9°$

14. $x = \sqrt{10^2 - 3^2} = \sqrt{91}$. Then $\sin\theta = \frac{3}{10}$, $\cos\theta = \frac{\sqrt{91}}{10}$, $\tan\theta = \frac{3}{\sqrt{91}}$, $\csc\theta = \frac{10}{3}$, $\sec\theta = \frac{10}{\sqrt{91}}$, and
   $\cot\theta = \frac{\sqrt{91}}{3}$.

16. $\cos 35° = \dfrac{2}{x} \quad\Leftrightarrow\quad x = \dfrac{2}{\cos 35°} \approx 2.44$, and $\tan 35° = \dfrac{y}{2} \quad\Leftrightarrow\quad y = 2\tan 35° \approx 1.40$

18. $\cos 30° = \dfrac{x}{4} \quad\Leftrightarrow\quad x = 4\cos 30° \approx 3.46$, and $\sin 30° = \dfrac{y}{x} \quad\Leftrightarrow\quad y = x\sin 30° = 3.46 \times 0.5$
    ≈ 1.73

20. The other angle is $90° - 60° = 30°$,

    $\tan 60° = \dfrac{l}{20} \quad\Leftrightarrow\quad l = 20\tan 60° \approx 34.64$,

    $\cos 60° = \dfrac{20}{h} \quad\Leftrightarrow\quad h = \dfrac{20}{\cos 60°} = 40$

22. Let h be the height of the tower in meters. Then $\tan 28.81° = \dfrac{h}{1000} \quad\Leftrightarrow\quad h = 1000$
    $\tan 28.81° \approx 550$ m.

24. As the crankshaft moves in its circular pattern, point Q is determined by the angle θ, namely it has
    coordinates $Q(2\cos\theta, 2\sin\theta)$. We split the triangle into two right triangles, $\triangle OQR$ and $\triangle PQR$ as
    shown in the figure. Let h be the height of the piston. We consider two cases, $0° \leq \theta < 180°$ and
    $180° \leq \theta < 360°$.

    If $0° \leq \theta < 180°$, then h is the sum of OR and RP. Using the Pythagorean Theorem, we find

$RP = \sqrt{8^2 - (2\cos\theta)^2}$, while OR is the y-coordinate of the point Q, $2\sin\theta$. Thus
$h = \sqrt{64 - 4\cos^2\theta} + 2\sin\theta.$

If $180° \leq \theta < 360°$, then h is the difference between RP and RO. Again,
$RP = \sqrt{64 - 4\cos^2\theta}$ and OR is the y-coordinate of the point Q, $2\sin\theta$. Thus
$h = \sqrt{64 - 4\cos^2\theta} - 2\,|\sin\theta|$. Since $\sin\theta < 0$ for $180° < \theta < 360°$, this also reduces to $h = \sqrt{64 - 4\cos^2\theta} + 2\sin\theta.$

Since we get the same result in both cases, the height of the piston in terms of θ is
$h = \sqrt{64 - 4\cos^2\theta} + 2\sin\theta.$

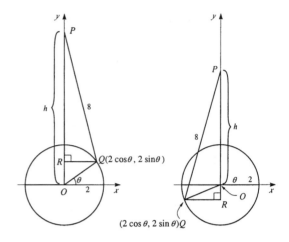

26. Let d_1 represent the horizontal distance from a point directly below the plane to the closer ship in ft, and d_2 represent the horizontal distance to the other ship in ft. Then $\tan 52° = \dfrac{35{,}000}{d_1}$ $\Leftrightarrow$

$d_1 = \frac{35{,}000}{\tan 52°}$, and similarly, $\tan 40° = \dfrac{35{,}000}{d_2}$ $\Leftrightarrow$ $d_2 = \dfrac{35{,}000}{\tan 40°}$. So the distance between the two ships is $d_2 - d_1 = \dfrac{35{,}000}{\tan 40°} - \dfrac{35{,}000}{\tan 52°} \approx 14{,}400$ ft.

28. $\csc \frac{9\pi}{4} = \csc \frac{\pi}{4} = \sqrt{2}$

30. $\cos\left(\frac{5\pi}{6}\right) = -\cos\frac{\pi}{6} = -\frac{\sqrt{3}}{2}$

32. $\sin 405° = \sin 45° = \frac{1}{\sqrt{2}} = \frac{\sqrt{2}}{2}$

34. $\sec\left(\frac{22\pi}{3}\right) = \sec\left(\frac{4\pi}{3}\right) = -\sec\frac{\pi}{3} = -2$

36. $\sec \frac{13\pi}{6} = \sec \frac{\pi}{6} = \frac{2\sqrt{3}}{3}$

38. $\tan \frac{23\pi}{4} = \tan \frac{3\pi}{4} = -\tan \frac{\pi}{4} = -1$

40. If θ is in standard position, then the terminal point of θ on the unit circle is simply $(\cos\theta, \sin\theta)$. Since the terminal point is given as $\left(-\frac{\sqrt{3}}{2}, \frac{1}{2}\right)$, $\sin\theta = \frac{1}{2}$.

42. $4y - 2x - 1 = 0$ $\Leftrightarrow$ $y = \frac{1}{2}x + \frac{1}{4}$. The slope of the line is $m = \frac{1}{2}$. Then $\tan\theta = m = \frac{1}{2}$ and $r = \sqrt{1^2 + 2^2} = \sqrt{5}$. So $\sin\theta = -\frac{1}{\sqrt{5}}$, $\cos\theta = -\frac{2}{\sqrt{5}}$, $\tan\theta = \frac{1}{2}$, $\csc\theta = -\sqrt{5}$, $\sec\theta = -\frac{\sqrt{5}}{2}$, and $\cot\theta = 2.$

44. $\sec\theta = \dfrac{1}{\cos\theta} = \dfrac{1}{-\sqrt{1 - \sin^2\theta}}$ (since $\cos\theta < 0$ in quadrant III)

46. $\csc^2\theta \cos^2\theta = \dfrac{1}{\sin^2\theta} \cdot \cos^2\theta = \dfrac{1 - \sin^2\theta}{\sin^2\theta} = \dfrac{1}{\sin^2\theta} - 1$

48. $\sec\theta = \frac{41}{40}$, $\csc\theta = -\frac{41}{9}$. Then $\sin\theta = -\frac{9}{41}$, $\cos\theta = \frac{40}{41}$, $\tan\theta = \dfrac{\sin\theta}{\cos\theta} = \dfrac{-\frac{9}{41}}{\frac{40}{41}} = -\frac{9}{40}$, and $\cot\theta = -\frac{40}{9}.$

50. $\sec\theta = -\frac{13}{5}$ and $\tan\theta > 0$. Then $\cos\theta = -\frac{5}{13}$, and θ must be in quadrant III $\Rightarrow$ $\sin\theta < 0$.

Therefore, $\sin\theta = -\sqrt{1 - \cos^2\theta} = -\sqrt{1 - \frac{25}{169}} = -\frac{12}{13}$, $\csc\theta = -\frac{13}{12}$, $\tan\theta = \frac{\sin\theta}{\cos\theta} = \frac{12}{5}$, and $\cot\theta = \frac{5}{12}$.

52. $\sin\theta = \frac{1}{2}$ for θ in quadrant I. Then $\tan\theta + \sec\theta = \frac{\sin\theta}{\cos\theta} + \frac{1}{\cos\theta} = \frac{\sin\theta + 1}{\cos\theta} = \frac{\sin\theta + 1}{\sqrt{1 - \sin^2\theta}}$

$= \frac{\frac{1}{2} + 1}{\sqrt{1 - \frac{1}{2}}} = \frac{2\sqrt{3}}{2} = \sqrt{3}$

54. $\cos\theta = -\frac{\sqrt{3}}{2}$ and $\frac{\pi}{2} < \theta < \pi$. Then $\theta = \frac{5\pi}{6}$ $\Rightarrow$ $2\theta = \frac{10\pi}{6} = \frac{5\pi}{3}$. So $\sin 2\theta = \sin\frac{5\pi}{3} = -\sin\frac{\pi}{3}$

$= -\frac{\sqrt{3}}{2}$

56. $x = \dfrac{2 \cdot \sin 45°}{\sin 105°} \approx 1.46$

58. $x^2 = 2^2 + 8^2 - 2(2)(8) \cdot \cos 120° = 84$ $\Leftrightarrow$ $x \approx \sqrt{84} \approx 9.17$

60. $\sin B = \dfrac{4 \cdot \sin 110°}{6} \approx 0.626$ $\Leftrightarrow$ $\angle B \approx 38.79°$. Then $\angle C \approx 180° - 110° - 38.79° = 31.21°$,

and so $x \approx \dfrac{6 \cdot \sin 31.21°}{\sin 110°} \approx 3.3$.

62. Let h represent the height of the building in feet, and x represent the horizontal distance from the building to point B. Then $\tan 24.1° = \dfrac{h}{x + 600}$ and $\tan 30.2° = \dfrac{h}{x}$ $\Leftrightarrow$ $x = h \cot 30.2°$.

Substituting for x gives $\tan 24.1° = \dfrac{h}{h \cot 30.2° + 600}$ $\Leftrightarrow$ $h = \tan 24.1° \, (h \cot 30.2° + 600)$

$\Leftrightarrow$ $h = \dfrac{600 \cdot \tan 24.1°}{1 - \tan 24.1° \cot 30.2°} \approx 1160$ ft.

64. $\angle C = 180° - 42.3° - 68.9° = 68.8°$. Then $b = \dfrac{120 \cdot \sin 68.9°}{\sin 68.8°} \approx 120.08$ miles. Let d be the shortest distance, in miles, to the shore. Then $d = b \sin A \approx 120.08 \sin 42.3° \approx 80.8$ miles.

66. $A = \frac{1}{2}ab \sin\theta = \frac{1}{2}(8)(14) \sin 35° \approx 32.12$

Focus on Problem Solving

2. Each face of the old polyhedron is represented by vertex in the new polyhedron, so $F_{\text{old}} = V_{\text{new}}$. Two vertices of the new polyhedron are connect if they share an edge in the old polyhedron, so the number of edges of a face of the old polyhedron is equal to the number of edges that meet at any one vertex. Also each vertex of the old polyhedron now corresponds to a face in the new polyhedron, so $V_{\text{old}} = F_{\text{new}}$. We also have $E_{\text{old}} = E_{\text{new}}$.

    Tetrahedron: 4 equilateral triangles, $F_{\text{old}} = 4$, $V_{\text{old}} = 4$. Since each vertex of a tetrahedron has 3 edges, the new polyhedron will have 4 faces that are triangles and 4 vertices. Thus the new polyhedron constructed this way is a tetrahedron.

    Octahedron: 8 equilateral triangles, $F_{\text{old}} = 8$, $V_{\text{old}} = 6$. Since each vertex of a octahedron: has 4 edges, the new polyhedron will have 6 faces that are squares and 6 vertices. Thus the new polyhedron constructed this way is a cube.

    Cube: 6 squares, $F_{\text{old}} = 6$, $V_{\text{old}} = 8$. Since each vertex of a cube has 3 edges, the new polyhedron will have 8 faces that are triangles and 8 vertices. Thus the new polyhedron constructed this way is an octahedron.

    Dodecahedron: 12 pentagons, $F_{\text{old}} = 12$, $V_{\text{old}} = 20$. Since each vertex of a dodecahedron has 3 edges, the new polyhedron will have 20 faces that are triangles and 12 vertices. Thus the new polyhedron constructed this way is an icosahedron.

    Icosahedron: 20 equilateral triangles, $F_{\text{old}} = 20$, $V_{\text{old}} = 12$. Since each vertex of an icosahedron has 5 edges, the new polyhedron will have 12 faces that are pentagons and 20 vertices. Thus the new polyhedron constructed this way is a dodecahedron.

4. (a) As shown in the figure for A_n, there are n equal triangles each having an interior angle of $\dfrac{2\pi}{n}$. The area of each triangle is

    $\frac{1}{2} \cdot b \cdot h = \frac{1}{2} \cdot 2 \cdot \sin \dfrac{\pi}{n} \cos \dfrac{\pi}{n} = \frac{1}{2}\sin \dfrac{2\pi}{n}$ (by the double angle formula for sine), and so $A_n = \dfrac{n}{2} \sin \dfrac{2\pi}{n}$.

    (b) $A_3 = \frac{3}{2} \sin \frac{2\pi}{3} = \frac{3\sqrt{3}}{4} \approx 1.299038$, $A_4 = \frac{4}{2} \sin \frac{2\pi}{4} = 2.000000$, $A_{100} = \frac{100}{2} \sin \frac{2\pi}{100} = 50 \sin \frac{\pi}{50} \approx 3.139526$, and $A_{1000} = \frac{1000}{2} \sin \frac{2\pi}{1000} = 500 \sin \frac{\pi}{500} \approx 3.141572$. The terms are approaching π because the area of a circle of radius 1 is $\pi r^2 = \pi \cdot 1^2 = \pi$.

6. (a) We redraw the figure and include the radii where the belt meets the pulleys and a line that joins the centers of the pulleys. Since the belt is tangent to the circle at the point where it meets the pulley, $\angle PAO$ is $90°$. And since $\triangle AOP$ and $\triangle BOP$ are similar triangles $\angle APO = 30°$. So $\triangle AOP$ and $\triangle BOP$ are $30°$-$60°$ triangles. Likewise, $\triangle CQP$ and $\triangle DQP$ are $30°$-$60°$ triangles. Since $|OA| = 2$ we have $|AP| = |BP| = 2\sqrt{3}$ and since $|CQ| = 1$ we have $|CP| = |DP| = \sqrt{3}$. Now the length of the belt is

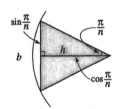

$\left(\begin{array}{c}\text{\textit{arc length around the}}\\ \text{\textit{2 inch pulley}}\end{array}\right) + \left(\begin{array}{c}\text{\textit{arc length around the}}\\ \text{\textit{1 inch pulley}}\end{array}\right) + |AD| + |BC|$. But $\angle AOB = 120°$ so the length of the arc around the 2 inch pulley is $\frac{240°}{360°} \times$ [circumference] $= \frac{2}{3} \times 2\pi r = \frac{8\pi}{3}$. Similarly, for the 1 inch pulley, the length of the arc is $\frac{2}{3} \times 2\pi(1) = \frac{4\pi}{3}$. Therefore the length of the belt is $\frac{8\pi}{3} + \frac{4\pi}{3} + 3\sqrt{3} + 3\sqrt{3} = 4\pi + 6\sqrt{3} \approx 22.96$ inches.

(b) We redraw and label the figure. Since the belt is tangent to the circle at the point where it meets the pulley, $\angle QAB = 90°$. Likewise, $\angle OBA = 90°$. Therefore $OBAA'$ is a rectangle and $\angle OA'Q = 90°$. Since $|A'Q| = 3$ and $|OQ| = 6$, $\triangle A'OQ$ is a 30°-60° right triangle.

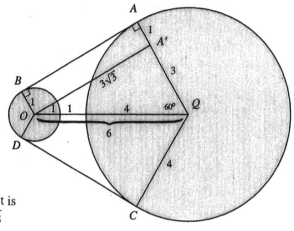

Since $|OQ| = 6$ we have $|OA'| = 3\sqrt{3}$, so $|BA| = |DC| = 3\sqrt{3}$. Now,
$\angle BOQ = \angle BOA' + \angle A'OQ$
$= 90° + 30° = 120°$, likewise,
$\angle DOQ = 120°$. Thus the length of the arc on the 1 inch pulley is
$\frac{120°}{360°} \times$ [circumference] $= \frac{1}{3} \times 2\pi r$
$= \frac{2\pi}{3}$. Now $\angle AQC = 120°$ so the length of the arc on the 4 inch pulley is $\frac{240°}{360°} \times$ [circumference] $= \frac{2}{3} \times 2\pi r$
$= \frac{16\pi}{3}$. Therefore the length of the belt is
$\frac{2\pi}{3} + \frac{16\pi}{3} + 3\sqrt{3} + 3\sqrt{3} = 6\pi + 6\sqrt{3}$
≈ 29.24 inches.

8. Applying the Law of Cosines we have $a^2 = b^2 + c^2 - 2bc \cos A$
$\Leftrightarrow \quad \cos A = \dfrac{b^2 + c^2 - a^2}{2bc}$. Since A, B, and C are rational numbers, $\dfrac{b^2 + c^2 - a^2}{2bc}$ must also be rational number since the set of rational numbers is closed under addition and multiplication. Likewise, $\cos B = \dfrac{a^2 + c^2 - b^2}{2ac}$ and $\cos C = \dfrac{a^2 + b^2 - c^2}{2ab}$ must also be rational.

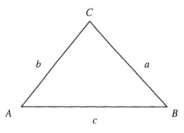

10. Let s represent the actual distance on the earth, and p represent the projected distance. (Let r be the radius of the earth.)

(a) $s = r\theta = r \cdot \frac{\pi}{180} \approx 0.01745\,r$. $p = r \tan 21° - r \tan 20° \approx 0.01989r$. Thus, the distortion factor is $\dfrac{p}{s} \approx \dfrac{0.01989\,r}{0.01745\,r} \approx 1.14$.

(b) $s = r\theta = r \cdot \frac{\pi}{180}$. $p = r \tan 41° - r \tan 40°$. The distortion factor is
$\dfrac{p}{s} = \dfrac{\tan 41° - \tan 40°}{\pi/180} \approx 1.7$.

(c) $s = r \cdot \frac{\pi}{180}$. $p = r \tan 81° - r \tan 80°$. The distortion factor is $\dfrac{p}{s} = \dfrac{\tan 81° - \tan 80°}{\pi/180} \approx 36.8$.

(d)   Let r_1 be the radius of the 20th parallel. So $\dfrac{r_1}{r} = \cos 20°$ $\Leftrightarrow$ $r_1 = r\cos 20°$. Then

$s = r_1\theta = r\cos 20° \cdot \frac{\pi}{180}$ and $p = r\theta = r \cdot \frac{\pi}{180}$. The distortion factor is

$$\frac{p}{s} = \frac{r \cdot \frac{\pi}{180}}{r\cos 20° \cdot \frac{\pi}{180}} = \frac{1}{\cos 20°} \approx 1.0.$$

(e)   In the same way as in part (a), the distortion factor is $\dfrac{p}{s} = \dfrac{1}{\cos 40°} \approx 1.31$.

(f)   In the same way as in part (a), the distortion factor is $\dfrac{p}{s} = \dfrac{1}{\cos 80°} \approx 5.76$.

12. Let p be an odd prime and label the other integer sides of the triangle as shown. Then $p^2 + b^2 = c^2$ $\Leftrightarrow$ $p^2 = c^2 - b^2$ $\Leftrightarrow$ $p^2 = (c - b)(c + b)$. Now, $c - b$ and $c + b$ are integer factors of p^2 where p is a prime.

Case 1: $c - b = p$ and $c + b = p$. Subtracting gives $b = 0$ which contradicts that b is the length of a side of a triangle.

Case 2: $c - b = 1$ and $c + b = p^2$. Adding gives $2c = 1 + p^2$ $\Leftrightarrow$ $c = \dfrac{1 + p^2}{2}$ and $b = \dfrac{p^2 - 1}{2}$.

Since p is odd, p^2 is odd. Thus $\dfrac{1 + p^2}{2}$ and $\dfrac{p^2 - 1}{2}$ both define integers and are the only solutions.
(For example, if we choose $p = 3$, then $c = 5$ and $b = 4$.)

14. (a) If $2p + 1$ is a perfect square, then $2p + 1 = n^2$ $\Leftrightarrow$ $2p = n^2 - 1$ $\Leftrightarrow$ $2p = (n + 1)(n - 1)$.

Case 1: $n + 1 = 2$ and $n - 1 = p$. Thus $n = 1$ $\Rightarrow$ $p = 0$ which contradicts the fact that p is prime.

Case 2: $n + 1 = p$ and $n - 1 = 2$. Thus $n = 3$ $\Rightarrow$ $p = 4$ which contradicts the fact that p is prime.

Thus there are no such primes.

(b) If $2p + 1$ is a perfect cube, then $2p + 1 = n^3$ $\Leftrightarrow$ $2p = n^3 - 1$ $\Leftrightarrow$ $2p = (n - 1)(n^2 + n + 1)$. Since p is prime we have 2 cases.

Case 1: $n - 1 = 2$ and $n^2 + n + 1 = p$. Thus $n = 3$ $\Rightarrow$ $p = n^2 + n + 1 = 9 + 3 + 1$ $= 13$. So $p = 13$ is a solution.

Case 2: $n - 1 = p$ and $n^2 + n + 1 = 2$. In this case $n^2 + n - 1 = 0$ $\Rightarrow$

$n = \dfrac{-1 \pm \sqrt{1+4}}{2} = \dfrac{-1 \pm \sqrt{5}}{2}$ which is not an integer..

Thus the only solution is $p = 13$.

Chapter Eight

Exercises 8.1

2. Since $\left(\frac{40}{41}\right)^2 + \left(\frac{9}{41}\right)^2 = \frac{1600}{1681} + \frac{81}{1681} = 1$, $P\left(\frac{40}{41}, \frac{9}{41}\right)$ lies on the unit circle.

4. Since $\left(-\frac{5}{13}\right)^2 + \left(-\frac{12}{13}\right)^2 = \frac{25}{169} + \frac{144}{169} = 1$, $P\left(-\frac{5}{13}, -\frac{12}{13}\right)$ lies on the unit circle.

6. $x^2 + \left(-\frac{1}{3}\right)^2 = 1 \quad \Leftrightarrow \quad x^2 = 1 - \frac{1}{9} \quad \Leftrightarrow \quad x^2 = \frac{8}{9} \quad \Leftrightarrow \quad x = \pm\frac{2\sqrt{2}}{3}$. Since P is in quadrant III, x is negative. Therefore, the point is $P\left(-\frac{2\sqrt{2}}{3}, -\frac{1}{3}\right)$.

8. $x^2 + \left(-\frac{\sqrt{5}}{5}\right)^2 = 1 \quad \Leftrightarrow \quad x^2 = 1 - \frac{5}{25} \quad \Leftrightarrow \quad x^2 = \frac{20}{25} \quad \Leftrightarrow \quad x = \pm\frac{2\sqrt{5}}{5}$. Since we know x is positive, the point is $P\left(\frac{2\sqrt{5}}{5}, -\frac{\sqrt{5}}{5}\right)$.

10. $\left(-\frac{2}{5}\right)^2 + y^2 = 1 \quad \Leftrightarrow \quad y^2 = 1 - \frac{4}{25} \quad \Leftrightarrow \quad y^2 = \frac{21}{25} \quad \Leftrightarrow \quad y = \pm\frac{\sqrt{21}}{5}$. Since P is in quadrant II, y is positive, and the point is $P\left(-\frac{2}{5}, \frac{\sqrt{21}}{5}\right)$.

12. Quadrant I

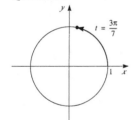

14. Quadrant III

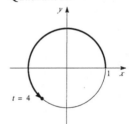

16. Quadrant I

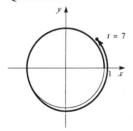

18. $P(x, y) = (0, 1)$

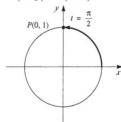

20. $P(x, y) = \left(-\frac{\sqrt{3}}{2}, -\frac{1}{2}\right)$

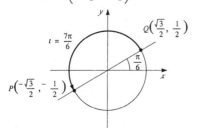

22. $P(x, y) = \left(-\frac{\sqrt{3}}{2}, -\frac{1}{2}\right)$

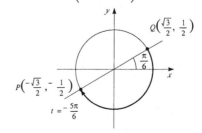

24. $P(x, y) = (0, -1)$

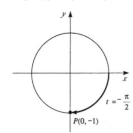

26. $P(x, y) = \left(\frac{\sqrt{3}}{2}, -\frac{1}{2}\right)$

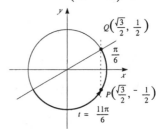

28. Let $Q(x, y) = \left(\frac{1}{3}, \frac{2\sqrt{2}}{3}\right)$ be the terminal point determined by t.

(a) $-t$ determines the point $P(x, -y) = \left(\frac{1}{3}, -\frac{2\sqrt{2}}{3}\right)$.

(b) $4\pi + t$ determines the point $P(x, y) = \left(\frac{1}{3}, \frac{2\sqrt{2}}{3}\right)$.

(c) $\pi - t$ determines the point $P(-x, y) = \left(-\frac{1}{3}, \frac{2\sqrt{2}}{3}\right)$.

(d) $t - \pi$ determines the point $P(-x, -y) = \left(-\frac{1}{3}, -\frac{2\sqrt{2}}{3}\right)$.

30. (a) $\overline{t} = \pi - \frac{5\pi}{7} = \frac{2\pi}{7}$ (b) $\overline{t} = \frac{9\pi}{8} - \pi = \frac{\pi}{8}$

    (c) $\overline{t} = 3.55 - \pi \approx 3.55 - 3.14 = 0.41$ (d) $\overline{t} = -2.9 + \pi \approx -2.9 + 3.14 = 0.24$

32. (a) $\overline{t} = \pi - 3 \approx 3.14 - 3 = 0.14$ (b) $\overline{t} = 2\pi - 6 \approx 6.28 - 6 = 0.28$

    (c) $\overline{t} = -3 + \pi \approx -3 + 3.14 = 0.14$ (d) $\overline{t} = -6 + \pi \approx -6 + 6.28 = 0.28$

34. (a) $\overline{t} = \frac{7\pi}{3} - 2\pi = \frac{\pi}{3}$ (b) $P\left(\frac{1}{2}, \frac{\sqrt{3}}{2}\right)$

36. (a) $\overline{t} = \frac{7\pi}{6} - \pi = \frac{\pi}{6}$ (b) $P\left(-\frac{\sqrt{3}}{2}, \frac{1}{2}\right)$

38. (a) $\overline{t} = \frac{13\pi}{6} - 2\pi = \frac{\pi}{6}$ (b) $P\left(\frac{\sqrt{3}}{2}, \frac{1}{2}\right)$

40. (a) $\overline{t} = \frac{17\pi}{4} - 4\pi = \frac{\pi}{4}$ (b) $P\left(\frac{\sqrt{2}}{2}, \frac{\sqrt{2}}{2}\right)$

42. (a) $\overline{t} = \frac{31\pi}{6} - 5\pi = \frac{\pi}{6}$ (b) $P\left(-\frac{\sqrt{3}}{2}, -\frac{1}{2}\right)$

44. (a) $\overline{t} = -10\pi - \left(-\frac{41\pi}{4}\right) = \frac{\pi}{4}$ (b) $P\left(\frac{\sqrt{2}}{2}, \frac{-\sqrt{2}}{2}\right)$

46. $t = 2.5 \quad \Rightarrow \quad P(-0.8, 0.6)$ **48.** $t = 4.2 \quad \Rightarrow \quad P(-0.6, -0.9)$

50. P is the reflection of Q about the line $y = x$. Since Q is the point $Q\left(\frac{\sqrt{3}}{2}, \frac{1}{2}\right)$ it follows that P is the point $P\left(\frac{1}{2}, \frac{\sqrt{3}}{2}\right)$.

Exercises 8.2

2.   (a) $\sin \pi = 0$ (b) $\cos \pi = -1$

4.   (a) $\cos \frac{\pi}{6} = \frac{\sqrt{3}}{2}$ (b) $\cos \frac{5\pi}{6} = -\frac{\sqrt{3}}{2}$

6.   (a) $\sin \frac{7\pi}{6} = -\frac{1}{2}$ (b) $\cos \frac{7\pi}{6} = -\frac{\sqrt{3}}{2}$

8.   (a) $\sin \frac{5\pi}{6} = \frac{1}{2}$ (b) $\sec \frac{5\pi}{6} = -\frac{2}{\sqrt{3}}$

10.   (a) $\sin \frac{3\pi}{4} = \frac{1}{\sqrt{2}} = \frac{\sqrt{2}}{2}$ (b) $\cos \frac{3\pi}{4} = -\frac{1}{\sqrt{2}} = -\frac{\sqrt{2}}{2}$

12.   (a) $\sin \frac{\pi}{6} = \frac{1}{2}$ (b) $\sin\left(-\frac{\pi}{6}\right) = -\frac{1}{2}$

14.   (a) $\tan \frac{\pi}{3} = \sqrt{3}$ (b) $\cot \frac{\pi}{3} = \frac{1}{\sqrt{3}} = \frac{\sqrt{3}}{3}$

16.   (a) $\sec \frac{13\pi}{6} = \frac{2}{\sqrt{3}} = \frac{2\sqrt{3}}{3}$ (b) $\sec \left(-\frac{13\pi}{6}\right) = \frac{2}{\sqrt{3}} = \frac{2\sqrt{3}}{3}$

18.   (a) $\sec \pi = -1$ (b) $\csc \frac{\pi}{2} = 1$

20.   (a) $\tan \frac{3\pi}{4} = -1$ (b) $\tan \frac{11\pi}{4} = -1$

22. $t = \frac{\pi}{2}$ $\Rightarrow$ $\sin t = 1, \cos t = 0, \csc t = 1, \cot t = 0, \tan t$ and $\sec t$ are undefined.

24. $t = \frac{3\pi}{2}$ $\Rightarrow$ $\sin t = -1, \cos t = 0, \csc t = -1, \cot t = 0, \tan t$ and $\sec t$ are undefined.

26. $\left(-\frac{3}{5}\right)^2 + \left(\frac{4}{5}\right)^2 = \frac{9}{25} + \frac{16}{25} = 1.$ So $\sin t = \frac{4}{5}, \cos t = -\frac{3}{5},$ and $\tan t = \dfrac{\frac{4}{5}}{-\frac{3}{5}} = -\dfrac{4}{3}.$

28. $\left(-\frac{1}{3}\right)^2 + \left(-\frac{2\sqrt{2}}{3}\right)^2 = \frac{1}{9} + \frac{8}{9} = 1.$ So $\sin t = -\frac{2\sqrt{2}}{3}, \cos t = -\frac{1}{3},$ and $\tan t = \dfrac{-\frac{2\sqrt{2}}{3}}{-\frac{1}{3}} = 2\sqrt{2}.$

30. $\left(-\frac{3}{5}\right)^2 + \left(-\frac{4}{5}\right)^2 = \frac{9}{25} + \frac{16}{25} = 1.$ So $\sin t = -\frac{4}{5}, \cos t = -\frac{3}{5},$ and $\tan t = \dfrac{-\frac{4}{5}}{-\frac{3}{5}} = \dfrac{4}{3}.$

32. $\left(\frac{\sqrt{5}}{5}\right)^2 + \left(\frac{2\sqrt{5}}{5}.\right)^2 = \frac{5}{25} + \frac{20}{25} = 1.$ So $\sin t = \frac{2\sqrt{5}}{5}, \cos t = \frac{\sqrt{5}}{5},$ and $\tan t = \dfrac{\frac{2\sqrt{5}}{5}}{\frac{\sqrt{5}}{5}} = 2.$

34.   (a) 0.7   (b) 0.69671

36.   (a) 0.3   (b) 0.28366

38.   (a) -3.6 (b) -3.60210

40.   (a) 0.9   (b) 0.88345

42. $\sin^2 t \cdot \cos t$ is positive in quadrant IV because $\sin^2 t$ is always positive and $\cos t$ is positive in quadrant IV.

44. $\cos t \cdot \sec t$ is positive in any quadrant, since $\cos t \cdot \sec t = \cos t \cdot \frac{1}{\cos t} = 1,$ provided $\cos t \neq 0.$

46.   quadrant III   48.   quadrant II

50. $\cos t = \sqrt{1 - \sin^2 t}$

52. $\tan t = -\dfrac{\sqrt{1 - \cos^2 t}}{\cos t}$

54. $\csc t = -\sqrt{1 + \cot^2 t}$

56. $\sin t = -\sqrt{1 - \cos^2 t} = -\sqrt{1 - \dfrac{1}{\sec^2 t}}$

58. $\sec^2 t \cdot \sin^2 t = \frac{1}{\cos^2 t} \cdot (1 - \cos^2 t) = \frac{1}{\cos^2 t} - 1$

60. $\cos t = -\frac{4}{5}$ and t lies in quadrant III, so the terminal point determined by t is $P\left(-\frac{4}{5},\, y\right)$. Since P is
     on the unit circle $\left(-\frac{4}{5}\right)^2 + y^2 = 1$. Solving for y gives $x = \pm\sqrt{1 - \frac{16}{25}} = \pm\sqrt{\frac{9}{25}} = \pm\frac{3}{5}$. Since t is
     in quadrant III, $y = -\frac{3}{5}$. Thus the terminal point is $P\left(-\frac{4}{5}, -\frac{3}{5}\right)$. Thus, $\sin t = -\frac{3}{5}$, $\tan t = \frac{3}{4}$,
     $\csc t = -\frac{5}{3}$, $\sec t = -\frac{5}{4}$, $\cot t = \frac{4}{3}$.

62. $\sec t = 3$ and t lies in quadrant IV. Thus, $\cos t = \frac{1}{3}$ and the terminal point determined by t is
     $P\left(\frac{1}{3}, y\right)$. Since P is on the unit circle $\left(\frac{1}{3}\right)^2 + y^2 = 1$. Solving for y gives $y = \pm\sqrt{1 - \frac{1}{9}}$
     $= \pm\sqrt{\frac{8}{9}} = \pm\frac{2\sqrt{2}}{3}$. Since t is in quadrant IV, $y = -\frac{2\sqrt{2}}{3}$. Thus the terminal point is $P\left(\frac{1}{3}, -\frac{2\sqrt{2}}{3}\right)$.
     Therefore, $\sin t = -\frac{2\sqrt{2}}{3}$, $\cos t = \frac{1}{3}$, $\tan t = -2\sqrt{2}$, $\csc t = -\frac{3}{2\sqrt{2}}$, $\cot t = -\frac{1}{2\sqrt{2}}$.

64. $\tan t = \frac{1}{4}$ and t lies in quadrant III. Since $\sec^2 t = \tan^2 t + 1$ we have $\sec^2 t = \left(\frac{1}{4}\right)^2 + 1 = \frac{1}{16} + 1$
     $= \frac{17}{16}$. Thus $\sec t = \pm\sqrt{\frac{17}{16}} = \pm\frac{\sqrt{17}}{4}$. Since $\sec t < 0$ in quadrant III we have $\sec t = -\frac{\sqrt{17}}{4}$, so $\cos$
     $t = \dfrac{1}{\sec t} = \dfrac{1}{-\frac{\sqrt{17}}{4}} = -\dfrac{4}{\sqrt{17}} = -\dfrac{4\sqrt{17}}{17}$. Since $\tan t \cdot \cos t = \sin t$ we have $\sin t = \left(\frac{1}{4}\right)\left(-\frac{4}{\sqrt{17}}\right)$
     $= -\dfrac{1}{\sqrt{17}} = -\dfrac{\sqrt{17}}{17}$. Thus, the terminal point determined by t is $P\left(-\frac{4\sqrt{17}}{17}, -\frac{\sqrt{17}}{17}\right)$. Therefore,
     $\sin t = -\frac{\sqrt{17}}{17}$, $\cos t = -\frac{4\sqrt{17}}{17}$, $\csc t = -\sqrt{17}$, $\sec t = -\frac{\sqrt{17}}{4}$, $\cot t = 4$.

66. $\tan t = -4$ and t lies in quadrant II. Since $\sec^2 t = \tan^2 t + 1$ we have $\sec^2 t = (-4)^2 + 1 = 16 + 1$
     $= 17$. Thus $\sec t = \pm\sqrt{17}$. Since $\sec t < 0$, we have $\sec t = -\sqrt{17}$ and $\cos t = \dfrac{1}{\sec t} = \dfrac{1}{-\sqrt{17}}$
     $= -\frac{\sqrt{17}}{17}$. Since $\tan t \cdot \cos t = \sin t$ we have $\sin t = (-4)\left(-\frac{\sqrt{17}}{17}\right) = \frac{4\sqrt{17}}{17}$. Thus, the terminal
     point determined by t is $P\left(-\frac{\sqrt{17}}{17}, \frac{4\sqrt{17}}{17}\right)$.   Thus, $\sin t = \frac{4\sqrt{17}}{17}$, $\cos t = -\frac{\sqrt{17}}{17}$, $\csc t = \frac{\sqrt{17}}{4}$,
     $\sec t = -\sqrt{17}$, $\cot t = -\frac{1}{4}$.

68. $f(-x) = (-x)^2 \cos 2(-x) = x^2 \cos 2x = f(x)$ so f is even.

70. $f(-x) = e^{(-x)}\sin(-x) = -e^{-x}\sin x$ which is neither $f(x)$ nor $-f(x)$, so f is neither even
     nor odd.

72. $f(-x) = -x\sin^3(-x) = -x\,[\sin(-x)]^3 = -x(-\sin x)^3 = x\sin^3 x = f(x)$ so f is even.

74. $f(-x) = \cos[\sin(-x)] = \cos(-\sin x) = \cos(\sin x) = f(x)$ so f is even.

76. To prove $\triangle AOB \cong \triangle CDO$, first note that $OB = OD = 1$ and $\angle OAB = \angle OCD = \frac{\pi}{2}$. Now,
     $\angle COD + \angle AOB + \frac{\pi}{2} = \pi \quad \Leftrightarrow \quad \angle COD = \frac{\pi}{2} - \angle AOB = \angle ABO$. Since we know two angles
     and one side to be equal, the triangles are (SAA) congruent. Thus $AB = OC$ and $OA = CD$, so if
     B has coordinates (x, y), then D has coordinates $(-y, x)$. Therefore,
     (a) $\sin\left(t + \frac{\pi}{2}\right) = x = \cos t$

(b) $\cos\left(t + \frac{\pi}{2}\right) = -y$, and $\sin t = y$. Therefore, $\cos\left(t + \frac{\pi}{2}\right) = -\sin t$.

(c) $\tan\left(t + \dfrac{\pi}{2}\right) = \dfrac{x}{-y} = -\dfrac{x}{y} = -\dfrac{\cos t}{\sin t} = -\cot t$

Exercises 8.3

2. $y = -\sin x$

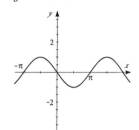

4. $y = -1 + \cos x$

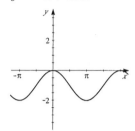

6. $y = -3\sin x$

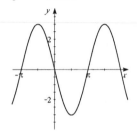

8. $y = 4 - 2\sin x$

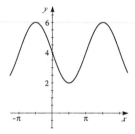

10. $y = |\cos x|$

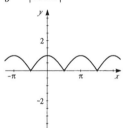

12. $y = -2\sin 2\pi x$
     amplitude $= 2$, period $= 1$

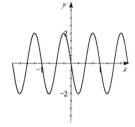

14. $y = \cos 10\pi x$
     amplitude $= 1$, period $= \frac{1}{5}$,

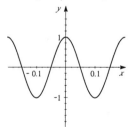

16. $y = \sin(-2x)$
     amplitude $= 1$, period $= \pi$

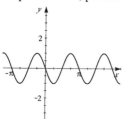

18. $y = 5 - 2\sin 2x$
     amplitude $= 2$, period $= \pi$

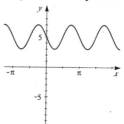

20. $y = 2\sin(x - \frac{\pi}{3})$
     amplitude $= 2$, period $= 2\pi$,
     phase shift $= \frac{\pi}{3}$

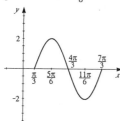

22. $y = 3\cos(x + \frac{\pi}{4})$
     amplitude $= 3$, period $= 2\pi$,
     phase shift $= \frac{\pi}{4}$

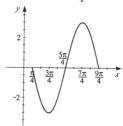

24. $y = -4\sin 2\left(x + \frac{\pi}{2}\right)$
     amplitude $= 4$, period $= \pi$,
     phase shift $= -\frac{\pi}{2}$

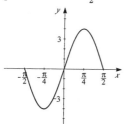

26. $y = \sin \frac{1}{2}\left(x + \frac{\pi}{4}\right)$
     amplitude $= 1$, period $= 4\pi$,
     phase shift $= -\frac{\pi}{4}$

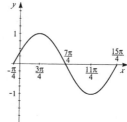

28. $y = 1 + \cos\left(3x + \frac{\pi}{2}\right) = 1 + \cos 3\left(x + \frac{\pi}{6}\right)$
     amplitude $= 1$, period $= \frac{2\pi}{3}$,
     phase shift $= -\frac{\pi}{6}$

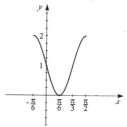

30. $y = 3 + 2\sin 3(x + 1)$
     amplitude $= 2$, period $= \frac{2\pi}{3}$,
     phase shift $= -1$

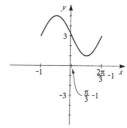

32. $y = \cos\left(\frac{\pi}{2} - x\right) = \cos\left(x - \frac{\pi}{2}\right)$

amplitude $= 1$, period $= 2\pi$,

phase shift $= \frac{\pi}{2}$

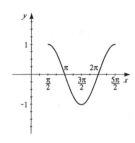

34. (a) amplitude $= a = 2$, period $= \frac{2\pi}{k} = \pi$, phase shift $= b = 0$

(b) $y = a\cos k(x - b) = 2\cos 2x$

36. (a) amplitude $= a = 4$, period $= \frac{2\pi}{k} = \frac{3}{2}$, phase shift $= b = -\frac{1}{2}$

(b) $y = 4\sin\frac{4\pi}{3}\left(x + \frac{1}{2}\right)$

38. (a) amplitude $= a = 5$, period $= \frac{2\pi}{k} = 1$, phase shift $= b = 0$

(b) $y = 5\cos 2\pi x$

40. $f(x) = 3\sin 120x$, $[-0.1, 0.1]$ by $[-4, 4]$

42. $f(x) = \cos\frac{x}{80}$, $[0, 500]$ by $[-1, 1]$

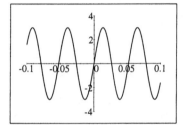

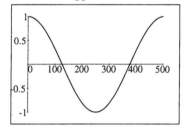

44. $y = \csc 40x$, $[-0.1, 0.1]$ by $[-10, 10]$

46. $y = \sqrt{\tan 10\pi x}$, $[-0.2, 0.2]$ by $[-1, 4]$

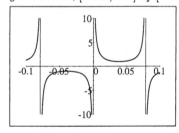

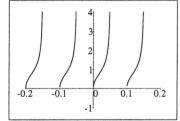

48. $f(x) = \sin x$, $g(x) = \sin 2x$

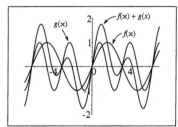

50. $y = x$, $y = -x$, $y = x \cos x$
     $y = x \cos x$ is a cosine curve that lies
     between the graphs of $y = x$ and $y = -x$.

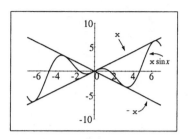

52. $y = \dfrac{1}{1 + x^2}$, $y = -\dfrac{1}{1 + x^2}$, $y = \dfrac{\cos 2\pi x}{1 + x^2}$

     $y = \dfrac{\cos 2\pi x}{1 + x^2}$ is a cosine curve that lies

     between the graphs of $y = \dfrac{1}{1 + x^2}$ and

     $y = -\dfrac{1}{1 + x^2}$.

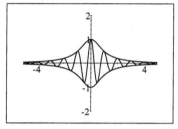

54. $y = \sin 2\pi x$, $y = -\sin 2\pi x$,
     $y = \sin 2\pi x \sin 10\pi x$
     $y = \sin 2\pi x \sin 10\pi x$ is a sine curve that lies
     between the graphs of $y = \sin 2\pi x$ and
     $y = \sin 2\pi x$.

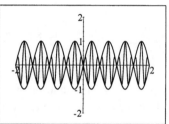

56. $y = \sin|x|$

     (a)
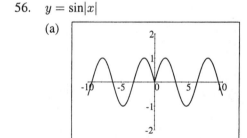

     (b) Function is not periodic. Note: While
          $\sin|x + 2\pi| = \sin|x|$ for many values of
          x it is false for $x \in (-2\pi, 0)$. For
          example $\sin\left|-\frac{\pi}{2}\right| = \sin\frac{\pi}{2} = 1$ while
          $\sin\left|-\frac{\pi}{2} + 2\pi\right| = \sin\frac{3\pi}{2} = -1$.

     (c) This function is even.

58. $y = 2^{\cos x}$

     (a)
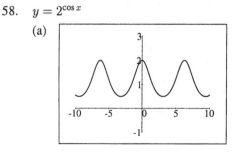

     (b) period $= 2\pi$

     (c) This function is even.

60. $y = \sin(x^2)$

(a)

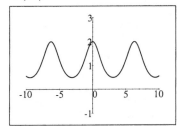

(b)   This function is not periodic.

(c)   This function is even.

62. $y = x - 2\sin x$, $0 \le x \le 2\pi$. Maximum value 6.97 when $x \approx 5.24$, minimum value -0.68 when $x \approx 1.05$.

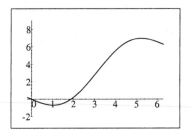

64. $y = \dfrac{\cos x}{2 + \sin x}$. The period is 2π, so we graph the function over one period. Maximum value 0.58 when $x \approx 5.76 + 2n\pi$ (exact value $x = \frac{11\pi}{6} + 2n\pi$); Minimum value -0.58 when $x \approx 3.67 + 2n\pi$ (exact value $x = \frac{7\pi}{6} + 2n\pi$) for $n = 0, \pm 1, \pm 2, \ldots$

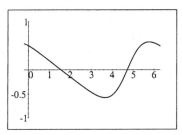

66. $\tan x = 2$, $x \in [0, \pi]$

$x \approx 1.11$

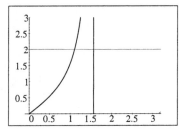

68. $\cos x = x$, $x \in [0, \pi]$

$x \approx 0.74$

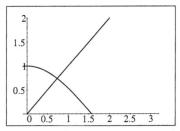

70. (a) $y = \sin\left(\sqrt{x}\right)$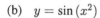

This graph looks like a $\sin x$ function
which has been stretched horizontally
(stretched more for larger values of x). It
is defined only for $x \geq 0$, so it is neither
even nor odd.

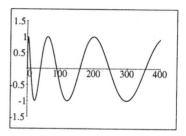

(b) $y = \sin\left(x^2\right)$

This graph looks like a $\sin |x|$ function
which has been shrunk for $|x| > 1$
(shrunk more for larger values of x), but
which is stretched when $|x| < 1$. It
is an even function, whereas $\sin x$ is odd.

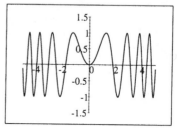

Exercises 8.4

2. $y = -3\tan x$, period $= \pi$

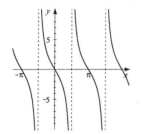

4. $y = -\frac{1}{2}\tan x$, period $= \pi$

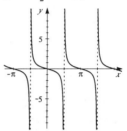

6. $y = \frac{1}{4}\cot x$, period $= \pi$

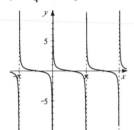

8. $y = \frac{1}{2}\csc x$, period $= 2\pi$

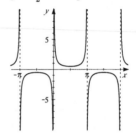

10. $y = \frac{1}{4}\sec x$, period $= 2\pi$

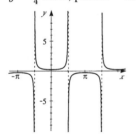

12. $y = \tan\left(x - \frac{\pi}{4}\right)$, period $= \pi$

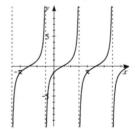

14. $y = \sec\left(x - \frac{\pi}{4}\right)$, period $= 2\pi$

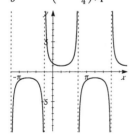

16. $y = 2\csc\left(x - \frac{\pi}{3}\right)$, period $= 2\pi$

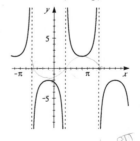

$\frac{6\pi}{6} \quad \frac{8\pi}{6} \quad \frac{4\pi}{3}$

18. $y = 3\csc\left(x - \frac{\pi}{2}\right)$, period $= 2\pi$

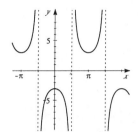

20. $y = \tan\left(\frac{1}{2}x\right)$, period $= \dfrac{\pi}{\left(\frac{1}{2}\right)} = 2\pi$

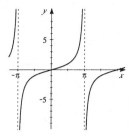

22. $y = \cot\left(\frac{\pi}{2}x\right)$, period $= \dfrac{\pi}{\left(\frac{\pi}{2}\right)} = 2$

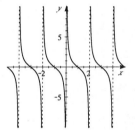

24. $y = 5\csc(3x)$, period $= \frac{2\pi}{3}$

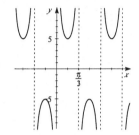

26. $y = \csc\left(\frac{1}{2}x\right)$, period $= \dfrac{2\pi}{\left(\frac{1}{2}\right)} = 4\pi$

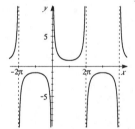

28. $y = 2\tan\left(\frac{\pi}{2}x\right)$, period $= \dfrac{\pi}{\left(\frac{\pi}{2}\right)} = 2$

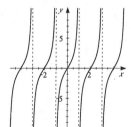

30. $y = 5\sec(2\pi x)$, period $= \frac{2\pi}{2\pi} = 1$

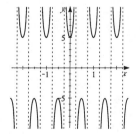

32. $y = \csc 2\left(x + \frac{\pi}{2}\right)$, period $= \frac{2\pi}{2} = \pi$

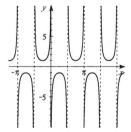

34. $y = \sec 2\left(x - \frac{\pi}{2}\right)$, period $= \frac{2\pi}{2} = \pi$

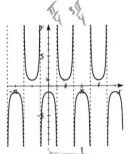

36. $y = \frac{1}{2}\tan(\pi x - \pi) = \frac{1}{2}\tan \pi(x - 1)$,

period $= \frac{\pi}{\pi} = 1$

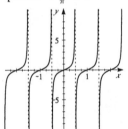

38. $y = 2\sec\left(\frac{1}{2}x - \frac{\pi}{3}\right) = 2\sec\frac{1}{2}\left(x - \frac{2\pi}{3}\right)$,

period $= \dfrac{2\pi}{\left(\frac{1}{2}\right)} = 4\pi$

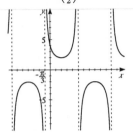

40. $y = \frac{1}{2}\sec(2\pi x - \pi) = \frac{1}{2}\sec 2\pi\left(x - \frac{1}{2}\right)$,

period $= \dfrac{2\pi}{2\pi} = 1$

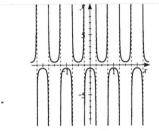

42. $y = \tan\frac{1}{2}\left(x + \frac{\pi}{4}\right)$, period $= \dfrac{\pi}{\left(\frac{1}{2}\right)} = 2\pi$

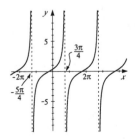

44. $y = \sec\left(3x + \frac{\pi}{2}\right) = \sec 3\left(x + \frac{\pi}{6}\right)$,

period $= \frac{2\pi}{3}$

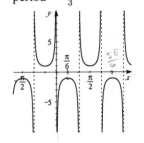

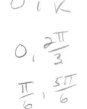

46. $y = 2\csc(3x + 3) = 2\csc 3(x + 1)$,
period $= \frac{2\pi}{3}$

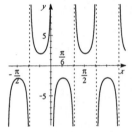

48. The graph of $y = -\cot x$ is the same as the graph of $y = \tan x$ shifted $\frac{\pi}{2}$ units to the right.
The graph of $y = \csc x$ is the same as the graph of $y = \sec x$ shifted $\frac{\pi}{2}$ units to the right.

Review Exercises for Chapter 8

2. (a) Since $\left(\frac{3}{5}\right)^2 + \left(-\frac{4}{5}\right)^2 = \frac{9}{25} + \frac{16}{25} = 1$, the point $P\left(\frac{3}{5}, -\frac{4}{5}\right)$ lies on the unit circle.

   (b) $\sin t = -\frac{4}{5}$, $\cos t = \frac{3}{5}$, $\tan t = \dfrac{-\frac{4}{5}}{\frac{3}{5}} = -\frac{4}{3}$.

4. $t = \frac{5\pi}{3}$

   (a) $\bar{t} = 2\pi - \frac{5\pi}{3} = \frac{\pi}{3}$

   (b) $P\left(\frac{1}{2}, -\frac{\sqrt{3}}{2}\right)$

   (c) $\sin t = -\frac{\sqrt{3}}{2}$, $\cos t = \frac{1}{2}$, $\tan t = -\sqrt{3}$, $\csc t = -\frac{2\sqrt{3}}{3}$, $\sec t = 2$, and $\cot t = -\frac{\sqrt{3}}{3}$.

6. $t = -\frac{7\pi}{6}$

   (a) $\bar{t} = \frac{7\pi}{6} - \pi = \frac{\pi}{6}$

   (b) $P\left(-\frac{\sqrt{3}}{2}, \frac{1}{2}\right)$

   (c) $\sin t = \frac{1}{2}$, $\cos t = -\frac{\sqrt{3}}{2}$, $\tan t = -\frac{\sqrt{3}}{3}$, $\csc t = 2$, $\sec t = -\frac{2\sqrt{3}}{3}$, $\cot t = -\sqrt{3}$.

8. (a) $\tan \frac{\pi}{3} = \sqrt{3}$ (b) $\tan\left(-\frac{\pi}{3}\right) = -\sqrt{3}$

10. (a) $\cos \frac{\pi}{5} \approx 0.80902$ (b) $\cos\left(-\frac{\pi}{5}\right) \approx 0.80902$

12. (a) $\sin \frac{\pi}{7} \approx 0.43388$ (b) $\csc \frac{\pi}{7} \approx 2.30476$

14. (a) $\sin 2\pi = 0$ (b) $\csc 2\pi$ is undefined

16. (a) $\cos \frac{\pi}{3} = \frac{1}{2}$ (b) $\sin \frac{\pi}{6} = \frac{1}{2}$

18. $\tan^2 t \cdot \sec t = \tan^2 t \cdot \dfrac{1}{\cos t} = \dfrac{\sin^2 t}{\cos^2 t} \cdot \dfrac{1}{\cos t} = \dfrac{1 - \cos^2 t}{\cos^3 t}$

20. $\sec t = \dfrac{1}{\cos t} = \dfrac{1}{\pm\sqrt{1 - \sin^2 t}} = \dfrac{1}{-\sqrt{1 - \sin^2 t}}$ (since t is in quadrant II $\;\Rightarrow\;$ $\cos t$ is negative)

22. $\sin t = -\frac{1}{2}$, $\cos t > 0$. Since $\sin t$ is negative and $\cos t$ is positive, t is in quadrant IV. Thus, t determines the terminal point $P\left(\frac{\sqrt{3}}{2}, -\frac{1}{2}\right)$, and $\cos t = \frac{\sqrt{3}}{2}$, $\tan t = -\frac{\sqrt{3}}{3}$, $\csc t = -2$, $\sec t = \frac{2\sqrt{3}}{3}$, $\cot t = -\sqrt{3}$.

24. $\cos t = -\frac{3}{5}$, $\tan t < 0$. Since $\cos t$ and $\tan t$ are both negative, t is in quadrant II. Thus, t determines the terminal point $P\left(-\frac{3}{5}, \frac{4}{5}\right)$, and $\sin t = \frac{4}{5}$, $\tan t = -\frac{4}{3}$, $\csc t = \frac{5}{4}$, $\sec t = -\frac{5}{3}$, $\cot t = -\frac{3}{4}$.

26. $\sin t = -\frac{8}{17}$, t is in quadrant IV $\;\Rightarrow\;$ $\csc t + \sec t = \dfrac{1}{\sin t} + \dfrac{1}{\cos t} = \dfrac{\cos t + \sin t}{\sin t \cos t}$

   $= \dfrac{\sqrt{1 - \sin^2 t} + \sin t}{\sin t \sqrt{1 - \sin^2 t}} = \dfrac{\frac{15}{17} + \frac{-8}{17}}{\frac{-8}{17} \cdot \frac{15}{17}} = \dfrac{7}{17} \cdot \dfrac{17^2}{-8 \cdot 15} = -\dfrac{7 \cdot 17}{8 \cdot 15} = \dfrac{119}{120} \approx -0.99167$ (since $\cos t$ is positive in quadrant IV)

28. The value of $\sec t$ is irrelevant, since $\sin^2 t + \cos^2 t = 1$ for all t.

30. $y = 4 \sin 2\pi x$ (b)

   (a) amplitude $= 4$, period $= \frac{2\pi}{2\pi} = 1$, phase shift $= 0$

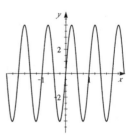

32. $y = 2 \sin\left(x - \frac{\pi}{4}\right)$ (b)

   (a) amplitude $= 2$, period $= 2\pi$, phase shift $= \frac{\pi}{4}$

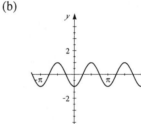

34. $y = \cos 2\left(x - \frac{\pi}{2}\right)$ (b)

   (a) amplitude $= 1$, period $= \frac{2\pi}{2} = \pi$, phase shift $= \frac{\pi}{2}$

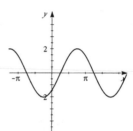

36. $y = 10 \sin\left(2x - \frac{\pi}{2}\right) = 10 \sin 2\left(x - \frac{\pi}{4}\right)$ (b)

   (a) amplitude $= 10$, period $= \frac{2\pi}{2} = \pi$, phase shift $= \frac{\pi}{4}$

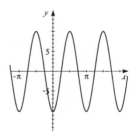

38. From the graph we see that the amplitude is 2, the period is 4 since $\frac{1}{4}$ of the period has been completed at $(1, 2)$, and there is no phase shift. Thus, $\frac{2\pi}{k} = 4 \quad \Leftrightarrow \quad k = \frac{\pi}{2}$. Therefore, the function is $y = 2 \sin \frac{\pi}{2} x$.

40. From the graph we see that the amplitude is 4, the period is $\frac{4\pi}{3}$. Thus, $\frac{2\pi}{k} = \frac{4\pi}{3} \quad \Leftrightarrow \quad k = \frac{3}{2}$. The phase shift is $-\frac{\pi}{3}$. Therefore, the function is $y = 4 \sin \frac{3}{2}\left(x + \frac{\pi}{3}\right)$.

42. $y = \tan \pi x$, period $= \frac{\pi}{\pi} = 1$ 44. $y = \sec\left(\frac{1}{2}x - \frac{\pi}{2}\right) = \sec \frac{1}{2}(x - \pi)$,

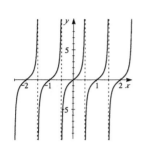

$$\text{period} = \frac{2\pi}{\left(\frac{1}{2}\right)} = 4\pi$$

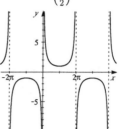

46. $y = \tan\left(x + \frac{\pi}{6}\right)$, period $= \pi$

48. $y = -4\sec\left(4\pi x\right)$, period $= \frac{2\pi}{4\pi} = \frac{1}{2}$

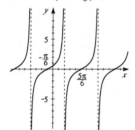

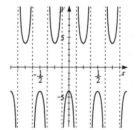

50.   (a) $y = \sin(\cos x)$

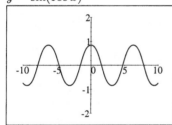

(b)   function has period 2π

(c)   function is even

52.   (a) $y = 1 + 2^{\cos x}$

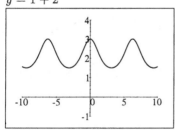

(b)   function has period 2π

(c)   function is even

54.   (a) $y = \ln x \sin x$ $(x > 0)$

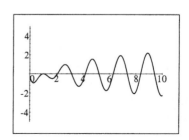

(c)   function is neither even nor odd

(b)   function is not periodic

56. $y = 2^{-x}$, $y = -2^{-x}$, $y = 2^{-x}\cos 4\pi x$

   $y = 2^{-x}\cos 4\pi x$ is a cosine function
   whose graph lies between the graphs of
   $y = 2^{-x}$ and $y = -2^{-x}$.

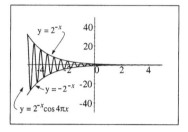

58. $y = \sin^2 x$, $y = \cos^2 x$, $y = \sin^2 x + \cos^2 x$

   $y = \sin^2 x + \cos^2 x$ is the sum of the two
   functions $y = \sin^2 x$ and $y = \cos^2 x$.
   Note that $\sin^2 x + \cos^2 x = 1$ for all x.

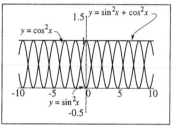

60. $y = \cos x + \sin^2 x$

   Since the period of this function is 2π, we
   graph this function over the interval $-\pi$
   to π. The maximum value is 1.25 when
   $x \approx 1.05 \pm 2n\pi$, the minimum value is
   -1 when $x = \frac{\pi}{2} \pm 2n\pi \approx 1.57 \pm 2n\pi$, n
   an integer.

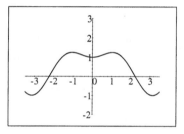

62.   We want to find solutions to $\cos 3x = x$
   in the interval $[0, \pi]$, so we plot the
   functions $y = \cos 3x$ and $y = x$ and look
   for their intersection. We see that
   $x \approx 0.390$.

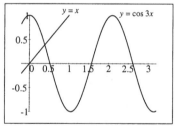

Focus on Modeling

2. From the graph we see that the amplitude is 6 feet and the period is 12 hours. Also, the sine curve is shifted 6 hours (exactly half its period) to the right, which is equivalent to reflecting the curve about the x-axis. Thus, the equation is $y = -(6) \sin\left(\frac{2\pi}{12}\right)x = -6 \sin \frac{\pi}{6}x$.

4. $a = 2$, $\dfrac{2\pi}{\omega} = 1 \quad \Leftrightarrow \quad \omega = 2\pi$. So $y = -2\cos 2\pi t$.

6. (a) $m = 10$ g, $k = 3$, $a = 5$ cm. Then $f(t) = 5\cos\left(\sqrt{\frac{3}{10}}\,t\right)$

   (b) The function $f(t) = a\cos\sqrt{k/m}\,t$ describes an object oscillating in simple harmonic motion, so by comparing it with the general equation $y = a\cos\omega t$ we see that $\omega = \sqrt{k/m}$. This means the frequency is $f = \dfrac{\omega}{2\pi} = \dfrac{\sqrt{k/m}}{2\pi} = \dfrac{1}{2\pi}\cdot\sqrt{\dfrac{k}{m}}$.

   (c) If the mass is increased, then the denominator of $\sqrt{\dfrac{k}{m}}$ increases, so overall the frequency decreases. If the frequency has decreased, then by definition the oscillations are slower.

   (d) If a stiffer spring is used, k is larger and so the numerator of $\sqrt{\dfrac{k}{m}}$ increases. Thus, overall the frequency increases. If the frequency has increased, then by definition the oscillations are faster.

8. Let $f(t)$ represent the measure of the angle θ at time t. The amplitude of this motion is 10. Since the period is 2s, we have $\dfrac{2\pi}{\omega} = 2 \quad \Leftrightarrow \quad \omega = \pi$. Thus $f(t) = 10\sin\pi t$.

10. $a = 1.5$, $\dfrac{\omega}{2\pi} = \dfrac{1}{5.4} \quad \Leftrightarrow \quad \omega = \dfrac{2\pi}{5.4}$. So $R(t) = 20 + 1.5\sin\left(\dfrac{2\pi}{5.4}t\right)$, where R is in millions of miles and t is in days.

12. $E_0 = 310$, frequency $= 100 \quad \Rightarrow \quad \frac{\omega}{2\pi} = 100 \quad \Leftrightarrow \quad \omega = 200\pi$. Then, $E(t) = 310\cos 200\pi t$. The maximum voltage produced occurs when $\cos 2\pi t = 1$, and hence is $E_{\max} = 310$V. The RMS voltage is $\frac{310}{\sqrt{2}} \approx 219$ V.

14. (a) $a = 10$, $\dfrac{\omega}{2\pi} = 20 \quad \Leftrightarrow \quad \omega = 40\pi$.
    Then $P(t) = 10\sin 40\pi t$, where P is in N/m^2 and t is in seconds.

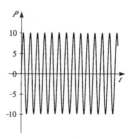

   (b) When the pitch is increased, the frequency increases. When the pitch is decreased, the frequency decreases.

16. $k = 6$, $c = 2.8$, and $\dfrac{\omega}{2\pi} = 2 \quad \Leftrightarrow \quad \omega = 4\pi$.

(a)   Since $f(0) = 6$, $f(t) = 6e^{-2.8t} \cos 4\pi t$.

(b)   The amplitude of the vibration is 0.5 when $6e^{-2.8t} = 0.5$ $\Rightarrow$ $e^{-2.8t} = \frac{1}{12}$ $\Rightarrow$
      $-2.8t = \ln \frac{1}{12}$ $\Rightarrow$ $t = -\frac{1}{2.8} \ln \frac{1}{12} = \frac{\ln 12}{2.8} \approx 0.88$ sec.

18.   (a) $\dfrac{ke^{-c \cdot 0}}{ke^{-c \cdot 2}} = \dfrac{3}{0.6} = 5$ $\Leftrightarrow$ $e^{2c} = 5$ $\Leftrightarrow$ $2c = \ln 5$ $\Leftrightarrow$ $c = \dfrac{1}{2} \ln 5 \approx 0.80$.

(b) $f(t) = 3e^{-0.8t} \cos \omega t$. If the frequency is 165 cycles per second, then $\frac{\omega}{2\pi} = 165$ $\Leftrightarrow$
      $\omega = 330\pi$. Thus, $f(t) = 3e^{-0.8t} \cos 330\pi t$.

Chapter Nine

Exercises 9.1

2. $\sin\theta\cos\theta\csc\theta = \sin\theta\cos\theta\,\dfrac{1}{\sin\theta} = \cos\theta$

4. $\dfrac{\tan x + \cot x}{\sec x\csc x} = \dfrac{\dfrac{\sin x}{\cos x} + \dfrac{\cos x}{\sin x}}{\dfrac{1}{\sin x\cos x}} = \left(\dfrac{\sin x}{\cos x} + \dfrac{\cos x}{\sin x}\right)\sin x\cos x = \sin^2 x + \cos^2 x = 1$

6. $\cos^2 x(1 + \tan^2 x) = \cos^2 x\left(1 + \dfrac{\sin^2 x}{\cos^2 x}\right) = \cos^2 x + \sin^2 x = 1$

8. $\cos^3 x + \sin^2 x\cos x = \cos x(\cos^2 x + \sin^2 x) = \cos x$

10. $\dfrac{\tan x}{\sec(-x)} = \dfrac{\tan x}{\sec x} = \dfrac{\sin x}{\cos x}\cdot\cos x = \sin x$

12. $\dfrac{\sec x - \cos x}{\tan x} = \dfrac{\dfrac{1}{\cos x} - \dfrac{\cos^2 x}{\cos x}}{\dfrac{\sin x}{\cos x}} = \dfrac{1 - \cos^2 x}{\sin x} = \dfrac{\sin^2 x}{\sin x} = \sin x$

14. $\dfrac{\sin x}{\csc x} + \dfrac{\cos x}{\sec x} = \sin x\sin x + \cos x\cos x = \sin^2 x + \cos^2 x = 1$

16. $\tan x\cos x\csc x = \dfrac{\sin x}{\cos x}\cdot\cos x\cdot\dfrac{1}{\sin x} = 1$

18. $\dfrac{1 + \cot A}{\csc A} = (1 + \cot A)\sin A = \sin A + \sin A\cot A = \sin A + \sin A\,\dfrac{\cos A}{\sin A} = \sin A + \cos A$

20. $\dfrac{\cos x}{\sec x + \tan x} = \dfrac{\cos x}{\dfrac{1}{\cos x} + \dfrac{\sin x}{\cos x}} = \dfrac{\cos^2 x}{1 + \sin x} = \dfrac{1 - \sin^2 x}{1 + \sin x} = \dfrac{(1 + \sin x)(1 - \sin x)}{1 + \sin x} = 1 - \sin x$

22. $\dfrac{\tan x}{\sec x} = \dfrac{\sin x}{\cos x}\cdot\cos x = \sin x$

24. $\dfrac{\cot x\sec x}{\csc x} = \dfrac{\cos x}{\sin x}\cdot\dfrac{1}{\cos x}\cdot\sin x = 1$

26. $\dfrac{\cos v}{\sec v\sin v} = \cos v\cdot\dfrac{\cos v}{\sin v} = \dfrac{1 - \sin^2 v}{\sin v} = \csc v - \sin v$

28. $\cos(-x) - \sin(-x) = \cos x - (-\sin x) = \cos x + \sin x$

30. $\csc x[\csc x + \sin(-x)] = \csc^2 x - \sin x\csc x = \csc^2 x - 1 = \cot^2 x$

32. $(\sin x + \cos x)^2 = \sin^2 x + 2\sin x\cos x + \cos^2 x = 1 + 2\sin x\cos x$

34. $\dfrac{\cos x}{\sec x} + \dfrac{\sin x}{\csc x} = \cos^2 x + \sin^2 x = 1$

36. $(\sin x + \cos x)^4 = \left[(\sin x + \cos x)^2\right]^2 = (\sin^2 x + 2\sin x\cos x + \cos^2 x)^2 = (1 + 2\sin x\cos x)^2$

38. $\dfrac{1 - \sin x}{1 + \sin x} = \dfrac{1 - \sin x}{1 + \sin x} \cdot \dfrac{1 - \sin x}{1 - \sin x} = \dfrac{1 - 2\sin x + \sin^2 x}{1 - \sin^2 x} = \dfrac{1 - 2\sin x + \sin^2 x}{\cos^2 x}$

$= \dfrac{1}{\cos^2 x} - \dfrac{2\sin x}{\cos^2 x} + \dfrac{\sin^2 x}{\cos^2 x} = \sec^2 x - 2\sec x \tan x + \tan^2 x = (\sec x - \tan x)^2$

40. $\csc x - \sin x = \dfrac{1}{\sin x} - \sin x = \dfrac{1 - \sin^2 x}{\sin x} = \dfrac{\cos^2 x}{\sin x} = \cos x \cot x$

42. $\sin^4\theta - \cos^4\theta = (\sin^2\theta)^2 - (\cos^2\theta)^2 = (\sin^2\theta - \cos^2\theta)(\sin^2\theta + \cos^2\theta) = \sin^2\theta - \cos^2\theta$

44. $\cos^2 x - \sin^2 x = \cos^2 x - (1 - \cos^2 x) = 2\cos^2 x - 1$

46. $\tan y + \cot y = \dfrac{\sin y}{\cos y} + \dfrac{\cos y}{\sin y} = \dfrac{\sin^2 y + \cos^2 y}{\sin y \cos y} = \dfrac{1}{\sin y \cos y} = \sec y \csc y$

48. $\sin^2\alpha + \cos^2\alpha + \tan^2\alpha = 1 + \tan^2\alpha = \sec^2\alpha$

50. $\dfrac{\sin w}{\sin w + \cos w} = \dfrac{\sin w}{\sin w + \cos w} \cdot \dfrac{\dfrac{1}{\cos w}}{\dfrac{1}{\cos w}} = \dfrac{\tan w}{1 + \tan w}$

52. $\sec t \csc t(\tan t + \cot t) = \dfrac{1}{\cos t}\dfrac{1}{\sin t}\left(\dfrac{\sin t}{\cos t} + \dfrac{\cos t}{\sin t}\right) = \dfrac{1}{\cos^2 t} + \dfrac{1}{\sin^2 t} = \sec^2 t + \csc^2 t$

54. $\dfrac{1 + \sec^2 x}{1 + \tan^2 x} = \dfrac{1 + \sec^2 x}{\sec^2 x} = \dfrac{1}{\sec^2 x} + 1 = \cos^2 x + 1$

56. $\dfrac{\sec x + \csc x}{\tan x + \cot x} = \dfrac{\dfrac{1}{\cos x} + \dfrac{1}{\sin x}}{\dfrac{\sin x}{\cos x} + \dfrac{\cos x}{\sin x}} = \dfrac{\dfrac{1}{\cos x} + \dfrac{1}{\sin x}}{\dfrac{\sin x}{\cos x} + \dfrac{\cos x}{\sin x}} \cdot \dfrac{\sin x \cos x}{\sin x \cos x} = \dfrac{\sin x + \cos x}{\sin^2 x + \cos^2 x} = \sin x + \cos x$

58. $\dfrac{\sin A}{1 - \cos A} - \cot A = \dfrac{\sin A}{1 - \cos A} \cdot \dfrac{1 + \cos A}{1 + \cos A} - \cot A = \dfrac{\sin A(1 + \cos A)}{1 - \cos^2 A} - \cot A$

$= \dfrac{\sin A(1 + \cos A)}{\sin^2 A} - \dfrac{\cos A}{\sin A} = \dfrac{1}{\sin A} + \dfrac{\cos A}{\sin A} - \dfrac{\cos A}{\sin A} = \dfrac{1}{\sin A} = \csc A$

60. $\dfrac{1 - \cos x}{\sin x} + \dfrac{\sin x}{1 - \cos x} = \dfrac{1 - \cos x}{\sin x} \cdot \dfrac{1 - \cos x}{1 - \cos x} + \dfrac{\sin x}{1 - \cos x} \cdot \dfrac{\sin x}{\sin x}$

$= \dfrac{1 - 2\cos x + \cos^2 x + \sin^2 x}{\sin x(1 - \cos x)} = \dfrac{2 - 2\cos x}{\sin x(1 - \cos x)} = \dfrac{2(1 - \cos x)}{\sin x(1 - \cos x)} = 2\csc x$

62. $\dfrac{\csc^2 x - \cot^2 x}{\sec^2 x} = \dfrac{1}{\sec^2 x} = \cos^2 x$

64. $\dfrac{\tan v \sin v}{\tan v + \sin v} = \dfrac{\tan v \sin v}{\tan v + \sin v} \cdot \dfrac{\tan v - \sin v}{\tan v - \sin v} = \dfrac{\tan v \sin v (\tan v - \sin v)}{\tan^2 v - \sin^2 v}$

$= \dfrac{\tan v \sin v (\tan v - \sin v)}{\sin^2 v (\sec^2 v - 1)} = \dfrac{\tan v \sin v (\tan v - \sin v)}{\tan^2 v \sin^2 v} = \dfrac{\tan v - \sin v}{\tan v \sin v}$

66. $\dfrac{\cos\theta}{1-\sin\theta} = \dfrac{\cos\theta}{1-\sin\theta}\cdot\dfrac{1+\sin\theta}{1+\sin\theta} = \dfrac{\cos\theta(1+\sin\theta)}{1-\sin^2\theta} = \dfrac{\cos\theta(1+\sin\theta)}{\cos^2\theta} = \dfrac{1}{\cos\theta}+\dfrac{\sin\theta}{\cos\theta}$

$= \sec\theta + \tan\theta$

68. $\dfrac{1+\tan x}{1-\tan x} = \dfrac{1+\dfrac{\sin x}{\cos x}}{1-\dfrac{\sin x}{\cos x}}\cdot\dfrac{\cos x}{\cos x} = \dfrac{\cos x+\sin x}{\cos x-\sin x}$

70. $\dfrac{1}{1-\sin x}-\dfrac{1}{1+\sin x} = \dfrac{(1+\sin x)-(1-\sin x)}{(1-\sin x)(1+\sin x)} = \dfrac{2\sin x}{1-\sin^2 x} = \dfrac{2\sin x}{\cos^2 x} = 2\,\dfrac{\sin x}{\cos x}\cdot\dfrac{1}{\cos x}$

$= 2\tan x\sec x$

72. $\dfrac{1+\sin x}{1-\sin x}-\dfrac{1-\sin x}{1+\sin x} = \dfrac{(1+\sin x)^2-(1-\sin x)^2}{(1-\sin x)(1+\sin x)} = \dfrac{1+2\sin x+\sin^2 x-1+2\sin x-\sin^2 x}{1-\sin^2 x}$

$= \dfrac{4\sin x}{\cos^2 x} = 4\,\dfrac{\sin x}{\cos x}\cdot\dfrac{1}{\cos x} = 4\tan x\sec x$

74. $\tan^2 x-\cot^2 x = (\sec^2 x-1)-(\csc^2 x-1) = \sec^2 x-\csc^2 x$

76. $\dfrac{\cot x+1}{\cot x-1} = \dfrac{\cot x+1}{\cot x-1}\cdot\dfrac{\tan x}{\tan x} = \dfrac{\tan x\cot x+\tan x}{\tan x\cot x-\tan x} = \dfrac{1+\tan x}{1-\tan x}$

78. $\dfrac{\tan v-\cot v}{\tan^2 v-\cot^2 v} = \dfrac{\tan v-\cot v}{(\tan v-\cot v)(\tan v+\cot v)} = \dfrac{1}{\tan v+\cot v} = \dfrac{1}{\dfrac{\sin v}{\cos v}+\dfrac{\cos v}{\sin v}} = \dfrac{1}{\dfrac{\sin v}{\cos v}+\dfrac{\cos v}{\sin v}}\cdot\dfrac{\sin v\cos v}{\sin v\cos v}$

$= \dfrac{\sin v\cos v}{\sin^2 v+\cos^2 v} = \sin v\cos v$

80. $\dfrac{\tan x+\tan y}{\cot x+\cot y} = \dfrac{\dfrac{\sin x}{\cos x}+\dfrac{\sin y}{\cos y}}{\dfrac{\cos x}{\sin x}+\dfrac{\cos y}{\sin y}} = \dfrac{\dfrac{\sin x\cos y+\cos x\sin y}{\cos x\cos y}}{\dfrac{\cos x\sin y+\sin x\cos y}{\sin x\sin y}}$

$= \left(\dfrac{\sin x\cos y+\cos x\sin y}{\cos x\cos y}\right)\left(\dfrac{\sin x\sin y}{\cos x\sin y+\sin x\cos y}\right) = \dfrac{\sin x\sin y}{\cos x\cos y} = \tan x\tan y$

82. $(\sin\alpha-\tan\alpha)(\cos\alpha-\cot\alpha) = \left(\sin\alpha-\dfrac{\sin\alpha}{\cos\alpha}\right)\left(\cos\alpha-\dfrac{\cos\alpha}{\sin\alpha}\right)$

$= \sin\alpha\left(1-\dfrac{1}{\cos\alpha}\right)\cdot\cos\alpha\left(1-\dfrac{1}{\sin\alpha}\right) = \cos\alpha\left(1-\dfrac{1}{\cos\alpha}\right)\sin\alpha\left(1-\dfrac{1}{\sin\alpha}\right)$

$= (\cos\alpha-1)(\sin\alpha-1)$

84. $x=\tan\theta$; then $\sqrt{1+x^2} = \sqrt{1+\tan^2\theta} = \sqrt{1+(\sec^2\theta-1)} = \sqrt{\sec^2\theta} = \sec\theta$ (since $\sec\theta\geq 0$ for $0\leq\theta\leq\frac{\pi}{2}$).

86. $x=2\tan\theta$; then $\dfrac{1}{x^2\sqrt{4+x^2}} = \dfrac{1}{(2\tan\theta)^2\sqrt{4+(2\tan\theta)^2}} = \dfrac{1}{4\tan^2\theta\cdot\sqrt{4(1+\tan^2\theta)}}$

$= \dfrac{1}{4\tan^2\theta\cdot 2\sqrt{\sec^2\theta}} = \dfrac{1}{8\tan^2\theta\cdot\sec\theta} = \dfrac{1}{8}\cdot\dfrac{\cos^3\theta}{\sin^2\theta}$, (since $\sec\theta>0$ for $0\leq\theta<\dfrac{\pi}{2}$).

88. $x = 5 \sec \theta$; then $\dfrac{\sqrt{x^2 - 25}}{x} = \dfrac{\sqrt{(5\sec\theta)^2 - 25}}{5\sec\theta} = \dfrac{\sqrt{25(\sec^2\theta - 1)}}{5\sec\theta} = \dfrac{5\sqrt{\tan^2\theta}}{5\sec\theta} = \dfrac{\tan\theta}{\sec\theta}$

$= \dfrac{\dfrac{\sin\theta}{\cos\theta}}{\dfrac{1}{\cos\theta}} = \sin\theta,$ (since $\tan\theta > 0$ for $0 \le \theta < \dfrac{\pi}{2}$).

90. Choose $x = \frac{\pi}{4}$ and $y = \frac{\pi}{4}$. Then $\sin(x + y) = \sin\frac{\pi}{2} = 1$ whereas $\sin x + \sin y = \sin\frac{\pi}{4} + \sin\frac{\pi}{4}$
$= \frac{1}{\sqrt{2}} + \frac{1}{\sqrt{2}} = \frac{2}{\sqrt{2}}$. Since these are not equal, the equation is not an identity.

92. Choose $x = \frac{\pi}{4}$. Then $\dfrac{1}{\sin x + \cos x} = \dfrac{1}{\sin\frac{\pi}{4} + \cos\frac{\pi}{4}} = \dfrac{1}{\frac{1}{\sqrt{2}} + \frac{1}{\sqrt{2}}} = \dfrac{1}{\sqrt{2}}$ whereas $\csc x + \sec x$

$= \csc\frac{\pi}{4} + \sec\frac{\pi}{4} = \sqrt{2} + \sqrt{2}$. Since these are not equal, the equation is not an identity.

94. $f(x) = \tan x\,(1 + \sin x),\ g(x) = \dfrac{\sin x \cos x}{1 + \sin x}$

From the graph this does not appear to be an identity. In order
to show this, let $x = \frac{\pi}{4}$. Then,

$f\left(\frac{\pi}{4}\right) = (1)\cdot\left[1 + \left(\frac{1}{\sqrt{2}}\right)\right] = \frac{\sqrt{2}+1}{\sqrt{2}}$. However,

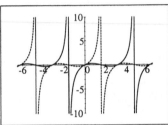

$g\left(\frac{\pi}{4}\right) = \dfrac{\frac{1}{\sqrt{2}}\cdot\frac{1}{\sqrt{2}}}{\left[1 + \left(\frac{1}{\sqrt{2}}\right)\right]} = \dfrac{1}{2}\cdot\dfrac{1}{\frac{\sqrt{2}+1}{\sqrt{2}}} = \dfrac{\sqrt{2}}{2\left(\sqrt{2}+1\right)}.$ since

$f\left(\frac{\pi}{4}\right) \ne g\left(\frac{\pi}{4}\right)$, this is not an identity.

96. $f(x) = \cos^4 x - \sin^4 x,\ g(x) = 2\cos^2 x - 1$

From the graph this appears to be an identity. In order to prove
this, simplify the expression $f(x)$: $f(x) = \cos^4 x - \sin^4 x =$
$(\cos^2 x - \sin^2 x)(\cos^2 x + \sin^2 x) = (\cos^2 x - \sin^2 x)(1)$
$= (2\cos^2 x - \cos^2 x) - \sin^2 x = 2\cos^2 x - (\cos^2 x + \sin^2 x)$
$= 2\cos^2 x - 1 = g(x)$

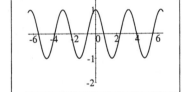

Since $f(x) = g(x)$ for all x, this is an identity.

98. No. All this proves is that $f(x) = g(x)$ for x in the range of the viewing rectangle. It does not prove
that these functions are equal for all values of x. For example, let $f(x) = 1 - \dfrac{x^2}{2} + \dfrac{x^4}{24} - \dfrac{x^6}{720}$ and
$g(x) = \cos x$. In the first viewing rectangle the graphs of these two functions appear identical.
However, when the domain is expanded in the second viewing rectangle, you can see that these two
functions are not identical.

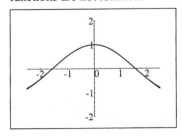
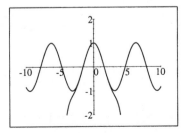

Exercises 9.2

2. $\cos 165° = \cos(120° + 45°) = \cos 120° \cos 45° - \sin 120° \sin 45°$

   $= (-\cos 60°)\cos 45° - (\sin 60°)\sin 45° = -\frac{1}{2} \cdot \frac{\sqrt{2}}{2} - \frac{\sqrt{3}}{2} \cdot \frac{\sqrt{2}}{2} = -\frac{\sqrt{2}+\sqrt{6}}{4}$

4. $\cos \frac{\pi}{12} = \cos\left(\frac{\pi}{4} - \frac{\pi}{6}\right) = \cos\frac{\pi}{4} \cos\frac{\pi}{6} + \sin\frac{\pi}{4} \sin\frac{\pi}{6} = \frac{\sqrt{2}}{2} \cdot \frac{\sqrt{3}}{2} + \frac{\sqrt{2}}{2} \cdot \frac{1}{2} = \frac{\sqrt{6}+\sqrt{2}}{4}$

6. $\sin 75° = \sin(45° + 30°) = \sin 45° \cos 30° + \cos 45° \sin 30° = \frac{\sqrt{2}}{2} \cdot \frac{\sqrt{3}}{2} + \frac{\sqrt{2}}{2} \cdot \frac{1}{2} = \frac{\sqrt{6}+\sqrt{2}}{4}$

8. $\cos \frac{3\pi}{7} \cos \frac{2\pi}{21} + \sin \frac{3\pi}{7} \sin \frac{2\pi}{21} = \cos\left(\frac{3\pi}{7} - \frac{2\pi}{21}\right) = \cos\left(\frac{9\pi-2\pi}{21}\right) = \cos \frac{\pi}{3} = \frac{1}{2}$

10. $\cos \frac{13\pi}{15} \cos\left(-\frac{\pi}{5}\right) - \sin \frac{13\pi}{15} \sin\left(-\frac{\pi}{5}\right) = \cos\left[\frac{13\pi}{15} + \left(-\frac{\pi}{5}\right)\right] = \cos \frac{10\pi}{15} = \cos \frac{2\pi}{3} = -\frac{1}{2}$

12. $\cot\left(\frac{\pi}{2} - u\right) = \dfrac{\cos\left(\frac{\pi}{2} - u\right)}{\sin\left(\frac{\pi}{2} - u\right)} = \dfrac{\cos \frac{\pi}{2} \cos u + \sin \frac{\pi}{2} \sin u}{\sin \frac{\pi}{2} \cos u - \cos \frac{\pi}{2} \sin u} = \dfrac{0 \cdot \cos u + 1 \cdot \sin u}{1 \cdot \cos u - 0 \cdot \sin u} = \dfrac{\sin u}{\cos u} = \tan u$

14. $\csc\left(\frac{\pi}{2} - u\right) = \dfrac{1}{\sin\left(\frac{\pi}{2} - u\right)} = \dfrac{1}{\sin \frac{\pi}{2} \cos u - \cos \frac{\pi}{2} \sin u} = \dfrac{1}{1 \cdot \cos u - 0 \cdot \sin u} = \dfrac{1}{\cos u} = \sec u$

16. $\cos(x - \frac{\pi}{2}) = \cos x \cos \frac{\pi}{2} + \sin x \sin \frac{\pi}{2} = 0 \cdot \cos x + 1 \cdot \sin x = \sin x$

18. $\cos(x - \pi) = \cos x \cos \pi + \sin x \sin \pi = -1 \cdot \cos x + 0 \cdot \sin x = -\cos x$

20. $\text{LHS} = \sin(\frac{\pi}{2} - x) = \sin \frac{\pi}{2} \cos x - \cos \frac{\pi}{2} \sin x = 1 \cdot \cos x - 0 \cdot \sin x = \cos x$

    $\text{RHS} = \sin(\frac{\pi}{2} + x) = \sin \frac{\pi}{2} \cos x + \cos \frac{\pi}{2} \sin x = 1 \cdot \cos x + 0 \cdot \sin x = \cos x$

    Therefore, LHS = RHS.

22. $\tan(x - \frac{\pi}{4}) = \dfrac{\tan x - \tan \frac{\pi}{4}}{1 + \tan x \tan \frac{\pi}{4}} = \dfrac{\tan x - 1}{1 + \tan x \cdot 1} = \dfrac{\tan x - 1}{\tan x + 1}$

24. $\cos(x + y) + \cos(x - y) = \cos x \cos y - \sin x \sin y + \cos x \cos y + \sin x \sin y = 2 \cos x \cos y$

26. $\cot(x + y) = \dfrac{1}{\tan(x + y)} = \dfrac{1 - \tan x \tan y}{\tan x + \tan y} = \dfrac{1 - \dfrac{1}{\cot x} \dfrac{1}{\cot y}}{\dfrac{1}{\cot x} + \dfrac{1}{\cot y}} \cdot \dfrac{\cot x \cot y}{\cot x \cot y} = \dfrac{\cot x \cot y - 1}{\cot x + \cot y}$

28. $1 - \tan x \tan y = 1 - \dfrac{\sin x \sin y}{\cos x \cos y} = \dfrac{\cos x \cos y - \sin x \sin y}{\cos x \cos y} = \dfrac{\cos(x + y)}{\cos x \cos y}$

30. $\cos(x + y) \cos(x - y) = [\cos x \cos y - \sin x \sin y][\cos x \cos y + \sin x \sin y]$

    $= \cos^2 x \cos^2 y - \sin^2 x \sin^2 y = \cos^2 x \, (1 - \sin^2 y) - (1 - \cos^2 x) \sin^2 y$

    $= \cos^2 x - \sin^2 y \cos^2 x + \sin^2 y \cos^2 x - \sin^2 y = \cos^2 x - \sin^2 y$

32. The addition formula for the tangent function can be written as
    $\tan A + \tan B = \tan(A + B)[1 - \tan A \tan B]$. Also note that $\tan(-A) = -\tan A$. Using these facts
    we get $\tan(x - y) + \tan(y - z) + \tan(z - x)$

    $= \tan(x - y + y - z)[1 - \tan(x - y) \tan(y - z)] + \tan(z - x)$

$$= \tan(x - z)[1 - \tan(x - y)\tan(y - z)] + \tan(z - x)$$
$$= \tan(x - z) + \tan(z - x) - \tan(x - y)\tan(y - z)\tan(x - z)$$
$$= \tan(x - z) - \tan(x - z) - \tan(x - y)\tan(y - z)\tan(x - z)$$
$$= 0 - \tan(x - y)\tan(y - z)\tan(x - z) = \tan(x - y)\tan(y - z)\tan(z - x)$$

34. $k = \sqrt{A^2 + B^2} = \sqrt{1^2 + 1^2} = \sqrt{2}$ and ϕ satisfies $\sin\phi = \frac{1}{\sqrt{2}}$, $\cos\phi = \frac{1}{\sqrt{2}}$ $\Leftrightarrow$ $\phi = \frac{\pi}{4}$.

Thus, $\sin x + \cos x = k\sin(x + \phi) = \sqrt{2}\sin(x + \frac{\pi}{4})$.

36. $k = \sqrt{A^2 + B^2} = \sqrt{3^2 + (3\sqrt{3})^2} = \sqrt{36} = 6$ and ϕ satisfies $\sin\phi = \frac{3\sqrt{3}}{6} = \frac{\sqrt{3}}{2}$, $\cos\phi = \frac{3}{6} = \frac{1}{2}$

$\Leftrightarrow$ $\phi = \frac{\pi}{3}$. Thus, $3\sin\pi x + 3\sqrt{3}\cos\pi x = k\sin(\pi x + \phi) = 6\sin(\pi x + \frac{\pi}{3}) = 6\sin\pi(x + \frac{1}{3})$.

38. $g(x) = \cos 2x + \sqrt{3}\sin 2x$ $\Rightarrow$

$k = \sqrt{1^2 + (\sqrt{3})^2} = \sqrt{4} = 2$, and ϕ satisfies

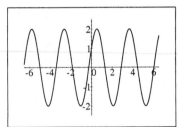

$\sin\phi = \frac{1}{2}$, $\cos\phi = \frac{\sqrt{3}}{2}$ $\Rightarrow$ $\phi = \frac{\pi}{6}$.

Thus, we can write $g(x) = k\sin(2x + \phi)$

$= 2\sin(2x + \frac{\pi}{6}) = 2\sin 2(x + \frac{\pi}{12})$. We see

that this is a sine curve with amplitude $= 2$,

period $= \pi$, and phase shift $= -\frac{\pi}{12}$.

40. $g(x) = \cos x$. Now $\dfrac{g(x + h) - g(x)}{h} = \dfrac{\cos(x + h) - \cos x}{h} = \dfrac{\cos x\cos h - \sin x\sin h - \cos x}{h}$

$= \dfrac{-\cos x(1 - \cos h) - \sin h(\sin x)}{h} = -\cos x\left(\dfrac{1 - \cos h}{h}\right) - \left(\dfrac{\sin h}{h}\right)\sin x$

42. (a) By definition, $m = \dfrac{\Delta y}{\Delta x}$ and $\tan\theta = \dfrac{\Delta y}{\Delta x}$. Thus, $m = \tan\theta$.

(b) $\tan\psi = \tan(\theta_2 - \theta_1) = \dfrac{\tan\theta_2 - \tan\theta_1}{1 + \tan\theta_2\tan\theta_1}$. From (a), we have $m_1 = \tan\theta_1$ and $m_2 = \tan\theta_2$.

Then, by substitution, $\tan\psi = \dfrac{m_2 - m_1}{1 + m_1 m_2}$.

(c) Let ψ be the unknown angle as in (b). Since $m_1 = \frac{1}{3}$ and $m_2 = -\frac{1}{2}$, and

$\tan\psi = \dfrac{m_2 - m_1}{1 + m_1 m_2} = \dfrac{-\frac{1}{2} - \frac{1}{3}}{1 + \frac{1}{3}(-\frac{1}{2})} = \dfrac{-\frac{5}{6}}{\frac{5}{6}} = -1$ $\Leftrightarrow$ $\psi = \dfrac{3\pi}{4}$.

(d) From part (b) we have $\cot\psi = \dfrac{1 + m_1 m_2}{m_2 - m_1}$. If the two lines are perpendicular then $\psi = 90°$

and so $\cot\psi = 0$. Thus we have $0 = \dfrac{1 + m_1 m_2}{m_2 - m_1}$ $\Leftrightarrow$ $0 = 1 + m_1 m_2$ $\Leftrightarrow$ $m_1 m_2 = -1$

$\Leftrightarrow$ $m_2 = -\dfrac{1}{m_1}$. Thus m_2 is the negative reciprocal of m_1.

44. (a) $y = -\frac{1}{2}\left[\cos(x+\pi) + \cos(x-\pi)\right]$

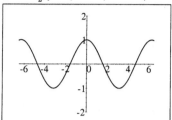

The graph of y appears to be the cosine function.

(b) $y = -\frac{1}{2}\left[\cos(x+\pi) + \cos(x-\pi)\right]$

$= -\frac{1}{2}\left[(\cos x \cos \pi - \sin x \sin \pi) + (\cos x \cos \pi + \sin x \sin \pi)\right]$

$= -\frac{1}{2}\left[(-\cos x - 0) + (-\cos x + 0)\right] = -\frac{1}{2}\left[-2\cos x\right] = \cos x$

46. $\sin(s+t) = \cos\left[\frac{\pi}{2} - (s+t)\right] = \cos\left[\left(\frac{\pi}{2} - s\right) - t\right] = \cos\left(\frac{\pi}{2} - s\right)\cos t + \sin\left(\frac{\pi}{2} - s\right)\sin t$

$= \sin s \cos t + \cos s \sin t.$ The last equality comes from again applying the cofunction identities.

Exercises 9.3

2. $\cos x = \frac{4}{5}$. Then, $\sin x = -\frac{3}{5}$ ($\csc x < 0$) and $\tan x = -\frac{3}{4}$.

$\sin 2x = 2\sin x \cos x = 2(-\frac{3}{5}) \cdot \frac{4}{5} = -\frac{24}{25}$

$\cos 2x = \cos^2 x - \sin^2 x = (\frac{4}{5})^2 - (-\frac{3}{5})^2 = \frac{16-9}{25} = \frac{7}{25}$

$\tan 2x = \dfrac{\sin 2x}{\cos 2x} = \dfrac{-\frac{24}{25}}{\frac{7}{25}} = -\frac{24}{25} \cdot \frac{25}{7} = -\frac{24}{7}$

4. $\csc x = 4$. Then $\sin x = \frac{1}{4}$, $\cos x = -\frac{\sqrt{15}}{4}$, and $\tan x = -\frac{1}{\sqrt{15}}$ ($\tan x < 0$).

$\sin 2x = 2\sin x \cos x = 2 \cdot \frac{1}{4}\left(-\frac{\sqrt{15}}{4}\right) = -\frac{\sqrt{15}}{8}$

$\cos 2x = \cos^2 x - \sin^2 x = \left(-\frac{\sqrt{15}}{4}\right)^2 - \left(\frac{1}{4}\right)^2 = \frac{15-1}{16} = \frac{7}{8}$

$\tan 2x = \dfrac{\sin 2x}{\cos 2x} = \dfrac{-\frac{\sqrt{15}}{8}}{\frac{7}{8}} = -\frac{\sqrt{15}}{8} \cdot \frac{8}{7} = -\frac{\sqrt{15}}{7}$

6. $\cot x = \frac{2}{3}$. Then $\tan x = \frac{3}{2}$, $\sin x = \frac{3}{\sqrt{13}}$ ($\sin x > 0$), and $\cos x = \frac{2}{\sqrt{13}}$.

$\sin 2x = 2\sin x \cos x = 2\left(\frac{3}{\sqrt{13}}\right)\left(\frac{2}{\sqrt{13}}\right) = \frac{12}{13}$

$\cos 2x = \cos^2 x - \sin^2 x = \left(\frac{2}{\sqrt{13}}\right)^2 - \left(\frac{3}{\sqrt{13}}\right)^2 = \frac{4-9}{13} = -\frac{5}{13}$

$\tan 2x = \dfrac{\sin 2x}{\cos 2x} = \dfrac{\frac{12}{13}}{-\frac{5}{13}} = \frac{12}{13} \cdot \left(-\frac{13}{5}\right) = -\frac{12}{5}$

8. $\cos^4 x = (\cos^2 x)^2 = \left(\dfrac{1 + \cos 2x}{2}\right)^2 = \frac{1}{4} + \frac{1}{2}\cos 2x + \frac{1}{4}\cos^2 2x$

$= \frac{1}{4} + \frac{1}{2}\cos 2x + \frac{1}{4} \cdot \dfrac{1 + \cos 4x}{2} = \frac{1}{4} + \frac{1}{2}\cos 2x + \frac{1}{8} + \frac{1}{8}\cos 4x = \frac{3}{8} + \frac{1}{2}\cos 2x + \frac{1}{8}\cos 4x$

$= \frac{1}{2}\left(\frac{3}{4} + \cos 2x + \frac{1}{4}\cos 4x\right)$

10. Using Example 4 we have: $\cos^4 x \sin^2 x = \cos^2 x(\cos^2 x \sin^2 x) = \frac{1}{2}(1 + \cos 2x) \cdot \frac{1}{8}(1 - \cos 4x)$
    $= \frac{1}{16}(1 - \cos 4x + \cos 2x - \cos 2x \cos 4x)$

12. Using the result of Exercise 8 we have:

$\cos^6 x = (\cos^2 x)^2 \cdot \cos^2 x = \left(\frac{3}{8} + \frac{1}{2}\cos 2x + \frac{1}{8}\cos 4x\right)\left(\frac{1}{2} + \frac{1}{2}\cos 2x\right)$

$= \frac{3}{16} + \frac{1}{4}\cos 2x + \frac{1}{16}\cos 4x + \frac{3}{16}\cos 2x + \frac{1}{16}\cos 2x \cos 4x$

$= \frac{3}{16} + \frac{7}{16}\cos 2x + \frac{1}{16}\cos 4x + \frac{1}{16}\cos 2x \cos 4x$

$= \frac{1}{16}(3 + 7\cos 2x + \cos 4x + \cos 2x \cos 4x)$

14. $\tan 15° = \dfrac{1 - \cos 30°}{\sin 30°} = \dfrac{1 - \frac{\sqrt{3}}{2}}{\frac{1}{2}} = 2 - \sqrt{3}$

16. $\tan\frac{\pi}{8} = \dfrac{1 - \cos\frac{\pi}{4}}{\sin\frac{\pi}{4}} = \dfrac{1 - \frac{1}{\sqrt{2}}}{\frac{1}{\sqrt{2}}} = \sqrt{2} - 1$

18. $\cos\frac{5\pi}{12} = \cos\left(\frac{1}{2}\cdot\frac{5\pi}{6}\right) = -\sqrt{\dfrac{1 + \cos\frac{5\pi}{6}}{2}} = -\sqrt{\dfrac{1 - \frac{\sqrt{3}}{2}}{2}} = -\sqrt{\dfrac{2 - \sqrt{3}}{4}} = -\dfrac{\sqrt{2 - \sqrt{3}}}{2}$. Note that
     we have chosen the negative root because $\cos\frac{5\pi}{12} < 0$ since $\frac{5\pi}{12}$ is in quadrant II.

20.   (a) $\dfrac{2\tan 7°}{1 - \tan^2 7°} = \tan 14°$ (b) $\dfrac{2\tan 7\theta}{1 - \tan^2 7\theta} = \tan 14\theta$

22.   (a) $\cos^2\frac{\theta}{2} - \sin^2\frac{\theta}{2} = \cos\theta$ (b) $2\sin\frac{\theta}{2}\cos\frac{\theta}{2} = \sin\theta$

24.   (a) $\sqrt{\dfrac{1 - \cos 30°}{2}} = \sin 15°$ (b) $\sqrt{\dfrac{1 - \cos 8\theta}{2}} = \sin 4\theta$

26. $\cos x = -\frac{4}{5}$. Since x is in quadrant III, $\sin x = -\frac{3}{5}$ and $\tan x = \frac{3}{4}$. Also, since $180° \le x \le 270°$,
     $90° \le \frac{x}{2} \le 135°$ and so $\frac{x}{2}$ is in quadrant II.

$$\sin\frac{x}{2} = \sqrt{\tfrac{1}{2}(1 - \cos x)} = \sqrt{\tfrac{1}{2}(1 + \tfrac{4}{5})} = \frac{3}{\sqrt{10}} = \frac{3\sqrt{10}}{10}$$

$$\cos\frac{x}{2} = -\sqrt{\tfrac{1}{2}(1 + \cos x)} = -\sqrt{\tfrac{1}{2}(1 - \tfrac{4}{5})} = -\frac{1}{\sqrt{10}} = -\frac{\sqrt{10}}{10}$$

$$\tan\frac{x}{2} = \frac{\sin\frac{x}{2}}{\cos\frac{x}{2}} = \frac{3}{\sqrt{10}}\cdot\frac{\sqrt{10}}{-1} = -3$$

28. $\tan x = 1$. Then $\sin x = \frac{\sqrt{2}}{2}$ and $\cos x = \frac{\sqrt{2}}{2}$, since x is in quadrant I. Also, since $0° \le x \le 90°$,
     $0° \le \frac{x}{2} \le 45°$ and so $\frac{x}{2}$ is also in quadrant I.

$$\sin\frac{x}{2} = \sqrt{\tfrac{1}{2}(1 - \cos x)} = \sqrt{\tfrac{1}{2}\left(1 - \tfrac{\sqrt{2}}{2}\right)} = \tfrac{1}{2}\sqrt{2 - \sqrt{2}}$$

$$\cos\frac{x}{2} = \sqrt{\tfrac{1}{2}(1 + \cos x)} = \sqrt{\tfrac{1}{2}\left(1 + \tfrac{\sqrt{2}}{2}\right)} = \tfrac{1}{2}\sqrt{2 + \sqrt{2}}$$

$$\tan\frac{x}{2} = \frac{1 - \cos x}{\sin x} = \frac{1 - \frac{\sqrt{2}}{2}}{\frac{\sqrt{2}}{2}} = \sqrt{2} - 1.$$

30. $\cot x = 5$. Then, $\cos x = -\frac{5}{\sqrt{26}}$ and $\sin x = -\frac{1}{\sqrt{26}}$ ($\csc x < 0$). Since $\cot x > 0$ and $\csc x < 0$ it
     follows that x is in quadrant III. Thus $180° \le x \le 270°$ and so $90° \le \frac{x}{2} \le 135°$. Thus $\frac{x}{2}$ is in
     quadrant II.

$$\sin\frac{x}{2} = \sqrt{\tfrac{1}{2}(1 - \cos x)} = \sqrt{\tfrac{1}{2}\left(1 + \tfrac{5}{\sqrt{26}}\right)} = \tfrac{1}{2}\sqrt{\tfrac{26 + 5\sqrt{26}}{13}}$$

$$\cos\frac{x}{2} = -\sqrt{\tfrac{1}{2}(1 + \cos x)} = -\sqrt{\tfrac{1}{2}\left(1 - \tfrac{5}{\sqrt{26}}\right)} = -\tfrac{1}{2}\sqrt{\tfrac{26 - 5\sqrt{26}}{13}}$$

$$\tan\frac{x}{2} = \frac{1 - \cos x}{\sin x} = \frac{1 + \frac{5}{\sqrt{26}}}{-\frac{1}{\sqrt{26}}} = -5 - \sqrt{26}.$$

32. $\sin x \sin 5x = \frac{1}{2}[\cos(x - 5x) - \cos(x + 5x)] = \frac{1}{2}(\cos 4x - \cos 6x)$

34. $11 \sin \frac{x}{2} \cos \frac{x}{4} = 11 \cdot \frac{1}{2}[\sin(\frac{x}{2} + \frac{x}{4}) + \sin(\frac{x}{2} - \frac{x}{4})] = \frac{11}{2} (\sin \frac{3x}{4} + \sin \frac{x}{4})$

36. $\sin x - \sin 4x = 2 \cos\left(\frac{x+4x}{2}\right) \sin\left(\frac{x-4x}{2}\right) = 2 \cos \frac{5x}{2} \sin \frac{-3x}{2} = -2 \cos \frac{5x}{2} \sin \frac{3x}{2}$

38. $\cos 9x + \cos 2x = 2 \cos\left(\frac{9x+2x}{2}\right) \cos\left(\frac{9x-2x}{2}\right) = 2 \cos \frac{11x}{2} \cos \frac{7x}{2}$

40. $\sin 3x + \sin 4x = 2 \sin\left(\frac{3x+4x}{2}\right) \cos\left(\frac{3x-4x}{2}\right) = 2 \sin \frac{7x}{2} \cos \frac{-x}{2} = 2 \sin \frac{7x}{2} \cos \frac{x}{2}$

42. $3 \cos 37.5° \cos 7.5° = \frac{3}{2} (\cos 45° + \cos 30°) = \frac{3}{2} \left(\frac{\sqrt{2}}{2} + \frac{\sqrt{3}}{2} \right) = \frac{3}{4} (\sqrt{2} + \sqrt{3})$

44. $\sin 75° + \sin 15° = 2 \sin(\frac{75°+15°}{2}) \cos(\frac{75°-15°}{2}) = 2 \sin 45° \cos 30° = 2 \cdot \frac{\sqrt{2}}{2} \cdot \frac{\sqrt{3}}{2} = \frac{\sqrt{6}}{2}$

46. $\cos \frac{\pi}{12} + \cos \frac{5\pi}{12} = 2 \cos[\frac{1}{2}(\frac{\pi}{12} + \frac{5\pi}{12})] \cos[\frac{1}{2}(\frac{\pi}{12} - \frac{5\pi}{12})] = 2 \cos \frac{\pi}{4} \cos \frac{\pi}{6} = 2 \cdot \frac{\sqrt{2}}{2} \cdot \frac{\sqrt{3}}{2} = \frac{\sqrt{6}}{2}$

48. $\sin 8x = \sin(2 \cdot 4x) = 2 \sin 4x \cos 4x$

50. $\dfrac{2 \tan x}{1 + \tan^2 x} = \dfrac{2 \tan x}{\sec^2 x} = 2 \cdot \dfrac{\sin x}{\cos x} \cos^2 x = 2 \sin x \cos x = \sin 2x$

52. $\dfrac{1 + \sin 2x}{\sin 2x} = \dfrac{1 + 2 \sin x \cos x}{2 \sin x \cos x} = 1 + \dfrac{1}{2 \sin x \cos x} = 1 + \frac{1}{2} \csc x \sec x$

54. $\cot 2x = \dfrac{1}{\tan 2x} = \dfrac{1}{\dfrac{2 \tan x}{1 - \tan^2 x}} = \dfrac{1 - \tan^2 x}{2 \tan x}$

56. $4(\sin^6 x + \cos^6 x) = 4[(\sin^2 x + \cos^2 x)^3 - 3(\sin^4 x \cos^2 x + \sin^2 x \cos^4 x)]$

     $= 4[1 - 3 \sin^2 x \cos^2 x (\sin^2 x + \cos^2 x)] = 4 - 12 \sin^2 x \cos^2 x = 4 - 3(2 \sin x \cos x)^2$

     $= 4 - 3 \sin^2 2x$

58.   Let $y = \frac{x}{2} + \frac{\pi}{4}$ $\Leftrightarrow$ $2y = x + \frac{\pi}{2}$. Then, $\tan^2(\frac{x}{2} + \frac{\pi}{4}) = \tan^2 y = \dfrac{1 - \cos 2y}{1 + \cos 2y} = \dfrac{1 - \cos(x + \frac{\pi}{2})}{1 + \cos(x + \frac{\pi}{2})}$

     $= \dfrac{1 - (-\sin x)}{1 + (-\sin x)} = \dfrac{1 + \sin x}{1 - \sin x}$

60. $\dfrac{\sin 3x + \sin 7x}{\cos 3x - \cos 7x} = \dfrac{2 \sin 5x \cos 2x}{-2 \sin 5x \sin(-2x)} = \dfrac{\cos 2x}{\sin 2x} = \cot 2x$

62. $\dfrac{\sin x + \sin 3x + \sin 5x}{\cos x + \cos 3x + \cos 5x} = \dfrac{\sin x + \sin 5x + \sin 3x}{\cos x + \cos 5x + \cos 3x} = \dfrac{2 \sin 3x \cos 2x + \sin 3x}{2 \cos 3x \cos 2x + \cos 3x}$

     $= \dfrac{\sin 3x \, (2 \cos 2x + 1)}{\cos 3x \, (2 \cos 2x + 1)} = \tan 3x$

64. $\dfrac{\sin(x + y) - \sin(x - y)}{\cos(x + y) + \cos(x - y)} = \dfrac{2 \sin\left(\frac{x+y+x-y}{2}\right) \cos\left(\frac{x+y-x+y}{2}\right)}{2 \cos\left(\frac{x+y+x-y}{2}\right) \cos\left(\frac{x+y-x+y}{2}\right)} = \dfrac{\sin x}{\cos x} = \tan x$

66. $\cos 87° + \cos 33° = 2\cos\frac{87°+33°}{2}\cos\frac{87°-33°}{2} = 2\cos 60°\cos 27° = 2\cdot\frac{1}{2}\cos 27° = \cos 27°$

   $= \sin(90° - 27°) = \sin 63°.$

68. $n = 1:$ $\sin(2^1 x) = 2\sin x\cos x = 2^1\sin x\cos(2^0 x)$

   $n = 2:$ $\sin(2^2 x) = \sin 4x = 2\sin 2x\cos 2x = 2(2\sin x\cos x)\cos 2x = 4\sin x\cos x\cos 2x$

   $= 2^2\sin x\cos x\cos(2^1 x)$

   $n = 3:$ $\sin(2^3 x) = \sin 8x = 2\sin 4x\cos 4x = 2(4\sin x\cos x\cos 2x)\cos 4x$

   $= 8\sin x\cos x\cos 2x\cos 4x = 2^3\sin x\cos x\cos 2x\cos(2^2 x)$

   Thus for a general $n > 0$ we have:

   $\sin(2^n x) = \sin 2(2^{n-1} x) = 2\sin(2^{n-1} x)\cos(2^{n-1} x)$

   $= 2[2^{n-1}\sin x\cos x\cos 2x\cos 4x\cos 8x\cdots\cos(2^{n-2} x)]\cos(2^{n-1} x)$

   $= 2^n\sin x\cos x\cos 2x\cos 4x\cos 8x\cdots\cos(2^{n-2} x)\cos(2^{n-1} x)$

70.   (a) $f(x) = \cos 2x + 2\sin^2 x$

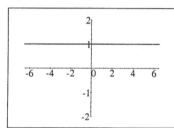

The function appears to have a constant value of 1.

   (b) $f(x) = \cos 2x + 2\sin^2 x$

   $= (\cos^2 x - \sin^2 x) + 2\sin^2 x$

   $= \cos^2 x + \sin^2 x = 1.$

72.   (a) $y = f_1(t) + f_2(t) = \cos 11t + \cos 13t$

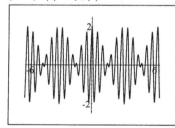

   (b)   Using the identity

   $\cos\alpha + \cos y = 2\cdot\cos\left(\dfrac{\alpha+y}{2}\right)\cos\left(\dfrac{\alpha-y}{2}\right),$

   we have $f(t) = \cos 11t + \cos 13t$

   $= 2\cdot\cos\left(\dfrac{11t+13t}{2}\right)\cos\left(\dfrac{11t-13t}{2}\right)$

   $= 2\cdot\cos 12t\cdot\cos(-t) = 2\cos 12t\cos t.$

   (c) $y = \cos 11t + \cos 13t$, with $y = 2\cos t$ and $y = -2\cos t$

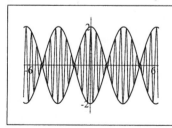

   The graph of f lies between the graphs of $y = 2\cos t$ and $y = -2\cos t$. Thus, the loudness of the sound varies between $y = \pm 2\cos t$.

74.   From Example 2 we have $\cos 3x = 4\cos^3 x - 3\cos x$. If $3x = \frac{\pi}{3}$, then

   $\cos\frac{\pi}{3} = \frac{1}{2} = 4\cos^3 x - 3\cos x$ $\Leftrightarrow$ $1 = 8\cos^3 x - 6\cos x$ $\Leftrightarrow$ $8\cos^3 x - 6\cos x - 1 = 0.$

   Substituting $y = \cos x$ gives $8y^3 - 6y - 1 = 0.$

76. Let c_1 and c_2 be the lengths of the segments shown in the figure. By the Law of Sines applied to

$\triangle ABC$ we have $\dfrac{c}{\sin 2x} = \dfrac{b}{\sin B}$ or $c = \dfrac{b \sin 2x}{\sin B}$.

Also by the Law of Sines applied to $\triangle BCD$

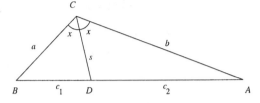

and $\triangle ACD$ we have $\dfrac{s}{\sin B} = \dfrac{c_1}{\sin x}$ and

$\dfrac{s}{\sin A} = \dfrac{c_2}{\sin x}$. So $c_1 = \dfrac{s \sin x}{\sin B}$ and $c_2 = \dfrac{s \sin x}{\sin A}$.

Since $c = c_1 + c_2$, we have $\dfrac{b \sin 2x}{\sin B} = \dfrac{s \sin x}{\sin B} + \dfrac{s \sin x}{\sin A} = s \sin x \left(\dfrac{1}{\sin B} + \dfrac{1}{\sin A} \right)$

By applying the Law of Sines to $\triangle ABC$, $\dfrac{b}{\sin B} = \dfrac{a}{\sin A} \quad \Leftrightarrow \quad \dfrac{1}{\sin A} = \dfrac{b}{a \sin B}$. Substituting

we

have $\dfrac{b \sin 2x}{\sin B} = s \sin x \left(\dfrac{1}{\sin B} + \dfrac{b}{a \sin B} \right) = s \dfrac{\sin x}{\sin B} \left(1 + \dfrac{b}{a} \right) \quad \Leftrightarrow \quad b \sin 2x = s \sin x \left(1 + \dfrac{b}{a} \right)$

$\Leftrightarrow \quad 2b \sin x \cos x = \sin x \left(1 + \dfrac{b}{a} \right) \quad \Leftrightarrow \quad 2b \cos x = s \left(1 + \dfrac{b}{a} \right) = s \left(\dfrac{a+b}{a} \right) \quad \Leftrightarrow$

$s = \dfrac{2ab \cos x}{a + b}$.

Exercises 9.4

2. (a) $\sin^{-1}\frac{\sqrt{3}}{2} = \frac{\pi}{3}$ (b) $\cos^{-1}\frac{\sqrt{3}}{2} = \frac{\pi}{6}$ (c) $\cos^{-1}(-\frac{\sqrt{3}}{2}) = \frac{5\pi}{6}$

4. (a) $\tan^{-1}\sqrt{3} = \frac{\pi}{3}$ (b) $\tan^{-1}(-\sqrt{3}) = -\frac{\pi}{3}$ (c) $\sin^{-1}\sqrt{3}$ is not defined.

6. (a) $\tan^{-1}1 = \frac{\pi}{4}$ (b) $\tan^{-1}(-1) = -\frac{\pi}{4}$ (c) $\tan^{-1}0 = 0$

8. (a) $\sin^{-1}0 = 0$ (b) $\cos^{-1}0 = \frac{\pi}{2}$ (c) $\cos^{-1}(-\frac{1}{2}) = \frac{2\pi}{3}$

10. (a) $\cos^{-1}(0.3388) \approx 1.22516$ (b) $\tan^{-1}(15.2000) \approx 1.505$

12. $\cos(\cos^{-1}\frac{3}{4}) = \frac{3}{4}$

14. $\sin(\sin^{-1}10)$ does not exist, 10 is not in the domain of the function $\sin^{-1}$.

16. $\tan^{-1}(\tan\frac{\pi}{6}) = \frac{\pi}{6}$ 18. Since $\sin\frac{5\pi}{6} = \sin\frac{\pi}{6}$, $\sin^{-1}(\sin\frac{5\pi}{6}) = \frac{\pi}{6}$

20. Since $\cos(-\frac{\pi}{4}) = \cos\frac{\pi}{4}$, $\cos^{-1}[\cos(-\frac{\pi}{4})] = \frac{\pi}{4}$

22. $\sin(\sin^{-1}0) = 0$ 24. $\tan(\sin^{-1}\frac{\sqrt{2}}{2}) = \tan\frac{\pi}{4} = 1$

26. $\cos^{-1}(\sqrt{3}\sin\frac{\pi}{6}) = \cos^{-1}(\sqrt{3}\cdot\frac{1}{2}) = \frac{\pi}{6}$

28. Let $u = \sin^{-1}\frac{4}{5}$, so $\sin u = \frac{4}{5}$. Then from the triangle $\tan(\sin^{-1}\frac{4}{5}) = \tan u = \frac{4}{3}$.

30. Let $u = \tan^{-1}5$, so $\tan u = 5$. Then from the triangle $\cos(\tan^{-1}5) = \cos u = \frac{1}{\sqrt{26}}$.

32. Let $\alpha = \cos^{-1}\frac{7}{25}$, so $\cos\alpha = \frac{7}{25}$. Then from the triangle $\csc(\cos^{-1}\frac{7}{25}) = \csc\alpha = \frac{25}{24}$.

34. Let $u = \sin^{-1}\frac{2}{3}$, so $\sin u = \frac{2}{3}$. Then from the triangle $\cot(\sin^{-1}\frac{2}{3}) = \cot u = \frac{\sqrt{5}}{2}$.

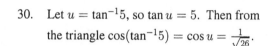

36. Let $u = \tan^{-1}\frac{5}{13}$, so $\tan u = \frac{5}{13}$. Then from the triangle

$$\tan(2\tan^{-1}\frac{5}{13}) = \tan 2u = \frac{2\tan u}{1 - \tan^2 u} = \frac{2\cdot\frac{5}{13}}{1 - \frac{25}{169}}$$

$$= \frac{10}{13}\cdot\frac{169}{144} = \frac{65}{72}.$$

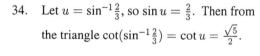

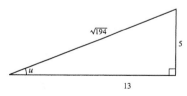

38. Let $\theta = \sin^{-1}\frac{3}{5}$ and $\gamma = \cos^{-1}\frac{3}{5}$, so $\sin\theta = \frac{3}{5}$ and $\cos\gamma = \frac{3}{5}$. From the triangle

$$\cos(\sin^{-1}\tfrac{3}{5} - \cos^{-1}\tfrac{3}{5}) = \cos(\sin^{-1}\tfrac{3}{5})\cos(\cos^{-1}\tfrac{3}{5}) + \sin(\sin^{-1}\tfrac{3}{5})\sin(\cos^{-1}\tfrac{3}{5})$$
$$= \cos\theta\cos\gamma + \sin\theta\sin\gamma = \tfrac{4}{5}\cdot\tfrac{3}{5} + \tfrac{3}{5}\cdot\tfrac{4}{5} = \tfrac{24}{25}.$$

40. Let $u = \tan^{-1}x$, so $\tan u = x$. Then from the triangle $\sin(\tan^{-1}x) = \sin u$

$$= \frac{x}{\sqrt{1+x^2}}.$$

42. Let $u = \tan^{-1}x$, so $\tan u = x$. Then from the triangle $\cos(\tan^{-1}x) = \cos u$

$$= \frac{1}{\sqrt{1+x^2}}.$$

44. Let $u = \sin^{-1}x$, so $\sin u = x$. From the triangle $\sin(2\sin^{-1}x) = \sin 2u$
$$= 2\sin u\cos u = 2x\sqrt{1-x^2}.$$

46. Let $u = \tan^{-1}x$ and $v = \sin^{-1}x$, so $\tan u = x$ and $\sin v = x$.
From the triangles we have
$$\sin(\tan^{-1}x - \sin^{-1}x) = \sin(u - v) = \sin u\cos v - \cos u\sin v$$
$$= \frac{x}{\sqrt{1+x^2}}\cdot\sqrt{1-x^2} - \frac{1}{\sqrt{1+x^2}}\cdot x = \frac{x\sqrt{1-x^2} - 1}{\sqrt{1+x^2}}.$$

48. $\sin\theta = \dfrac{h}{680} \quad\Rightarrow\quad \theta = \sin^{-1}\left(\dfrac{h}{680}\right)$

50. (a) $y = \tan^{-1}x + \tan^{-1}\left(\dfrac{1}{x}\right)$

conjecture: $y = \begin{cases} \frac{\pi}{2}, & \text{if } x > 0 \\ -\frac{\pi}{2}, & \text{if } x < 0 \end{cases}$

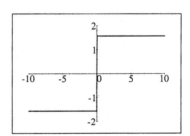

(b) To prove this conjecture, let $\tan^{-1}x = u \quad\Leftrightarrow\quad \tan u = x$, for $-\frac{\pi}{2} < u < \frac{\pi}{2}$. Then,
$$\frac{1}{x} = \frac{1}{\tan u} = \cot u = \tan\left(\tfrac{\pi}{2} - u\right) \text{ by the cofunction identity. So,}$$

$$\tan^{-1}x + \tan^{-1}\left(\frac{1}{x}\right) = u + \tan^{-1}\left(\tan(\tfrac{\pi}{2} - u)\right).$$

If $x > 0$, then $\frac{\pi}{2} > u > 0$, so $0 < \frac{\pi}{2} - u < \frac{\pi}{2} \quad\Rightarrow\quad \frac{\pi}{2} - u$ is in quadrant I. Therefore,
$$\tan^{-1}\left(\tan(\tfrac{\pi}{2} - u)\right) = \tfrac{\pi}{2} - u, \text{ so } \tan^{-1}x + \tan^{-1}\left(\frac{1}{x}\right) = u + \left(\tfrac{\pi}{2} - u\right) = \tfrac{\pi}{2}.$$

If $x < 0$, then $-\frac{\pi}{2} < u < 0$, so $\pi > \frac{\pi}{2} - u > \frac{\pi}{2}$ $\Rightarrow$ $\frac{\pi}{2} - u$ is in quadrant II. Thus, $\tan^{-1}\left(\tan(\frac{\pi}{2} - u)\right) = \left(\frac{\pi}{2} - u\right) - \pi = -\frac{\pi}{2} - u$, and hence

$$\tan^{-1}x + \tan^{-1}\left(\frac{1}{x}\right) = u + \left(-\frac{\pi}{2} - u\right) = -\frac{\pi}{2}.$$

52. (a) $y = \sin^{-1}x - \cos^{-1}x$

From the graph, we see that $y = 0$ when $x \approx 0.71$.

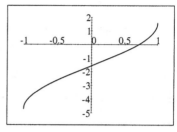

(b) To find the exact solution, we set $\sin^{-1}x - \cos^{-1}x = 0$ $\Leftrightarrow$ $\sin^{-1}x = \cos^{-1}x$ $\Rightarrow$ $\sin(\sin^{-1}x) = \sin(\cos^{-1}x)$ $\Rightarrow$ $x = \sqrt{1 - x^2}$ $\Rightarrow$ $x^2 = 1 - x^2$ $\Leftrightarrow$ $2x^2 = 1$ $\Rightarrow$ $x = \pm\frac{1}{\sqrt{2}}$. But $x = \sqrt{1 - x^2} \geq 0$, so $x = \frac{1}{\sqrt{2}}$.

Exercises 9.5

2. $\sqrt{2}\sin x - 1 = 0 \quad \Leftrightarrow \quad \sqrt{2}\sin x = 1 \quad \Leftrightarrow \quad \sin x = \frac{1}{\sqrt{2}}$. The solutions in the interval $[0, 2\pi)$ are $x = \frac{\pi}{4}, \frac{3\pi}{4}$. Thus the solutions are $x = \frac{\pi}{4} + 2k\pi, \frac{3\pi}{4} + 2k\pi$.

4. $\tan x + 1 = 0 \quad \Leftrightarrow \quad \tan x = -1$. The solution in the interval $[0, \pi)$ are $x = -\frac{\pi}{4}$. Thus, the solutions are $x = k\pi - \frac{\pi}{4}$, for any integer k.

6. $2\cos^2 x - 1 = 0 \quad \Leftrightarrow \quad \cos^2 x = \frac{1}{2} \quad \Leftrightarrow \quad \cos x = \pm\frac{1}{\sqrt{2}} \quad \Leftrightarrow \quad x = \frac{\pi}{4}, \frac{3\pi}{4}, \frac{5\pi}{4}, \frac{7\pi}{4}$ in $[0, 2\pi)$. Thus $x = \frac{\pi}{4} + k\pi, \frac{3\pi}{4} + k\pi$, for any integer k.

8. $\csc^2 x - 4 = 0 \quad \Leftrightarrow \quad \csc^2 x = 4 \quad \Leftrightarrow \quad \csc x = \pm 2 \quad \Leftrightarrow \quad \sin x = \pm\frac{1}{2} \quad \Leftrightarrow \quad x = \frac{\pi}{6}, \frac{5\pi}{6}, \frac{7\pi}{6}, \frac{11\pi}{6}$ for x in $[0, 2\pi)$. Thus $x = \frac{\pi}{6} + k\pi, \frac{5\pi}{6} + k\pi$, for any integer k.

10. $\sec x\, (2\cos x - \sqrt{2}) = 0 \quad \Leftrightarrow \quad \sec x = 0$ or $2\cos x - \sqrt{2} = 0$. Since $|\sec x| \geq 1$, $\sec x = 0$ has no solution. Thus $2\cos x - \sqrt{2} = 0 \quad \Leftrightarrow \quad 2\cos x = \sqrt{2} \quad \Leftrightarrow \quad \cos x = \frac{\sqrt{2}}{2} \quad \Leftrightarrow \quad x = \frac{\pi}{4}, \frac{7\pi}{4}$ in $[0, 2\pi)$. Thus $x = \frac{\pi}{4} + 2k\pi, \frac{7\pi}{4} + 2k\pi$, for any integer k

12. $(2\cos x + \sqrt{3}\,)(2\sin x - 1) = 0 \quad \Leftrightarrow \quad 2\cos x + \sqrt{3} = 0$ or $2\sin x - 1 = 0 \quad \Leftrightarrow \quad \cos x = -\frac{\sqrt{3}}{2}$ or $\sin x = \frac{1}{2} \quad \Leftrightarrow \quad x = \frac{\pi}{6}, \frac{5\pi}{6}, \frac{7\pi}{6}$ in $[0, 2\pi)$. Thus $x = \frac{\pi}{6} + k\pi, \frac{5\pi}{6} + 2k\pi$, for any integer k.

14. $\tan x \sin x + \sin x = 0 \quad \Leftrightarrow \quad \sin x\,(\tan x + 1) = 0 \quad \Leftrightarrow \quad \sin x = 0$ or $\tan x + 1 = 0$. Now $\sin x = 0$ when $x = k\pi$ and $\tan x + 1 = 0 \quad \Leftrightarrow \quad \tan x = -1 \quad \Rightarrow \quad x = \frac{3\pi}{4} + k\pi$. Thus the solutions are $x = k\pi, \frac{3\pi}{4} + k\pi$, for any integer k.

16. $2\sin^2 x - \sin x - 1 = 0 \quad \Leftrightarrow \quad (2\sin x + 1)(\sin x - 1) = 0 \quad \Leftrightarrow \quad 2\sin x + 1 = 0$ or $\sin x - 1 = 0$. Since $2\sin x + 1 = 0 \quad \Leftrightarrow \quad 2\sin x = -\frac{1}{2} \quad \Leftrightarrow \quad x = \frac{7\pi}{6}, \frac{11\pi}{6}$ in $[0, 2\pi)$ and $\sin x = 1 \quad \Leftrightarrow \quad x = \frac{\pi}{2}$ in $[0, 2\pi)$. Thus the solutions are $x = \frac{7\pi}{6} + 2k\pi, \frac{11\pi}{6} + 2k\pi, \frac{\pi}{2} + 2k\pi$, for any integer k.

18. $3\tan^3 x = \tan x \quad \Leftrightarrow \quad 3\tan^3 x - \tan x = 0 \quad \Leftrightarrow \quad \tan x\,(3\tan^2 x - 1) = 0 \quad \Leftrightarrow \quad \tan x = 0$ or $3\tan^2 x - 1 = 0$. Now $\tan x = 0 \quad \Rightarrow \quad x = k\pi$ and $3\tan^2 x - 1 = 0 \quad \Leftrightarrow \quad \tan^2 x = \frac{1}{3} \quad \Rightarrow \quad \tan x = \pm\frac{1}{\sqrt{3}} \quad \Rightarrow \quad x = \frac{\pi}{6} + k\pi, \frac{5\pi}{6} + k\pi$. Thus the solutions are $x = k\pi, \frac{\pi}{6} + k\pi, \frac{5\pi}{6} + k\pi$, for any integer k.

20. $2\cos^2 x + \sin x = 1 \quad \Leftrightarrow \quad 2(1 - \sin^2 x) + \sin x - 1 = 0 \quad \Leftrightarrow \quad -2\sin^2 x + \sin x + 1 = 0 \quad \Leftrightarrow \quad 2\sin^2 x - \sin x - 1 = 0$ which we solved in Exercise 16. Thus $x = \frac{7\pi}{6} + 2k\pi, \frac{11\pi}{6} + 2k\pi, \frac{\pi}{2} + 2k\pi$, for any integer k.

22. $\sqrt{3}\sin 2x = \cos 2x \quad \Leftrightarrow \quad \tan 2x = \frac{1}{\sqrt{3}}$ (if $\cos 2x \neq 0$) $\quad \Leftrightarrow \quad 2x = \frac{\pi}{6} + k\pi \quad \Leftrightarrow \quad x = \frac{\pi}{12} + \frac{1}{2}k\pi$, for any integer k.

24. $\csc 3x = \sin 3x \quad \Leftrightarrow \quad \dfrac{1}{\sin 3x} = \sin 3x \quad \Leftrightarrow \quad \sin^2 3x = 1 \quad \Leftrightarrow \quad \sin 3x = \pm 1 \quad \Leftrightarrow \quad 3x = \frac{\pi}{2} + k\pi \quad \Leftrightarrow \quad x = \frac{\pi}{6} + \frac{k\pi}{3}$, for any integer k. Notice that multiplying by $\sin 3x$ in the first step did not introduce extraneous roots.

26. $3\tan^3 x - 3\tan^2 x - \tan x + 1 = 0$ $\Leftrightarrow$ $(\tan x - 1)(3\tan^2 x - 1) = 0$ $\Leftrightarrow$ $\tan x = 1$ or
$3\tan^2 x = 1$ $\Leftrightarrow$ $\tan x = 1$ or $\tan x = \pm\frac{1}{\sqrt{3}}$ $\Leftrightarrow$ $x = \frac{\pi}{4}, \frac{\pi}{6}, \frac{5\pi}{6}$, for $x \in [0, \pi)$. Thus
$x = \frac{\pi}{4} + k\pi, \frac{\pi}{6} + k\pi, \frac{5\pi}{6} + k\pi$, for any integer k.

28. $\sin 2x = 2\tan 2x$ $\Leftrightarrow$ $\sin 2x = \dfrac{2\sin 2x}{\cos 2x}$ $\Leftrightarrow$ $\sin 2x \cos 2x - 2\sin 2x = 0$ $\Leftrightarrow$
$\sin 2x (\cos 2x - 2) = 0$ $\Leftrightarrow$ $\cos 2x = 2$ (which is impossible since $|\cos u| \le 1$) or $\sin 2x = 0$
$\Leftrightarrow$ $2x = k\pi$ $\Leftrightarrow$ $x = \frac{1}{2}k\pi$, for any integer k.

30. $\sec x - \tan x = \cos x$ $\Leftrightarrow$ $\cos x(\sec x - \tan x) = \cos x(\cos x)$ $\Leftrightarrow$ $1 - \sin x = \cos^2 x$ $\Leftrightarrow$
$1 - \sin x = 1 - \sin^2 x$ $\Leftrightarrow$ $\sin x = \sin^2 x$ $\Leftrightarrow$ $\sin^2 x - \sin x = 0$ $\Leftrightarrow$ $\sin x(\sin x - 1) = 0$
$\Leftrightarrow$ $\sin x = 0$ or $\sin x = 1$ $\Leftrightarrow$ $x = 0, \pi$ or $x = \frac{\pi}{2}, \frac{3\pi}{2}$ in $[0, 2\pi)$. However, since the equation
is undefined when $x = \frac{\pi}{2}, \frac{3\pi}{2}$, the solutions are $x = k\pi$ for any integer k.

32. $3\csc^2 x = 4$ $\Leftrightarrow$ $\csc^2 x = \frac{4}{3}$ $\Rightarrow$ $\csc x = \pm\frac{2}{\sqrt{3}}$ $\Leftrightarrow$ $\sin x = \pm\frac{\sqrt{3}}{2}$ $\Rightarrow$ $x = \frac{\pi}{3}, \frac{2\pi}{3}$, in
$[0, 2\pi)$.

34. $\sec x \tan x - \cos x \cot x = \sin x$ $\Leftrightarrow$ $\dfrac{1}{\cos x}\dfrac{\sin x}{\cos x} - \cos x \cdot \dfrac{\cos x}{\sin x} = \sin x$ $\Leftrightarrow$
$\dfrac{\sin x}{\cos^2 x} - \dfrac{\cos^2 x}{\sin x} = \sin x$. Multiplying both sides by the common denominator $\cos^2 x \sin x$ gives
$\sin^2 x - \cos^4 x = \sin^2 x \cos^2 x$ $\Leftrightarrow$ $\sin^2 x - \cos^4 x = (1 - \cos^2 x)\cos^2 x$ $\Leftrightarrow$
$\sin^2 x - \cos^4 x = \cos^2 x - \cos^4 x$ $\Leftrightarrow$ $\sin^2 x = \cos^2 x$ $\Leftrightarrow$ $\sin^2 x = 1 - \sin^2 x$ $\Leftrightarrow$
$2\sin^2 x = 1$ $\Leftrightarrow$ $\sin x = \pm\frac{1}{\sqrt{2}}$ $\Leftrightarrow$ $x = \frac{\pi}{4}, \frac{3\pi}{4}, \frac{5\pi}{4}, \frac{7\pi}{4}$. Since we multiplied the above
equation by $\cos^2 x \sin x$ (which could be zero) we must check to see if we have introduced
extraneous solutions. However, each of the values of x satisfies the original equation and so the
solutions on $[0, 2\pi)$ are $x = \frac{\pi}{4}, \frac{3\pi}{4}, \frac{5\pi}{4}, \frac{7\pi}{4}$.

36. $2\sin^2 x - \cos x = 1$ $\Leftrightarrow$ $2(1 - \cos^2 x) - \cos x - 1 = 0$ $\Leftrightarrow$ $-2\cos^2 x - \cos x + 1 = 0$
$\Leftrightarrow$ $(2\cos x - 1)(\cos x + 1) = 0$ $\Leftrightarrow$ $2\cos x - 1 = 0$ or $\cos x + 1 = 0$ $\Leftrightarrow$ $\cos x = \frac{1}{2}$ or
$\cos x = -1$ $\Leftrightarrow$ $x = \frac{\pi}{3}, \frac{5\pi}{3}, \pi$ in $[0, 2\pi)$.

38. $3\sec^2 x + 8\cos^2 x = 7$ $\Leftrightarrow$ $\dfrac{3}{\cos^2 x} + 4\cos^2 x - 7 = 0$ (for $\cos x \ne 0$) $\Leftrightarrow$

$3 + 4\cos^4 x - 7\cos^2 x = 0$ $\Leftrightarrow$ $4\cos^4 x - 7\cos^2 x + 3 = 0$ $\Leftrightarrow$
$(4\cos^2 x - 3)(\cos^2 x - 1) = 0$ $\Leftrightarrow$ $4\cos^2 x - 3 = 0$ or $\cos^2 x - 1 = 0$ $\Leftrightarrow$ $\cos x = \pm\frac{\sqrt{3}}{2}$ or
$\cos x = \pm 1$ $\Leftrightarrow$ $x = \frac{\pi}{6}, \frac{5\pi}{6}, \frac{7\pi}{6}, \frac{11\pi}{6}$ or $x = 0, \pi$ in $[0, 2\pi)$. So, the solutions are $x = 0, \frac{\pi}{6}, \frac{5\pi}{6}, \pi$,
$\frac{7\pi}{6}, \frac{11\pi}{6}$.

40. (a) $2\tan x = 13$ $\Leftrightarrow$ $\tan x = \frac{13}{2}$ $\Rightarrow$ $x \approx 1.41815$. Since the period for tangent is π, the
        other solution in $[0, 2\pi]$ is $x \approx 1.41815 + \pi \approx 4.55974$.

     (b) Since the period is π, the solutions are of the form $x \approx 1.41815 + k\pi$, for any integer k.

42. (a) Since $\cos x = 0$ is not a solution, we divide both sides by $\cos x$. $3\sin x = 7\cos x$ $\Leftrightarrow$
        $\tan x = \frac{7}{3}$ $\Rightarrow$ $x \approx 1.16590$. Since the period for tangent is π, the other solution in $[0, 2\pi]$
        is $x \approx 1.16590 + \pi \approx 4.30750$.

(b) Since the period is π, the solutions are of the form $x \approx 1.16590 + k\pi$, for any integer k.

44. (a) $2\sin 2x - \cos x = 0 \quad \Leftrightarrow \quad 2(2\sin x \cos x) - \cos x = 0 \quad \Leftrightarrow \quad 4\sin x \cos x - \cos x = 0$
$\Leftrightarrow \quad \cos x(4\sin x - 1) = 0 \quad \Leftrightarrow \quad \cos x = 0$ or $4\sin x - 1 = 0$. Now $\cos x = 0 \quad \Leftrightarrow$
$x = \frac{\pi}{2}, \frac{3\pi}{2}$ and $4\sin x - 1 = 0 \quad \Leftrightarrow \quad \sin x = \frac{1}{4} \quad \Rightarrow \quad x \approx 0.25268$ or $x \approx \pi - 0.25268$
≈ 2.88891. Thus the solutions in $[0, 2\pi)$ are $x \approx 0.25268, 1.57080, 2.88891, 4.71239$.

(b) Since the period is 2π, the solutions are of the form $x \approx 1.57080 + k\pi, x \approx 0.25268 + 2k\pi,$
$x \approx 2.88891 + 2k\pi$, for any integer k.

46. (a) $\tan^4 x - 13\tan^2 x + 36 = 0 \quad \Leftrightarrow \quad (\tan^2 x - 4)(\tan^2 x - 9) = 0 \quad \Leftrightarrow \quad \tan x = \pm 2$ or
$\tan x = \pm 3 \quad \Rightarrow \quad x \approx 1.10715, -1.10715, 1.24905, -1.24905$ in $(-\frac{\pi}{2}, \frac{\pi}{2})$. Since the period
for tangent is π, the solutions in $[0, 2\pi)$ are $x \approx 1.10715, 1.24905, 1.89255, 2.03444, 4.24874,$
4.39064, 5.03414, 5.17604. *doesn't match book φ*

(b) Since the period is π, the solutions are of the form $x \approx 1.10715 + k\pi, x \approx 2.03444 + k\pi,$
$x \approx 1.24905 + k\pi, x \approx 1.89255 + k\pi,$ for any integer k.

48. $f(x) = \sin 2x; g(x) = 2\sin 2x + 1$.
$f(x) = g(x)$ when $\sin 2x = 2\sin 2x + 1$
$\Leftrightarrow \quad \sin 2x = -1 \quad \Leftrightarrow \quad 2x = \frac{3\pi}{2} + 2k\pi$
$\Leftrightarrow \quad x = \frac{3\pi}{4} + k\pi$, for any integer k.

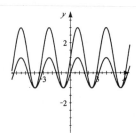

50. $f(x) = \sin x - 1; g(x) = \cos x.$ $f(x) = g(x)$ when $\sin x - 1 = \cos x$
$\Rightarrow \quad (\sin x - 1)^2 = \cos^2 x \quad \Leftrightarrow \quad \sin^2 x - 2\sin x + 1 = \cos^2 x$
$\Leftrightarrow \quad \sin^2 x - 2\sin x + 1 - \cos^2 x = 0 \quad \Leftrightarrow \quad 2\sin^2 x - 2\sin x = 0$
$\Leftrightarrow \quad 2\sin x(\sin x - 1) = 0 \quad \Leftrightarrow \quad \sin x = 0$ or $\sin x = 1 \quad \Leftrightarrow$
$x = k\pi, \frac{\pi}{2} + 2k\pi$. However, $x = k\pi$ is not a solution when k is even
(extraneous solutions introduced by squaring both sides). So, the
solutions are $x = (2k+1)\pi, \frac{\pi}{2} + 2k\pi$, and the intersection points are
$(\pi + 2k\pi, -1), (\frac{\pi}{2} + 2k\pi, 0)$, for any integer k.

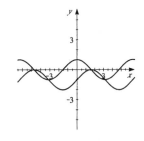

Alternative solution. $\sin x - 1 = \cos x \quad \Leftrightarrow \quad \sin x - \cos x = 1 \quad \Leftrightarrow$
$\sqrt{2}\left(\frac{1}{\sqrt{2}}\sin x - \frac{1}{\sqrt{2}}\cos x\right) = 1 \quad \Leftrightarrow \quad \frac{\sqrt{2}}{2}\sin x - \frac{\sqrt{2}}{2}\cos x = \frac{\sqrt{2}}{2}$. Since $\sin\frac{\pi}{4} = \cos\frac{\pi}{4} = \frac{\sqrt{2}}{2}$ we
may write $\frac{\sqrt{2}}{2}\sin x - \frac{\sqrt{2}}{2}\cos x = \cos\frac{\pi}{4}\sin x - \sin\frac{\pi}{4}\cos x = \frac{\sqrt{2}}{2} \quad \Leftrightarrow \quad \sin(x - \frac{\pi}{4}) = \frac{\sqrt{2}}{2} \quad \Leftrightarrow$
$x - \frac{\pi}{4} = \frac{\pi}{4}, \frac{3\pi}{4} \quad \Leftrightarrow \quad x = \frac{\pi}{2}, \pi$ in $[0, 2\pi)$. So, the solutions are $x = (2k+1)\pi, \frac{\pi}{2} + 2k\pi$, and the
intersection points are $(\pi + 2k\pi, -1), (\frac{\pi}{2} + 2k\pi, 0)$, for any integer k.

52. $\cos x \cos 2x + \sin x \sin 2x = \frac{1}{2} \quad \Leftrightarrow \quad \cos(x - 2x) = \frac{1}{2} \quad \Leftrightarrow \quad \cos(-x) = \frac{1}{2} \quad \Leftrightarrow \quad \cos x = \frac{1}{2}$
$\Leftrightarrow \quad x = \frac{\pi}{3}, \frac{5\pi}{3}$ in $[0, 2\pi)$.

54. $\sin 3x \cos x - \cos 3x \sin x = 0 \quad \Leftrightarrow \quad \sin(3x - x) = 0 \quad \Leftrightarrow \quad \sin 2x = 0 \quad \Leftrightarrow \quad 2x = 0, \pi, 2\pi,$
$3\pi, 4\pi$ in $[0, 4\pi) \quad \Leftrightarrow \quad x = 0, \frac{\pi}{2}, \pi, \frac{3\pi}{2}$ in $[0, 2\pi)$.

56. $\tan\frac{x}{2} - \sin x = 0$ $\Leftrightarrow$ $\dfrac{\sin x}{1+\cos x} - \sin x = 0$ $\Leftrightarrow$ $\sin x - \sin x\,(1+\cos x) = 0$ (and $\cos x \neq -1$ $\Leftrightarrow$ $x \neq \pi$) $\Leftrightarrow$ $\sin x\,(-\cos x) = 0$ $\Leftrightarrow$ $\sin x = 0$ or $\cos x = 0$ $\Leftrightarrow$ $x = 0, \frac{\pi}{2}, \frac{3\pi}{2}$ in $[0, 2\pi)$ ($x = \pi$ is inadmissible).

58. $\tan x + \cot x = 4\sin 2x$ $\Leftrightarrow$ $\dfrac{\sin x}{\cos x} + \dfrac{\cos x}{\sin x} = 8\sin x \cos x$ $\Leftrightarrow$

$\left(\dfrac{\sin x}{\cos x} + \dfrac{\cos x}{\sin x}\right) \cdot \sin x \cos x = (8\sin x \cos x) \cdot \sin x \cos x$ $\Leftrightarrow$

$\sin^2 x + \cos^2 x = 8\sin^2 x \cos^2 x$ $\Leftrightarrow$ $1 = 2\,(2\sin x \cos x)^2$ $\Leftrightarrow$ $(\sin 2x)^2 = \frac{1}{2}$ $\Leftrightarrow$

$\sin 2x = \pm\frac{1}{\sqrt{2}}$. Therefore, $2x = \frac{\pi}{4} + k\pi$ or $2x = \frac{3\pi}{4} + k\pi$ $\Leftrightarrow$ $x = \frac{\pi}{8} + \frac{k\pi}{2}$ or $x = \frac{3\pi}{8} + \frac{k\pi}{2}$.

Thus on the interval $[0, 2\pi)$ the solutions are $x = \frac{\pi}{8}, \frac{5\pi}{8}, \frac{9\pi}{8}, \frac{13\pi}{8}$ and $\frac{3\pi}{8}, \frac{7\pi}{8}, \frac{11\pi}{8}, \frac{15\pi}{8}$. Together we write the solutions as $x = \frac{\pi}{8}, \frac{3\pi}{8}, \frac{5\pi}{8}, \frac{7\pi}{8}, \frac{9\pi}{8}, \frac{11\pi}{8}, \frac{13\pi}{8}, \frac{15\pi}{8}$, which are odd multiples of $\frac{\pi}{8}$. So we can express the general solution as $x = \frac{(2k+1)\pi}{8}$, where k is any integer.

60. $\cos 5x - \cos 7x = 0$ $\Leftrightarrow$ $-2\sin 6x \sin(-x) = 0$ $\Leftrightarrow$ $\sin 6x \sin x = 0$ $\Leftrightarrow$ $\sin 6x = 0$ or $\sin x = 0$ $\Leftrightarrow$ $6x = k\pi$ or $x = k\pi$ $\Leftrightarrow$ $x = \frac{k\pi}{6}$, for any integer k.

62. $\sin 5x - \sin 3x = \cos 4x$ $\Leftrightarrow$ $2\cos 4x \sin x = \cos 4x$ $\Leftrightarrow$ $\cos 4x\,(2\sin x - 1) = 0$ $\Leftrightarrow$ $\cos 4x = 0$ or $\sin x = \frac{1}{2}$ $\Leftrightarrow$ $4x = \frac{\pi}{2} + k\pi$ or $x = \frac{\pi}{6} + 2k\pi$, $\frac{5\pi}{6} + 2k\pi$ $\Leftrightarrow$ $x = \frac{\pi}{8} + \frac{k\pi}{4}$, $\frac{\pi}{6} + 2k\pi$, $\frac{5\pi}{6} + 2k\pi$. ($x = \frac{\pi}{8} + \frac{k\pi}{4}$ can also be expressed as $x = \frac{(2k+1)\pi}{8}$).

64. $\cos x = \frac{x}{3}$

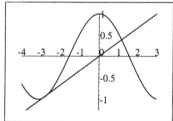

3 solutions: $x = 1.17, -2.66, -2.94$

66. $\sin x = x^3$

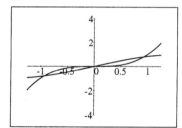

3 solutions: $x = 0, \pm 0.93$

68. $\sin x = \frac{1}{2}\left(e^x - e^{-x}\right)$

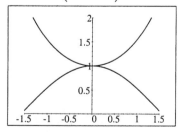

1 solution: $x = 0$

70. $\sin(\cos x)$ is a function *of* a function, that is, a composition of trigonometric functions (see Section 2.6). Most of the other equations involve sums, products, differences, or quotients of trigonometric functions.

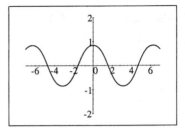

$\sin(\cos x) = 0 \quad \Leftrightarrow \quad \cos x = 0$ or $\cos x = \pi$. However, since $|\cos x| \le 1$ the only solution is $\cos x = 0 \quad \Rightarrow \quad x = \frac{\pi}{2} + k\pi$. The graph of $f(x) = \sin(\cos x)$ is shown at the right.

Exercises 9.6

2. $1 - \sqrt{3}\,i$. Then $\tan\theta = -\sqrt{3}$ with θ in quadrant IV $\Rightarrow$ $\theta = \frac{5\pi}{3}$, and $r = \sqrt{1+3} = 2$. Hence, $1 - \sqrt{3}\,i = 2\left(\cos\frac{5\pi}{3} + i\sin\frac{5\pi}{3}\right)$.

4. $1 - i$. Then $\tan\theta = -1$ with θ in quadrant IV $\Rightarrow$ $\theta = \frac{7\pi}{4}$, and $r = \sqrt{1+1} = \sqrt{2}$. Hence, $1 - i = \sqrt{2}\left(\cos\frac{7\pi}{4} + i\sin\frac{7\pi}{4}\right)$.

6. $-1 + i$. Then $\tan\theta = -1$ with θ in quadrant II $\Rightarrow$ $\theta = \frac{3\pi}{4}$, and $r = \sqrt{1+1} = \sqrt{2}$. Hence, $-1 + i = \sqrt{2}\left(\cos\frac{3\pi}{4} + i\sin\frac{3\pi}{4}\right)$.

8. $-3 - 3\sqrt{3}\,i$. Then $\tan\theta = \sqrt{3}$ with θ in quadrant III $\Rightarrow$ $\theta = \frac{4\pi}{3}$, and $r = \sqrt{9+27} = 6$. Hence, $-3 - 3\sqrt{3}\,i = 6\left(\cos\frac{4\pi}{3} + i\sin\frac{4\pi}{3}\right)$.

10. 4. Then $\theta = 0$, and $r = \sqrt{16+0} = 4$. Hence, $4 = 4\left(\cos 0 + i\sin 0\right)$.

12. $8i$. Then $\theta = \frac{\pi}{2}$, and $r = 8$. Hence, $8i = 8\left(\cos\frac{\pi}{2} + i\sin\frac{\pi}{2}\right)$.

14. $\sqrt{3} + i$. Then $\tan\theta = \frac{1}{\sqrt{3}}$ with θ in quadrant I $\Rightarrow$ $\theta = \frac{\pi}{6}$, and $r = \sqrt{3+1} = 2$. Hence, $\sqrt{3} + i = 2\left(\cos\frac{\pi}{6} + i\sin\frac{\pi}{6}\right)$.

16. $i\left(2 - 2i\right) = 2 + 2i$. Then $\tan\theta = 1$ with θ in quadrant I $\Rightarrow$ $\theta = \frac{\pi}{4}$, and $r = \sqrt{4+4} = 2\sqrt{2}$. Hence, $i\left(2 - 2i\right) = 2\sqrt{2}\left(\cos\frac{\pi}{4} + i\sin\frac{\pi}{4}\right)$.

18. $2\left(1 - i\right) = 2 - 2i$. Then $\tan\theta = -1$ with θ in quadrant IV $\Rightarrow$ $\theta = \frac{7\pi}{4}$, and $r = \sqrt{4+4} = 2\sqrt{2}$. Hence, $2\left(1 - i\right) = 2\sqrt{2}\left(\cos\frac{7\pi}{4} + i\sin\frac{7\pi}{4}\right)$.

20. $-3 - 3i$. Then $\tan\theta = 1$ with θ in quadrant III $\Rightarrow$ $\theta = \frac{5\pi}{4}$, and $r = \sqrt{9+9} = 3\sqrt{2}$. Hence, $-3 - 3i = 3\sqrt{2}\left(\cos\frac{5\pi}{4} + i\sin\frac{5\pi}{4}\right)$.

22. $3 + \sqrt{3}\,i$. Then $\tan\theta = \frac{1}{\sqrt{3}}$ with θ in quadrant I $\Rightarrow$ $\theta = \frac{\pi}{6}$, and $r = \sqrt{9+3} = 2\sqrt{3}$. Hence, $3 + \sqrt{3}\,i = 2\sqrt{3}\left(\cos\frac{\pi}{6} + i\sin\frac{\pi}{6}\right)$.

24. $-\pi i$. Then $\theta = \frac{3\pi}{2}$, and $r = \pi$. Hence $-\pi i = \pi\left(\cos\frac{3\pi}{2} + i\sin\frac{3\pi}{2}\right)$.

26. $z_1 = 3\left(\cos\frac{\pi}{6} + i\sin\frac{\pi}{6}\right)$, $z_2 = 5\left(\cos\frac{4\pi}{3} + i\sin\frac{4\pi}{3}\right)$

$z_1 z_2 = 3\cdot 5\left[\cos\left(\frac{\pi}{6} + \frac{4\pi}{3}\right) + i\sin\left(\frac{\pi}{6} + \frac{4\pi}{3}\right)\right] = 15\left(\cos\frac{9\pi}{6} + i\sin\frac{9\pi}{6}\right) = 15\left(\cos\frac{3\pi}{2} + i\sin\frac{3\pi}{2}\right)$

$z_1 / z_2 = \frac{3}{5}\left[\cos\left(\frac{\pi}{6} - \frac{4\pi}{3}\right) + i\sin\left(\frac{\pi}{6} - \frac{4\pi}{3}\right)\right] = \frac{3}{5}\left[\cos\left(-\frac{7\pi}{6}\right) + i\sin\left(-\frac{7\pi}{6}\right)\right] = \frac{3}{5}\left[\cos\left(\frac{7\pi}{6}\right) - i\sin\left(\frac{7\pi}{6}\right)\right]$

28. $z_1 = \sqrt{2}\left(\cos 75° + i\sin 75°\right)$, $z_2 = 3\sqrt{2}\left(\cos 60° + i\sin 60°\right)$

$z_1 z_2 = \sqrt{2}\cdot 3\sqrt{2}\cdot\left[\cos(75° + 60°) + i\sin(75° + 60°)\right] = 6\left(\cos 135° + i\sin 135°\right)$

$z_1 / z_2 = \frac{\sqrt{2}}{3\sqrt{2}}\left[\cos(75° - 60°) + i\sin(75° - 60°)\right] = \frac{1}{3}\left(\cos 15° + i\sin 15°\right)$

30. $z_1 = \frac{4}{5}\left(\cos 25° + i\sin 25°\right)$, $z_2 = \frac{1}{5}\left(\cos 155° + i\sin 155°\right)$

$z_1 z_2 = \frac{4}{5}\cdot\frac{1}{5}\cdot\left[\cos(25° + 155°) + i\sin(25° + 155°)\right] = \frac{4}{25}\left(\cos 180° + i\sin 180°\right)$

$z_1/z_2 = \dfrac{\frac{4}{5}}{\frac{1}{5}}[\cos(25° - 155°) + i\sin(25° - 155°)] = 4[\cos(-130° + i\sin(-130°)]$

$= 4(\cos 130° - i\sin 130°)$

32. $z_1 = \sqrt{2} - \sqrt{2}\,i$. Then $\tan\theta_1 = -1$ with θ_1 in quadrant IV $\Rightarrow$ $\theta_1 = \frac{7\pi}{4}$, and
$r_1 = \sqrt{2+2} = 2$.

$z_2 = 1 - i$. Then $\tan\theta_2 = -1$ with θ_2 in quadrant IV $\Rightarrow$ $\theta_2 = \frac{7\pi}{4}$, and $r_2 = \sqrt{1+1} = \sqrt{2}$.

Hence, $z_1 = 2\left(\cos\frac{7\pi}{4} + i\sin\frac{7\pi}{4}\right)$ and $z_2 = \sqrt{2}\left(\cos\frac{7\pi}{4} + i\sin\frac{7\pi}{4}\right)$.

$z_1 z_2 = 2 \cdot \sqrt{2}[\cos(\frac{7\pi}{4} + \frac{7\pi}{4}) + i\sin(\frac{7\pi}{4} + \frac{7\pi}{4})] = 2\sqrt{2}(\cos\frac{7\pi}{2} + i\sin\frac{7\pi}{2}) = 2\sqrt{2}\left(\cos\frac{\pi}{2} + i\sin\frac{\pi}{2}\right)$

$z_1/z_2 = \frac{2}{\sqrt{2}}[\cos(\frac{7\pi}{4} - \frac{7\pi}{4}) + i\sin(\frac{7\pi}{4} - \frac{7\pi}{4})] = \sqrt{2}(\cos 0 + i\sin 0)$

$1/z_1 = \frac{1}{2}\left[\cos(-\frac{7\pi}{4}) + i\sin(-\frac{7\pi}{4})\right] = \frac{1}{2}\left(\cos\frac{7\pi}{4} - i\sin\frac{7\pi}{4}\right)$

34. $z_1 = -\sqrt{2}\,i$. Then $\theta_1 = \frac{3\pi}{2}$, and $r_1 = \sqrt{2}$.

$z_2 = -3 - 3\sqrt{3}\,i$. Then $\tan\theta_2 = \sqrt{3}$ with θ_2 in quadrant IV $\Rightarrow$ $\theta_2 = \frac{4\pi}{3}$, and
$r_2 = \sqrt{9+27} = 6$.

Hence, $z_1 = \sqrt{2}\left(\cos\frac{3\pi}{2} + i\sin\frac{3\pi}{2}\right)$ and $z_2 = 6\left(\cos\frac{4\pi}{3} + i\sin\frac{4\pi}{3}\right)$.

$z_1 z_2 = \sqrt{2} \cdot 6\left[\cos(\frac{3\pi}{2} + \frac{4\pi}{3}) + i\sin(\frac{3\pi}{2} + \frac{4\pi}{3})\right] = 6\sqrt{2}\left(\cos\frac{5\pi}{6} + i\sin\frac{5\pi}{6}\right)$

$z_1/z_2 = \frac{\sqrt{2}}{6}\left[\cos(\frac{3\pi}{2} - \frac{4\pi}{3}) + i\sin(\frac{3\pi}{2} - \frac{4\pi}{3})\right] = \frac{\sqrt{2}}{6}\left(\cos\frac{\pi}{6} + i\sin\frac{\pi}{6}\right)$

$1/z_1 = \frac{1}{\sqrt{2}}\left[\cos(-\frac{3\pi}{2}) + i\sin(-\frac{3\pi}{2})\right] = \frac{1}{\sqrt{2}}\left(\cos\frac{3\pi}{2} - i\sin\frac{3\pi}{2}\right)$.

36. $z_1 = 4\sqrt{3} - 4i$. Then $\tan\theta_1 = \frac{-4}{4\sqrt{3}} = -\frac{1}{\sqrt{3}}$ with θ_1 in quadrant III $\Rightarrow$ $\theta_1 = \frac{11\pi}{6}$, and
$r_1 = \sqrt{48+16} = 8$.

$z_2 = 8i$. Then $\theta_2 = \frac{\pi}{2}$, and $r_2 = 8$.

Hence, $z_1 = 8\left(\cos\frac{11\pi}{6} + i\sin\frac{11\pi}{6}\right)$ and $z_2 = 8\left(\cos\frac{\pi}{2} + i\sin\frac{\pi}{2}\right)$.

$z_1 z_2 = 8 \cdot 8\left[\cos(\frac{11\pi}{6} + \frac{\pi}{2}) + i\sin(\frac{11\pi}{6} + \frac{\pi}{2})\right] = 64\left(\cos\frac{\pi}{3} + i\sin\frac{\pi}{3}\right)$

$z_1/z_2 = \frac{8}{8}\left[\cos(\frac{11\pi}{6} - \frac{\pi}{2}) + i\sin(\frac{11\pi}{6} - \frac{\pi}{2})\right] = \cos\frac{4\pi}{3} + i\sin\frac{4\pi}{3}$

$1/z_1 = \frac{1}{8}\left(\cos\frac{11\pi}{6} - i\sin\frac{11\pi}{6}\right)$

38. $z_1 = 3 + 4i$. Then $\tan\theta_1 = \frac{4}{3}$ with θ_1 in quadrant I $\Rightarrow$ $\theta_1 = \tan^{-1}\frac{4}{3}$, and $r_1 = \sqrt{9+16} = 5$.

$z_2 = 2 - 2i$. Then $\tan\theta_2 = -1$ with θ_2 in quadrant IV $\Rightarrow$ $\theta_2 = \frac{7\pi}{4}$, and $r_2 = \sqrt{4+4} = 2\sqrt{2}$.

Hence, $z_1 = 5[\cos(\tan^{-1}\frac{4}{3}) + i\sin(\tan^{-1}\frac{4}{3})] \approx 5(\cos 53.13° + i\sin 53.13°)$ and

$z_2 = 2\sqrt{2}\left(\cos\frac{7\pi}{4} + i\sin\frac{7\pi}{4}\right)$.

$z_1 z_2 = 5 \cdot 2\sqrt{2}[\cos(\tan^{-1}\frac{4}{3} + \frac{7\pi}{4}) + i\sin(\tan^{-1}\frac{4}{3} + \frac{7\pi}{4})]$

$z_1/z_2 = \frac{5}{2\sqrt{2}}[\cos(\tan^{-1}\frac{4}{3} - \frac{7\pi}{4}) + i\sin(\tan^{-1}\frac{4}{3} - \frac{7\pi}{4})]$

$= \frac{5\sqrt{2}}{4}[\cos(\tan^{-1}\frac{4}{3} - \frac{7\pi}{4}) + i\sin(\tan^{-1}\frac{4}{3} - \frac{7\pi}{4})]$

$1/z_1 = \frac{1}{5}[\cos(\tan^{-1}\frac{4}{3}) - i\sin(\tan^{-1}\frac{4}{3})]$

40. From Exercise 2: $1 - \sqrt{3}\,i = 2\left(\cos\frac{5\pi}{3} + i\sin\frac{5\pi}{3}\right)$. Thus, $(1 - \sqrt{3}\,i)^5 = 2^5\left(\cos\frac{25\pi}{3} + i\sin\frac{25\pi}{3}\right)$

$\quad = 32\left(\cos\frac{\pi}{3} + i\sin\frac{\pi}{3}\right) = 32\left(\frac{1}{2} + i\frac{\sqrt{3}}{2}\right) = 16 + 16\sqrt{3}\,i$

42. From Exercise 4: $1 - i = \sqrt{2}\left(\cos\frac{7\pi}{4} + i\sin\frac{7\pi}{4}\right)$. Thus, $(1 - i)^8 = (\sqrt{2})^8\left(\cos 14\pi + i\sin 14\pi\right)$
$\quad = 16(1 + 0i) = 16$

44. $r = \sqrt{3 + 1} = 2$ and $\tan\theta = \frac{-1}{\sqrt{3}}$ with θ in quadrant IV $\quad\Rightarrow\quad \theta = \frac{11\pi}{6}$. Thus

$\quad \sqrt{3} - i = 2\left(\cos\frac{11\pi}{6} + i\sin\frac{11\pi}{6}\right)$. So, $(\sqrt{3} - i)^{-10} = \left(\frac{1}{2}\right)^{10}\left(\cos\frac{-110\pi}{6} + i\sin\frac{-110\pi}{6}\right)$

$\quad = \frac{1}{1024}\left(\cos\frac{2\pi}{3} - i\sin\frac{2\pi}{3}\right) = \frac{1}{1024}\left(-\frac{1}{2} + \frac{\sqrt{3}}{2}i\right) = \frac{1}{2048}\left(-1 + \sqrt{3}\,i\right)$

46. $r = \sqrt{\frac{1}{4} + \frac{3}{4}} = 1$ and $\tan\theta = \sqrt{3}$ with θ in quadrant III $\quad\Rightarrow\quad \theta = -\frac{4\pi}{3}$. Thus

$\quad -\frac{1}{2} - \frac{\sqrt{3}}{2}i = \cos\frac{4\pi}{3} + i\sin\frac{4\pi}{3}$. So, $\left(-\frac{1}{2} - \frac{\sqrt{3}}{2}i\right)^{15} = \cos\frac{60\pi}{3} + i\sin\frac{60\pi}{3} = \cos 20\pi + i\sin 20\pi = 1$

48. $r = \sqrt{9 + 3} = 2\sqrt{3}$ and $\tan\theta = \frac{\sqrt{3}}{3}$ with θ in quadrant I $\quad\Rightarrow\quad \theta = \frac{\pi}{6}$. Thus

$\quad 3 + \sqrt{3}\,i = 2\sqrt{3}\left(\cos\frac{\pi}{6} + i\sin\frac{\pi}{6}\right)$. Therefore, $(3 + \sqrt{3}\,i)^4 = 144\left(\cos\frac{2\pi}{3} + i\sin\frac{2\pi}{3}\right)$

$\quad = 144\left(-\frac{1}{2} + \frac{\sqrt{3}}{2}i\right) = 72\left(-1 + \sqrt{3}\,i\right)$

50. $r = \sqrt{1 + 1} = \sqrt{2}$ and $\tan\theta = -1$ with θ in quadrant IV $\quad\Rightarrow\quad \theta = \frac{7\pi}{4}$. Thus

$\quad 1 - i = \sqrt{2}\left(\cos\frac{7\pi}{4} + i\sin\frac{7\pi}{4}\right)$. So, $(1 - i)^{-8} = \frac{1}{16}\left(\cos\frac{-56\pi}{4} + i\sin\frac{-56\pi}{4}\right)$

$\quad = \frac{1}{16}\left(\cos 14\pi - i\sin 14\pi\right) = \frac{1}{16}$

52. $r = \sqrt{48 + 16} = 8$ and $\tan\theta = \frac{4}{4\sqrt{3}} = \frac{1}{\sqrt{3}} \quad\Rightarrow\quad \theta = \frac{\pi}{6}$. Thus

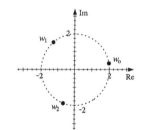

$\quad 4\sqrt{3} + 4i = 8\left(\cos\frac{\pi}{6} + i\sin\frac{\pi}{6}\right)$. So,

$\quad (4\sqrt{3} + 4i)^{1/3} = 2\left[\cos\left(\frac{\pi/6 + 2k\pi}{3}\right) + i\sin\left(\frac{\pi/6 + 2k\pi}{3}\right)\right]$ for $k = 0, 1, 2$.

Thus the three roots are $w_0 = 2\left(\cos\frac{\pi}{18} + i\sin\frac{\pi}{18}\right)$,

$\quad w_1 = 2\left(\cos\frac{13\pi}{18} + i\sin\frac{13\pi}{8}\right)$, $w_2 = 2\left(\cos\frac{25\pi}{18} + i\sin\frac{25\pi}{18}\right)$.

54. $32 = 32\left(\cos 0 + i\sin 0\right)$. Thus, $32^{1/5}\left(\cos\frac{2k\pi}{5} + i\sin\frac{2k\pi}{5}\right)$ for $k = 0$,

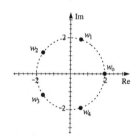

$\quad 1, 2, 3, 4$. Thus the five roots are $w_0 = 2\left(\cos 0 + i\sin 0\right)$,

$\quad w_1 = 2\left(\cos\frac{2\pi}{5} + i\sin\frac{2\pi}{5}\right)$, $w_2 = 2\left(\cos\frac{4\pi}{5} + i\sin\frac{4\pi}{5}\right)$,

$\quad w_3 = 2\left(\cos\frac{6\pi}{5} + i\sin\frac{6\pi}{5}\right)$, $w_4 = 2\left(\cos\frac{8\pi}{5} + i\sin\frac{8\pi}{5}\right)$

56. From Exercise 1: $1 + i = \sqrt{2}\left(\cos\frac{\pi}{4} + i\sin\frac{\pi}{4}\right)$. So,

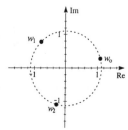

$\quad (1 + i)^{1/3} = (\sqrt{2})^{1/3}\left[\cos\left(\frac{\pi/4 + 2k\pi}{3}\right) + i\sin\left(\frac{\pi/4 + 2k\pi}{3}\right)\right]$ for $k = 0, 1$,

$\quad 2$. Thus the three roots are $w_0 = 2^{1/6}\left(\cos\frac{\pi}{12} + i\sin\frac{\pi}{12}\right)$,

$\quad w_1 = 2^{1/6}\left(\cos\frac{9\pi}{12} + i\sin\frac{9\pi}{12}\right)$, $w_3 = 2^{1/6}\left(\cos\frac{17\pi}{12} + i\sin\frac{17\pi}{12}\right)$

58. $i = \cos\frac{\pi}{2} + i\sin\frac{\pi}{2}$. So, $i^{1/5} = \cos\left(\frac{\pi/2+2k\pi}{5}\right) + i\sin\left(\frac{\pi/2+2k\pi}{5}\right)$ for
      $k = 0, 1, 2, 3, 4$. Thus the five roots are $w_0 = \cos\frac{\pi}{10} + i\sin\frac{\pi}{10}$,
      $w_1 = \cos\frac{\pi}{2} + i\sin\frac{\pi}{2}$, $w_2 = \cos\frac{9\pi}{10} + i\sin\frac{9\pi}{10}$,
      $w_3 = \cos\frac{13\pi}{10} + i\sin\frac{13\pi}{10}$, $w_4 = \cos\frac{17\pi}{10} + i\sin\frac{17\pi}{10}$

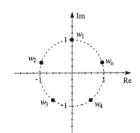

60. $r = \sqrt{16^2\left(1+3\right)} = 32$ and $\tan\theta = \frac{16\sqrt{3}}{16} = \sqrt{3}$ with θ in quadrant
      III $\Rightarrow$ $\theta = \frac{4\pi}{3}$. Thus $-16 - 16\sqrt{3}\,i = 32\left(\cos\frac{4\pi}{3} + i\sin\frac{4\pi}{3}\right)$.
      So, $(-16 - 16\sqrt{3}\,i)^{1/5} = 32^{1/5}\left[\cos\left(\frac{4\pi/3+2k\pi}{5}\right) + i\sin\left(\frac{4\pi/3+2k\pi}{5}\right)\right]$ for
      $k = 0, 1, 2, 3, 4$. Thus the five roots are $w_0 = 2\left(\cos\frac{4\pi}{15} + i\sin\frac{4\pi}{15}\right)$,
      $w_1 = 2\left(\cos\frac{2\pi}{3} + i\sin\frac{2\pi}{3}\right)$, $w_2 = 2\left(\cos\frac{16\pi}{15} + i\sin\frac{16\pi}{15}\right)$,
      $w_3 = 2\left(\cos\frac{22\pi}{15} + i\sin\frac{22\pi}{15}\right)$, $w_4 = 2\left(\cos\frac{28\pi}{15} + i\sin\frac{28\pi}{15}\right)$

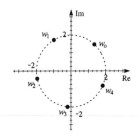

62. $z^8 - i = 0$ $\Rightarrow$ $x = i^{1/8}$. Since $i = \cos\frac{\pi}{2} + i\sin\frac{\pi}{2}$, then, $z = i^{1/8} = \cos\left(\frac{\pi/2+2k\pi}{8}\right) + i$
      $\sin\left(\frac{\pi/2+2k\pi}{8}\right)$ for $k = 0, 1, 2, 3, 4, 5, 6, 7$. Thus there are eight solutions: $z = \cos\frac{\pi}{16} + i\sin\frac{\pi}{16}$,
      $\cos\frac{5\pi}{16} + i\sin\frac{5\pi}{16}$, $\cos\frac{9\pi}{16} + i\sin\frac{9\pi}{16}$, $\cos\frac{13\pi}{16} + i\sin\frac{13\pi}{16}$, $\cos\frac{17\pi}{16} + i\sin\frac{17\pi}{16}$, $\cos\frac{21\pi}{16} + i\sin\frac{21\pi}{16}$,
      $\cos\frac{25\pi}{16} + i\sin\frac{25\pi}{16}$, and $\cos\frac{29\pi}{16} + i\sin\frac{29\pi}{16}$.

64. $z^6 - 1 = 0$ $\Leftrightarrow$ $z = 1^{1/6}$. Since $1 = \cos 0 + i\sin 0$, $z = 1^{1/6} = \cos\frac{2k\pi}{6} + i\sin\frac{2k\pi}{6}$ for $k = 0, 1$,
      $2, 3, 4, 5$. Thus there are six solutions: $z = \pm 1, \pm\frac{1}{2} \pm \frac{\sqrt{3}}{2}\,i$.

66. $z^3 - 1 = 0$ $\Rightarrow$ $z = 1^{1/3}$. Since $1 = \cos 0 + i\sin 0$, $z = 1^{1/3} = \cos\frac{2k\pi}{3} + i\sin\frac{2k\pi}{3}$ for $k = 0, 1$,
      2. Thus the three solutions to this equation are $z = \cos 0 + i\sin 0$, $\cos\frac{2\pi}{3} + i\sin\frac{2\pi}{3}$, and
      $\cos\frac{4\pi}{3} + i\sin\frac{4\pi}{3}$ or $z = 1, -\frac{1}{2} + \frac{\sqrt{3}}{2}\,i, -\frac{1}{2} - \frac{\sqrt{3}}{2}\,i$.

68.   The cube roots of 1 are $w^0 = 1$, $w^1 = \cos\frac{2\pi}{3} + i\sin\frac{2\pi}{3} = -\frac{1}{2} + \frac{\sqrt{3}}{2}\,i$, $w^2 = \cos\frac{4\pi}{3} + i\sin\frac{4\pi}{3}$
      $= \frac{1}{2} - \frac{\sqrt{3}}{2}\,i$ so $w^0 + w^1 + w^2 = 1 + \left(-\frac{1}{2} + \frac{\sqrt{3}}{2}\,i\right) + \left(\frac{1}{2} - \frac{\sqrt{3}}{2}\,i\right) = 0$

      The fourth roots of 1 are $w^0 = 1$, $w^1 = i$, $w^2 = -1$, $w^3 = -i$. So the sum of the four fourth roots
      of 1 is: $w^0 + w^1 + w^2 + w^3 = 1 + i - 1 - i = 0$

      The sixth roots of 1 are $w^0 = 1$, $w^1 = \cos\frac{\pi}{3} + i\sin\frac{\pi}{3} = \frac{1}{2} + \frac{\sqrt{3}}{2}\,i$, $w^2 = \cos\frac{2\pi}{3} + i\sin\frac{2\pi}{3}$
      $= -\frac{1}{2} + \frac{\sqrt{3}}{2}\,i$, $w^3 = -1$, $w^4 = \cos\frac{4\pi}{3} + i\sin\frac{4\pi}{3} = -\frac{1}{2} - \frac{\sqrt{3}}{2}\,i$, $w^5 = \cos\frac{5\pi}{3} + i\sin\frac{5\pi}{3} = \frac{1}{2} - \frac{\sqrt{3}}{2}\,i$.
      So the sum of the six sixth roots of 1 is:

      $1 + \left(\frac{1}{2} + \frac{\sqrt{3}}{2}\,i\right) + \left(-\frac{1}{2} + \frac{\sqrt{3}}{2}\,i\right) - 1 + \left(-\frac{1}{2} - \frac{\sqrt{3}}{2}\,i\right) + \left(\frac{1}{2} - \frac{\sqrt{3}}{2}\,i\right) = 0$

      The eight roots of 1 are $w^0 = 1$, $w^1 = \cos\frac{\pi}{4} + i\sin\frac{\pi}{4} = \frac{\sqrt{2}}{2} + \frac{\sqrt{2}}{2}\,i$, $w^2 = i$,
      $w^3 = \cos\frac{3\pi}{4} + i\sin\frac{3\pi}{4} = -\frac{\sqrt{2}}{2} + \frac{\sqrt{2}}{2}\,i$, $w^4 = -1$,
      $w^5 = \cos\frac{5\pi}{4} + i\sin\frac{5\pi}{4} = -\frac{\sqrt{2}}{2} - \frac{\sqrt{2}}{2}\,i$, $w^6 = -i$, $w^7 = \cos\frac{7\pi}{4} + i\sin\frac{7\pi}{4} = \frac{\sqrt{2}}{2} - \frac{\sqrt{2}}{2}\,i$. So the sum
      of the eight eighth roots of 1 is:

40. From Exercise 2: $1 - \sqrt{3}\,i = 2\left(\cos\frac{5\pi}{3} + i\sin\frac{5\pi}{3}\right)$. Thus, $(1 - \sqrt{3}\,i)^5 = 2^5\left(\cos\frac{25\pi}{3} + i\sin\frac{25\pi}{3}\right)$

$= 32\left(\cos\frac{\pi}{3} + i\sin\frac{\pi}{3}\right) = 32\left(\frac{1}{2} + i\frac{\sqrt{3}}{2}\right) = 16 + 16\sqrt{3}\,i$

42. From Exercise 4: $1 - i = \sqrt{2}\left(\cos\frac{7\pi}{4} + i\sin\frac{7\pi}{4}\right)$. Thus, $(1 - i)^8 = (\sqrt{2})^8\left(\cos 14\pi + i\sin 14\pi\right)$
$= 16\,(1 + 0i) = 16$

44. $r = \sqrt{3 + 1} = 2$ and $\tan\theta = \frac{-1}{\sqrt{3}}$ with θ in quadrant IV $\Rightarrow$ $\theta = \frac{11\pi}{6}$. Thus
$\sqrt{3} - i = 2\left(\cos\frac{11\pi}{6} + i\sin\frac{11\pi}{6}\right)$. So, $(\sqrt{3} - i)^{-10} = \left(\frac{1}{2}\right)^{10}\left(\cos\frac{-110\pi}{6} + i\sin\frac{-110\pi}{6}\right)$
$= \frac{1}{1024}\left(\cos\frac{2\pi}{3} - i\sin\frac{2\pi}{3}\right) = \frac{1}{1024}\left(-\frac{1}{2} + \frac{\sqrt{3}}{2}i\right) = \frac{1}{2048}\left(-1 + \sqrt{3}\,i\right)$

46. $r = \sqrt{\frac{1}{4} + \frac{3}{4}} = 1$ and $\tan\theta = \sqrt{3}$ with θ in quadrant III $\Rightarrow$ $\theta = -\frac{4\pi}{3}$. Thus
$-\frac{1}{2} - \frac{\sqrt{3}}{2}i = \cos\frac{4\pi}{3} + i\sin\frac{4\pi}{3}$. So, $\left(-\frac{1}{2} - \frac{\sqrt{3}}{2}i\right)^{15} = \cos\frac{60\pi}{3} + i\sin\frac{60\pi}{3} = \cos 20\pi + i\sin 20\pi = 1$

48. $r = \sqrt{9 + 3} = 2\sqrt{3}$ and $\tan\theta = \frac{\sqrt{3}}{3}$ with θ in quadrant I $\Rightarrow$ $\theta = \frac{\pi}{6}$. Thus
$3 + \sqrt{3}\,i = 2\sqrt{3}\left(\cos\frac{\pi}{6} + i\sin\frac{\pi}{6}\right)$. Therefore, $(3 + \sqrt{3}\,i)^4 = 144\left(\cos\frac{2\pi}{3} + i\sin\frac{2\pi}{3}\right)$
$= 144\left(-\frac{1}{2} + \frac{\sqrt{3}}{2}i\right) = 72\left(-1 + \sqrt{3}\,i\right)$

50. $r = \sqrt{1 + 1} = \sqrt{2}$ and $\tan\theta = -1$ with θ in quadrant IV $\Rightarrow$ $\theta = \frac{7\pi}{4}$. Thus
$1 - i = \sqrt{2}\left(\cos\frac{7\pi}{4} + i\sin\frac{7\pi}{4}\right)$. So, $(1 - i)^{-8} = \frac{1}{16}\left(\cos\frac{-56\pi}{4} + i\sin\frac{-56\pi}{4}\right)$
$= \frac{1}{16}\left(\cos 14\pi - i\sin 14\pi\right) = \frac{1}{16}$

52. $r = \sqrt{48 + 16} = 8$ and $\tan\theta = \frac{4}{4\sqrt{3}} = \frac{1}{\sqrt{3}}$ $\Rightarrow$ $\theta = \frac{\pi}{6}$. Thus
$4\sqrt{3} + 4i = 8\left(\cos\frac{\pi}{6} + i\sin\frac{\pi}{6}\right)$. So,
$(4\sqrt{3} + 4i)^{1/3} = 2\left[\cos\left(\frac{\pi/6 + 2k\pi}{3}\right) + i\sin\left(\frac{\pi/6 + 2k\pi}{3}\right)\right]$ for $k = 0, 1, 2$.
Thus the three roots are $w_0 = 2\left(\cos\frac{\pi}{18} + i\sin\frac{\pi}{18}\right)$,
$w_1 = 2\left(\cos\frac{13\pi}{18} + i\sin\frac{13\pi}{8}\right)$, $w_2 = 2\left(\cos\frac{25\pi}{18} + i\sin\frac{25\pi}{18}\right)$.

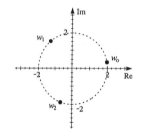

54. $32 = 32\left(\cos 0 + i\sin 0\right)$. Thus, $32^{1/5}\left(\cos\frac{2k\pi}{5} + i\sin\frac{2k\pi}{5}\right)$ for $k = 0$,
$1, 2, 3, 4$. Thus the five roots are $w_0 = 2\left(\cos 0 + i\sin 0\right)$,
$w_1 = 2\left(\cos\frac{2\pi}{5} + i\sin\frac{2\pi}{5}\right)$, $w_2 = 2\left(\cos\frac{4\pi}{5} + i\sin\frac{4\pi}{5}\right)$,
$w_3 = 2\left(\cos\frac{6\pi}{5} + i\sin\frac{6\pi}{5}\right)$, $w_4 = 2\left(\cos\frac{8\pi}{5} + i\sin\frac{8\pi}{5}\right)$

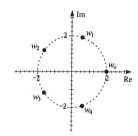

56. From Exercise 1: $1 + i = \sqrt{2}\left(\cos\frac{\pi}{4} + i\sin\frac{\pi}{4}\right)$. So,
$(1 + i)^{1/3} = (\sqrt{2})^{1/3}\left[\cos\left(\frac{\pi/4 + 2k\pi}{3}\right) + i\sin\left(\frac{\pi/4 + 2k\pi}{3}\right)\right]$ for $k = 0, 1,$
2. Thus the three roots are $w_0 = 2^{1/6}\left(\cos\frac{\pi}{12} + i\sin\frac{\pi}{12}\right)$,
$w_1 = 2^{1/6}\left(\cos\frac{9\pi}{12} + i\sin\frac{9\pi}{12}\right)$, $w_3 = 2^{1/6}\left(\cos\frac{17\pi}{12} + i\sin\frac{17\pi}{12}\right)$

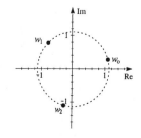

58. $i = \cos\frac{\pi}{2} + i\sin\frac{\pi}{2}$. So, $i^{1/5} = \cos\left(\frac{\pi/2+2k\pi}{5}\right) + i\sin\left(\frac{\pi/2+2k\pi}{5}\right)$ for
$k = 0, 1, 2, 3, 4$. Thus the five roots are $w_0 = \cos\frac{\pi}{10} + i\sin\frac{\pi}{10}$,
$w_1 = \cos\frac{\pi}{2} + i\sin\frac{\pi}{2}$, $w_2 = \cos\frac{9\pi}{10} + i\sin\frac{9\pi}{10}$,
$w_3 = \cos\frac{13\pi}{10} + i\sin\frac{13\pi}{10}$, $w_4 = \cos\frac{17\pi}{10} + i\sin\frac{17\pi}{10}$

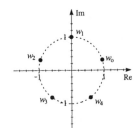

60. $r = \sqrt{16^2(1+3)} = 32$ and $\tan\theta = \frac{16\sqrt{3}}{16} = \sqrt{3}$ with θ in quadrant
III $\Rightarrow$ $\theta = \frac{4\pi}{3}$. Thus $-16 - 16\sqrt{3}\,i = 32\left(\cos\frac{4\pi}{3} + i\sin\frac{4\pi}{3}\right)$.
So, $(-16 - 16\sqrt{3}\,i)^{1/5} = 32^{1/5}\left[\cos\left(\frac{4\pi/3+2k\pi}{5}\right) + i\sin\left(\frac{4\pi/3+2k\pi}{5}\right)\right]$ for
$k = 0, 1, 2, 3, 4$. Thus the five roots are $w_0 = 2\left(\cos\frac{4\pi}{15} + i\sin\frac{4\pi}{15}\right)$,
$w_1 = 2\left(\cos\frac{2\pi}{3} + i\sin\frac{2\pi}{3}\right)$, $w_2 = 2\left(\cos\frac{16\pi}{15} + i\sin\frac{16\pi}{15}\right)$,
$w_3 = 2\left(\cos\frac{22\pi}{15} + i\sin\frac{22\pi}{15}\right)$, $w_4 = 2\left(\cos\frac{28\pi}{15} + i\sin\frac{28\pi}{15}\right)$

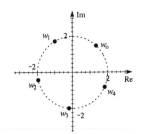

62. $z^8 - i = 0$ $\Rightarrow$ $x = i^{1/8}$. Since $i = \cos\frac{\pi}{2} + i\sin\frac{\pi}{2}$, then, $z = i^{1/8} = \cos\left(\frac{\pi/2+2k\pi}{8}\right) + i\sin\left(\frac{\pi/2+2k\pi}{8}\right)$ for $k = 0, 1, 2, 3, 4, 5, 6, 7$. Thus there are eight solutions: $z = \cos\frac{\pi}{16} + i\sin\frac{\pi}{16}$,
$\cos\frac{5\pi}{16} + i\sin\frac{5\pi}{16}$, $\cos\frac{9\pi}{16} + i\sin\frac{9\pi}{16}$, $\cos\frac{13\pi}{16} + i\sin\frac{13\pi}{16}$, $\cos\frac{17\pi}{16} + i\sin\frac{17\pi}{16}$, $\cos\frac{21\pi}{16} + i\sin\frac{21\pi}{16}$,
$\cos\frac{25\pi}{16} + i\sin\frac{25\pi}{16}$, and $\cos\frac{29\pi}{16} + i\sin\frac{29\pi}{16}$.

64. $z^6 - 1 = 0$ $\Leftrightarrow$ $z = 1^{1/6}$. Since $1 = \cos 0 + i\sin 0$, $z = 1^{1/6} = \cos\frac{2k\pi}{6} + i\sin\frac{2k\pi}{6}$ for $k = 0, 1,$
$2, 3, 4, 5$. Thus there are six solutions: $z = \pm 1, \pm\frac{1}{2} \pm \frac{\sqrt{3}}{2}\,i$.

66. $z^3 - 1 = 0$ $\Rightarrow$ $z = 1^{1/3}$. Since $1 = \cos 0 + i\sin 0$, $z = 1^{1/3} = \cos\frac{2k\pi}{3} + i\sin\frac{2k\pi}{3}$ for $k = 0, 1,$
2. Thus the three solutions to this equation are $z = \cos 0 + i\sin 0$, $\cos\frac{2\pi}{3} + i\sin\frac{2\pi}{3}$, and
$\cos\frac{4\pi}{3} + i\sin\frac{4\pi}{3}$ or $z = 1, -\frac{1}{2} + \frac{\sqrt{3}}{2}\,i, -\frac{1}{2} - \frac{\sqrt{3}}{2}\,i$.

68. The cube roots of 1 are $w^0 = 1$, $w^1 = \cos\frac{2\pi}{3} + i\sin\frac{2\pi}{3} = -\frac{1}{2} + \frac{\sqrt{3}}{2}\,i$, $w^2 = \cos\frac{4\pi}{3} + i\sin\frac{4\pi}{3}$
$= \frac{1}{2} - \frac{\sqrt{3}}{2}\,i$ so $w^0 + w^1 + w^2 = 1 + \left(-\frac{1}{2} + \frac{\sqrt{3}}{2}\,i\right) + \left(\frac{1}{2} - \frac{\sqrt{3}}{2}\,i\right) = 0$

The fourth roots of 1 are $w^0 = 1$, $w^1 = i$, $w^2 = -1$, $w^3 = -i$. So the sum of the four fourth roots
of 1 is: $w^0 + w^1 + w^2 + w^3 = 1 + i - 1 - i = 0$

The sixth roots of 1 are $w^0 = 1$, $w^1 = \cos\frac{\pi}{3} + i\sin\frac{\pi}{3} = \frac{1}{2} + \frac{\sqrt{3}}{2}\,i$, $w^2 = \cos\frac{2\pi}{3} + i\sin\frac{2\pi}{3}$
$= -\frac{1}{2} + \frac{\sqrt{3}}{2}\,i$, $w^3 = -1$, $w^4 = \cos\frac{4\pi}{3} + i\sin\frac{4\pi}{3} = -\frac{1}{2} - \frac{\sqrt{3}}{2}\,i$, $w^5 = \cos\frac{5\pi}{3} + i\sin\frac{5\pi}{3} = \frac{1}{2} - \frac{\sqrt{3}}{2}\,i$.
So the sum of the six sixth roots of 1 is:
$1 + \left(\frac{1}{2} + \frac{\sqrt{3}}{2}\,i\right) + \left(-\frac{1}{2} + \frac{\sqrt{3}}{2}\,i\right) - 1 + \left(-\frac{1}{2} - \frac{\sqrt{3}}{2}\,i\right) + \left(\frac{1}{2} - \frac{\sqrt{3}}{2}\,i\right) = 0$

The eight roots of 1 are $w^0 = 1$, $w^1 = \cos\frac{\pi}{4} + i\sin\frac{\pi}{4} = \frac{\sqrt{2}}{2} + \frac{\sqrt{2}}{2}\,i$, $w^2 = i$,
$w^3 = \cos\frac{3\pi}{4} + i\sin\frac{3\pi}{4} = -\frac{\sqrt{2}}{2} + \frac{\sqrt{2}}{2}\,i$, $w^4 = -1$,
$w^5 = \cos\frac{5\pi}{4} + i\sin\frac{5\pi}{4} = -\frac{\sqrt{2}}{2} - \frac{\sqrt{2}}{2}\,i$, $w^6 = -i$, $w^7 = \cos\frac{7\pi}{4} + i\sin\frac{7\pi}{4} = \frac{\sqrt{2}}{2} - \frac{\sqrt{2}}{2}\,i$. So the sum
of the eight eighth roots of 1 is:

$$1 + \left(\tfrac{\sqrt{2}}{2} + \tfrac{\sqrt{2}}{2}i\right) + i + \left(-\tfrac{\sqrt{2}}{2} + \tfrac{\sqrt{2}}{2}\right) - 1 + \left(-\tfrac{\sqrt{2}}{2} - \tfrac{\sqrt{2}}{2}i\right) - i + \left(\tfrac{\sqrt{2}}{2} - \tfrac{\sqrt{2}}{2}i\right) = 0$$

It seems like the sum of the roots is 0.

Proof.

To prove this note that the sum of the roots of the polynomial equation
$x^n + a_{n-1}x^{n-1} + \cdots + a_1 x + a_0 = 0$ is $-a_{n-1}$, the negative of the coefficient of x^{n-1}. (See Focus
on Problem Solving following Chapter 5, Problem 8(c), page 376.) Since the nth root of 1 are the
roots of the polynomial equation $z^n - 1 = 0$, it follows that the sum is the negative of the coefficient
of z^{n-1} in this equation, which is clearly zero.

Exercises 9.7

2. $-\mathbf{v} = -\langle 3, 4 \rangle = \langle -3, -4 \rangle$

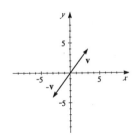

4. $\mathbf{u} - \mathbf{v} = \langle -2, 3 \rangle - \langle 3, 4 \rangle = \langle -2 - 3, 3 - 4 \rangle$
    $= \langle -5, -1 \rangle$

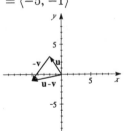

6. $2\mathbf{u} + \mathbf{v} = 2\langle -2, 3 \rangle + \langle 3, 4 \rangle$
    $= \langle 2(-2) + 3, 2(3) + 4 \rangle = \langle -1, 10 \rangle$

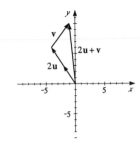

In Exercises 8 – 16, $\mathbf{v}$ represents the vector with initial point P and terminal point Q.

8. $P(2, 1), Q(-3, 4)$. $\mathbf{v} = \langle -3 - 2, 4 - 1 \rangle = \langle -5, 3 \rangle$

10. $P(3, 1), Q(1, -2)$. $\mathbf{v} = \langle 3 - 1, -2 - 1 \rangle = \langle 2, -3 \rangle$

12. $P(1, 1), Q(9, 9)$. $\mathbf{v} = \langle 9 - 1, 9 - 1 \rangle = \langle 8, 8 \rangle$

14. $P(-1, 3), Q(-6, -1)$. $\mathbf{v} = \langle -6 - (-1), -1 - 3 \rangle = \langle -5, -4 \rangle$

16. $P(-8, -6), Q(-1, -1)$. $\mathbf{v} = \langle -1 - (-8), -1 - (-6) \rangle = \langle 7, 5 \rangle$

18. $\mathbf{u} = \langle -2, 5 \rangle$, $\mathbf{v} = \langle 2, -8 \rangle$.

    $2\mathbf{u} = 2 \cdot \langle -2, 5 \rangle = \langle -4, 10 \rangle$; $-3\mathbf{v} = -3 \cdot \langle 2, -8 \rangle = \langle -6, 24 \rangle$; $\mathbf{u} + \mathbf{v} = \langle -2, 5 \rangle + \langle 2, -8 \rangle$
    $= \langle 0, -3 \rangle$; $3\mathbf{u} - 4\mathbf{v} = \langle -6, 15 \rangle - \langle 8, -32 \rangle = \langle -14, 47 \rangle$

20. $\mathbf{u} = \mathbf{i}$, $\mathbf{v} = -2\mathbf{j}$. $2\mathbf{u} = 2\mathbf{i}$; $-3\mathbf{v} = -3(-2\mathbf{j}) = 6\mathbf{j}$; $\mathbf{u} + \mathbf{v} = \mathbf{i} - 2\mathbf{j}$; $3\mathbf{u} - 4\mathbf{v} = 3\mathbf{i} + 8\mathbf{j}$

22. $\mathbf{u} = \mathbf{i} + \mathbf{j}$, $\mathbf{v} = \mathbf{i} - \mathbf{j}$. $2\mathbf{u} = 2\mathbf{i} + 2\mathbf{j}$, $-3\mathbf{v} = -3\mathbf{i} + 3\mathbf{j}$, $\mathbf{u} + \mathbf{v} = \mathbf{i} + \mathbf{j} + \mathbf{i} - \mathbf{j} = 2\mathbf{i}$;
    $3\mathbf{u} - 4\mathbf{v} = 3(\mathbf{i} + \mathbf{j}) - 4(\mathbf{i} - \mathbf{j}) = -\mathbf{i} + 7\mathbf{j}$

24. $\mathbf{u} = -2\mathbf{i} + 3\mathbf{j}$, $\mathbf{v} = \mathbf{i} - 2\mathbf{j}$. Then $|\mathbf{u}| = \sqrt{4 + 9} = \sqrt{13}$; $|\mathbf{v}| = \sqrt{1 + 4} = \sqrt{5}$; $2\mathbf{u} = -4\mathbf{i} + 6\mathbf{j}$;
    $|2\mathbf{u}| = \sqrt{16 + 36} = 2\sqrt{13}$; $\frac{1}{2}\mathbf{v} = \frac{1}{2}\mathbf{i} - \mathbf{j}$; $|\frac{1}{2}\mathbf{v}| = \sqrt{\frac{1}{4} + 1} = \frac{1}{2}\sqrt{5}$; $\mathbf{u} + \mathbf{v} = -\mathbf{i} + \mathbf{j}$;
    $|\mathbf{u} + \mathbf{v}| = \sqrt{1 + 1} = \sqrt{2}$; $\mathbf{u} - \mathbf{v} = -3\mathbf{i} + 5\mathbf{j}$; $|\mathbf{u} - \mathbf{v}| = \sqrt{9 + 25} = \sqrt{34}$;
    $|\mathbf{u}| - |\mathbf{v}| = \sqrt{13} - \sqrt{5}$

26. $\mathbf{u} = \langle -6, 6 \rangle$, $\mathbf{v} = \langle -2, -1 \rangle$. Then $|\mathbf{u}| = \sqrt{36 + 36} = 6\sqrt{2}$; $|\mathbf{v}| = \sqrt{4 + 1} = \sqrt{5}$;

$2\mathbf{u} = \langle -12, 12 \rangle$; $|2\mathbf{u}| = \sqrt{144 + 144} = 12\sqrt{2}$; $\frac{1}{2}\mathbf{v} = \langle -1, -\frac{1}{2} \rangle$; $|\frac{1}{2}\mathbf{v}| = \sqrt{1 + \frac{1}{4}} = \frac{1}{2}\sqrt{5}$;

$\mathbf{u} + \mathbf{v} = \langle -8, 5 \rangle$; $|\mathbf{u} + \mathbf{v}| = \sqrt{64 + 25} = \sqrt{89}$; $\mathbf{u} - \mathbf{v} = \langle -4, 7 \rangle$; $|\mathbf{u} - \mathbf{v}| = \sqrt{16 + 49} = \sqrt{63}$;

$|\mathbf{u}| - |\mathbf{v}| = 6\sqrt{2} - \sqrt{5}$

In Exercises 28 – 32, x represents the horizontal component and y the vertical component.

28. $|\mathbf{v}| = 50$, direction $\theta = 120°$. $x = 50 \cos 120° = -25$, $y = 50 \sin 120° = 25\sqrt{3}$. Thus,

$\mathbf{v} = x\mathbf{i} + y\mathbf{j} = -25\mathbf{i} + 25\sqrt{3}\mathbf{j}$

30. $|\mathbf{v}| = 800$, direction $\theta = 125°$. $x = 800 \cos 125° \approx -458.86$, and $y = 800 \sin 125° \approx 655.32$.

Thus, $\mathbf{v} = x\mathbf{i} + y\mathbf{j} = (800 \cos 125°)\,\mathbf{i} + (800 \sin 125°)\,\mathbf{j} \approx -458.86\mathbf{i} + 655.32\mathbf{j}$

32. $|\mathbf{v}| = \sqrt{3}$, direction $\theta = 300°$. $x = \sqrt{3}\cos 300° = \frac{\sqrt{3}}{2}$, $y = \sqrt{3}\sin 300° = -\frac{3}{2}$. Thus,

$\mathbf{v} = x\mathbf{i} + y\mathbf{j} = \frac{\sqrt{3}}{2}\mathbf{i} - \frac{3}{2}\mathbf{j}$

34. $|\mathbf{v}| = 500$, direction $\theta = 70°$. $x = 500 \cos 70° \approx 171.01$, $y = 500 \sin 70° \approx 469.85$. So, the east component of the velocity is 171.01 mi/h and the north component is 469.85 mi/h.

36. $\mathbf{v} = \langle -\frac{\sqrt{2}}{2}, -\frac{\sqrt{2}}{2} \rangle$. The magnitude is $|\mathbf{v}| = \sqrt{\frac{1}{2} + \frac{1}{2}} = 1$. The direction is θ where $\tan \theta = 1$ with θ in quadrant III $\Leftrightarrow$ $\theta = \tan^{-1}1 = 225°$

38. $\mathbf{v} = \langle 40, 9 \rangle$. The magnitude is $|\mathbf{v}| = \sqrt{1600 + 81} = 41$. The direction is θ where $\tan \theta = \frac{9}{40}$ with θ in quadrant I $\Leftrightarrow$ $\theta = \tan^{-1}\frac{9}{40} \approx 12.68°$

40. $\mathbf{v} = \mathbf{i} + \mathbf{j}$. The magnitude is $|\mathbf{v}| = \sqrt{1 + 1} = \sqrt{2}$. The direction is θ where $\tan \theta = 1$ with θ in quadrant I $\Leftrightarrow$ $\theta = \tan^{-1}1 = 45°$

42. (a) Let the vectors $\mathbf{w}$ and $\mathbf{v}$ represent the velocities of the wind and jet respectively. Then

$\mathbf{w} = 55 \cos 60°\mathbf{i} + 55 \sin 60°\mathbf{j} = \frac{55}{2}\mathbf{i} + \frac{55\sqrt{3}}{2}\mathbf{j}$ and $\mathbf{v} = 765 \frac{\sqrt{2}}{2}\mathbf{i} + 765 \frac{\sqrt{2}}{2}\mathbf{j}$. The resulting

velocity vector of the jet is $\mathbf{v} + \mathbf{w} = \left(\frac{55}{2} + \frac{765\sqrt{2}}{2} \right)\mathbf{i} + \left(\frac{55\sqrt{3}}{2} + \frac{765\sqrt{2}}{2} \right)\mathbf{j} \approx 568.44\mathbf{i} + 588.57\mathbf{j}$

$= \langle 568.44, 588.57 \rangle$

(b) The true speed of the jet is $|\mathbf{w} + \mathbf{v}| \approx \sqrt{568.44^2 + 588.57^2} \approx 818$ mi/h. The direction of the

vector $\mathbf{w} + \mathbf{v}$ is $\theta \approx \tan^{-1}\left(\frac{588.57}{568.44} \right) \approx 46°$. Thus the true direction of the jet is approximately N 44° E.

44. Let $\mathbf{v}$ be the velocity vector of the jet and let θ be the direction of this vector. Thus $\mathbf{v} = (765 \cos \theta)\mathbf{i} + (765 \sin \theta)\mathbf{j}$. If $\mathbf{w}$ is the velocity vector of the wind then the true course of the jet is $\mathbf{v} + \mathbf{w} = \left(765 \cos \theta + \frac{55}{2} \right)\mathbf{i} + \left(765 \sin \theta + \frac{55\sqrt{3}}{2} \right)\mathbf{j}$. To achieve a course of true north, the east-west component (the $\mathbf{i}$ component) of the jet's velocity vector must be 0. That is

$765 \cos \theta + \frac{55}{2} = 0$ $\Leftrightarrow$ $\cos \theta = \frac{-27.5}{765}$ $\Leftrightarrow$ $\theta = \cos^{-1}\left(\frac{-27.5}{765} \right) \approx 92.1°$. Thus the pilot should head his plane in the direction N 2.1° W.

46. Let $\mathbf{w}$ be the velocity vector of the water, let $\mathbf{v}$ be the velocity vector of the boat, and let θ be the direction of $\mathbf{v}$. Then $\mathbf{v} = (20 \cos \theta)\mathbf{i} + (20 \sin \theta)\mathbf{j}$ and $\mathbf{w} = 10\mathbf{i}$. The true course of the boat is $\mathbf{v} + \mathbf{w} = (20 \cos \theta + 10)\mathbf{i} + (20 \sin \theta)\mathbf{j}$. To achieve a course of true north, the east-west component

of the boat's velocity vector must be 0. Thus, $20 \cos \theta + 10 = 0 \iff \cos \theta = \frac{-10}{20} = -\frac{1}{2} \iff$
$\theta = \cos^{-1}(-\frac{1}{2}) = 120°$. Thus the boater should head her boat in the direction N 30° W.

48. Let $\mathbf{w}$ represent the velocity of the woman and $\mathbf{l}$ the velocity of the ocean liner. Then $\mathbf{w} = \langle -2, 0 \rangle$,
and $\mathbf{l} = \langle 0, 25 \rangle$, and so $\mathbf{r} = \langle -2 + 0, 0 + 25 \rangle$. Hence, relative to the water, the woman's speed is
$|\mathbf{r}| = \sqrt{4 + 625} \approx 25.08$ mi/h, and her direction is $\theta = \tan^{-1} \frac{25}{-2} \approx 94.57°$ or approximately
N 4.57° W.

50. $\mathbf{F_1} = \langle 3, -7 \rangle$, $\mathbf{F_2} = \langle 4, -2 \rangle$, and $\mathbf{F_3} = \langle -7, 9 \rangle$.

   (a) Then $\mathbf{F_1} + \mathbf{F_2} + \mathbf{F_3} = \langle 3 + 4 - 7, -7 - 2 + 9 \rangle = \langle 0, 0 \rangle$.

   (b) No additional force is required.

52. $\mathbf{F_1} = \mathbf{i} - \mathbf{j}$, $\mathbf{F_2} = \mathbf{i} + \mathbf{j}$, and $\mathbf{F_3} = -2\mathbf{i} + \mathbf{j}$.

   (a) $\mathbf{F_1} + \mathbf{F_2} + \mathbf{F_3} = (1 + 1 - 2)\mathbf{i} + (-1 + 1 + 1)\mathbf{j} = 0\mathbf{i} + \mathbf{j}$.

   (b) The additional force required is $\mathbf{F_4} = 0\mathbf{i} + 0\mathbf{j} - (0\mathbf{i} + \mathbf{j}) = -\mathbf{j}$.

54. $\mathbf{F_1} = \langle 3, -1 \rangle$, $\mathbf{F_2} = \langle 1, 2 \rangle$, $\mathbf{F_3} = \langle -2, -1 \rangle$, and $\mathbf{F_4} = \langle 0, -4 \rangle$.

   (a) $\mathbf{F_1} + \mathbf{F_2} + \mathbf{F_3} + \mathbf{F_4} = \langle 3 + 1 - 2 + 0, -1 + 2 - 1 - 4 \rangle = \langle 2, -4 \rangle$

   (b) The additional force required is $\mathbf{F_5} = \langle 0, 0 \rangle - \langle 2, -4 \rangle = \langle -2, 4 \rangle$.

56. From the figure we see that $\mathbf{T_1} = -|\mathbf{T_1}| \cos 22.3° \mathbf{i} + |\mathbf{T_1}| \sin 22.3° \mathbf{j}$ and
$\mathbf{T_2} = |\mathbf{T_2}| \cos 41.5° \mathbf{i} + |\mathbf{T_2}| \sin 41.5° \mathbf{j}$. Since $\mathbf{T_1} + \mathbf{T_2} = 18{,}278\mathbf{j}$ we get
$-|\mathbf{T_1}| \cos 22.3° + |\mathbf{T_2}| \cos 41.5° = 0$ and $|\mathbf{T_1}| \sin 22.3° + |\mathbf{T_2}| \sin 41.5° = 18{,}278$.
From the first equation $|\mathbf{T_2}| = |\mathbf{T_1}| \frac{\cos 22.3°}{\cos 41.5°}$ and substituting into the second equation gives
$|\mathbf{T_1}| \sin 22.3° + |\mathbf{T_1}| \frac{\cos 22.3° \sin 41.5°}{\cos 41.5°} = 18{,}278 \iff$
$|\mathbf{T_1}| (\sin 22.3° \cos 41.5° + \cos 22.3° \sin 41.5°) = 18{,}278 \cos 41.5° \iff$
$|\mathbf{T_1}| \sin(22.3° + 41.5°) = 18{,}278 \cos 41.5° \iff |\mathbf{T_1}| = 18{,}278 \frac{\cos 41.5°}{\sin 63.8°} \approx 15{,}257$. Similarly,
solving for $|\mathbf{T_1}|$ in the first equation gives $|\mathbf{T_1}| = |\mathbf{T_2}| \frac{\cos 41.5°}{\cos 22.3°}$ and substituting gives
$|\mathbf{T_2}| \frac{\cos 41.5° \sin 22.3°}{\cos 22.3°} + |\mathbf{T_2}| \sin 41.5° = 18{,}278 \iff$
$|\mathbf{T_2}| (\sin 22.3° \cos 41.5° + \sin 41.5° \cos 22.3°) = 18{,}278 \cos 22.3° \iff$
$|\mathbf{T_2}| = \frac{18{,}278 \cos 22.3°}{\sin 63.8°} \approx 18{,}847$.
Thus $\mathbf{T_1} \approx (-15{,}257 \cos 22.3°)\mathbf{i} + (15{,}257 \sin 22.3°)\mathbf{j} \approx -14{,}116\mathbf{i} + 5{,}789\mathbf{j}$ and
$\mathbf{T_2} \approx (18{,}847 \cos 41.5°)\mathbf{i} + (18{,}847 \sin 41.5°)\mathbf{j} \approx 14{,}116\mathbf{i} + 12{,}488\mathbf{j}$.

Exercises 9.8

2. (a) $\mathbf{u} \cdot \mathbf{v} = \langle 1, \sqrt{3} \rangle \cdot \langle -\sqrt{3}, 1 \rangle = -\sqrt{3} + \sqrt{3} = 0$

   (b) $\cos \theta = \dfrac{\mathbf{u} \cdot \mathbf{v}}{|\mathbf{u}|\,|\mathbf{v}|} = 0 \quad \Rightarrow \quad \theta = 90°$

4. (a) $\mathbf{u} \cdot \mathbf{v} = \langle -6, 6 \rangle \cdot \langle 1, -1 \rangle = -6 + (-6) = -12$

   (b) $\cos \theta = \dfrac{\mathbf{u} \cdot \mathbf{v}}{|\mathbf{u}|\,|\mathbf{v}|} = \dfrac{-12}{6\sqrt{2} \cdot \sqrt{2}} = -\dfrac{12}{12} = -1 \quad \Rightarrow \quad \theta = 180°$

6. (a) $\mathbf{u} \cdot \mathbf{v} = \langle 2, 1 \rangle \cdot \langle 3, -2 \rangle = 6 + (-2) = 4$

   (b) $\cos \theta = \dfrac{\mathbf{u} \cdot \mathbf{v}}{|\mathbf{u}|\,|\mathbf{v}|} = \dfrac{4}{\sqrt{5} \cdot \sqrt{13}} \quad \Rightarrow \quad \theta = \cos^{-1}\left(\dfrac{4}{\sqrt{65}}\right) \approx 60.3°$

8. (a) $\mathbf{u} \cdot \mathbf{v} = \langle 1, 1 \rangle \cdot \langle 1, -1 \rangle = 1 + (-1) = 0$

   (b) $\cos \theta = \dfrac{\mathbf{u} \cdot \mathbf{v}}{|\mathbf{u}|\,|\mathbf{v}|} = \dfrac{0}{\sqrt{2} \cdot \sqrt{2}} = 0 \quad \Rightarrow \quad \theta = 90°$

10. $\mathbf{u} \cdot \mathbf{v} = 0 + 0 = 0 \quad \Rightarrow \quad$ vectors are orthogonal

12. $\mathbf{u} \cdot \mathbf{v} = 0 + 0 = 0 \quad \Rightarrow \quad$ vectors are orthogonal

14. $\mathbf{u} \cdot \mathbf{v} = -4 + 0 = -4 \quad \Rightarrow \quad$ vectors are not orthogonal

16. $\mathbf{u} \cdot (\mathbf{v} + \mathbf{w}) = \langle 2, 1 \rangle \cdot [\langle 1, -3 \rangle + \langle 3, 4 \rangle] = \langle 2, 1 \rangle \cdot \langle 4, 1 \rangle = 8 + 1 = 9$

18. $(\mathbf{u} \cdot \mathbf{v})(\mathbf{u} \cdot \mathbf{w}) = (\langle 2, 1 \rangle \cdot \langle 1, -3 \rangle)\,(\langle 2, 1 \rangle \cdot \langle 3, 4 \rangle) = (-1)(10) = -10$

20. $x = \dfrac{\mathbf{u} \cdot \mathbf{v}}{|\mathbf{v}|} = \dfrac{-\frac{3}{\sqrt{2}} + \frac{5}{\sqrt{2}}}{1} = \dfrac{2}{\sqrt{2}} = \sqrt{2}$

22. $x = \dfrac{\mathbf{u} \cdot \mathbf{v}}{|\mathbf{v}|} = \dfrac{56 + 0}{10} = \dfrac{28}{5}$

23. $W = \mathbf{F} \cdot \mathbf{d} = \langle 4, -5 \rangle \cdot \langle 3, 8 \rangle = -28$

24. $W = \mathbf{F} \cdot \mathbf{d} = \langle 400, 50 \rangle \cdot \langle 201, 0 \rangle = 80{,}400$

26. $W = \mathbf{F} \cdot \mathbf{d} = \langle -4, 20 \rangle \cdot \langle 5, 15 \rangle = 280$

28. The displacement of the object is $\mathbf{D} = \langle 11, 13 \rangle - \langle 2, 5 \rangle = \langle 9, 8 \rangle$. Hence, the work done is
    $W = \mathbf{F} \cdot \mathbf{D} = \langle 2, 8 \rangle \cdot \langle 9, 8 \rangle = 18 + 64 = 82$ ft-lb.

30. $W = \mathbf{F} \cdot \mathbf{d}$, and in this problem $\mathbf{F} = \langle 0, -2500 \rangle$, $\mathbf{d} = \langle 500 \cos 12°, 500 \sin 12° \rangle$ Thus,
    $W = \langle 0, -2500 \rangle \cdot \langle 500 \cos 12°, 500 \sin 12° \rangle \approx 0 - (2500)(104.0) = -260{,}000$ ft-lb. This is the
    work done by gravity; the car does (positive) work in overcoming the force of gravity. So, the work
    done by the car is 260,000 ft-lb.

32. (a) Since the force parallel to the driveway is $490 = |\mathbf{w}| \sin 10° \quad \Leftrightarrow \quad |\mathbf{w}| = \dfrac{490}{\sin 10°} \approx 2821.8$,
        and thus the weight of the car is about 2822 lb.

   (b) The force exerted against the driveway is $2821.8 \cos 10° \approx 2779$ lb.

34. (a) The angle formed by the vector **w** representing
         the wind and vector **S** representing the sail is 25°.
         Thus the component of the wind perpendicular to the
         sail is the length of the vector **P** in the figure.
         $|\mathbf{P}| = |\mathbf{w}| \sin 25° = 220 \sin 25° \approx 93$ lb.

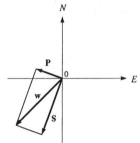

    (b) The angle formed by the vector **P** found in
         part (a) and the keel is 70°. The effective force
         of the wind that drives the boat is the component of
         P that is parallel to the keel. This force is the length
         of the vector **k** shown in the figure.
         $|\mathbf{k}| = |\mathbf{P}| \cos 70° \approx 93 \cos 70° \approx 32$ lb.

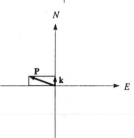

36. Let $\mathbf{u} = \langle u_1, u_2 \rangle$ and $\mathbf{v} = \langle v_1, v_2 \rangle$. Then
    $$(a\mathbf{u}) \cdot \mathbf{v} = (a \langle u_1, u_2 \rangle) \cdot \langle v_1, v_2 \rangle = \langle au_1, au_2 \rangle \cdot \langle v_1, v_2 \rangle = au_1 v_1 + au_2 v_2$$
    $$= a(u_1 v_1 + u_2 v_2) = a(\mathbf{u} \cdot \mathbf{v})$$
    $$= u_1 a v_1 + u_2 a v_2 = \langle u_1, u_2 \rangle \cdot \langle av_1, av_2 \rangle = \mathbf{u} \cdot (a\mathbf{v})$$

38. Let $\mathbf{u} = \langle u_1, u_2 \rangle$ and $\mathbf{v} = \langle v_1, v_2 \rangle$. So
    $$(\mathbf{u} - \mathbf{v}) \cdot (\mathbf{u} + \mathbf{v}) = (\langle u_1, u_2 \rangle - \langle v_1, v_2 \rangle) \cdot (\langle u_1, u_2 \rangle + \langle v_1, v_2 \rangle)$$
    $$= \langle u_1 - v_1, u_2 - v_2 \rangle \cdot \langle u_1 + v_1, u_2 + , v_2 \rangle = u_1^2 - v_1^2 + u_2^2 - v_2^2$$
    $$= (u_1^2 + u_2^2) - (v_1^2 + v_2^2)$$
    $$= \left(\sqrt{u_1^2 + u_2^2}\right)^2 - \left(\sqrt{v_1^2 + v_2^2}\right)^2 = |\mathbf{u}|^2 - |\mathbf{v}|^2$$

Review Exercises for Chapter 9

2. $\dfrac{1}{1 - \sin^2 x} = \dfrac{1}{\cos^2 x} = \sec^2 x = 1 + \tan^2 x$

4. $\dfrac{1 + \sec x}{\sec x} = \dfrac{1}{\sec x} + 1 = 1 + \cos x = (1 + \cos x) \cdot \dfrac{1 - \cos x}{1 - \cos x} = \dfrac{1 - \cos^2 x}{1 - \cos x} = \dfrac{\sin^2 x}{1 - \cos x}$

6. $(1 - \tan x)(1 - \cot x) = 1 - \cot x - \tan x + \tan x \cot x = 2 - (\cot x + \tan x)$

$\displaystyle = 2 - \left(\dfrac{\cos x}{\sin x} + \dfrac{\sin x}{\cos x} \right) = 2 - \dfrac{\cos^2 x + \sin^2 x}{\cos x \sin x} = 2 - \dfrac{1}{\cos x \sin x} = 2 - \sec x \csc x$

8. $(\tan x + \cot x)^2 = \left(\dfrac{\sin x}{\cos x} + \dfrac{\cos x}{\sin x} \right)^2 = \left(\dfrac{\sin^2 x + \cos^2 x}{\cos x \sin x} \right)^2 = \left(\dfrac{1}{\cos x \sin x} \right)^2$

$= (\sec x \csc x)^2 = \csc^2 x \sec^2 x$

10. $\dfrac{\cos(x + y)}{\cos x \sin y} = \dfrac{\cos x \cos y - \sin x \sin y}{\cos x \sin y} = \dfrac{\cos x \cos y}{\cos x \sin y} - \dfrac{\sin x \sin y}{\cos x \sin y} = \dfrac{\cos y}{\sin y} - \dfrac{\sin x}{\cos x} = \cot y - \tan x$

12. $\dfrac{\sin(x + y) + \sin(x - y)}{\cos(x + y) + \cos(x - y)} = \dfrac{2 \sin\left(\frac{(x+y)+(x-y)}{2} \right) \cos\left(\frac{(x+y)-(x-y)}{2} \right)}{2 \cos\left(\frac{(x+y)+(x-y)}{2} \right) \cos\left(\frac{(x+y)-(x-y)}{2} \right)} = \dfrac{2 \sin x \cos y}{2 \cos x \cos y} = \dfrac{\sin x}{\cos x} = \tan x$

14. $\csc x - \tan \frac{x}{2} = \csc x - \dfrac{1 - \cos x}{\sin x} = \csc x - (\csc x - \cot x) = \cot x$

16. $\dfrac{\sin 3x + \cos 3x}{\cos x - \sin x} = \dfrac{\sin(x + 2x) + \cos(x + 2x)}{\cos x - \sin x}$

$= \dfrac{\sin x \cos 2x + \cos x \sin 2x + \cos x \cos 2x - \sin x \sin 2x}{\cos x - \sin x}$

$= \dfrac{\cos 2x (\sin x + \cos x) + \sin 2x (\cos x - \sin x)}{\cos x - \sin x} = \dfrac{\cos 2x (\sin x + \cos x)}{\cos x - \sin x} + \sin 2x$

$= \dfrac{(\cos^2 x - \sin^2 x)(\sin x + \cos x)}{\cos x - \sin x} + \sin 2x = (\cos x + \sin x)(\sin x + \cos x) + \sin 2x$

$= \sin^2 x + \cos^2 x + 2 \sin x \cos x + \sin 2x = 1 + \sin 2x + \sin 2x = 1 + 2 \sin 2x$

18. $\dfrac{\cos 3x - \cos 7x}{\sin 3x + \sin 7x} = \dfrac{-2 \sin\left(\frac{3x+7x}{2} \right) \sin\left(\frac{3x-7x}{2} \right)}{2 \sin\left(\frac{3x+7x}{2} \right) \cos\left(\frac{3x-7x}{2} \right)} = \dfrac{-2 \sin 5x \sin(-2x)}{2 \sin 5x \cos(-2x)} = \dfrac{2 \sin 5x \sin 2x}{2 \sin 5x \cos 2x}$

$= \dfrac{\sin 2x}{\cos 2x} = \tan 2x$

20. $(\cos x + \cos y)^2 + (\sin x - \sin y)^2 = \cos^2 x + 2 \cos x \cos y + \cos^2 y + \sin^2 x - 2 \sin x \sin y + \sin^2 y$

$= (\cos^2 x + \sin^2 x) + (\sin^2 y + \cos^2 y) + 2 (\cos x \cos y - \sin x \sin y) = 2 + 2 \cos(x + y)$

22. $\dfrac{\sec x - 1}{\sin x \sec x} = \dfrac{\frac{1}{\cos x} - 1}{\sin x \frac{1}{\cos x}} = \dfrac{\frac{1}{\cos x} - 1}{\sin x \frac{1}{\cos x}} \cdot \dfrac{\cos x}{\cos x} = \dfrac{1 - \cos x}{\sin x} = \tan \frac{x}{2}$

24. (a) $f(x) = \sin x + \cos x,$

$g(x) = \sqrt{\sin^2 x + \cos^2 x}$

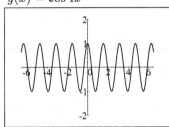

(b) The graphs suggest $f(x) \neq g(x)$ in general. For example, choose $x = \frac{\pi}{6}$ and evaluate the functions: $f(\frac{\pi}{6}) = \frac{1}{2} + \frac{\sqrt{3}}{2} = \frac{1+\sqrt{3}}{2}$, whereas $g(\frac{\pi}{6}) = \sqrt{\frac{1}{4} + \frac{3}{4}} = \sqrt{1} = 1$, so $f(x) \neq g(x)$.

26. (a) $f(x) = 1 - 8\sin^2 x + 8\sin^4 x,$

$g(x) = \cos 4x$

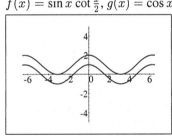

(b) The graphs suggest that $f(x) = g(x)$ is an identity. To show this, expand $g(x)$ by using double-angle identities:

$g(x) = \cos 4x = \cos(2(2x)) = 1 - 2\sin^2 2x$
$= 1 - 2(2\sin x \cos x)^2$
$= 1 - 2(4\sin^2 x \cos^2 x)$
$= 1 - 8\sin^2 x \cdot (1 - \sin^2 x)$
$= 1 - 8\sin^2 x + 8\sin^4 x = f(x)$

28. (a) $f(x) = \sin x \cot \frac{x}{2}, \ g(x) = \cos x$

(b) Proof: $f(x) = \sin x \cot \frac{x}{2} = \sin x \cdot \left(\dfrac{\cos \frac{x}{2}}{\sin \frac{x}{2}} \right)$

$= \left(2 \sin \frac{x}{2} \cos \frac{x}{2}\right) \cdot \left(\dfrac{\cos \frac{x}{2}}{\sin \frac{x}{2}} \right) = 2 \cos^2 \frac{x}{2}$

Now, subtract and add 1 so that
$f(x) = 2 \cos^2 \frac{x}{2} - 1 + 1 = \cos x + 1$
$= g(x) + 1.$

Conjecture: $f(x) = g(x) + 1$

30. $\sin x - 2\sin^2 x = 0 \quad \Leftrightarrow \quad \sin x (1 - 2\sin x) = 0 \quad \Leftrightarrow \quad \sin x = 0 \text{ or } \sin x = \frac{1}{2} \quad \Leftrightarrow \quad x = 0, \pi$
or $x = \frac{\pi}{6}, \frac{5\pi}{6}$. Therefore, the solutions in $[0, 2\pi)$ are $x = 0, \frac{\pi}{6}, \frac{5\pi}{6}, \pi$.

32. $\sin x - \cos x - \tan x = -1 \quad \Leftrightarrow \quad \sin x \cos x - \cos^2 x - \sin x = -\cos x \quad \Leftrightarrow$
$\sin x \cos x - \sin x - \cos^2 x + \cos x = 0 \quad \Leftrightarrow \quad \sin x (\cos x - 1) - \cos x (\cos x - 1) = 0 \quad \Leftrightarrow$
$(\sin x - \cos x)(\cos x - 1) = 0 \quad \Leftrightarrow \quad \sin x = \cos x \text{ or } \cos x = 1 \quad \Leftrightarrow \quad \tan x = 1 \text{ or } \cos x = 1$
$\Leftrightarrow \quad x = \frac{\pi}{4}, \frac{5\pi}{4} \text{ or } x = 0$. Therefore, the solutions in $[0, 2\pi)$ are $x = 0, \frac{\pi}{4}, \frac{5\pi}{4}$.

34. $4\sin^2 x + 2\cos^2 x = 3 \quad \Leftrightarrow \quad 2\sin^2 x + 2(\sin^2 x + \cos^2 x) - 3 = 0 \quad \Leftrightarrow \quad 2\sin^2 x + 2 - 3 = 0$
$\Leftrightarrow \quad 2\sin^2 x = 1 \quad \Leftrightarrow \quad \sin x = \pm \frac{1}{\sqrt{2}}$. So the solution in $[0, 2\pi)$ are $x = \frac{\pi}{4}, \frac{3\pi}{4}, \frac{5\pi}{4}, \frac{7\pi}{4}$.

36. $\sin x = \cos 2x \quad \Leftrightarrow \quad \sin x = 1 - 2\sin^2 x \quad \Leftrightarrow \quad 2\sin^2 x + \sin x - 1 = 0 \quad \Leftrightarrow$
$(2\sin x - 1)(\sin x + 1) = 0 \quad \Leftrightarrow \quad \sin x = \frac{1}{2} \text{ or } \sin x = -1 \quad \Leftrightarrow \quad x = \frac{\pi}{6}, \frac{5\pi}{6} \text{ or } x = \frac{3\pi}{2}$. Thus,
the solutions in $[0, 2\pi)$ are $x = \frac{\pi}{6}, \frac{3\pi}{2}, \frac{5\pi}{6}$.

38. $\cos 2x \csc^2 x = 2 \cos 2x \quad \Leftrightarrow \quad \cos 2x \csc^2 x - 2 \cos 2x = 0 \quad \Leftrightarrow \quad \cos 2x (\csc^2 x - 2) = 0 \quad \Leftrightarrow$
$\cos 2x = 0$ or $\csc^2 x = 2 \quad \Leftrightarrow \quad \cos 2x = 0$ or $\sin^2 x = \frac{1}{2} \quad \Leftrightarrow \quad \cos 2x = 0$ or $\sin x = \pm\frac{1}{\sqrt{2}}$. For
$\cos 2x = 0$ the solutions in $[0, 4\pi)$ are $2x = \frac{\pi}{2}, \frac{3\pi}{2}, \frac{5\pi}{2}, \frac{7\pi}{2} \quad \Leftrightarrow \quad$ the solutions in $[0, 2\pi)$ are
$x = \frac{\pi}{4}, \frac{3\pi}{4}, \frac{5\pi}{4}, \frac{7\pi}{4}$. For $\sin x = \pm\frac{1}{\sqrt{2}}$ the solutions in $[0, 2\pi)$ are $x = \frac{\pi}{4}, \frac{3\pi}{4}, \frac{5\pi}{4}, \frac{7\pi}{4}$. Thus, the
solutions of the equation in $[0, 2\pi)$ are $x = \frac{\pi}{4}, \frac{3\pi}{4}, \frac{5\pi}{4}, \frac{7\pi}{4}$.

40. $\cos 3x + \cos 2x + \cos x = 0 \quad \Leftrightarrow \quad \cos 2x \cos x - \sin 2x \sin x + \cos 2x + \cos x = 0 \quad \Leftrightarrow$
$\cos 2x \cos x + \cos 2x - \sin 2x \sin x + \cos x = 0 \quad \Leftrightarrow$
$\cos 2x (\cos x + 1) - 2 \sin^2 x \cos x + \cos x = 0 \quad \Leftrightarrow \quad \cos 2x (\cos x + 1) + \cos x (1 - 2\sin^2 x) = 0$
$\Leftrightarrow \quad \cos 2x (\cos x + 1) + \cos x \cos 2x = 0 \quad \Leftrightarrow \quad \cos 2x (\cos x + 1 + \cos x) = 0 \quad \Leftrightarrow$
$\cos 2x (2 \cos x + 1) = 0 \quad \Leftrightarrow \quad \cos 2x = 0$ or $\cos x = -\frac{1}{2} \quad \Leftrightarrow \quad 2x = \frac{\pi}{2}, \frac{3\pi}{2}, \frac{5\pi}{2}, \frac{7\pi}{2}$ (in $[0, 4\pi)$)
or $x = \frac{2\pi}{3}, \frac{4\pi}{3}$ (in $[0, 2\pi)$). Thus the solutions in $[0, 2\pi)$ are $x = \frac{\pi}{4}, \frac{3\pi}{4}, \frac{5\pi}{4}, \frac{7\pi}{4}, \frac{2\pi}{3}, \frac{4\pi}{3}$.

42. $2 \cos x - 3 \tan x = 0 \quad \Leftrightarrow \quad 2 \cos x - 3 \dfrac{\sin x}{\cos x} = 0 \quad \Leftrightarrow \quad 2 \cos^2 x - 3 \sin x = 0 \quad (\cos x \neq 0)$
$\Leftrightarrow \quad 2 (1 - \sin^2 x) - 3 \sin x = 0 \quad \Leftrightarrow \quad 2 \sin^2 x + 3 \sin x - 2 = 0 \quad \Leftrightarrow$
$(2 \sin x - 1)(\sin x + 2) = 0 \quad \Leftrightarrow \quad \sin x = \frac{1}{2}$ or $\sin x = -2$ (which has no solutions) $\quad \Leftrightarrow$
$x = \frac{\pi}{6}, \frac{5\pi}{6}$.

44. We graph $f(x) = e^{\sin x}$ and $g(x) = x$ in the viewing rectangle $[0, 6.5]$ by $[-1, 3]$. The two functions intersect at only one point, $x \approx 2.22$.

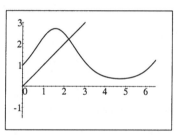

46. $\sin \frac{5\pi}{12} = \sin(\frac{\pi}{4} + \frac{\pi}{6}) = \sin \frac{\pi}{4} \cos \frac{\pi}{6} + \cos \frac{\pi}{4} \sin \frac{\pi}{6} = \frac{1}{\sqrt{2}} \cdot \frac{\sqrt{3}}{2} + \frac{1}{\sqrt{2}} \cdot \frac{1}{2} = \frac{1+\sqrt{3}}{2\sqrt{2}} = \frac{\sqrt{2}+\sqrt{6}}{4}$

48. $2 \sin \frac{\pi}{12} \cos \frac{\pi}{12} = \sin(2 \cdot \frac{\pi}{12}) = \sin \frac{\pi}{6} = \frac{1}{2}$.

50. $\dfrac{\tan 66° - \tan 6°}{1 + \tan 66° \tan 6°} = \tan(66° - 6°) = \tan 60° = \sqrt{3}$.

52. $\frac{1}{2} \cos \frac{\pi}{12} + \frac{\sqrt{3}}{2} \sin \frac{\pi}{12} = \sin \frac{\pi}{6} \cos \frac{\pi}{12} + \cos \frac{\pi}{6} \sin \frac{\pi}{12} = \sin(\frac{\pi}{6} + \frac{\pi}{12}) = \sin \frac{\pi}{4} = \frac{1}{\sqrt{2}} = \frac{\sqrt{2}}{2}$.

54. $\cos 67.5° + \cos 22.5° = 2 \cos\left(\dfrac{67.5° + 22.5°}{2}\right) \cos\left(\dfrac{67.5° - 22.5°}{2}\right) = 2 \cos 45° \cos 22.5°$

$= 2 \cdot \dfrac{1}{\sqrt{2}} \cdot \sqrt{\dfrac{1 + \cos 45°}{2}} = \sqrt{1 + \cos 45°} = \sqrt{1 + \frac{1}{\sqrt{2}}} = \sqrt{\dfrac{2+\sqrt{2}}{2}}$.

In Exercises 56 – 60, since x and y are in quadrant I, we know that $\sec x = \frac{3}{2} \quad \Rightarrow \quad \cos x = \frac{2}{3}$, so
$\sin x = \frac{\sqrt{5}}{3}$ and $\tan x = \frac{\sqrt{5}}{2}$. Also, $\csc y = 3 \quad \Rightarrow \quad \sin y = \frac{1}{3}$, and so $\cos y = \frac{2\sqrt{2}}{3}$ and
$\tan y = \frac{1}{2\sqrt{2}} = \frac{\sqrt{2}}{4}$.

56. $\cos(x - y) = \cos x \cos y + \sin x \sin y = \frac{2}{3} \cdot \frac{2\sqrt{2}}{3} + \frac{\sqrt{5}}{3} \cdot \frac{1}{3} = \frac{1}{9}\left(4\sqrt{2} + \sqrt{5}\right)$.

58. $\sin 2x = 2 \sin x \cos x = 2 \cdot \frac{\sqrt{5}}{3} \cdot \frac{2}{3} = \frac{4\sqrt{5}}{9}$.

60. $\tan\frac{y}{2} = \dfrac{1-\cos y}{\sin y} = \dfrac{1-\frac{2\sqrt{2}}{3}}{\frac{1}{3}} = \dfrac{3-2\sqrt{2}}{1} = 3-2\sqrt{2}.$

62. $\tan^{-1}(\frac{\sqrt{3}}{3}) = \frac{\pi}{6}$

64. $\sin(\cos^{-1}\frac{\sqrt{3}}{2}) = \sin\frac{\pi}{6} = \frac{1}{2}.$

66. Let $u = \cos^{-1}\frac{3}{8}$ then $\cos u = \frac{3}{8}$. From the triangle we have $\sin(\cos^{-1}\frac{3}{8}) = \sin u = \frac{\sqrt{55}}{8}.$

68. Let $u = \sin^{-1}\frac{5}{13}$ and $v = \cos^{-1}\frac{4}{5}$. Then $\sin u = \frac{5}{13}$ and $\cos v = \frac{4}{5}$. So, from the triangles we have $\cos(\sin^{-1}\frac{5}{13} - \cos^{-1}\frac{4}{5}) = \cos(u-v) = \cos u \cos v + \sin u \sin v = \frac{12}{13}\cdot\frac{4}{5} + \frac{5}{13}\cdot\frac{3}{5} = \frac{63}{65}.$

70. Let $\theta = \sin^{-1}x$. Then $\sin\theta = x$. From the triangle we have $\sec(\sin^{-1}x) = \sec\theta = \dfrac{1}{\sqrt{1-x^2}}.$

72. $\tan\theta = \dfrac{x}{2} \Rightarrow \theta = \tan^{-1}\left(\dfrac{x}{2}\right)$

74. From Exercise 73, we know that $\cos\left(\dfrac{s}{2r}\right) = \dfrac{r}{r+h} \Rightarrow \cos\left(\dfrac{2450}{2(3960)}\right) \approx 0.9525 = \dfrac{3960}{3960+h}.$
Thus, $h + 3960 = \frac{3960}{0.9525} \approx 4157 \Rightarrow h \approx 4157 - 3960 = 197$. Therefore, the satellite would have to be approximately 197 miles above the earth.

76. $-10i$ has $r = 10$, and $\theta = \frac{3\pi}{2}$. Thus, $-10i = 10\left(\cos\frac{3\pi}{2} + i\sin\frac{3\pi}{2}\right).$

78. $1 + \sqrt{3}\,i$ has $r = \sqrt{1+3} = 2$, and $\theta = \tan^{-1}\sqrt{3} = \frac{\pi}{3}$ (since θ is in quadrant I). Thus, $1 + \sqrt{3}\,i = 2\left(\cos\frac{\pi}{3} + i\sin\frac{\pi}{3}\right).$

80. -20 has $r = 20$ and $\theta = \pi$. Thus, $-20 = 20\left(\cos\pi + i\sin\pi\right).$

82. $1 + i$ has $r = \sqrt{1+1} = \sqrt{2}$ and $\theta = \frac{\pi}{4}$. Thus, $1+i = \sqrt{2}\left(\cos\frac{\pi}{4} + i\sin\frac{\pi}{4}\right)$, and so $(1+i)^8 = (\sqrt{2})^8\left(\cos 2\pi + i\sin 2\pi\right) = 16\left(1 + i\cdot 0\right) = 16.$

84. $\frac{1}{2} + \frac{\sqrt{3}}{2}\,i$ has $r = \sqrt{\frac{1}{4} + \frac{3}{4}} = 1$ and $\theta = \tan^{-1}\frac{\sqrt{3}/2}{1/2} = \frac{\pi}{3}$ (since θ is in quadrant I). So,
$\frac{1}{2} + \frac{\sqrt{3}}{2}\,i = \cos\frac{\pi}{3} + i\sin\frac{\pi}{3}$. Thus $\left(\frac{1}{2} + \frac{\sqrt{3}}{2}i\right)^{20} = 1^{20}\left(\cos\frac{20\pi}{3} + i\sin\frac{20\pi}{3}\right) = \cos\frac{2\pi}{3} + i\sin\frac{2\pi}{3}$
$= -\frac{1}{2} + \frac{\sqrt{3}}{2}\,i = \frac{1}{2}(-1 + i\sqrt{3})$

86. $4 + 4\sqrt{3}\,i$ has $r = \sqrt{16+48} = 8$ and $\theta = \tan^{-1}\frac{4\sqrt{3}}{4} = \frac{\pi}{3}$. Therefore,
$4 + 4\sqrt{3}\,i = 8\left(\cos\frac{\pi}{3} + i\sin\frac{\pi}{3}\right)$. Thus $(4 + 4\sqrt{3}\,i)^{1/3} = \sqrt[3]{8}\left[\cos\left(\frac{\pi+6k\pi}{9}\right) + i\sin\left(\frac{\pi+6k\pi}{9}\right)\right]$ for
$k = 0, 1, 2$. Thus the three roots are $w_0 = 2\left(\cos\frac{\pi}{9} + i\sin\frac{\pi}{9}\right)$, $w_1 = 2\left(\cos\frac{7\pi}{9} + i\sin\frac{7\pi}{9}\right)$, and
$w_2 = 2\left(\cos\frac{13\pi}{9} + i\sin\frac{13\pi}{9}\right).$

88. $i = \cos\frac{\pi}{2} + i\sin\frac{\pi}{2}$. Then, $i^{1/8} = \cos\left(\frac{\pi/2 + 2k\pi}{8}\right) + i\sin\left(\frac{\pi/2 + 2k\pi}{8}\right) = \cos\left(\frac{\pi+4k\pi}{16}\right) + i\sin\left(\frac{\pi+4k\pi}{16}\right)$ for

$k = 0, 1, 2, 3, 4, 5, 6, 7$. Thus the eight roots are $w_0 = \cos\frac{\pi}{16} + i\sin\frac{\pi}{16}$, $w_1 = \cos\frac{5\pi}{16} + i\sin\frac{5\pi}{16}$, $w_2 = \cos\frac{9\pi}{16} + i\sin\frac{9\pi}{16}$, $w_3 = \cos\frac{13\pi}{16} + i\sin\frac{13\pi}{16}$, $w_4 = \cos\frac{17\pi}{16} + i\sin\frac{17\pi}{16}$, $w_5 = \cos\frac{21\pi}{16} + i\sin\frac{21\pi}{6}$, $w_6 = \cos\frac{25\pi}{16} + i\sin\frac{25\pi}{16}$, and $w_7 = \cos\frac{29\pi}{16} + i\sin\frac{29\pi}{16}$.

90. $\mathbf{u} = 2\mathbf{i} + \mathbf{j}$ and $\mathbf{v} = \mathbf{i} - 2\mathbf{j}$. Then $|\mathbf{u}| = \sqrt{2^2 + 1^2} = \sqrt{5}$ and $\mathbf{u} + \mathbf{v} = (2+1)\mathbf{i} + (1-2)\mathbf{j} = 3\mathbf{i} - \mathbf{j}$; $\mathbf{u} - \mathbf{v} = (2-1)\mathbf{i} + (1+2)\mathbf{j} = \mathbf{i} + 3\mathbf{j}$; $2\mathbf{u} = 4\mathbf{i} + 2\mathbf{j}$; and $3\mathbf{u} - 2\mathbf{v} = (6-2)\mathbf{i} + (3+4)\mathbf{j} = 4\mathbf{i} + 7\mathbf{j}$.

92. $\mathbf{u} = (|\mathbf{u}|\cos\theta)\mathbf{i} + (|\mathbf{u}|\sin\theta)\mathbf{j} = 20\cos 60°\mathbf{i} + 20\sin 60°\mathbf{j} = 10\mathbf{i} + 10\sqrt{3}\mathbf{j}$

94. $\tan\theta = \frac{-5}{2}$ with θ in quadrant IV $\Leftrightarrow$ $\theta = \tan^{-1}(-2.5) \approx -68.2°$.

96. (a) The initial velocity of the plane is $\mathbf{v} = 600\cos 30°\mathbf{i} + 600\sin 30°\mathbf{j} = \langle 300\sqrt{3}, 300\rangle$. The tail wind has a velocity $\mathbf{w} = 50\cos 60°\mathbf{i} + 50\sin 60°\mathbf{j} = \langle 25, 25\sqrt{3}\rangle$. Thus, the resultant velocity is $\mathbf{r} = \langle 300\sqrt{3} + 25, 300 + 25\sqrt{3}\rangle$.

   (b) The true speed of the plane is $|\mathbf{r}| = \sqrt{(300\sqrt{3} + 25)^2 + (300 + 25\sqrt{3})^2} \approx 643.8$ mi/h. since
   $$\tan\theta = \frac{300 + 25\sqrt{3}}{300\sqrt{3} + 25} \approx 0.63036, \theta \approx \tan^{-1}(0.63036) \approx 32.2°,$$ and the true direction is N $57.8°$ E.

98. $\mathbf{u} = \langle 5, 12\rangle$ and $\mathbf{v} = \langle 10, -4\rangle$. Then $|\mathbf{u}| = \sqrt{(5)^2 + (12)^2} = \sqrt{169} = 13$;
    $\mathbf{u} \cdot \mathbf{u} = \langle 5, 12\rangle \cdot \langle 5, 12\rangle = (5)(5) + (12)(12) = 25 + 144 = 169$;
    $\mathbf{u} \cdot \mathbf{v} = \langle 5, 12\rangle \cdot \langle 10, -4\rangle = (5)(10) + (12)(-4) = 50 - 48 = 2$.

100. $\mathbf{u} = 10\mathbf{j}$ and $\mathbf{v} = 5\mathbf{i} - 3\mathbf{j}$. Then $|\mathbf{u}| = \sqrt{(0)^2 + (10)^2} = \sqrt{100} = 10$;
     $\mathbf{u} \cdot \mathbf{u} = 10\mathbf{j} \cdot 10\mathbf{j} = (0)(0) + (10)(10) = 100$;
     $\mathbf{u} \cdot \mathbf{v} = 10\mathbf{j} \cdot 5\mathbf{i} - 3\mathbf{j} = (0)(5) + (10)(-3) = -30$.

102. $\mathbf{u} = \langle 5, 3\rangle$ and $\mathbf{v} = \langle -2, 6\rangle$. Then $\cos\theta = \frac{\mathbf{u} \cdot \mathbf{v}}{|\mathbf{u}|\,|\mathbf{v}|} = \frac{-10+18}{\sqrt{34}\cdot\sqrt{40}} = \frac{5}{2\sqrt{340}} = \frac{5}{4\sqrt{85}}$. Thus, $\theta = \cos^{-1}\frac{5}{4\sqrt{85}} \approx 82.2°$.

104. $\mathbf{u} = \mathbf{i} - \mathbf{j}$ and $\mathbf{v} = \mathbf{i} + \mathbf{j}$. Then $\cos\theta = \frac{\mathbf{u} \cdot \mathbf{v}}{|\mathbf{u}|\,|\mathbf{v}|} = \frac{1-1}{\sqrt{2}\cdot\sqrt{2}} = 0$, so the vectors are orthogonal. Thus, $\theta = \cos^{-1} 0 = 90°$.

106. $\mathbf{u} = \langle -8, 6\rangle$ and $\mathbf{v} = \langle 20, 20\rangle$. Then the component of $\mathbf{u}$ along $\mathbf{v}$ is
     $\frac{\mathbf{u} \cdot \mathbf{v}}{|\mathbf{v}|} = \frac{\langle -8,6\rangle\cdot\langle 20,20\rangle}{\sqrt{\langle 20,20\rangle\cdot\langle 20,20\rangle}} = \frac{-160+120}{\sqrt{400+400}} = \frac{-40}{\sqrt{800}} = \frac{-40}{20\sqrt{2}} = \frac{-2}{\sqrt{2}}$.

108. $W = \mathbf{F} \cdot \mathbf{D} = 3800$ ft-lb. But $\mathbf{F} \cdot \mathbf{D} = |\mathbf{F}|\,|\mathbf{D}|\cos\theta \Leftrightarrow \cos\theta = \frac{\mathbf{F} \cdot \mathbf{D}}{|\mathbf{F}|\,|\mathbf{D}|} = \frac{3800}{(250)(20)} = 0.76$.
     Therefore, $\theta = \cos^{-1}(0.76) \approx 40.5°$.

Focus on Problem Solving

2. The solutions to the equation are the points of intersection of the graphs of the functions $y = \cos x$ and $y = \dfrac{x^2}{400}$. We first find the number of positive solutions. The graph of $y = \dfrac{x^2}{400}$ is a parabola. One the interval $[2k\pi, 2(k+1)\pi]$ the graphs intersect at two points, one in the subinterval $[2k\pi, 2k\pi + \frac{\pi}{2}]$ and one in the subinterval $[2k\pi + \frac{3\pi}{2}, 2(k+1)\pi]$. This pattern continues as long as $\dfrac{x^2}{400} \leq 1 \iff x^2 \leq 400$. So we need to know how many of the intervals described lie between 0 and 20. Since $\frac{20}{2\pi} \approx 3.18$, there are three intervals with two intersections each. Now as x approaches 20, $\frac{x^2}{400}$ approaches 1 and the intersection occurs closer to $2k\pi$ in the interval $[2k\pi, 2k\pi + \frac{\pi}{2}]$. Thus there are $2 \cdot 3 + 1 = 7$ positive points of intersection. When $x < 0$, we again have two points of intersection, one in $[2k\pi, 2k\pi + \frac{\pi}{2}]$ and one in $[2k\pi + \frac{3\pi}{2}, 2(k+1)\pi]$. Again there are three intervals with two intersections each. Now as x approaches -20, $\frac{x^2}{400}$ approaches 1 and the intersection occurs closer to $2(k+1)\pi$ in the interval $[2k\pi + \frac{3\pi}{2}, 2(k+1)\pi]$. Therefore, the total number of solutions of the given equation is $7 + 7 = 14$.

4. In the figure shown, P and Q are the centers of the circles. Since the circles are tangent to the cone, $\angle OAP$ and $\angle OBQ$ are right angles. Thus $\triangle OAP$ is similar to $\triangle OBQ$. We have $PQ = a + b$ and $\dfrac{OP}{a} = \csc\dfrac{\theta}{2} \iff OP = a\csc\dfrac{\theta}{2}$.

Using the similar triangles $\triangle OAP$ and $\triangle OBQ$ we get
$$\dfrac{AP}{OP} = \dfrac{BQ}{OQ} \iff \dfrac{a}{a\csc(\theta/2)} = \dfrac{b}{a + b + a\csc(\theta/2)} \iff$$
$$a + b + a\csc\dfrac{\theta}{2} = b\csc\dfrac{\theta}{2} \iff b\csc\dfrac{\theta}{2} - b = a + a\csc\dfrac{\theta}{2} \iff b\left(\csc\dfrac{\theta}{2} - 1\right) = a\left(1 + \csc\dfrac{\theta}{2}\right)$$
$$\iff b = a \cdot \dfrac{\csc(\theta/2) + 1}{\csc(\theta/2) - 1} = a \cdot \dfrac{1 + \sin(\theta/2)}{1 - \sin(\theta/2)} \text{ where in the last step the numerator and denominator}$$
are multiplied by $\sin(\theta/2)$.

6. Clearly $C = \frac{\pi}{4}$. Now $\tan(A + B) = \dfrac{\tan A + \tan B}{1 - \tan A \tan B} = \dfrac{\frac{1}{3} + \frac{1}{2}}{1 - \frac{1}{3} \cdot \frac{1}{2}} = 1$. Thus $A + B = \frac{\pi}{4}$.

Therefore $A + B + C = \frac{\pi}{4} + \frac{\pi}{4} = \frac{\pi}{2}$.

8. Since $\tan^{-1}$ is one-to-one, we will show that the tangents of each side of this equation are equal. Let $A = \tan^{-1}\frac{1}{2}$, $B = \tan^{-1}\frac{1}{5}$, and $C = \tan^{-1}\frac{1}{8}$ so that $\tan A = \frac{1}{2}$, $\tan B = \frac{1}{5}$, and $\tan C = \frac{1}{8}$. Then

$$\tan(A + B) = \dfrac{\tan A + \tan B}{1 - \tan A \tan B} = \dfrac{\frac{1}{2} + \frac{1}{5}}{1 - \frac{1}{2} \cdot \frac{1}{5}} = \dfrac{\frac{7}{10}}{\frac{9}{10}} = \frac{7}{9}. \text{ So}$$

$$\tan(A + B + C) = \dfrac{\tan(A + B) + \tan C}{1 - \tan(A + B)\tan C} = \dfrac{\frac{7}{9} + \frac{1}{8}}{1 - \frac{7}{9} \cdot \frac{1}{8}} = \dfrac{\frac{56+9}{72}}{\frac{65}{72}} = 1. \text{ Since } \tan\frac{\pi}{4} = 1, \text{ this proves}$$

that $A + B + C = \frac{\pi}{4}$ which proves the assertion.

10. $|\tan x| \le 1 \quad \Leftrightarrow \quad -1 \le \tan x \le 1$. Now, $y = \tan x$ is an one–one, increasing function on $\left(-\frac{\pi}{2}, \frac{\pi}{2}\right)$. Also, $\tan-\frac{\pi}{4} = -1$ and $\tan \frac{\pi}{4} = 1$, so the solution on $\left(-\frac{\pi}{2}, \frac{\pi}{2}\right)$ is $-\frac{\pi}{4} \le x \le \frac{\pi}{4}$. However, $\tan x$ is periodic with period π, so any interval of the form $-\frac{\pi}{4} + n\pi \le x \le \frac{\pi}{4} + n\pi$, $n = 0, \pm1, \pm2, \ldots$ is also a solution.

12. If $\log_2 5$ is rational, then $\log_2 5 = \dfrac{m}{n}$, where m and n are positive integers. Then, $2^{m/n} = 5 \quad \Leftrightarrow \quad 2^m = 5^n$. But this is impossible since 2^m is even and 5^n is odd. Therefore $\log_2 5$ is irrational.

14. Using the Change of Base formula, we have $\dfrac{1}{\log_2 x} + \dfrac{1}{\log_3 x} + \dfrac{1}{\log_5 x} = \log_x 2 + \log_x 3 + \log_x 5 = \log_x(2 \cdot 3 \cdot 5) = \log_x 30 = \dfrac{1}{\log_{30} x}$.

Chapter Ten

Exercises 10.1

2. $\begin{cases} 2x + y = 7 \\ 3x - y = 13 \end{cases}$ Solving the first equation for y, we get $y = 7 - 2x$ and substituting this into the second equation, gives $2x + (7 - 2x) = 13 \quad \Leftrightarrow \quad 5x = 20 \quad \Leftrightarrow \quad x = 4$. Substituting for x we get $y = 7 - 2x = 7 - 2(4) = -1$. Thus the solution is $(4, -1)$.

4. $\begin{cases} x^2 + y^2 = 25 \\ y = \frac{3}{4}x \end{cases}$ Substituting for y in the first equation gives $x^2 + \left(\frac{3}{4}x\right)^2 = 25 \quad \Leftrightarrow \quad \frac{25}{16}x^2 = 25$
$\Leftrightarrow \quad x^2 = 16 \quad \Rightarrow \quad x = \pm 4$. When $x = 4$ then $y = \frac{3}{4}(4) = 3$, and when $x = -4$ then $y = \frac{3}{4}(-4) = -3$. Thus the solutions are $(4, 3)$ and $(-4, -3)$.

6. $\begin{cases} x^2 + y = 9 \\ x - y + 3 = 0 \end{cases}$ Solving the first equation for y, we get $y = 9 - x^2$. Substituting this into the second equation gives $x - (9 - x^2) + 3 = 0 \quad \Leftrightarrow \quad x^2 + x - 6 = 0 \quad \Leftrightarrow \quad (x + 3)(x - 2) = 0$
$\Leftrightarrow \quad x = -3$ or $x = 2$. If $x = -3$, then $y = 9 - (-3)^2 = 0$, and if $x = 2$, then $y = 9 - (2)^2 = 5$. Thus the solutions are $(-3, 0)$ and $(2, 5)$.

8. $\begin{cases} 4x - 3y = 10 \\ 9x + 4y = 1 \end{cases}$ Multiplying the first equation by 4 and the second by 3 gives the system
$\begin{cases} 16x - 12y = 40 \\ 27x + 12y = 3 \end{cases}$. Adding, we get $43x = 43 \quad \Leftrightarrow \quad x = 1$. Substituting this value into the second equation gives $9(1) + 4y = 1 \quad \Leftrightarrow \quad 4y = -8 \quad \Leftrightarrow \quad y = -2$. Thus the solution is $(1, -2)$.

10. $\begin{cases} 3x^2 + 4y = 17 \\ 2x^2 + 5y = 2 \end{cases}$ Multiplying the first equation by 2 and the second by 3 gives the system
$\begin{cases} 6x^2 + 8y = 34 \\ -6x^2 - 15y = -6 \end{cases}$. Adding we get $-7y = 28 \quad \Rightarrow \quad y = -4$. Substituting this value into the second equation gives $2x^2 + 5(-4) = 2 \quad \Rightarrow \quad 2x^2 = 22 \quad \Leftrightarrow \quad x^2 = 11 \quad \Leftrightarrow \quad x = \pm\sqrt{11}$. Thus the solutions are $(\sqrt{11}, -4)$ and $(-\sqrt{11}, -4)$.

12. $\begin{cases} 2x^2 + 4y = 13 \\ x^2 - y^2 = \frac{7}{2} \end{cases}$ Multiplying the second by 2 gives the system $\begin{cases} 2x^2 + 4y = 13 \\ 2x^2 - 2y^2 = 7 \end{cases}$. Subtracting the equations gives $4y + 2y^2 = 6 \quad \Leftrightarrow \quad y^2 + 2y - 3 = 0 \quad \Leftrightarrow \quad (y + 3)(y - 1) = 0 \quad \Leftrightarrow$
$y = -3, y = 1$. If $y = -3$, then $2x^2 + 4(-3) = 13 \quad \Leftrightarrow \quad x^2 = \frac{25}{2} \quad \Leftrightarrow \quad x = \pm\frac{5\sqrt{2}}{2}$. If $y = 1$, then $2x^2 + 4(1) = 13 \quad \Leftrightarrow \quad x^2 = \frac{9}{2} \quad \Leftrightarrow \quad x = \pm\frac{3\sqrt{2}}{2}$. Hence, the solutions are $\left(\pm\frac{5\sqrt{2}}{2}, -3\right)$ and $\left(\pm\frac{3\sqrt{2}}{2}, 1\right)$.

14. $\begin{cases} x - y^2 = 0 \\ y - x^2 = 0 \end{cases}$ Solving the first equation for x and the second equation for y gives $\begin{cases} x = y^2 \\ y = x^2 \end{cases}$.
Substituting for y in the first equation gives $x = x^4 \quad \Leftrightarrow \quad x(x^3 - 1) = 0 \quad \Leftrightarrow \quad x = 0, x = 1$. Thus, the solutions are $(0, 0)$ and $(1, 1)$.

16. $\begin{cases} y = 4 - x^2 \\ y = x^2 - 4 \end{cases}$ Setting the two equations equal, we get $4 - x^2 = x^2 - 4 \Leftrightarrow 2x^2 = 8 \Leftrightarrow$
$x = \pm 2$. Therefore, the solutions are $(2, 0)$ and $(-2, 0)$.

18. $\begin{cases} xy = 24 \\ 2x^2 - y^2 + 4 = 0 \end{cases}$ Since $x = 0$ is not a solution, from the first equation we get $y = \dfrac{24}{x}$.
Substituting into the second equation, we get $2x^2 + 4 = \left(\frac{24}{x}\right)^2 \Rightarrow 2x^4 + 4x^2 = 576 \Leftrightarrow$
$x^4 + 2x^2 - 288 = 0 \Leftrightarrow (x^2 + 18)(x^2 - 16) = 0$. Since $x^2 + 18$ cannot be 0 if x is real, we
have $x^2 - 16 = 0 \Leftrightarrow x = \pm 4$. So $y = \frac{24}{\pm 4} = \pm 6$. Thus the solutions are $(4, 6)$ and $(-4, -6)$.

20. $\begin{cases} x + \sqrt{y} = 0 \\ y^2 - 4x^2 = 12 \end{cases}$ Solving the first equation for x, we get $x = -\sqrt{y}$. Substituting for x gives
$y^2 - 4(-\sqrt{y})^2 = 12 \Leftrightarrow y^2 - 4y - 12 = 0 \Leftrightarrow (y - 6)(y + 2) = 0 \Rightarrow y = 6, y = -2$.
Since $x = -\sqrt{-2}$ is not a real solution, the only solution is $(-\sqrt{6}, 6)$.

22. $\begin{cases} x^2 + 2y^2 = 2 \\ 2x^2 - 3y = 15 \end{cases}$ Multiplying the first equation by 2 gives the system $\begin{cases} 2x^2 + 4y^2 = 4 \\ 2x^2 - 3y = 15 \end{cases}$.
Subtracting the two equations gives $4y^2 + 3y = -11 \Leftrightarrow 4y^2 + 3y + 11 = 0 \Rightarrow$
$y = \frac{-3 \pm \sqrt{9 - 4(4)(11)}}{2(4)}$ which is not a real number. Therefore, there are no real solutions.

24. $\begin{cases} x^4 - y^3 = 15 \\ 3x^4 + 5y^3 = 53 \end{cases}$ Multiplying the first equation by 3 gives the system $\begin{cases} 3x^4 - 3y^3 = 45 \\ 3x^4 + 5y^3 = 53 \end{cases}$.
Subtracting the equations gives $8y^3 = 8 \Leftrightarrow y^3 = 1 \Rightarrow y = 1$, and then $x^4 - 1 = 15 \Leftrightarrow$
$x = \pm 2$. Therefore, the solutions are $(2, 1)$ and $(-2, 1)$.

26. $\begin{cases} \dfrac{4}{x^2} + \dfrac{6}{y^4} = \dfrac{7}{2} \\ \dfrac{1}{x^2} - \dfrac{2}{y^4} = 0 \end{cases}$ If we let $u = \dfrac{1}{x^2}$ and $v = \dfrac{1}{y^4}$, the system is equivalent to $\begin{cases} 4u + 6v = \frac{7}{2} \\ u - 2v = 0 \end{cases}$, and

multiplying the second equation by 3, gives $\begin{cases} 4u + 6v = \frac{7}{2} \\ 3u - 6v = 0 \end{cases}$. Adding the equations gives $7u = \frac{7}{2}$
$\Leftrightarrow u = \frac{1}{2}$, and $v = \frac{1}{4}$. Therefore, $x^2 = 2 \Leftrightarrow x = \pm\sqrt{2}$, and $y^4 = 4 \Leftrightarrow y = \pm\sqrt{2}$.
Thus, the solutions are $(\sqrt{2}, \sqrt{2})$, $(\sqrt{2}, -\sqrt{2})$, $(-\sqrt{2}, \sqrt{2})$, and $(-\sqrt{2}, -\sqrt{2})$.

28. $\begin{cases} y = x^2 \\ y = x + 3 \end{cases}$
The solutions are approximately $(2.30, 5.30)$
and $(-1.30, 1.70)$.

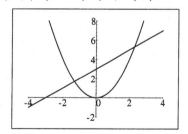

30. $\begin{cases} y = x^2 - 4x \\ 2x - y = 2 \end{cases}$ ⇔

$\begin{cases} y = x^2 - 4x \\ y = 2x - 2 \end{cases}$

The solutions are approximately $(0.35, -1.30)$
and $(5.65, 9.30)$.

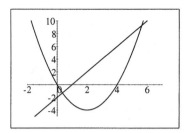

32. $\begin{cases} x^2 + y^2 = 17 \\ x^2 - 2x + y^2 = 13 \end{cases}$ ⇔

$\begin{cases} y = \pm\sqrt{17 - x^2} \\ y = \pm\sqrt{13 + 2x - x^2} \end{cases}$

The solutions are approximately $(2, \pm 3.61)$.

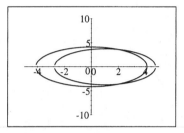

34. $\begin{cases} x^2 - y^2 = 3 \\ y = x^2 - 2x - 8 \end{cases}$ ⇔

$\begin{cases} y = \pm\sqrt{x^2 - 3} \\ y = x^2 - 2x - 8 \end{cases}$

The solutions are approximately
$(-2.22, 1.40)$, $(-1.88, -0.72)$, $(3.45, -2.99)$,
and $(4.65, 4.31)$.

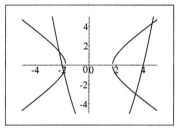

36. $\begin{cases} y = e^x + e^{-x} \\ y = 5 - x^2 \end{cases}$

The solutions are approximately $(1.19, 3.59)$
and $(-1.19, 3.59)$.

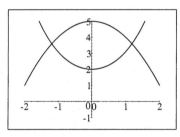

38. Let b be the length of the base of the triangle, in feet, and h be the height of the triangle, in feet.
Then, $\begin{cases} \frac{1}{2}bh = 84 \\ b^2 + h^2 = 25^2 = 625 \end{cases}$. The first equation gives $b = \dfrac{168}{h}$. By substitution,

$\left(\dfrac{168}{h}\right)^2 + h^2 = 625$ ⇔ $h^4 - 625h^2 + 168^2 = 0$ ⇔ $(h^2 - 49)(h^2 - 576) = 0$ ⇒

$h = 7$ or $h = 24$. Thus, the lengths of the other two sides are 7 ft and 24 ft.

40. Let w be the width and l be the length of the rectangle, in inches. From the figure, the diagonals of
the rectangle are simply diameters of the circle. Then, $\begin{cases} wl = 160 \\ w^2 + l^2 = 20^2 = 400 \end{cases}$ ⇔ $w = \dfrac{160}{l}$.

By substitution, $\dfrac{160^2}{l^2} + l^2 = 400$ ⇔ $l^4 - 400l^2 + 160^2 = 0$ ⇔ $(l^2 - 80)(l^2 - 320) = 0$

⇒ $l = \sqrt{80} = 4\sqrt{5}$ or $l = \sqrt{320} = 8\sqrt{5}$. Therefore, the dimensions of the rectangle are $4\sqrt{5}$
in. by $8\sqrt{5}$ in..

42. Let x be the circumference and y be length of the stove pipe. Using the circumference we can determine the radius, $2\pi r = x \Leftrightarrow r = \dfrac{x}{2\pi}$. Thus the volume is $\pi\left(\dfrac{x}{2\pi}\right)^2 y = \dfrac{1}{4\pi}x^2 y$. So the system is given by $\begin{cases} xy = 1200 \\ \frac{1}{4\pi}x^2 y = 600 \end{cases}$. Substituting for xy in the second equation gives

$\frac{1}{4\pi}x^2 y = \frac{1}{4\pi}x(xy) = \frac{1}{4\pi}x(1200) = 600 \Leftrightarrow x = 2\pi$. So $y = \dfrac{1200}{x} = \dfrac{1200}{2\pi} = \dfrac{600}{\pi}$. Thus the dimensions of the sheet metal are 2π by $\frac{600}{\pi}$.

44. $\begin{cases} x - y = 3 \\ x^3 - y^3 = 387 \end{cases}$. Solving the first equation for x gives $x = 3 + y$ and using the hint,

$x^3 - y^3 = 387 \Leftrightarrow (x - y)(x^2 + xy + y^2) = 387$. Next, substituting for x, we get
$3[(3 + y)^2 + y(3 + y) + y^2] = 387 \Leftrightarrow 9 + 6y + y^2 + 3y + y^2 + y^2 = 129 \Leftrightarrow$
$3y^2 + 9y + 9 = 129 \Leftrightarrow (y + 8)(y - 5) = 0 \Rightarrow y = -8$ or $y = 5$. If $y = -8$, then
$x = 3 + (-8) = -5$, and if $y = 5$, then $x = 3 + 5 = 8$. Thus the solutions are $(-5, -8)$ and $(8, 5)$.

46. $\begin{cases} 2^x + 2^y = 10 \\ 4^x + 4^y = 68 \end{cases} \Leftrightarrow \begin{cases} 2^x + 2^y = 10 \\ 2^{2x} + 2^{2y} = 68 \end{cases}$

If we let $u = 2^x$ and $v = 2^y$, the system becomes $\begin{cases} u + v = 10 \\ u^2 + v^2 = 68 \end{cases}$.

Solving the first equation for u, and substituting this into the second equation gives $u + v = 10$
$\Leftrightarrow u = 10 - v$, so $(10 - v)^2 + v^2 = 68 \Leftrightarrow 100 - 20v + v^2 + v^2 = 68 \Leftrightarrow$
$v^2 - 10v + 16 = 0 \Leftrightarrow (v - 8)(v - 2) = 0 \Rightarrow v = 2$ or $v = 8$. If $v = 2$, then $u = 8$, and
so $y = 1$ and $x = 3$. If $v = 8$, then $u = 2$, and so $y = 3$ and $x = 1$. Thus, the solutions are $(1, 3)$
and $(3, 1)$.

48. The graphs of $y = x^2$ and $y = x + k$ for various values of k are shown. If we solve the system $\begin{cases} y = x^2 \\ y = x + k \end{cases}$, we get
$x^2 - x - k = 0$. Using the quadratic formula, we have
$x = \dfrac{-1 \pm \sqrt{1 + 4k}}{2}$. So there will be no solutions when $\sqrt{1 + 4k}$ is
undefined, that is, when $1 + 4k < 0 \Leftrightarrow k < -\frac{1}{4}$. There
will be exactly one solution when $1 + 4k = 0 \Leftrightarrow k < -\frac{1}{4}$,
and there will be two solutions when $1 + 4k > 0 \Leftrightarrow$
$k > -\frac{1}{4}$.

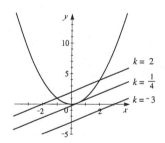

Exercises 10.2

2. $\begin{cases} 3x + 2y = 3 \\ -x + 5y = 16 \end{cases}$

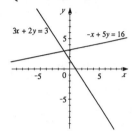

The solution is $x = -1$, $y = 3$.

4. $\begin{cases} 3x + 5y = 15 \\ x + \frac{5}{3}y = 5 \end{cases}$

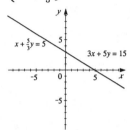

The solution is $(x, -\frac{3}{5}x + 3)$, for any real number x.

6. $\begin{cases} -4x + 14y = 28 \\ 10x - 35y = 70 \end{cases}$

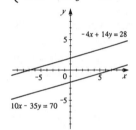

No solution. The lines are parallel, so there is no intersection.

8. $9x - y = -6$ $\Leftrightarrow$ $y = 9x + 6$. Substituting for y into $4x - 3y = 28$ gives $4x - 3(9x + 6) = 28$ $\Leftrightarrow$ $-23x = 46$ $\Leftrightarrow$ $x = -2$, and so $y = 9(-2) + 6 = -12$. Thus, the solution is $(-2, -12)$.

10. $-4x + 12y = 0$ $\Leftrightarrow$ $x = 3y$. Substituting for x into $12x + 4y = 160$ gives $12(3y) + 4y = 160$ $\Leftrightarrow$ $40y = 160$ $\Leftrightarrow$ $y = 4$, and so $x = 3(4) = 12$. Therefore, the solution is $(12, 4)$.

12. $0.2x - 0.2y = -1.8$ $\Leftrightarrow$ $x = y - 9$. Substituting for x into $-0.3x + 0.5y = 3.3$ gives $-0.3(y - 9) + 0.5y = 3.3$ $\Leftrightarrow$ $0.2y = 0.6$ $\Leftrightarrow$ $y = 3$, and so $x = (3) - 9 = -6$. Hence, the solution is $(-6, 3)$.

14. $\begin{cases} 4x + 2y = 16 \\ x - 5y = 70 \end{cases}$ Adding the first equation to -4 times the second equation gives

$\begin{array}{r} 4x + 2y = 16 \\ -4x + 20y = -280 \\ \hline 22y = -264 \end{array}$ $\Leftrightarrow$ $y = -12$.

So $4x + 2(-12) = 16$ $\Leftrightarrow$ $x = 10$, and the solution is $(10, -12)$.

16. $\begin{cases} -3x + 5y = 2 \\ 9x - 15y = 6 \end{cases}$ Adding 3 times the first equation to the second equation gives

$\begin{array}{r} -9x + 15y = 6 \\ 9x - 15y = 6 \\ \hline 0 = 12 \end{array}$, which is false. Therefore, there is no solution to this system.

18. $\begin{cases} 2x - 3y = -8 \\ 14x - 21y = 3 \end{cases}$ Adding 7 times the first equation to -1 times the second equation gives

$14x - 21y = -56$
$-14x + 21y = -3$
$\overline{\ 0 = -59}$, which is false. Therefore, there is no solution to this system.

20. $\begin{cases} 25x - 75y = 100 \\ -10x + 30y = -40 \end{cases}$ Adding $\frac{1}{23}$ times the first equation to $\frac{1}{10}$ times the second equation gives

$x - 3y = 4$
$-x + 3y = -4$
$\overline{\ 0 = 0}$, which is always true.

We now put the equation in slope-intercept form. We have $x - 3y = 4$ $\Leftrightarrow$ $-3y = -x + 4$ $\Leftrightarrow$ $y = \frac{1}{3}x - \frac{4}{3}$, so a solution is any pair of the form $\left(x, \frac{1}{3}x - \frac{4}{3}\right)$, where x is any real number.

22. $\begin{cases} u - 30v = -5 \\ -3u + 80v = 5 \end{cases}$ Adding 3 times the first equation to the second equation gives

$3u - 90v = -15$
$-3u + 80v = 5$
$\overline{-10v = -10}$ $\Leftrightarrow$ $v = 1$.

So $u - 30(1) = -5$ $\Leftrightarrow$ $u = 25$. Thus, the solution is $(u, v) = (25, 1)$.

24. $\begin{cases} \frac{3}{2}x - \frac{1}{3}y = \frac{1}{2} \\ 2\,x - \frac{1}{2}y = -\frac{1}{2} \end{cases}$ Adding -6 times the first equation to 4 times the second equation gives

$-9x + 2y = -3$
$8x - 2y = -2$
$\overline{-x\ = -5}$ $\Leftrightarrow$ $x = 5$. So $9(5) - 2y = 3$ $\Leftrightarrow$ $y = 21$. Thus the solution is $(5, 21)$.

26. $\begin{cases} x - 3y = 4x - 6y - 10 \\ 2x = 12y + 10 \end{cases}$ Simplifying the first equation rearranging the second equation gives the

system $\begin{cases} -3x + 3y = -10 \\ 2x - 12y = 10 \end{cases}$. Adding 2 times the first equation to 3 times the second equation gives

$-6x + 6y = -20$
$6x - 36y = 30$
$\overline{-30y = 10}$ $\Leftrightarrow$ $y = -\frac{1}{3}$.

So $2x - 12\left(-\frac{1}{3}\right) = 10$ $\Leftrightarrow$ $2x + 4 = 10$ $\Leftrightarrow$ $x = 3$. Thus the solution is $\left(3, -\frac{1}{3}\right)$.

28. $\begin{cases} x = 2x + y \\ x = 2y + 1 \end{cases}$ Rearranging the second equation gives the system $\begin{cases} x + y = 0 \\ x - 2y = 1 \end{cases}$. Adding the first

equation to -1 times the second equation gives $\quad x + y = 0$
$\ -x + 2y = -1$
$\overline{3y = -1}$ $\Leftrightarrow$ $y = -\frac{1}{3}$.

So $x + \left(-\frac{1}{3}\right) = 0$ $\Leftrightarrow$ $x = \frac{1}{3}$. Thus, the solution is $\left(\frac{1}{3}, -\frac{1}{3}\right)$.

30. $ax + by = 0 \quad\quad \times -1 \quad\quad\quad -ax - by = 0$
$x + y = 1 \quad\quad \times a \quad \Rightarrow \quad ax + ay = a$
$\overline{(a - b)y = a} \quad\quad \Leftrightarrow \quad y = \frac{a}{a-b}, a \neq b.$

So $x + \left(\frac{a}{a-b}\right) = 1 \quad \Leftrightarrow \quad x = \frac{b}{b-a}$. Hence, the solution is $\left(\frac{b}{b-a}, \frac{a}{a-b}\right)$.

32. $\begin{array}{lll} ax + by = 0 & \times -a & -a^2x - aby = 0 \\ a^2x + b^2y = 1 & \times 1 \Rightarrow & \underline{\quad a^2x + b^2y = 1 \quad} \\ & & b(b-a)y = 1 \quad \Leftrightarrow \quad y = \frac{1}{b(b-a)}. \end{array}$

So $ax + \frac{b}{b(b-a)} = 0 \quad \Leftrightarrow \quad x = -\frac{1}{a(b-a)}$. Hence, the solution is

$$\left(-\frac{1}{a(b-a)}, \frac{1}{b(b-a)}\right) = \left(\frac{1}{a^2 - ab}, \frac{1}{b^2 - ab}\right).$$

34. Let x be the larger number and y be the other number. This gives

$\begin{array}{lll} x + y = 2(x-y) & & -x + 3y = 0 \\ x = 6 + 2y & \Rightarrow & \underline{\quad x - 2y = 6 \quad} \\ & & y = 6. \end{array}$

So $x = 6 + 2(6) = 18$. Therefore, the two numbers are 18 and 6.

36. Let c be the number of children and a be the number of adults. This gives

$\begin{array}{lll} c + a = 2200 & \times -3 & -3c - 3a = -6600 \\ 1.50c + 4.00a = 5050 & \times 2 \Rightarrow & \underline{\quad 3c + 8a = 10100 \quad} \\ & & 5a = 3500 \quad \Leftrightarrow \quad a = 700. \end{array}$

So $c + 700 = 2200 \quad \Leftrightarrow \quad c = 1500$. Therefore, the number of children admitted was 1500 and the number of adults was 700.

38. Let x be speed of the boat in still water and y be speed of the river flow.

$\begin{array}{llll} \text{Down river:} & x + y = 20 & \times 5 & 5x + 5y = 100 \\ \text{Up river:} & 2.5x - 2.5y = 20 & \times 2 \Rightarrow & \underline{\quad 5x - 5y = 40 \quad} \\ & & & 10x \quad\quad = 140 \quad \Leftrightarrow \quad x = 14 \end{array}$

So $14 + y = 20 \quad \Leftrightarrow \quad y = 6$. Therefore, the boat's speed is 14 mph and the current in the river flows at 6 mph.

40. Let x and y be the number of milliliters of the two brine solutions.

$\begin{array}{llll} \text{Quantity:} & x + y = 1000 & \times -1 & -x - y = -1000 \\ \text{Concentrations:} & 0.05x + 0.20y = 0.14 & \times 20 \Rightarrow & \underline{\quad x + 4y = 2800 \quad} \\ & & & 3y = 1800 \quad \Leftrightarrow \quad y = 600 \end{array}$

So $x + 600 = 1000 \quad \Leftrightarrow \quad x = 400$. Therefore, 400 milliliters of the 5% solution and 600 milliliters of the 20% solution should be mixed.

42. Let x be the number of pounds of Kenyan coffee and y be the number of pounds of Sri Lankan coffee. This gives

$\begin{array}{llll} 3.50x + 5.60y = 11.55 & \times -10 & 35x + 56y = 115.5 \\ x + y = 3 & \times -35 \Rightarrow & \underline{\quad -35x - 35y = 105 \quad} \\ & & 21y = 10.5 \quad \Leftrightarrow \quad y = 0.5 \end{array}$

So $x + (2.5) = 3 \quad \Leftrightarrow \quad x = 2.5$. Thus, 2.5 pounds of Kenyan coffee and 0.5 pounds of Sri Lankan coffee should be mixed.

44. Let x be the amount she invests at 5% and let y be the amount she invests at 8%.

Total invested: $x + y = 20,000$ $\times -5$ $-5x - 5y = -100,000$
Interest earned: $0.05x + 0.08y = 1180$ $\times 100$ $\Rightarrow$ $\underline{5x + 8y = 118,000}$
                                                                      $3y = 18,000$ $\Leftrightarrow$ $y = 6,000$

So $x + 6,000 = 20,000$ $\Leftrightarrow$ $x = 14,000$. She invests \$14,000 at 5% and \$6,000 at 8%.

46. Let x be the length of time John drives and y be the length of time Mary drives. Then $y = x + 0.25$, so $-x + y = 0.25$, and multiplying by 40, we get $-40x + 40y = 10$. Comparing the distances, we get $60x = 40y + 35$, or $60x - 40y = 35$. This gives the system $\begin{cases} -40x + 40y = 10 \\ 60x - 40y = 35 \end{cases}$. Subtracting, we get $-40x + 40y = 10$

$\underline{60x - 40y = 35}$
$20x = 45$ $\Leftrightarrow$ $x = 2.25$.

So $y = 2.25 + 0.25 = 2.5$. Thus, John travels for $2\frac{1}{4}$ hours and Mary travels for $2\frac{1}{2}$ hours.

48. First, let us find the intersection point of the two lines. The y-coordinate of the intersection point is the height of the triangle. We have

$y = 2x - 4$ $2y = 4x - 8$
$y = -4x + 20$ Adding 2 times the first equation to the second equation gives $\underline{y = -4x + 20}$
$3y = 12$

So the triangle has height 4. Furthermore, $y = 2x - 4$ intersects the x-axis at $x = 2$, and $y = -4x + 20$ intersects the x-axis at $x = 5$. Thus the base has length $5 - 2 = 3$. Therefore, the area of the triangle is $A = \frac{1}{2} \cdot base \cdot height = \frac{1}{2} \cdot 3 \cdot 4 = 6$ square units.

50. $\begin{cases} 18.72x - 14.91y = 12.33 & l_1 \\ 6.21x - 12.92y = 17.82 & l_2 \end{cases}$

The solution is approximately $(-0.71, -1.72)$.

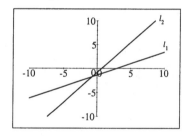

52. $\begin{cases} -435x + 912y = 0 & l_1 \\ 132x + 455\,y = 994 & l_2 \end{cases}$

The solution is approximately $(2.85, 1.36)$.

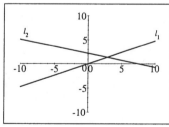

Exercises 10.3

2. The equation $x_1^2 + x_2^2 + x_3^2 = 36$ is not linear, since it contains squares of variables.

4. The system $\begin{cases} x - 3xy + 5y = 0 \\ 12x + 321y = 123 \end{cases}$ is not a linear system, since the first equation contains a product of variables.

6. (a) Yes, the matrix is in echelon form.
    (b) No, this matrix not in reduced echelon form. There must be a 0 above the leading 1 in the second row.
    (c) $x + 3y = -3$

    $y = 5$

8. (a) Yes, the matrix is in echelon form.
    (b) Yes, the matrix is in reduced echelon form.
    (c) $x - 7z = 0$

    $y + 3z = 0$

    $0 = 1$

10. (a) Yes, the matrix is in echelon form.
    (b) Yes, the matrix is in reduced echelon form.
    (c) $x = 1$

    $y = 2$

    $z = 3$

12. $\begin{bmatrix} 1 & 1 & 6 & 3 \\ 1 & 1 & 3 & 3 \\ 1 & 2 & 4 & 7 \end{bmatrix} \xrightarrow{R_2-R_1 \to R_2} \begin{bmatrix} 1 & 1 & 6 & 3 \\ 0 & 0 & -3 & 0 \\ 1 & 2 & 4 & 7 \end{bmatrix} \xrightarrow[R_3-R_1 \to R_3]{-\frac{1}{3}R_2} \begin{bmatrix} 1 & 1 & 6 & 3 \\ 0 & 0 & 1 & 0 \\ 0 & 1 & -2 & 4 \end{bmatrix}$

$\xrightarrow{R_3 \leftrightarrow R_2} \begin{bmatrix} 1 & 1 & 6 & 3 \\ 0 & 1 & -2 & 4 \\ 0 & 0 & 1 & 0 \end{bmatrix}$

Thus, $z = 0$; $y - 2z = y - 0 = y = 4$; and $x + y + 6z = 3 \quad \Leftrightarrow \quad x + 4 - 0 = 3 \quad \Leftrightarrow x = -1$. Therefore, the solution is $(-1, 4, 0)$.

14. $\begin{bmatrix} 1 & 1 & 1 & 4 \\ -1 & 2 & 3 & 17 \\ 2 & -1 & 0 & -7 \end{bmatrix} \xrightarrow[R_3-2R_1 \to R_3]{R_2+R_1 \to R_2} \begin{bmatrix} 1 & 1 & 1 & 4 \\ 0 & 3 & 4 & 21 \\ 0 & -3 & -2 & -15 \end{bmatrix} \xrightarrow{R_3+R_2 \to R_3}$

$\begin{bmatrix} 1 & 1 & 1 & 4 \\ 0 & 3 & 4 & 21 \\ 0 & 0 & 2 & 6 \end{bmatrix}$

Thus, $2z = 6 \quad \Leftrightarrow \quad z = 3$; $3y + 4(3) = 21 \quad \Leftrightarrow \quad y = 3$; and $x + (3) + (3) = 4 \quad \Leftrightarrow$ $x = -2$. The solution is $(-2, 3, 3)$.

16. $\begin{bmatrix} 0 & 2 & 1 & 4 \\ 1 & 1 & 0 & 4 \\ 3 & 3 & -1 & 10 \end{bmatrix} \xrightarrow{R_1 \leftrightarrow R_2} \begin{bmatrix} 1 & 1 & 0 & 4 \\ 0 & 2 & 1 & 4 \\ 3 & 3 & -1 & 10 \end{bmatrix} \xrightarrow{R_3-3R_1 \to R_3} \begin{bmatrix} 1 & 1 & 0 & 4 \\ 0 & 2 & 1 & 4 \\ 0 & 0 & -1 & -2 \end{bmatrix}$

Thus, $-z = -2$ $\Leftrightarrow$ $z = 2$; $2y + (2) = 4$ $\Leftrightarrow$ $y = 1$; and $x + (1) = 4$ $\Leftrightarrow$ $x = 3$.
The solution is $(3, 1, 2)$

18. $\begin{bmatrix} 2 & 1 & 0 & 7 \\ 2 & -1 & 1 & 6 \\ 3 & -2 & 4 & 11 \end{bmatrix}$ $\begin{matrix} R_2 - R_1 \to R_2 \\ 2R_3 - 3R_1 \to R_3 \end{matrix}$ $\begin{bmatrix} 2 & 1 & 0 & 7 \\ 0 & -2 & 1 & -1 \\ 0 & -7 & 8 & 1 \end{bmatrix}$ $\xrightarrow{2R_3 - 7R_2 \to R_3}$

$\begin{bmatrix} 2 & 1 & 0 & 7 \\ 0 & -2 & 1 & -1 \\ 0 & 0 & 9 & 9 \end{bmatrix}$

Then, $9x_3 = 9$ $\Leftrightarrow$ $x_3 = 1$; $-2x_2 + 1 = -1$ $\Leftrightarrow$ $x_2 = 1$; and $2x_1 + 1 = 7$ $\Leftrightarrow$ $x_1 = 3$.
Therefore, the solution is $(x_1, x_2, x_3) = (3, 1, 1)$.

20. $\begin{bmatrix} 10 & 10 & -20 & 60 \\ 15 & 20 & 30 & -25 \\ -5 & 30 & -10 & 45 \end{bmatrix}$ $\begin{matrix} 2R_2 - 3R_1 \to R_2 \\ 2R_3 + R_1 \to R_3 \end{matrix}$ $\begin{bmatrix} 10 & 10 & -20 & 60 \\ 0 & 10 & 120 & -230 \\ 0 & 70 & -40 & 150 \end{bmatrix}$ $\xrightarrow{R_3 - 7R_2 \to R_3}$

$\begin{bmatrix} 10 & 10 & -20 & 60 \\ 0 & 10 & 120 & -230 \\ 0 & 0 & -880 & 1760 \end{bmatrix}$

Thus, $-880z = 1760$ $\Leftrightarrow$ $z = -2$; $10y + 120(-2) = -230$ $\Leftrightarrow$ $y = 1$; and
$10x + 10 + 40 = 60$ $\Leftrightarrow$ $x = 1$. Therefore, the solution is $(1, 1, -2)$.

22. $\begin{bmatrix} 1 & 0 & 3 & 3 \\ 2 & 1 & -2 & 5 \\ 0 & -1 & 8 & 1 \end{bmatrix}$ $\xrightarrow{R_2 - 2R_1 \to R_2}$ $\begin{bmatrix} 1 & 0 & 3 & 3 \\ 0 & 1 & -8 & -1 \\ 0 & -1 & 8 & 1 \end{bmatrix}$ $\xrightarrow{R_3 + R_2 \to R_3}$ $\begin{bmatrix} 1 & 0 & 3 & 3 \\ 0 & 1 & -8 & -1 \\ 0 & 0 & 0 & 0 \end{bmatrix}$

The system is dependent; there are infinitely many solutions, given by $x + 3z = 3$ $\Leftrightarrow$
$x = 3 - 3z$; and $y - 8z = -1$ $\Leftrightarrow$ $y = 8z - 1$. The solutions are $(3 - 3z, 8z - 1, z)$, where z is
any real number.

24. $\begin{bmatrix} 1 & -2 & 5 & 3 \\ -2 & 6 & -11 & 1 \\ 3 & -16 & 20 & -26 \end{bmatrix}$ $\begin{matrix} R_2 + 2R_1 \to R_2 \\ R_3 - 3R_1 \to R_3 \end{matrix}$ $\begin{bmatrix} 1 & -2 & 5 & 3 \\ 0 & 2 & -1 & 7 \\ 0 & -10 & 5 & -35 \end{bmatrix}$ $\xrightarrow{R_3 + 5R_2 \to R_3}$

$\begin{bmatrix} 1 & -2 & 5 & 3 \\ 0 & 2 & -1 & 7 \\ 0 & 0 & 0 & 0 \end{bmatrix}$

The system is dependent; there are infinitely many solutions, given by $2y - z = 7$ $\Leftrightarrow$
$2y = z + 7$ $\Leftrightarrow$ $y = \frac{1}{2}z + \frac{7}{2}$; and $x - 2y + 5z = 3$ $\Leftrightarrow$ $x - 2\left(\frac{1}{2}z + \frac{7}{2}\right) + 5z = 3$ $\Leftrightarrow$
$x - z - 7 + 5z = 3$ $\Leftrightarrow$ $x = -4z + 10$. The solutions are $\left(-4z + 10, \frac{1}{2}z + \frac{7}{2}, z\right)$, where z is
any real number.

26. $\begin{bmatrix} -2 & 6 & -2 & -12 \\ 1 & -3 & 2 & 10 \\ -1 & 3 & 2 & 6 \end{bmatrix}$ $\xrightarrow{-\frac{1}{2}R_1}$ $\begin{bmatrix} 1 & -3 & 1 & 6 \\ 1 & -3 & 2 & 10 \\ -1 & 3 & 2 & 6 \end{bmatrix}$ $\begin{matrix} R_2 - R_1 \to R_2 \\ R_3 + R_1 \to R_3 \end{matrix}$ $\begin{bmatrix} 1 & -3 & 1 & 6 \\ 0 & 0 & 1 & 4 \\ 0 & 0 & 3 & 12 \end{bmatrix}$

$\xrightarrow{R_3 - 3R_2 \to R_3}$ $\begin{bmatrix} 1 & -3 & 1 & 6 \\ 0 & 0 & 1 & 4 \\ 0 & 0 & 0 & 0 \end{bmatrix}$

The system is dependent; there are infinitely many solutions, given by $z = 4$, and $x - 3y = 6$, so
$x - 3y + 4 = 6$ $\Leftrightarrow$ $x = 3y + 2$. The solutions are $(3y + 2, y, 4)$, where y is any real number.

28. $\begin{bmatrix} 3 & 2 & -3 & 10 \\ 1 & -1 & -1 & -5 \\ 1 & 4 & -1 & 20 \end{bmatrix}$ $\xrightarrow{R_1 \leftrightarrow R_2}$ $\begin{bmatrix} 1 & -1 & -1 & -5 \\ 3 & 2 & -3 & 10 \\ 1 & 4 & -1 & 20 \end{bmatrix}$ $\xrightarrow[R_3-R_1 \to R_3]{R_2-3R_1 \to R_2}$

$\begin{bmatrix} 1 & -1 & -1 & -5 \\ 0 & 5 & 0 & 25 \\ 0 & 5 & 0 & 25 \end{bmatrix}$ $\xrightarrow{R_3-R_2 \to R_3}$ $\begin{bmatrix} 1 & -1 & -1 & -5 \\ 0 & 5 & 0 & 25 \\ 0 & 0 & 0 & 0 \end{bmatrix}$

The system is dependent; there are infinitely many solutions, given by $5s = 25$ $\Leftrightarrow$ $s = 5$, and $r - 5 - t = -5$ $\Leftrightarrow$ $r = t$. Hence, the solutions are $(c, 5, c)$, where c is any real number.

30. $\begin{bmatrix} 0 & 1 & -5 & 7 \\ 3 & 2 & 0 & 12 \\ 3 & 0 & 10 & 80 \end{bmatrix}$ $\xrightarrow{R_1 \leftrightarrow R_2}$ $\begin{bmatrix} 3 & 2 & 0 & 12 \\ 0 & 1 & -5 & 7 \\ 3 & 0 & 10 & 80 \end{bmatrix}$ $\xrightarrow{R_3-R_1 \to R_3}$ $\begin{bmatrix} 3 & 2 & 0 & 12 \\ 0 & 1 & -5 & 7 \\ 0 & -2 & 10 & 68 \end{bmatrix}$

$\xrightarrow{R_3+2R_2 \to R_3}$ $\begin{bmatrix} 3 & 2 & 0 & 12 \\ 0 & 1 & -5 & 7 \\ 0 & 0 & 0 & 82 \end{bmatrix}$ Therefore, the system is inconsistent and has no solution.

32. $\begin{bmatrix} 2 & -3 & 5 & 14 \\ 4 & -1 & -2 & -17 \\ -1 & -1 & 1 & 3 \end{bmatrix}$ $\xrightarrow[-R_1]{R_1 \leftrightarrow R_3}$ $\begin{bmatrix} 1 & 1 & -1 & -3 \\ 4 & -1 & -2 & -17 \\ 2 & -3 & 5 & 14 \end{bmatrix}$ $\xrightarrow[R_3-2R_1 \to R_3]{R_2-4R_1 \to R_2}$

$\begin{bmatrix} 1 & 1 & -1 & -3 \\ 0 & -5 & 2 & -5 \\ 0 & -5 & 7 & 20 \end{bmatrix}$ $\xrightarrow{R_3-R_2 \to R_3}$ $\begin{bmatrix} 1 & 1 & -1 & -3 \\ 0 & -5 & 2 & -5 \\ 0 & 0 & 5 & 25 \end{bmatrix}$

Thus $5z = 25$ $\Leftrightarrow$ $z = 5$; $-5y + 2(5) = -5$ $\Leftrightarrow$ $-5y = -15$ $\Leftrightarrow$ $y = 3$; and $x + (3) - (5) = -3$ $\Leftrightarrow$ $x = -1$. Hence, the solution is $(-1, 3, 5)$.

34. $\begin{bmatrix} 3 & -1 & 2 & -1 \\ 4 & -2 & 1 & -7 \\ -1 & 3 & -2 & -1 \end{bmatrix}$ $\xrightarrow[-R_1]{R_1 \leftrightarrow R_3}$ $\begin{bmatrix} 1 & -3 & 2 & 1 \\ 4 & -2 & 1 & -7 \\ 3 & -1 & 2 & -1 \end{bmatrix}$ $\xrightarrow[R_3-3R_1 \to R_3]{R_2-4R_1 \to R_2}$

$\begin{bmatrix} 1 & -3 & 2 & 1 \\ 0 & 10 & -7 & -11 \\ 0 & 8 & -4 & -4 \end{bmatrix}$ $\xrightarrow{R_2 \leftrightarrow \frac{1}{4}R_3}$ $\begin{bmatrix} 1 & -3 & 2 & 1 \\ 0 & 2 & -1 & -1 \\ 0 & 10 & -7 & -11 \end{bmatrix}$ $\xrightarrow{R_3-5R_2 \to R_3}$

$\begin{bmatrix} 1 & -3 & 2 & 1 \\ 0 & 2 & -1 & -1 \\ 0 & 0 & -2 & -6 \end{bmatrix}$

Thus $-2z = -6$ $\Leftrightarrow$ $z = 3$; $2y - (3) = -1$ $\Leftrightarrow$ $2y = 2$ $\Leftrightarrow$ $y = 1$; and $x - 3(1) + 2(3) = 1$ $\Leftrightarrow$ $x = -2$. Hence, the solution is $(-2, 1, 3)$.

36. $\begin{bmatrix} 1 & 1 & -1 & -1 & 6 \\ 2 & 0 & 1 & -3 & 8 \\ 1 & -1 & 0 & 4 & -10 \\ 3 & 5 & -1 & -1 & 20 \end{bmatrix}$ $\xrightarrow[R_4-3R_1 \to R_4]{R_2-2R_1 \to R_2,\ R_3-R_1 \to R_3}$ $\begin{bmatrix} 1 & 1 & -1 & -1 & 6 \\ 0 & -2 & 3 & -1 & -4 \\ 0 & -2 & 1 & 5 & -16 \\ 0 & 2 & 2 & 2 & 2 \end{bmatrix}$

$\xrightarrow[R_3+R_4 \to R_3,\ \frac{1}{2}R_4]{R_2+R_4 \to R_2}$ $\begin{bmatrix} 1 & 1 & -1 & -1 & 6 \\ 0 & 0 & 5 & 1 & -2 \\ 0 & 0 & 3 & 7 & -14 \\ 0 & 1 & 1 & 1 & 1 \end{bmatrix}$ $\xrightarrow[R_3 \leftrightarrow R_4]{R_4 \leftrightarrow R_2}$ $\begin{bmatrix} 1 & 1 & -1 & -1 & 6 \\ 0 & 1 & 1 & 1 & 1 \\ 0 & 0 & 5 & 1 & -2 \\ 0 & 0 & 3 & 7 & -14 \end{bmatrix}$

$$\xrightarrow{5R_4-3R_3 \to R_4} \begin{bmatrix} 1 & 1 & -1 & -1 & 6 \\ 0 & 1 & 1 & 1 & 1 \\ 0 & 0 & 5 & 1 & -2 \\ 0 & 0 & 0 & 32 & -64 \end{bmatrix}$$

Thus $32w = -64 \iff w = -2$; $5z + (-2) = -2 \iff 5z = 0 \iff z = 0$; $y + 0 + (-2) = 1 \iff y = 3$; and $x + 3 - 0 - (-2) = 6 \iff x = 1$. Hence the solution is $(1, 3, 0, -2)$.

38.
$$\begin{bmatrix} 1 & -3 & 2 & 1 & -2 \\ 1 & -2 & 0 & -2 & -10 \\ 0 & 0 & 1 & 5 & 15 \\ 3 & 0 & 2 & 1 & -3 \end{bmatrix} \xrightarrow[R_4-3R_1 \to R_4]{R_2-R_1 \to R_2} \begin{bmatrix} 1 & -3 & 2 & 1 & -2 \\ 0 & 1 & -2 & -3 & -8 \\ 0 & 0 & 1 & 5 & 15 \\ 0 & 9 & -4 & -2 & 3 \end{bmatrix} \xrightarrow{R_4-9R_2 \to R_4}$$

$$\begin{bmatrix} 1 & -3 & 2 & 1 & -2 \\ 0 & 1 & -2 & -3 & -8 \\ 0 & 0 & 1 & 5 & 15 \\ 0 & 0 & 14 & 25 & 75 \end{bmatrix} \xrightarrow{R_4-14R_3 \to R_4} \begin{bmatrix} 1 & -3 & 2 & 1 & -2 \\ 0 & 1 & -2 & -3 & -8 \\ 0 & 0 & 1 & 5 & 15 \\ 0 & 0 & 0 & -45 & -135 \end{bmatrix}$$

Thus $-45w = -135 \iff w = 3$; $z + 5(3) = 15 \iff z = 0$; $y - 2(0) - 3(3) = -8 \iff y = 1$; and $x - 3(1) + 2(0) + (3) = -2 \iff x = -2$. Hence, the solution is $(-2, 1, 0, 3)$.

40.
$$\begin{bmatrix} 0 & 1 & -1 & 2 & 0 \\ 3 & 2 & 0 & 1 & 0 \\ 2 & 0 & 0 & 4 & 12 \\ -2 & 0 & -2 & 5 & 6 \end{bmatrix} \xrightarrow[R_4+R_3 \to R_4, \frac{1}{2}R_3]{R_2-R_3 \to R_2} \begin{bmatrix} 0 & 1 & -1 & 2 & 0 \\ 1 & 2 & 0 & -3 & -12 \\ 1 & 0 & 0 & 2 & 6 \\ 0 & 0 & -2 & 9 & 18 \end{bmatrix} \xrightarrow[R_2-R_1 \to R_2]{R_1 \leftrightarrow R_3}$$

$$\begin{bmatrix} 1 & 0 & 0 & 2 & 6 \\ 0 & 2 & 0 & -5 & -18 \\ 0 & 1 & -1 & 2 & 0 \\ 0 & 0 & -2 & 9 & 18 \end{bmatrix} \xrightarrow[R_2 \leftrightarrow R_3]{R_2-2R_3 \to R_2} \begin{bmatrix} 1 & 0 & 0 & 2 & 6 \\ 0 & 1 & -1 & 2 & 0 \\ 0 & 0 & 2 & -9 & -18 \\ 0 & 0 & -2 & 9 & 18 \end{bmatrix} \xrightarrow{R_4+R_3 \to R_4}$$

$$\begin{bmatrix} 1 & 0 & 0 & 2 & 6 \\ 0 & 1 & -1 & 2 & 0 \\ 0 & 0 & 2 & -9 & -18 \\ 0 & 0 & 0 & 0 & 0 \end{bmatrix}$$

Thus, the system has infinitely many solutions, given by $-2z + 9w = 18 \iff z = \frac{9}{2}w - 9$; $y - \left(\frac{9}{2}w - 9\right) + 2w = 0 \iff y = \frac{5}{2}w - 9$; and $x + 2w = 6 \iff x = -2w + 6$. So, the solutions are $\left(-2w + 6, \frac{5}{2}w - 9, \frac{9}{2}w - 9, w\right)$, where w is any real number.

42.
$$\begin{bmatrix} 2 & -1 & 2 & 1 & 5 \\ -1 & 1 & 4 & -1 & 3 \\ 3 & -2 & -1 & 0 & 0 \end{bmatrix} \xrightarrow[-R_1]{R_1 \leftrightarrow R_2} \begin{bmatrix} 1 & -1 & -4 & 1 & -3 \\ 2 & -1 & 2 & 1 & 5 \\ 3 & -2 & -1 & 0 & 0 \end{bmatrix} \xrightarrow[R_3-3R_1 \to R_3]{R_2-2R_1 \to R_2}$$

$$\begin{bmatrix} 1 & -1 & -4 & 1 & -3 \\ 0 & 1 & 10 & -1 & 11 \\ 0 & 1 & 11 & -3 & 9 \end{bmatrix} \xrightarrow{R_3-R_2 \to R_3} \begin{bmatrix} 1 & -1 & -4 & 1 & -3 \\ 0 & 1 & 10 & -1 & 11 \\ 0 & 0 & 1 & -2 & -2 \end{bmatrix}$$

Thus, the system has infinitely many solutions, given by $z - 2w = -2 \iff z = -2 + 2w$; $y + 10(-2 + 2w) - w = 11 \iff y = 31 - 19w$; and $x - (31 - 19w) - 4(-2 + 2w) + w = -3 \iff x = 20 - 12w$. Hence, the solutions are $(20 - 12w, 31 - 19w, -2 + 2w, w)$, where w is any real number.

44. Let x be the quantity, in mL, of 10% acid, y be the quantity of 20% acid, and z be the quantity of 40% acid. Then,

$$\begin{cases} 0.1x + 0.2y + 0.4z = 18 \\ x + y + z = 100 \\ x - 4z = 0 \end{cases}$$. Writing this equation in matrix form, we get

$$\begin{bmatrix} 1 & 1 & 1 & 100 \\ 0.1 & 0.2 & 0.4 & 18 \\ 1 & 0 & -4 & 0 \end{bmatrix} \xrightarrow[\substack{10R_2,\, R_2-R_1 \to R_2 \\ R_3-R_1 \to R_3}]{} \begin{bmatrix} 1 & 1 & 1 & 100 \\ 0 & 1 & 3 & 80 \\ 0 & -1 & -5 & -100 \end{bmatrix} \xrightarrow[\substack{R_3+R_2 \to R_3 \\ -R_3}]{}$$

$$\begin{bmatrix} 1 & 1 & 1 & 100 \\ 0 & 1 & 3 & 80 \\ 0 & 0 & 2 & 20 \end{bmatrix}.$$

Thus $2z = 20 \iff z = 10$; $y + 30 = 80 \iff y = 50$; and $x + 50 + 10 = 100 \iff x = 40$. So he should mix together 40 mL of 10% acid, 50 mL of 20% acid, and 10 mL of 40% acid.

46. Let a, b, and c be the number of students in classrooms A, B, and C, respectively, where $a, b, c \geq 0$. Then, the system of equations is

$$\begin{cases} a + b + c = 100 \\ \frac{1}{2}a = \frac{1}{5}b \\ \frac{1}{5}b = \frac{1}{3}c \end{cases} \iff \begin{cases} a + b + c = 100 \\ b = \frac{5}{2}a \\ c = \frac{3}{5}b = \frac{3}{2}a \end{cases}$$

By substitution, $a + \frac{5}{2}a + \frac{3}{2}a = 100 \iff a = 20$; $b = \frac{5}{2}(20) = 50$; and $c = \frac{3}{2}(20) = 30$. So there are 20 students in classroom A, 50 students in classroom B, and 30 students in classroom C.

48. The number of cars entering each intersection must equal the number of cars leaving that intersection. This leads to the following equations:

$$\begin{cases} 200 + 180 = x + z \\ x + 70 = 20 + w \\ w + 200 = y + 30 \\ y + z = 400 + 200 \end{cases}$$ Simplifying and writing this in matrix form, we get:

$$\begin{bmatrix} 1 & 0 & 1 & 0 & 380 \\ 1 & 0 & 0 & -1 & -50 \\ 0 & 1 & 0 & -1 & 170 \\ 0 & 1 & 1 & 0 & 600 \end{bmatrix} \xrightarrow[\substack{R_2-R_1 \to R_2 \\ R_4-R_3 \to R_4}]{} \begin{bmatrix} 1 & 0 & 1 & 0 & 380 \\ 0 & 0 & -1 & -1 & -430 \\ 0 & 1 & 0 & -1 & 170 \\ 0 & 0 & 1 & 1 & 430 \end{bmatrix} \xrightarrow[]{R_2 \leftrightarrow R_3}$$

$$\begin{bmatrix} 1 & 0 & 1 & 0 & 380 \\ 0 & 1 & 0 & -1 & 170 \\ 0 & 0 & -1 & -1 & -430 \\ 0 & 0 & 1 & 1 & 430 \end{bmatrix}$$

Therefore, $z + w = 430 \iff z = 430 - w$; $y - w = 170 \iff y = 170 + w$; and $x + 430 - w = 380 \iff x = w - 50$. Since $x, y, z, w \geq 0$, it follows that $50 \leq w \leq 430$, and so the solutions are $(w - 50, 170 + w, 430 - w)$, where $50 \leq w \leq 430$.

50. Line containing the points $(0, 0)$, $(1, 12)$:

Using the general form of a line, $y = ax + b$, we substitute for x and y and solve for a and b. This gives $(0, 0) \quad 0 = a(0) + b \quad \Rightarrow \quad b = 0$;
$(1, 12) \quad 12 = a(1) + b \quad \Rightarrow \quad a = 12.$

Since $a = 12$ and $b = 0$, the equation of the line is $y = 12x$.

Quadratic containing the points $(0, 0)$, $(1, 12)$, $(3, 6)$:

Using the general form of a quadratic, $y = ax^2 + bx + c$, we substitute for x and y and solve for a, b, and c. This gives

$$(0,0) \quad 0 = a(0)^2 + b(0) + c \quad \Rightarrow \quad c = 0;$$
$$(1,12) \quad 12 = a(1)^2 + b(1) + c \quad \Rightarrow \quad a + b = 12 \quad \times -3 \quad -3a - 3b = -36$$
$$(3,6) \quad 6 = a(3)^2 + b(3) + c \quad \Rightarrow \quad 9a + 3b = 6 \qquad\qquad \underline{\quad 9a + 3b = 6 \quad}$$
$$6a = -30 \quad \Leftrightarrow$$

$a = -5$. So $a + b = 12 \quad \Leftrightarrow \quad b = 12 - a \quad \Rightarrow \quad b = 17$. Since $a = -5$, $b = 17$, and $c = 0$, the equation of the quadratic is $y = -5x^2 + 17x$.

Cubic containing the points $(0, 0)$, $(1, 12)$, $(3, 6)$, $(-1, -14)$:

Using the general form of a cubic, $y = ax^3 + bx^2 + cx + d$, we substitute for x and y and solve for a, b, c, and d. This gives

$$(0,0) \quad 0 = a(0)^3 + b(0)^2 + c(0) + d \quad \Rightarrow \quad d = 0;$$
$$(1,12) \quad 12 = a(1)^3 + b(1)^2 + c(1) + d \quad \Rightarrow \quad a + b + c = 12;$$
$$(3,6) \quad 6 = a(3)^3 + b(3)^2 + c(3) + d \quad \Rightarrow \quad 27a + 9b + 3c = 6;$$
$$(-1,-14) \quad -14 = a(-1)^3 + b(-1)^2 + c(-1) + d \quad \Rightarrow \quad -a + b - c = -14.$$

Adding the second and fourth equation gives:
$$
\begin{array}{r}
a + b + c = 12 \\
-a + b - c = -14 \\
\hline
2b = -2 \quad \Leftrightarrow \quad b = -1.
\end{array}
$$

Substituting $b = -1$ into the second and third equations gives:

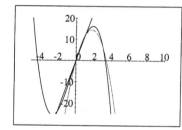

$$
\begin{array}{llll}
a + c = 13 & \times -1 & -a - c = -13 \\
27a + 3c = 15 & \times \frac{1}{3} & 9a + c = 5 \\
\cline{3-3}
& & 8a = -8
\end{array}
$$

$\Rightarrow \quad a = -1$. Thus $a + c = 13 \quad \Rightarrow \quad c = 13 - a = 14$.

So the cubic is $y = -x^3 - x^2 + 14x$.

Exercises 10.4

In Exercises 2 – 20, the matrices $A, B, C, D, E, F,$ and G are defined as follows:

$$A = \begin{bmatrix} 2 & -5 \\ 0 & 7 \end{bmatrix} \qquad B = \begin{bmatrix} 3 & \frac{1}{2} & 5 \\ 1 & -1 & 3 \end{bmatrix} \qquad C = \begin{bmatrix} 2 & -\frac{5}{2} & 0 \\ 0 & 2 & -3 \end{bmatrix} \qquad D = [7 \quad 3]$$

$$E = \begin{bmatrix} 1 \\ 2 \\ 0 \end{bmatrix} \qquad F = \begin{bmatrix} 1 & 0 & 0 \\ 0 & 1 & 0 \\ 0 & 0 & 1 \end{bmatrix} \qquad G = \begin{bmatrix} 5 & -3 & 10 \\ 6 & 1 & 0 \\ -5 & 2 & 2 \end{bmatrix}$$

2. $B + F$ is undefined because B (2×3) and F (3×3) have incompatible dimensions.

4. $5A = 5 \begin{bmatrix} 2 & -5 \\ 0 & 7 \end{bmatrix} = \begin{bmatrix} 10 & -25 \\ 0 & 35 \end{bmatrix}$

6. $C - 5A$ is undefined because C (2×3) and A (2×2) have incompatible dimensions.

8. $DA = [7 \quad 3] \begin{bmatrix} 2 & -5 \\ 0 & 7 \end{bmatrix} = [14 \quad -14]$

10. BC is undefined because B (2×3) and C (2×3) have incompatible dimensions.

12. $GF = \begin{bmatrix} 5 & -3 & 10 \\ 6 & 1 & 0 \\ -5 & 2 & 2 \end{bmatrix} \begin{bmatrix} 1 & 0 & 0 \\ 0 & 1 & 0 \\ 0 & 0 & 1 \end{bmatrix} = \begin{bmatrix} 5 & -3 & 10 \\ 6 & 1 & 0 \\ -5 & 2 & 2 \end{bmatrix}$

14. $D(AB) = [7 \quad 3] \begin{bmatrix} 2 & -5 \\ 0 & 7 \end{bmatrix} \begin{bmatrix} 3 & \frac{1}{2} & 5 \\ 1 & -1 & 3 \end{bmatrix} = [7 \quad 3] \begin{bmatrix} 1 & 6 & -5 \\ 7 & -7 & 21 \end{bmatrix} = [28 \quad 21 \quad 28]$

16. $A^2 = \begin{bmatrix} 2 & -5 \\ 0 & 7 \end{bmatrix} \begin{bmatrix} 2 & -5 \\ 0 & 7 \end{bmatrix} = \begin{bmatrix} 4 & -45 \\ 0 & 49 \end{bmatrix}$

18. $DB + DC = D(B + C) = [7 \quad 3] \left(\begin{bmatrix} 3 & \frac{1}{2} & 5 \\ 1 & -1 & 3 \end{bmatrix} + \begin{bmatrix} 2 & -\frac{5}{2} & 0 \\ 0 & 2 & -3 \end{bmatrix} \right)$

$= [7 \quad 3] \begin{bmatrix} 5 & -2 & 5 \\ 1 & 1 & 0 \end{bmatrix} = [38 \quad -11 \quad 35]$

20. $F^2 = \begin{bmatrix} 1 & 0 & 0 \\ 0 & 1 & 0 \\ 0 & 0 & 1 \end{bmatrix} \begin{bmatrix} 1 & 0 & 0 \\ 0 & 1 & 0 \\ 0 & 0 & 1 \end{bmatrix} = \begin{bmatrix} 1 & 0 & 0 \\ 0 & 1 & 0 \\ 0 & 0 & 1 \end{bmatrix}$

22. Suppose A is $n \times m$ and B is $i \times j$. If the product AB is defined, then $m = i$. If the product BA is defined, then $j = n$. Thus if both products are defined and if A is $n \times m$, then B must be $m \times n$.

24. $\begin{cases} 6x - y + z = 12 \\ 2x + z = 7 \\ y - 2z = 4 \end{cases}$ written as a matrix equation is $\begin{bmatrix} 6 & -1 & 1 \\ 2 & 0 & 1 \\ 0 & 1 & -2 \end{bmatrix} \begin{bmatrix} x \\ y \\ z \end{bmatrix} = \begin{bmatrix} 12 \\ 7 \\ 4 \end{bmatrix}$.

26. $\begin{cases} x - y + z = 2 \\ 4x - 2y - z = 2 \\ x + y + 5z = 2 \\ -x - y - z = 2 \end{cases}$ written as a matrix equation is $\begin{bmatrix} 1 & -1 & 1 \\ 4 & -2 & -1 \\ 1 & 1 & 5 \\ -1 & -1 & -1 \end{bmatrix} \begin{bmatrix} x \\ y \\ z \end{bmatrix} = \begin{bmatrix} 2 \\ 2 \\ 2 \\ 2 \end{bmatrix}$.

28. $\begin{bmatrix} 2 & 5 \\ 1 & 3 \end{bmatrix} \begin{bmatrix} x \\ y \end{bmatrix} = \begin{bmatrix} -2 \\ -3 \end{bmatrix}$. Thus we must solve the system $\begin{cases} 2x + 5y = -2 \\ x + 3y = -3 \end{cases}$. This gives

$\begin{bmatrix} 2 & 5 & -2 \\ 1 & 3 & -3 \end{bmatrix} \xrightarrow{R_2 \leftrightarrow R_1} \begin{bmatrix} 1 & 3 & -3 \\ 2 & 5 & -2 \end{bmatrix} \xrightarrow{R_2 - 2R_1 \to R_2} \begin{bmatrix} 1 & 3 & -3 \\ 0 & -1 & 4 \end{bmatrix}$

So $-y = 4 \Leftrightarrow y = -4; x + 3(-4) = -3 \Leftrightarrow x = 9$. Thus the solutions are $x = 9$, $y = -4$.

30. $5(X - C) = D \Leftrightarrow X - C = \frac{1}{5}D \Leftrightarrow X = \frac{1}{5}D + C = \frac{1}{5}\begin{bmatrix} 10 & 20 \\ 30 & 20 \\ 10 & 0 \end{bmatrix} + \begin{bmatrix} 2 & 3 \\ 1 & 0 \\ 0 & 2 \end{bmatrix}$

$= \begin{bmatrix} 2 & 4 \\ 6 & 4 \\ 2 & 0 \end{bmatrix} + \begin{bmatrix} 2 & 3 \\ 1 & 0 \\ 0 & 2 \end{bmatrix} = \begin{bmatrix} 4 & 7 \\ 7 & 4 \\ 2 & 2 \end{bmatrix}$.

32. $A + D = 3X \Leftrightarrow X = \frac{1}{3}(A + D)$, which is undefined because the dimensions, (2×2) and (3×2), are incompatible.

34. (a) $AB = \begin{bmatrix} 12 & 10 & 0 \\ 4 & 4 & 20 \\ 8 & 9 & 12 \end{bmatrix} \begin{bmatrix} \$1000 & \$500 \\ \$2000 & \$1200 \\ \$1500 & \$1000 \end{bmatrix} = \begin{bmatrix} \$32{,}000 & \$18{,}000 \\ \$42{,}000 & \$26{,}800 \\ \$44{,}000 & \$26{,}800 \end{bmatrix}$

(b) The daily profit in January from the Biloxi plant is the (2nd row, 1st column) matrix entry, and hence is $42,000.

(c) The total daily profit (from all three plants) in February was
$18,000 + $26,800 + $26,800 = $71,600.

36. Let $A = \begin{bmatrix} a & b \\ c & d \end{bmatrix}$ and $B = \begin{bmatrix} e & f \\ g & h \end{bmatrix}$. Then, $A + B = \begin{bmatrix} a+e & b+f \\ c+g & d+h \end{bmatrix}$, and

$(A + B)^2 = \begin{bmatrix} a+e & b+f \\ c+g & d+h \end{bmatrix} \begin{bmatrix} a+e & b+f \\ c+g & d+h \end{bmatrix}$

$= \begin{bmatrix} (a+e)^2 + (b+f)(c+g) & (a+e)(b+f) + (b+f)(d+h) \\ (c+g)(a+e) + (d+h)(c+g) & (c+g)(b+f) + (d+h)^2 \end{bmatrix}$;

$A^2 = \begin{bmatrix} a & b \\ c & d \end{bmatrix} \begin{bmatrix} a & b \\ c & d \end{bmatrix} = \begin{bmatrix} a^2 + bc & ab + bd \\ ac + cd & bc + d^2 \end{bmatrix}$;

$B^2 = \begin{bmatrix} e & f \\ g & h \end{bmatrix} \begin{bmatrix} e & f \\ g & h \end{bmatrix} = \begin{bmatrix} e^2 + fg & ef + fh \\ eg + gh & fg + h^2 \end{bmatrix}$;

$AB = \begin{bmatrix} a & b \\ c & d \end{bmatrix} \begin{bmatrix} e & f \\ g & h \end{bmatrix} = \begin{bmatrix} ae + bg & af + bh \\ ce + dg & cf + dh \end{bmatrix}$;

$BA = \begin{bmatrix} e & f \\ g & h \end{bmatrix} \begin{bmatrix} a & b \\ c & d \end{bmatrix} = \begin{bmatrix} ae + cf & be + df \\ ag + ch & bg + dh \end{bmatrix}$.

Then, $A^2 + AB + BA + B^2$

$= \begin{bmatrix} a^2 + bc + ae + bg + ae + cf + e^2 + fg & ab + bd + ef + fh + af + bh + be + df \\ ac + cd + eg + gh + ce + dg + ag + ch & bc + d^2 + fg + h^2 + cf + dh + bg + dh \end{bmatrix}$

$= \begin{bmatrix} a^2 + 2ae + e^2 + b(c+g) + f(c+g) & a(b+f) + e(b+f) + b(d+h) + f(d+h) \\ c(a+e) + g(a+e) + d(c+g) + h(c+g) & c(b+f) + g(b+f) + d^2 + 2dh + h^2 \end{bmatrix}$

$$= \begin{bmatrix} (a+e)^2 + (b+f)(c+g) & (a+e)(b+f) + (b+f)(d+h) \\ (c+g)(a+e) + (d+h)(c+g) & (c+g)(b+f) + (d+h)^2 \end{bmatrix} = (A+B)^2.$$

38. $A = \begin{bmatrix} 1 & 1 \\ 0 & 1 \end{bmatrix}$;

$A^2 = \begin{bmatrix} 1 & 1 \\ 0 & 1 \end{bmatrix} \begin{bmatrix} 1 & 1 \\ 0 & 1 \end{bmatrix} = \begin{bmatrix} 1 & 2 \\ 0 & 1 \end{bmatrix}$;

$A^3 = A \cdot A^2 = \begin{bmatrix} 1 & 1 \\ 0 & 1 \end{bmatrix} \begin{bmatrix} 1 & 2 \\ 0 & 1 \end{bmatrix} = \begin{bmatrix} 1 & 3 \\ 0 & 1 \end{bmatrix}$;

$A^4 = A \cdot A^3 = \begin{bmatrix} 1 & 1 \\ 0 & 1 \end{bmatrix} \begin{bmatrix} 1 & 3 \\ 0 & 1 \end{bmatrix} = \begin{bmatrix} 1 & 4 \\ 0 & 1 \end{bmatrix}$.

Therefore, it seems that $A^n = \begin{bmatrix} 1 & n \\ 0 & 1 \end{bmatrix}$.

40. Let $A = \begin{bmatrix} a & b \\ c & d \end{bmatrix}$. Then $A^2 = \begin{bmatrix} a & b \\ c & d \end{bmatrix} \cdot \begin{bmatrix} a & b \\ c & d \end{bmatrix} = \begin{bmatrix} a^2 + bc & ab + bd \\ ac + cd & bc + d^2 \end{bmatrix}$

$= \begin{bmatrix} a^2 + bc & b(a+d) \\ c(a+d) & bc + d^2 \end{bmatrix}$. So $A^2 = \begin{bmatrix} 4 & 0 \\ 0 & 9 \end{bmatrix} \Leftrightarrow \begin{matrix} a^2 + bc = 4 & b(a+d) = 0 \\ c(a+d) = 0 & bc + d^2 = 9 \end{matrix}$.

If $a + d = 0$ then $a = -d$; so $4 = a^2 + bc = (-d)^2 + bc = d^2 + bc = 9$, which is a contradiction. Thus $a + d \neq 0$. Since $b(a+d) = 0$ and $c(a+d) = 0$, we must have $b = 0$ and $c = 0$. So the first equation becomes $a^2 = 4 \implies a = \pm 2$, and the fourth equation becomes $d^2 = 9 \implies d = \pm 3$. Thus the square roots of $\begin{bmatrix} 4 & 0 \\ 0 & 9 \end{bmatrix}$ are $A_1 = \begin{bmatrix} 2 & 0 \\ 0 & 3 \end{bmatrix}$, $A_2 = \begin{bmatrix} 2 & 0 \\ 0 & -3 \end{bmatrix}$, $A_3 = \begin{bmatrix} -2 & 0 \\ 0 & 3 \end{bmatrix}$,

and $A_4 = \begin{bmatrix} -2 & 0 \\ 0 & -3 \end{bmatrix}$. We have $A^2 = \begin{bmatrix} 1 & 5 \\ 0 & 9 \end{bmatrix} \Leftrightarrow \begin{matrix} a^2 + bc = 1 & b(a+d) = 5 \\ c(a+d) = 0 & bc + d^2 = 9 \end{matrix}$.

Since $a + d \neq 0$ and $c(a+d) = 0$, we must have $c = 0$. The equations then simplify into the system

$$\begin{matrix} a^2 = 1 \\ b(a+d) = 5 \\ d^2 = 9 \end{matrix} \implies \begin{matrix} a = \pm 1 \\ b(a+d) = 5 \\ d = \pm 3 \end{matrix}$$. We consider the four possible values of a and d.

If $a = 1$ and $d = 3$, then $b(a+d) = 5 \implies b(4) = 5 \implies b = \frac{5}{4}$.

If $a = 1$ and $d = -3$, then $b(a+d) = 5 \implies b(-2) = 5 \implies b = -\frac{5}{2}$.

If $a = -1$ and $d = 3$, then $b(a+d) = 5 \implies b(2) = 5 \implies b = \frac{5}{2}$.

If $a = -1$ and $d = -3$, then $b(a+d) = 5 \implies b(-4) = 5 \implies b = -\frac{5}{4}$.

Thus the square roots of $\begin{bmatrix} 1 & 5 \\ 0 & 9 \end{bmatrix}$ are $A_1 = \begin{bmatrix} 1 & \frac{5}{4} \\ 0 & 3 \end{bmatrix}$, $A_2 = \begin{bmatrix} 1 & -\frac{5}{2} \\ 0 & -3 \end{bmatrix}$, $A_3 = \begin{bmatrix} -1 & \frac{5}{2} \\ 0 & 3 \end{bmatrix}$, and

$A_4 = \begin{bmatrix} -1 & -\frac{5}{4} \\ 0 & -3 \end{bmatrix}$.

Exercises 10.5

2. $B = \begin{bmatrix} 1 & 3 & 2 \\ 0 & 2 & 2 \\ -2 & -1 & 0 \end{bmatrix}$. We begin with a 3×6 matrix whose left half is B and whose right half is I_3.

$$\begin{bmatrix} 1 & 3 & 2 & 1 & 0 & 0 \\ 0 & 2 & 2 & 0 & 1 & 0 \\ -2 & -1 & 0 & 0 & 0 & 1 \end{bmatrix} \xrightarrow{R_3+2R_1 \to R_3} \begin{bmatrix} 1 & 3 & 2 & 1 & 0 & 0 \\ 0 & 2 & 2 & 0 & 1 & 0 \\ 0 & 5 & 4 & 2 & 0 & 1 \end{bmatrix} \xrightarrow{2R_3-5R_2 \to R_3}$$

$$\begin{bmatrix} 1 & 3 & 2 & 1 & 0 & 0 \\ 0 & 2 & 2 & 0 & 1 & 0 \\ 0 & 0 & -2 & 4 & -5 & 2 \end{bmatrix} \xrightarrow[-\frac{1}{2}R_3]{\frac{1}{2}R_2} \begin{bmatrix} 1 & 3 & 2 & 1 & 0 & 0 \\ 0 & 1 & 1 & 0 & \frac{1}{2} & 0 \\ 0 & 0 & 1 & -2 & \frac{5}{2} & -1 \end{bmatrix} \xrightarrow[R_2-R_3 \to R_2]{R_1-3R_2 \to R_1}$$

$$\begin{bmatrix} 1 & 0 & -1 & 1 & -\frac{3}{2} & 0 \\ 0 & 1 & 0 & 2 & -2 & 1 \\ 0 & 0 & 1 & -2 & \frac{5}{2} & -1 \end{bmatrix} \xrightarrow{R_1+R_3 \to R_1} \begin{bmatrix} 1 & 0 & 0 & -1 & 1 & -1 \\ 0 & 1 & 0 & 2 & -2 & 1 \\ 0 & 0 & 1 & -2 & \frac{5}{2} & -1 \end{bmatrix}$$

Then $B^{-1} = \begin{bmatrix} -1 & 1 & -1 \\ 2 & -2 & 1 \\ -2 & \frac{5}{2} & -1 \end{bmatrix}$;

$$B^{-1}B = \begin{bmatrix} -1 & 1 & -1 \\ 2 & -2 & 1 \\ -2 & \frac{5}{2} & -1 \end{bmatrix} \begin{bmatrix} 1 & 3 & 2 \\ 0 & 2 & 2 \\ -2 & -1 & 0 \end{bmatrix} = \begin{bmatrix} 1 & 0 & 0 \\ 0 & 1 & 0 \\ 0 & 0 & 1 \end{bmatrix}; \text{ and}$$

$$BB^{-1} = \begin{bmatrix} 1 & 3 & 2 \\ 0 & 2 & 2 \\ -2 & -1 & 0 \end{bmatrix} \begin{bmatrix} -1 & 1 & -1 \\ 2 & -2 & 1 \\ -2 & \frac{5}{2} & -1 \end{bmatrix} = \begin{bmatrix} 1 & 0 & 0 \\ 0 & 1 & 0 \\ 0 & 0 & 1 \end{bmatrix}.$$

4. $\begin{bmatrix} 3 & 4 \\ 7 & 9 \end{bmatrix}^{-1} = \frac{1}{27-28} \begin{bmatrix} 9 & -4 \\ -7 & 3 \end{bmatrix} = -\begin{bmatrix} 9 & -4 \\ -7 & 3 \end{bmatrix} = \begin{bmatrix} -9 & 4 \\ 7 & -3 \end{bmatrix}$

6. $\begin{bmatrix} -7 & 4 \\ 8 & -5 \end{bmatrix}^{-1} = \frac{1}{35-32} \begin{bmatrix} -5 & -4 \\ -8 & -7 \end{bmatrix} = \begin{bmatrix} -\frac{5}{3} & -\frac{4}{3} \\ -\frac{8}{3} & -\frac{7}{3} \end{bmatrix}$

8. $\begin{bmatrix} \frac{1}{2} & \frac{1}{3} \\ 5 & 4 \end{bmatrix}^{-1} = \frac{1}{2-\frac{5}{3}} \begin{bmatrix} 4 & -\frac{1}{3} \\ -5 & \frac{1}{2} \end{bmatrix} = \begin{bmatrix} 12 & -1 \\ -15 & \frac{3}{2} \end{bmatrix}$

10.
$$\begin{bmatrix} 4 & 2 & 3 & 1 & 0 & 0 \\ 3 & 3 & 2 & 0 & 1 & 0 \\ 1 & 0 & 1 & 0 & 0 & 1 \end{bmatrix} \xrightarrow[4R_3-R_1 \to R_3]{4R_2-3R_1 \to R_2} \begin{bmatrix} 4 & 2 & 3 & 1 & 0 & 0 \\ 0 & 6 & -1 & -3 & 4 & 0 \\ 0 & -2 & 1 & -1 & 0 & 4 \end{bmatrix} \xrightarrow[3R_3+R_2 \to R_3]{R_1+R_3 \to R_1}$$

$$\begin{bmatrix} 4 & 0 & 4 & 0 & 0 & 4 \\ 0 & 6 & -1 & -3 & 4 & 0 \\ 0 & 0 & 2 & -6 & 4 & 12 \end{bmatrix} \xrightarrow[\frac{1}{2}R_3]{\frac{1}{4}R_1} \begin{bmatrix} 1 & 0 & 1 & 0 & 0 & 1 \\ 0 & 6 & -1 & -3 & 4 & 0 \\ 0 & 0 & 1 & -3 & 2 & 6 \end{bmatrix} \xrightarrow[R_2+R_3 \to R_2]{R_1-R_3 \to R_1}$$

$$\begin{bmatrix} 1 & 0 & 0 & 3 & -2 & -5 \\ 0 & 6 & 0 & -6 & 6 & 6 \\ 0 & 0 & 1 & -3 & 2 & 6 \end{bmatrix} \xrightarrow{\frac{1}{6}R_2} \begin{bmatrix} 1 & 0 & 0 & 3 & -2 & -5 \\ 0 & 1 & 0 & -1 & 1 & 1 \\ 0 & 0 & 1 & -3 & 2 & 6 \end{bmatrix}$$

Therefore, the inverse matrix is $\begin{bmatrix} 3 & -2 & -5 \\ -1 & 1 & 1 \\ -3 & 2 & 6 \end{bmatrix}$.

12. $\begin{bmatrix} 5 & 7 & 4 & 1 & 0 & 0 \\ 3 & -1 & 3 & 0 & 1 & 0 \\ 6 & 7 & 5 & 0 & 0 & 1 \end{bmatrix}$ $\xrightarrow[R_1 \leftrightarrow R_3]{R_3 - R_1 \to R_3}$ $\begin{bmatrix} 1 & 0 & 1 & -1 & 0 & 1 \\ 3 & -1 & 3 & 0 & 1 & 0 \\ 5 & 7 & 4 & 1 & 0 & 0 \end{bmatrix}$ $\xrightarrow[R_3 - 5R_1 \to R_3]{R_2 - 3R_1 \to R_2}$

$\begin{bmatrix} 1 & 0 & 1 & -1 & 0 & 1 \\ 0 & -1 & 0 & 3 & 1 & -3 \\ 0 & 7 & -1 & 6 & 0 & -5 \end{bmatrix}$ $\xrightarrow{R_3 + 7R_2 \to R_3}$ $\begin{bmatrix} 1 & 0 & 1 & -1 & 0 & 1 \\ 0 & -1 & 0 & 3 & 1 & -3 \\ 0 & 0 & -1 & 27 & 7 & -26 \end{bmatrix}$

$\xrightarrow[-R_2, -R_3]{R_1 + R_3 \to R_1}$ $\begin{bmatrix} 1 & 0 & 0 & 26 & 7 & -25 \\ 0 & 1 & 0 & -3 & -1 & 3 \\ 0 & 0 & 1 & -27 & -7 & 26 \end{bmatrix}$

Therefore, the inverse matrix is $\begin{bmatrix} 26 & 7 & -25 \\ -3 & -1 & 3 \\ -27 & -7 & 26 \end{bmatrix}$.

14. $\begin{bmatrix} 2 & 1 & 0 & 1 & 0 & 0 \\ 1 & 1 & 4 & 0 & 1 & 0 \\ 2 & 1 & 2 & 0 & 0 & 1 \end{bmatrix}$ $\xrightarrow{R_1 \leftrightarrow R_2}$ $\begin{bmatrix} 1 & 1 & 4 & 0 & 1 & 0 \\ 2 & 1 & 0 & 1 & 0 & 0 \\ 2 & 1 & 2 & 0 & 0 & 1 \end{bmatrix}$ $\xrightarrow[R_3 - 2R_1 \to R_3]{R_2 - 2R_1 \to R_2}$

$\begin{bmatrix} 1 & 1 & 4 & 0 & 1 & 0 \\ 0 & -1 & -8 & 1 & -2 & 0 \\ 0 & -1 & -6 & 0 & -2 & 1 \end{bmatrix}$ $\xrightarrow[R_3 - R_2 \to R_3]{R_1 + R_2 \to R_1}$ $\begin{bmatrix} 1 & 0 & -4 & 1 & -1 & 0 \\ 0 & -1 & -8 & 1 & -2 & 0 \\ 0 & 0 & 2 & -1 & 0 & 1 \end{bmatrix}$

$\xrightarrow[R_2 + 4R_3 \to R_2]{R_1 + 2R_3 \to R_1}$ $\begin{bmatrix} 1 & 0 & 0 & -1 & -1 & 2 \\ 0 & -1 & 0 & -3 & -2 & 4 \\ 0 & 0 & 2 & -1 & 0 & 1 \end{bmatrix}$ $\xrightarrow[\frac{1}{2}R_3]{-R_2}$ $\begin{bmatrix} 1 & 0 & 0 & -1 & -1 & 2 \\ 0 & 1 & 0 & 3 & 2 & -4 \\ 0 & 0 & 1 & -\frac{1}{2} & 0 & \frac{1}{2} \end{bmatrix}$

Therefore, the inverse matrix is $\begin{bmatrix} -1 & -1 & 2 \\ 3 & 2 & -4 \\ -\frac{1}{2} & 0 & \frac{1}{2} \end{bmatrix}$.

16. $\begin{bmatrix} 3 & -2 & 0 & 1 & 0 & 0 \\ 5 & 1 & 1 & 0 & 1 & 0 \\ 2 & -2 & 0 & 0 & 0 & 1 \end{bmatrix}$ $\xrightarrow{R_1 - R_3 \to R_1}$ $\begin{bmatrix} 1 & 0 & 0 & 1 & 0 & -1 \\ 5 & 1 & 1 & 0 & 1 & 0 \\ 2 & -2 & 0 & 0 & 0 & 1 \end{bmatrix}$ $\xrightarrow[R_3 - 2R_1 \to R_3]{R_2 - 5R_1 \to R_2}$

$\begin{bmatrix} 1 & 0 & 0 & 1 & 0 & -1 \\ 0 & 1 & 1 & -5 & 1 & 5 \\ 0 & -2 & 0 & -2 & 0 & 3 \end{bmatrix}$ $\xrightarrow{R_3 + 2R_2 \to R_3}$ $\begin{bmatrix} 1 & 0 & 0 & 1 & 0 & -1 \\ 0 & 1 & 1 & -5 & 1 & 5 \\ 0 & 0 & 2 & -12 & 2 & 13 \end{bmatrix}$

$\xrightarrow[R_2 - R_3 \to R_2]{\frac{1}{2}R_3}$ $\begin{bmatrix} 1 & 0 & 0 & 1 & 0 & -1 \\ 0 & 1 & 0 & 1 & 0 & -\frac{3}{2} \\ 0 & 0 & 1 & -6 & 1 & \frac{13}{2} \end{bmatrix}$

Therefore, the inverse matrix is $\begin{bmatrix} 1 & 0 & -1 \\ 1 & 0 & -\frac{3}{2} \\ -6 & 1 & \frac{13}{2} \end{bmatrix}$.

18.
$$\begin{bmatrix} 1 & 0 & 1 & 0 & 1 & 0 & 0 & 0 \\ 0 & 1 & 0 & 1 & 0 & 1 & 0 & 0 \\ 1 & 1 & 1 & 0 & 0 & 0 & 1 & 0 \\ 1 & 1 & 1 & 1 & 0 & 0 & 0 & 1 \end{bmatrix} \xrightarrow[R_3-R_1 \to R_3]{R_4-R_1 \to R_4} \begin{bmatrix} 1 & 0 & 1 & 0 & 1 & 0 & 0 & 0 \\ 0 & 1 & 0 & 1 & 0 & 1 & 0 & 0 \\ 0 & 1 & 0 & 0 & -1 & 0 & 1 & 0 \\ 0 & 1 & 0 & 1 & -1 & 0 & 0 & 1 \end{bmatrix}$$

$$\xrightarrow[R_3-R_2 \to R_3]{R_4-R_2 \to R_4} \begin{bmatrix} 1 & 0 & 1 & 0 & 1 & 0 & 0 & 0 \\ 0 & 1 & 0 & 1 & 0 & 1 & 0 & 0 \\ 0 & 0 & 0 & -1 & -1 & -1 & 1 & 0 \\ 0 & 0 & 0 & 0 & -1 & -1 & 0 & 1 \end{bmatrix}$$

Therefore, there is no inverse matrix.

20. $\begin{cases} 3x + 4y = 10 \\ 7x + 9y = 20 \end{cases}$ is equivalent to the matrix equation $\begin{bmatrix} 3 & 4 \\ 7 & 9 \end{bmatrix} \begin{bmatrix} x \\ y \end{bmatrix} = \begin{bmatrix} 10 \\ 20 \end{bmatrix}$ $\Leftrightarrow$

$\begin{bmatrix} x \\ y \end{bmatrix} = \begin{bmatrix} -9 & 4 \\ 7 & -3 \end{bmatrix} \begin{bmatrix} 10 \\ 20 \end{bmatrix} = \begin{bmatrix} -10 \\ 10 \end{bmatrix}$. Therefore, $x = -10$ and $y = 10$.

22. $\begin{cases} -7x + 4y = 0 \\ 8x - 5y = 100 \end{cases}$ is equivalent to the matrix equation $\begin{bmatrix} -7 & 4 \\ 8 & -5 \end{bmatrix} \begin{bmatrix} x \\ y \end{bmatrix} = \begin{bmatrix} 0 \\ 100 \end{bmatrix}$ $\Leftrightarrow$

$\begin{bmatrix} x \\ y \end{bmatrix} = \begin{bmatrix} -\frac{5}{3} & -\frac{4}{3} \\ -\frac{8}{3} & -\frac{7}{3} \end{bmatrix} \begin{bmatrix} 0 \\ 100 \end{bmatrix} = \begin{bmatrix} -\frac{400}{3} \\ -\frac{700}{3} \end{bmatrix}$. Therefore, $x = -\frac{400}{3}$ and $y = -\frac{700}{3}$.

24. $\begin{cases} 5x + 7y + 4z = 1 \\ 3x - y + 3z = 1 \\ 6x + 7y + 5z = 1 \end{cases}$ is equivalent to the matrix equation $\begin{bmatrix} 5 & 7 & 4 \\ 3 & -1 & 3 \\ 6 & 7 & 5 \end{bmatrix} \begin{bmatrix} x \\ y \\ z \end{bmatrix} = \begin{bmatrix} 1 \\ 1 \\ 1 \end{bmatrix}$ $\Leftrightarrow$

$\begin{bmatrix} x \\ y \\ z \end{bmatrix} = \begin{bmatrix} 26 & 7 & -25 \\ -3 & -1 & 3 \\ -27 & -7 & 26 \end{bmatrix} \begin{bmatrix} 1 \\ 1 \\ 1 \end{bmatrix} = \begin{bmatrix} 8 \\ -1 \\ -8 \end{bmatrix}$. Therefore, $x = 8$, $y = -1$, and $z = -8$.

26. $\begin{cases} x + 2y + \quad 3w = 0 \\ \quad y + z + w = 1 \\ \quad y + \quad w = 2 \\ x + 2y + \quad 2w = 3 \end{cases}$ is equivalent to the matrix equation $\begin{bmatrix} 1 & 2 & 0 & 3 \\ 0 & 1 & 1 & 1 \\ 0 & 1 & 0 & 1 \\ 1 & 2 & 0 & 2 \end{bmatrix} \begin{bmatrix} x \\ y \\ z \\ w \end{bmatrix} = \begin{bmatrix} 0 \\ 1 \\ 2 \\ 3 \end{bmatrix}$ $\Leftrightarrow$

$\begin{bmatrix} x \\ y \\ z \\ w \end{bmatrix} = \begin{bmatrix} 0 & 0 & -2 & 1 \\ -1 & 0 & 1 & 1 \\ 0 & 1 & -1 & 0 \\ 1 & 0 & 0 & -1 \end{bmatrix} \begin{bmatrix} 0 \\ 1 \\ 2 \\ 3 \end{bmatrix} = \begin{bmatrix} -1 \\ 5 \\ -1 \\ -3 \end{bmatrix}$. Therefore, $x = -1$, $y = 5$, $z = -1$, and $w = -3$.

28. Using the inverse matrix from Exercise 15, we see that

$\begin{bmatrix} -\frac{9}{2} & -1 & 4 \\ 3 & 1 & -3 \\ \frac{7}{2} & 1 & -3 \end{bmatrix} \begin{bmatrix} 3 & 6 \\ 6 & 12 \\ 0 & 0 \end{bmatrix} = \begin{bmatrix} -\frac{39}{2} & -39 \\ 15 & 30 \\ \frac{33}{2} & 33 \end{bmatrix}$. Hence, $\begin{bmatrix} x & u \\ y & v \\ z & w \end{bmatrix} = \begin{bmatrix} -\frac{39}{2} & -39 \\ 15 & 30 \\ \frac{33}{2} & 33 \end{bmatrix}$.

30. $\begin{bmatrix} 3 & 1 & 4 & 1 & 0 & 0 \\ 4 & 2 & 6 & 0 & 1 & 0 \\ 3 & 2 & 5 & 0 & 0 & 1 \end{bmatrix} \xrightarrow[R_3-R_1 \to R_3]{R_2-R_1 \to R_2} \begin{bmatrix} 3 & 1 & 4 & 1 & 0 & 0 \\ 1 & 1 & 2 & -1 & 1 & 0 \\ 0 & 1 & 1 & -1 & 0 & 1 \end{bmatrix} \xrightarrow{R_1 \leftrightarrow R_2}$

$$\begin{bmatrix} 1 & 1 & 2 & -1 & 1 & 0 \\ 3 & 1 & 4 & 1 & 0 & 0 \\ 0 & 1 & 1 & -1 & 0 & 1 \end{bmatrix} \xrightarrow{R_2-3R_1 \to R_2} \begin{bmatrix} 1 & 1 & 2 & -1 & 1 & 0 \\ 0 & -2 & -2 & 4 & -3 & 0 \\ 0 & 1 & 1 & -1 & 0 & 1 \end{bmatrix} \xrightarrow{R_3+\frac{1}{2}R_2 \to R_3}$$

$$\begin{bmatrix} 1 & 1 & 2 & -1 & 1 & 0 \\ 0 & -2 & -2 & 4 & -3 & 0 \\ 0 & 0 & 0 & 1 & -\frac{3}{2} & 1 \end{bmatrix}$$

Since the inverse matrix does not exist, it would not be possible to use matrix inversion in the solution of parts (b), (c), and (d).

32. $$\begin{bmatrix} x & 1 \\ -1 & \frac{1}{x} \end{bmatrix}^{-1} = \frac{1}{1+1} \begin{bmatrix} \frac{1}{x} & -1 \\ 1 & x \end{bmatrix} = \begin{bmatrix} \frac{1}{2x} & -\frac{1}{2} \\ \frac{1}{2} & \frac{x}{2} \end{bmatrix}$$

34. $$\begin{bmatrix} 1 & e^x & 0 & 1 & 0 & 0 \\ e^x & -e^{2x} & 0 & 0 & 1 & 0 \\ 0 & 0 & 2 & 0 & 0 & 1 \end{bmatrix} \xrightarrow{R_2-e^x R_1 \to R_2} \begin{bmatrix} 1 & e^x & 0 & 1 & 0 & 0 \\ 0 & -2e^{2x} & 0 & -e^x & 1 & 0 \\ 0 & 0 & 2 & 0 & 0 & 1 \end{bmatrix} \xrightarrow[\frac{1}{2}R_3]{-\frac{1}{2}e^{-2x} R_2}$$

$$\begin{bmatrix} 1 & e^x & 0 & 1 & 0 & 0 \\ 0 & 1 & 0 & \frac{1}{2}e^{-x} & -\frac{1}{2}e^{-2x} & 0 \\ 0 & 0 & 1 & 0 & 0 & \frac{1}{2} \end{bmatrix} \xrightarrow{R_1-e^x R_2 \to R_1} \begin{bmatrix} 1 & 0 & 0 & \frac{1}{2} & \frac{1}{2}e^{-x} & 0 \\ 0 & 1 & 0 & \frac{1}{2}e^{-x} & -\frac{1}{2}e^{-2x} & 0 \\ 0 & 0 & 1 & 0 & 0 & \frac{1}{2} \end{bmatrix}$$

Therefore, the inverse matrix is $$\begin{bmatrix} \frac{1}{2} & \frac{1}{2}e^{-x} & 0 \\ \frac{1}{2}e^{-x} & -\frac{1}{2}e^{-2x} & 0 \\ 0 & 0 & \frac{1}{2} \end{bmatrix}.$$

36. $$\begin{bmatrix} a & 0 & 0 & 0 & 1 & 0 & 0 & 0 \\ 0 & b & 0 & 0 & 0 & 1 & 0 & 0 \\ 0 & 0 & c & 0 & 0 & 0 & 1 & 0 \\ 0 & 0 & 0 & d & 0 & 0 & 0 & 1 \end{bmatrix} \xrightarrow[\frac{1}{c}R_3, \frac{1}{d}R_4]{\frac{1}{a}R_1, \frac{1}{b}R_2} \begin{bmatrix} 1 & 0 & 0 & 0 & \frac{1}{a} & 0 & 0 & 0 \\ 0 & 1 & 0 & 0 & 0 & \frac{1}{b} & 0 & 0 \\ 0 & 0 & 1 & 0 & 0 & 0 & \frac{1}{c} & 0 \\ 0 & 0 & 0 & 1 & 0 & 0 & 0 & \frac{1}{d} \end{bmatrix}$$

Thus the matrix $$\begin{bmatrix} a & 0 & 0 & 0 \\ 0 & b & 0 & 0 \\ 0 & 0 & c & 0 \\ 0 & 0 & 0 & d \end{bmatrix}$$ has inverse $$\begin{bmatrix} \frac{1}{a} & 0 & 0 & 0 \\ 0 & \frac{1}{b} & 0 & 0 \\ 0 & 0 & \frac{1}{c} & 0 \\ 0 & 0 & 0 & \frac{1}{d} \end{bmatrix}.$$

Exercises 10.6

2. The matrix $\begin{bmatrix} 0 \end{bmatrix}$ has determinant $|D| = 0$.

4. The matrix $\begin{bmatrix} -2 & 1 \\ 3 & -2 \end{bmatrix}$ has determinant $|D| = (-2)(-2) - (1)(3) = 1$.

6. The matrix $\begin{bmatrix} 3 \\ 0 \end{bmatrix}$ does not have a determinant because the matrix is not square.

8. The matrix $\begin{bmatrix} 2.2 & -1.4 \\ 0.5 & 1.0 \end{bmatrix}$ has determinant $|D| = (2.2)(1.0) - (0.5)(-1.4) = 2.2 + 0.7 = 2.9$.

In Exercises 10–14, the matrix is $A = \begin{bmatrix} 1 & 0 & \frac{1}{2} \\ -3 & 5 & 2 \\ 0 & 0 & 4 \end{bmatrix}$.

10. $M_{33} = 1 \cdot 5 + 3 \cdot 0 = 5$, $A_{33} = (-1)^6 \, M_{33} = 5$

12. $M_{13} = -3 \cdot 0 - 0 \cdot 5 = 0$, $A_{13} = (-1)^4 \, M_{13} = 0$

14. $M_{32} = 1 \cdot 2 + 3 \cdot \frac{1}{2} = \frac{7}{2}$, $A_{32} = (-1)^5 \, M_{32} = -\frac{7}{2}$

16. $M = \begin{bmatrix} -2 & -\frac{3}{2} & \frac{1}{2} \\ 2 & 4 & 0 \\ \frac{1}{2} & 2 & 1 \end{bmatrix}$. Therefore, $|M| = \frac{1}{2} \begin{vmatrix} 2 & 4 \\ \frac{1}{2} & 2 \end{vmatrix} + 1 \begin{vmatrix} -2 & -\frac{3}{2} \\ 2 & 4 \end{vmatrix} = \frac{1}{2}(4 - 2) + (-8 + 3)$

$= 1 - 5 = -4$, and the matrix has an inverse.

18. $M = \begin{bmatrix} 1 & 2 & 5 \\ -2 & -3 & 2 \\ 3 & 5 & 3 \end{bmatrix}$. Therefore, $|M| = 1 \begin{vmatrix} -3 & 2 \\ 5 & 3 \end{vmatrix} - 2 \begin{vmatrix} -2 & 2 \\ 3 & 3 \end{vmatrix} + 5 \begin{vmatrix} -2 & -3 \\ 3 & 5 \end{vmatrix}$

$= (-9 - 10) - 2(-6 - 6) + 5(-10 + 9) = -19 + 24 - 5 = 0$, and so the matrix does not have an inverse.

20. $M = \begin{bmatrix} 1 & 2 & 0 & 2 \\ 3 & -4 & 0 & 4 \\ 0 & 1 & 6 & 0 \\ 1 & 0 & 2 & 0 \end{bmatrix}$. Therefore, $|M| = -1 \begin{vmatrix} 2 & 0 & 2 \\ -4 & 0 & 4 \\ 1 & 6 & 0 \end{vmatrix} - 2 \begin{vmatrix} 1 & 2 & 2 \\ 3 & -4 & 4 \\ 0 & 1 & 0 \end{vmatrix}$

$= 6 \begin{vmatrix} 2 & 2 \\ -4 & 4 \end{vmatrix} + 2 \begin{vmatrix} 1 & 2 \\ 3 & 4 \end{vmatrix} = 6 \cdot 16 - 2 \cdot 2 = 92$, and so M^{-1} exists.

22. $M = \begin{bmatrix} -2 & 3 & -1 & 7 \\ 4 & 6 & -2 & 3 \\ 7 & 7 & 0 & 5 \\ 3 & -12 & 4 & 0 \end{bmatrix}$. Then, $|M| = \begin{vmatrix} -2 & 3 & -1 & 7 \\ 4 & 6 & -2 & 3 \\ 7 & 7 & 0 & 5 \\ 3 & -12 & 4 & 0 \end{vmatrix} = \begin{vmatrix} -2 & 0 & -1 & 7 \\ 4 & 0 & -2 & 3 \\ 7 & 7 & 0 & 5 \\ 3 & 0 & 4 & 0 \end{vmatrix}$, by

replacing C_2 with $C_2 + 3C_3$. So expanding about the second column, $|M| = -7 \begin{vmatrix} -2 & -1 & 7 \\ 4 & -2 & 3 \\ 3 & 4 & 0 \end{vmatrix}$

$= -7 \left(7 \begin{vmatrix} 4 & -2 \\ 3 & 4 \end{vmatrix} - 3 \begin{vmatrix} -2 & -1 \\ 3 & 4 \end{vmatrix} \right) = -7 \, (7 \cdot 22 + 3 \cdot 5) = -1183$.

24. $M = \begin{bmatrix} 2 & -1 & 6 & 4 \\ 7 & 2 & -2 & 5 \\ 4 & -2 & 10 & 8 \\ 6 & 1 & 1 & 4 \end{bmatrix}$. Then, $|M| = \begin{vmatrix} 2 & -1 & 6 & 4 \\ 7 & 2 & -2 & 5 \\ 4 & -2 & 10 & 8 \\ 6 & 1 & 1 & 4 \end{vmatrix} = \begin{vmatrix} 0 & -1 & 6 & 4 \\ 11 & 2 & -2 & 5 \\ 0 & -2 & 10 & 8 \\ 8 & 1 & 1 & 4 \end{vmatrix}$, by replacing

C_1 with $C_1 + 2C_2$. So $|M| = -11 \begin{vmatrix} -1 & 6 & 4 \\ -2 & 10 & 8 \\ 1 & 1 & 4 \end{vmatrix} - 8 \begin{vmatrix} -1 & 6 & 4 \\ 2 & -2 & 5 \\ -2 & 10 & 8 \end{vmatrix}$

$= -11 \begin{vmatrix} -1 & 6 & 0 \\ -2 & 10 & 0 \\ 1 & 1 & 8 \end{vmatrix} - 8 \begin{vmatrix} -1 & 6 & 0 \\ 2 & -2 & 13 \\ -2 & 10 & 0 \end{vmatrix} = -88 \begin{vmatrix} -1 & 6 \\ -2 & 10 \end{vmatrix} + 104 \begin{vmatrix} -1 & 6 \\ -2 & 10 \end{vmatrix}$

$= -88 \cdot 2 + 104 \cdot 2 = 32.$

26. $\begin{cases} x + 2y + 6z = 5 \\ -3x - 6y + 5z = 8 \\ 2x + 6y + 9z = 7 \end{cases}$

(a) If $x = -1$, $y = 0$, and $z = 1$, then $x + 2y + 6z = (-1) + 2(0) + 6(1) = 5$,
    $-3x - 6y + 5z = -3(-1) - 6(0) + 5(1) = 8$, and $2x + 6y + 9z = 2(-1) + 6(0) + 9(1)$
    $= 7$. Therefore, $x = -1$, $y = 0$, $z = 1$ is a solution of the system.

(b) $M = \begin{bmatrix} 1 & 2 & 6 \\ -3 & -6 & 5 \\ 2 & 6 & 9 \end{bmatrix}$. Then, $|M| = \begin{vmatrix} 1 & 2 & 6 \\ -3 & -6 & 5 \\ 2 & 6 & 9 \end{vmatrix} = \begin{vmatrix} 1 & 0 & 6 \\ -3 & 0 & 5 \\ 2 & 2 & 9 \end{vmatrix}$ (replacing C_2 with

$C_2 - 2C_1$), so $|M| = -2 \begin{vmatrix} 1 & 6 \\ -3 & 5 \end{vmatrix} = -2 (5 + 18) = -46.$

(c) We can write the system as a matrix equation:
$$\begin{bmatrix} 1 & 2 & 6 \\ -3 & -6 & 5 \\ 2 & 6 & 9 \end{bmatrix} \begin{bmatrix} x \\ y \\ z \end{bmatrix} = \begin{bmatrix} 5 \\ 8 \\ 7 \end{bmatrix}$$, or $MX = B$. Since $|M| \neq 0$, M has an inverse. If we
multiply both sides of the matrix equation by M^{-1}, then we get a unique solution for X, given
by $X = M^{-1}B$ (see Section 7.5). Thus the equation has no other solutions.

(d) Yes, since $|M| \neq 0$.

28. $\begin{cases} 6x + 12y = 33 \\ 4x + 7y = 20 \end{cases}$ Then, $|D| = \begin{vmatrix} 6 & 12 \\ 4 & 7 \end{vmatrix} = -6$, $|D_x| = \begin{vmatrix} 33 & 12 \\ 20 & 7 \end{vmatrix} = -9$, and

$|D_y| = \begin{vmatrix} 6 & 33 \\ 4 & 20 \end{vmatrix} = -12$. Hence, $x = \dfrac{|D_x|}{|D|} = \dfrac{-9}{-6} = \dfrac{3}{2}$ and $y = \dfrac{|D_y|}{|D|} = \dfrac{-12}{-6} = 2$, and so the

solution is $\left(\frac{3}{2}, 2\right)$.

30. $\begin{cases} \frac{1}{2}x + \frac{1}{3}y = 1 \\ \frac{1}{4}x - \frac{1}{6}y = -\frac{3}{2} \end{cases}$ Then, $|D| = \begin{vmatrix} \frac{1}{2} & \frac{1}{3} \\ \frac{1}{4} & -\frac{1}{6} \end{vmatrix} = -\frac{1}{6}$, $|D_x| = \begin{vmatrix} 1 & \frac{1}{3} \\ -\frac{3}{2} & -\frac{1}{6} \end{vmatrix} = \frac{1}{3}$,

and $|D_y| = \begin{vmatrix} \frac{1}{2} & 1 \\ \frac{1}{4} & -\frac{3}{2} \end{vmatrix} = -1$. Hence, $x = \dfrac{|D_x|}{|D|} = \dfrac{\frac{1}{3}}{-\frac{1}{6}} = -2$, $y = \dfrac{|D_y|}{|D|} = \dfrac{-1}{-\frac{1}{6}} = 6$, and so

the solution is $(-2, 6)$.

32. $\begin{cases} 10x - 17y = 21 \\ 20x - 31y = 39 \end{cases}$. Then, $|D| = \begin{vmatrix} 10 & -17 \\ 20 & -31 \end{vmatrix} = 30$, $|D_x| = \begin{vmatrix} 21 & -17 \\ 39 & -31 \end{vmatrix} = 12$, and

$|D_y| = \begin{vmatrix} 10 & 21 \\ 20 & 39 \end{vmatrix} = -30$. Hence, $x = \frac{|D_x|}{|D|} = \frac{12}{30} = \frac{2}{5}$, $y = \frac{|D_y|}{|D|} = \frac{-30}{30} = -1$, and so the solution is $\left(\frac{2}{5}, -1\right)$.

34. $\begin{cases} 5x - 3y + z = 6 \\ 4y - 6z = 22 \\ 7x + 10y = -13 \end{cases}$. Then,

$|D| = \begin{vmatrix} 5 & -3 & 1 \\ 0 & 4 & -6 \\ 7 & 10 & 0 \end{vmatrix} = 1\begin{vmatrix} 0 & 4 \\ 7 & 10 \end{vmatrix} + 6\begin{vmatrix} 5 & -3 \\ 7 & 10 \end{vmatrix} = -28 + 426 = 398,$

$|D_x| = \begin{vmatrix} 6 & -3 & 1 \\ 22 & 4 & -6 \\ -13 & 10 & 0 \end{vmatrix} = 1\begin{vmatrix} 22 & 4 \\ -13 & 10 \end{vmatrix} + 6\begin{vmatrix} 6 & -3 \\ -13 & 10 \end{vmatrix} = 272 + 126 = 398,$

$|D_y| = \begin{vmatrix} 5 & 6 & 1 \\ 0 & 22 & -6 \\ 7 & -13 & 0 \end{vmatrix} = 1\begin{vmatrix} 0 & 22 \\ 7 & -13 \end{vmatrix} + 6\begin{vmatrix} 5 & 6 \\ 7 & -13 \end{vmatrix} = -154 - 642 = -796,$ and

$|D_z| = \begin{vmatrix} 5 & -3 & 6 \\ 0 & 4 & 22 \\ 7 & 10 & -13 \end{vmatrix} = 4\begin{vmatrix} 5 & 6 \\ 7 & -13 \end{vmatrix} - 22\begin{vmatrix} 5 & -3 \\ 7 & 10 \end{vmatrix} = -428 - 1562 = -1990.$ Therefore, the

solution is $x = \frac{398}{398} = 1$, $y = \frac{-796}{398} = -2$, and $z = \frac{-1990}{398} = -5$.

36. $\begin{cases} -2a + c = 2 \\ a + 2b - c = 9 \\ 3a + 5b + 2c = 22 \end{cases}$. Then,

$|D| = \begin{vmatrix} -2 & 0 & 1 \\ 1 & 2 & -1 \\ 3 & 5 & 2 \end{vmatrix} = -2\begin{vmatrix} 2 & -1 \\ 5 & 2 \end{vmatrix} + 1\begin{vmatrix} 1 & 2 \\ 3 & 5 \end{vmatrix} = -18 - 1 = -19,$

$|D_a| = \begin{vmatrix} 2 & 0 & 1 \\ 9 & 2 & -1 \\ 22 & 5 & 2 \end{vmatrix} = 2\begin{vmatrix} 2 & -1 \\ 5 & 2 \end{vmatrix} + 1\begin{vmatrix} 9 & 2 \\ 22 & 5 \end{vmatrix} = 18 + 1 = 19,$

$|D_b| = \begin{vmatrix} -2 & 2 & 1 \\ 1 & 9 & -1 \\ 3 & 22 & 2 \end{vmatrix} = -2\begin{vmatrix} 9 & -1 \\ 22 & 2 \end{vmatrix} - 2\begin{vmatrix} 1 & -1 \\ 3 & 2 \end{vmatrix} + 1\begin{vmatrix} 1 & 9 \\ 3 & 22 \end{vmatrix} = -80 - 10 - 5 = -95,$ and

$|D_c| = \begin{vmatrix} -2 & 0 & 2 \\ 1 & 2 & 9 \\ 3 & 5 & 22 \end{vmatrix} = -2\begin{vmatrix} 2 & 9 \\ 5 & 22 \end{vmatrix} + 2\begin{vmatrix} 1 & 2 \\ 3 & 5 \end{vmatrix} = 2 - 2 = 0.$

Hence, the solution is $a = -1$, $b = 5$, and $c = 0$.

38. $\begin{cases} 2x - y = 5 \\ 5x + 3z = 19 \\ 4y + 7z = 17 \end{cases}$ Then, $|D| = \begin{vmatrix} 2 & -1 & 0 \\ 5 & 0 & 3 \\ 0 & 4 & 7 \end{vmatrix} = 2\begin{vmatrix} 0 & 3 \\ 4 & 7 \end{vmatrix} + 1\begin{vmatrix} 5 & 3 \\ 0 & 7 \end{vmatrix} = -24 + 35 = 11,$

$$|D_x| = \begin{vmatrix} 5 & -1 & 0 \\ 19 & 0 & 3 \\ 17 & 4 & 7 \end{vmatrix} = 5\begin{vmatrix} 0 & 3 \\ 4 & 7 \end{vmatrix} + 1\begin{vmatrix} 19 & 3 \\ 17 & 7 \end{vmatrix} = -60 + 82 = 22,$$

$$|D_y| = \begin{vmatrix} 2 & 5 & 0 \\ 5 & 19 & 3 \\ 0 & 17 & 7 \end{vmatrix} = 2\begin{vmatrix} 19 & 3 \\ 17 & 7 \end{vmatrix} - 5\begin{vmatrix} 5 & 3 \\ 0 & 7 \end{vmatrix} = 164 - 175 = -11, \text{ and}$$

$$|D_z| = \begin{vmatrix} 2 & -1 & 5 \\ 5 & 0 & 19 \\ 0 & 4 & 17 \end{vmatrix} = -4\begin{vmatrix} 2 & 5 \\ 5 & 19 \end{vmatrix} + 17\begin{vmatrix} 2 & -1 \\ 5 & 0 \end{vmatrix} = -52 + 85 = 33. \text{ Thus, the solution is}$$

$x = 2, y = -1,$ and $z = 3.$

40. $\begin{cases} 2x - 5y = 4 \\ x + y - z = 8. \text{ Then,} \\ 3x + 5z = 0 \end{cases}$

$$|D| = \begin{vmatrix} 2 & -5 & 0 \\ 1 & 1 & -1 \\ 3 & 0 & 5 \end{vmatrix} = 2\begin{vmatrix} 1 & -1 \\ 0 & 5 \end{vmatrix} + 5\begin{vmatrix} 1 & -1 \\ 3 & 5 \end{vmatrix} = 10 + 40 = 50,$$

$$|D_x| = \begin{vmatrix} 4 & -5 & 0 \\ 8 & 1 & -1 \\ 0 & 0 & 5 \end{vmatrix} = 5\begin{vmatrix} 4 & -5 \\ 8 & 1 \end{vmatrix} = 220,$$

$$|D_y| = \begin{vmatrix} 2 & 4 & 0 \\ 1 & 8 & -1 \\ 3 & 0 & 5 \end{vmatrix} = 2\begin{vmatrix} 8 & -1 \\ 0 & 5 \end{vmatrix} - 4\begin{vmatrix} 1 & -1 \\ 3 & 5 \end{vmatrix} = 80 - 32 = 48, \text{ and}$$

$$|D_z| = \begin{vmatrix} 2 & -5 & 4 \\ 1 & 1 & 8 \\ 3 & 0 & 0 \end{vmatrix} = 3\begin{vmatrix} -5 & 4 \\ 1 & 8 \end{vmatrix} = -132. \text{ Thus, } x = \frac{22}{5}, y = \frac{24}{25}, \text{ and } z = -\frac{66}{25}.$$

42. $\begin{cases} x + y = 1 \\ y + z = 2 \\ z + w = 3 \\ w - x = 4 \end{cases}$. Then $|D| = \begin{vmatrix} 1 & 1 & 0 & 0 \\ 0 & 1 & 1 & 0 \\ 0 & 0 & 1 & 1 \\ -1 & 0 & 0 & 1 \end{vmatrix} = 1\begin{vmatrix} 1 & 1 & 0 \\ 0 & 1 & 1 \\ 0 & 0 & 1 \end{vmatrix} - 1\begin{vmatrix} 0 & 1 & 0 \\ 0 & 1 & 1 \\ -1 & 0 & 1 \end{vmatrix}$

$$= 1\begin{vmatrix} 1 & 1 \\ 0 & 1 \end{vmatrix} - (-1)\begin{vmatrix} 1 & 0 \\ 1 & 1 \end{vmatrix} = 1 + 1 = 2,$$

$$|D_x| = \begin{vmatrix} 1 & 1 & 0 & 0 \\ 2 & 1 & 1 & 0 \\ 3 & 0 & 1 & 1 \\ 4 & 0 & 0 & 1 \end{vmatrix} = 1\begin{vmatrix} 1 & 1 & 0 \\ 0 & 1 & 1 \\ 0 & 0 & 1 \end{vmatrix} - 1\begin{vmatrix} 2 & 1 & 0 \\ 3 & 1 & 1 \\ 4 & 0 & 1 \end{vmatrix} = \begin{vmatrix} 1 & 1 \\ 0 & 1 \end{vmatrix} - \left(2\begin{vmatrix} 1 & 1 \\ 0 & 1 \end{vmatrix} - 1\begin{vmatrix} 3 & 1 \\ 4 & 1 \end{vmatrix} \right)$$

$$= 1 - 3 = -2,$$

$$|D_y| = \begin{vmatrix} 1 & 1 & 0 & 0 \\ 0 & 2 & 1 & 0 \\ 0 & 3 & 1 & 1 \\ -1 & 4 & 0 & 1 \end{vmatrix} = 1\begin{vmatrix} 2 & 1 & 0 \\ 3 & 1 & 1 \\ 4 & 0 & 1 \end{vmatrix} - 1\begin{vmatrix} 0 & 1 & 0 \\ 0 & 1 & 1 \\ -1 & 0 & 1 \end{vmatrix}$$

$$= \left(2\begin{vmatrix} 1 & 1 \\ 0 & 1 \end{vmatrix} - 1\begin{vmatrix} 3 & 1 \\ 4 & 1 \end{vmatrix} \right) - (-1)\begin{vmatrix} 1 & 0 \\ 1 & 1 \end{vmatrix} = 3 + 1 = 4,$$

$$|D_z| = \begin{vmatrix} 1 & 1 & 1 & 0 \\ 0 & 1 & 2 & 0 \\ 0 & 0 & 3 & 1 \\ -1 & 0 & 4 & 1 \end{vmatrix} = 1\begin{vmatrix} 1 & 2 & 0 \\ 0 & 3 & 1 \\ 0 & 4 & 1 \end{vmatrix} + 1\begin{vmatrix} 1 & 1 & 0 \\ 1 & 2 & 0 \\ 0 & 3 & 1 \end{vmatrix} = 1\begin{vmatrix} 3 & 1 \\ 4 & 1 \end{vmatrix} + 1\begin{vmatrix} 1 & 1 \\ 1 & 2 \end{vmatrix} = -1 + 1 = 0,$$

$$|D_w| = \begin{vmatrix} 1 & 1 & 0 & 1 \\ 0 & 1 & 1 & 2 \\ 0 & 0 & 1 & 3 \\ -1 & 0 & 0 & 4 \end{vmatrix} = 1\begin{vmatrix} 1 & 1 & 2 \\ 0 & 1 & 3 \\ 0 & 0 & 4 \end{vmatrix} + 1\begin{vmatrix} 1 & 0 & 1 \\ 1 & 1 & 2 \\ 0 & 1 & 3 \end{vmatrix} = \begin{vmatrix} 1 & 3 \\ 0 & 4 \end{vmatrix} + \left(1\begin{vmatrix} 1 & 2 \\ 1 & 3 \end{vmatrix} - 1\begin{vmatrix} 0 & 1 \\ 1 & 3 \end{vmatrix}\right)$$

$= 4 + 2 = 6$. Hence, the solution is $x = \dfrac{|D_x|}{|D|} = \dfrac{-2}{2} = -1$, $y = \dfrac{|D_y|}{|D|} = \dfrac{4}{2} = 2$,

$z = \dfrac{|D_z|}{|D|} = \dfrac{0}{2} = 0$, and $w = \dfrac{|D_w|}{|D|} = \dfrac{6}{2} = 3$.

44. $\begin{vmatrix} a & a & a & a & a \\ 0 & a & a & a & a \\ 0 & 0 & a & a & a \\ 0 & 0 & 0 & a & a \\ 0 & 0 & 0 & 0 & a \end{vmatrix} = a\begin{vmatrix} a & a & a & a \\ 0 & a & a & a \\ 0 & 0 & a & a \\ 0 & 0 & 0 & a \end{vmatrix} = a^2\begin{vmatrix} a & a & a \\ 0 & a & a \\ 0 & 0 & a \end{vmatrix} = a^3\begin{vmatrix} a & a \\ 0 & a \end{vmatrix} = a^5.$

46. $\begin{vmatrix} x & 1 & 1 \\ 1 & 1 & x \\ x & 1 & x \end{vmatrix} = x\begin{vmatrix} 1 & x \\ 1 & x \end{vmatrix} - \begin{vmatrix} 1 & x \\ x & x \end{vmatrix} + \begin{vmatrix} 1 & 1 \\ x & 1 \end{vmatrix} = x(0) - (x - x^2) + 1 - x = x^2 - 2x + 1 = 0$

    $\Leftrightarrow \quad (x - 1)^2 = 0 \quad \Leftrightarrow \quad x = 1.$

48. $\begin{vmatrix} a & b & x - a \\ x & x + b & x \\ 0 & 1 & 1 \end{vmatrix} = -1\begin{vmatrix} a & x - a \\ x & x \end{vmatrix} + \begin{vmatrix} a & b \\ x & x + b \end{vmatrix} = -1[ax - x(x - a)] + a(x + b) - bx$

    $= -ax + x^2 - ax + ax + ab - bx = x^2 - ax - bx + ab = (x - a)(x - b) = 0 \quad \Leftrightarrow \quad x = a$ or
    $x = b.$

50.   The student should prefer Gaussian elimination, since six 5×5 determinants are much harder to evaluate than one 5-equation Gaussian elimination.

Exercises 10.7

2. $y > -3$

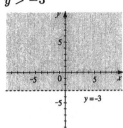

4. $y < x + 2$

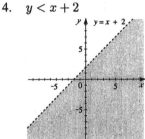

6. $y < -x + 5$

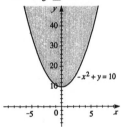

8. $3x + 4y + 12 > 0$

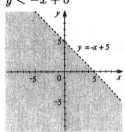

10. $-x^2 + y \geq 10$

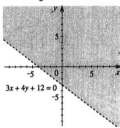

12. $x^2 + y^2 \geq 5$

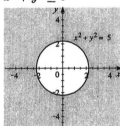

14. $\begin{cases} 2x + 3y > 12 \\ 3x - y < 21 \end{cases}$ The vertices occur where $\begin{cases} 2x + 3y = 12 \\ 3x - y = 21 \end{cases}$ $\Leftrightarrow$

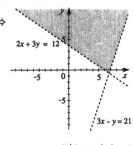

$\begin{cases} 2x + 3y = 12 \\ 9x - 3y = 63 \end{cases}$, and adding the two equations gives $11x = 75$

$\Leftrightarrow$ $x = \frac{75}{11}$. Then $2\left(\frac{75}{11}\right) + 3y = 12$ $\Leftrightarrow$

$3y = \frac{132-150}{11} = \frac{-18}{11}$ $\Leftrightarrow$ $y = -\frac{6}{11}$. Therefore, the vertex is

$\left(\frac{75}{11}, -\frac{6}{11}\right)$, and the solution set is not bounded.

16. $\begin{cases} x - y > 0 \\ 4 + y \leq 2x \end{cases}$

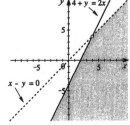

The vertices occur where $\begin{cases} x - y = 0 \quad \Leftrightarrow \quad y = x \\ 4 + y = 2x \end{cases}$.

Substituting for y gives $4 + x = 2x$ $\Leftrightarrow$ $x = 4$, so $y = 4$.
Hence, the vertex is $(4, 4)$, and the solution set is not bounded.

18. $\begin{cases} x > 2 \\ y < 12 \\ 2x - 4y > 8 \end{cases}$ From the graph, the vertices occur at $(2, -1)$

and $(28, 12)$. The solution set is not bounded.

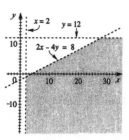

20. $\begin{cases} y \ge x^2 \\ x + y \ge 6 \end{cases}$ The vertices occur where $\begin{cases} y = x^2 \\ x + y = 6 \end{cases}$.

Substituting for y gives $x^2 + x = 6 \quad \Leftrightarrow \quad x^2 + x - 6 = 0 \quad \Leftrightarrow$
$(x + 3)(x - 2) = 0 \quad \Rightarrow \quad x = -3, x = 2$. Since $y = x^2$, the
vertices are $(-3, 9)$ and $(2, 4)$, and the solution set is not bounded.

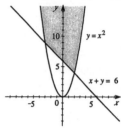

22. $\begin{cases} x > 0 \\ y > 0 \\ x + y < 10 \\ x^2 + y^2 > 9 \end{cases}$ From the graph, the vertices are $(0, 3)$, $(0, 10)$,

$(3, 0)$, and $(10, 0)$. The solution set is bounded.

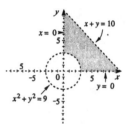

24. $\begin{cases} x^2 + y^2 < 9 \\ 2x + y^2 \ge 1 \end{cases}$ The vertices occur where $\begin{cases} x^2 + y^2 = 9 \\ 2x + y^2 = 1 \end{cases}$.

Subtracting the equations gives $x^2 - 2x = 8 \quad \Leftrightarrow$
$x^2 - 2x - 8 = 0 \quad \Leftrightarrow \quad (x - 4)(x + 2) = 0 \quad \Leftrightarrow \quad x = -2$,
$x = 4$. Therefore, the vertices are $(-2, -\sqrt{5})$ and $(-2, \sqrt{5})$,
since $x = 4$ does not give a real solution for y. The solution set
is bounded.

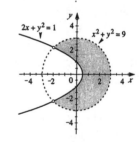

26. $\begin{cases} y < x + 6 \\ 3x + 2y \ge 12 \\ x - 2y \le 2 \end{cases}$

To find where the line $y = x + 6$ intersects the lines $3x + 2y = 12$
and $x - 2y = 2$ we substitute for y: $3x + 2(x + 6) = 12 \quad \Leftrightarrow$
$x = 0$, and $y = 6$; $x - 2(x + 6) = 2 \quad \Leftrightarrow \quad x = -14$, and
$y = -8$. Next, adding the equations $3x + 2y = 12$ and $x - 2y = 2$
yields $4x = 14 \quad \Leftrightarrow \quad x = \frac{7}{2}$. So these lines intersect at the point
$\left(\frac{7}{2}, \frac{3}{4}\right)$. Since the vertex $(-14, -8)$ is not part of the solution set, the vertices are $(0, 6)$ and $\left(\frac{7}{2}, \frac{3}{4}\right)$,
and the solution set is not bounded.

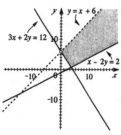

28.
$$\begin{cases} x \geq 0 \\ y \geq 0 \\ y \leq 4 \\ 2x + y \leq 8 \end{cases}$$

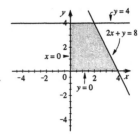

The points of intersection are $(0, 8)$, $(0, 4)$, $(4, 0)$, $(2, 4)$, and $(3, 2)$. However, the point $(0, 8)$ is not in the solution set. Therefore, the vertices are $(0, 4)$, $(2, 4)$, $(4, 0)$, and $(0, 0)$. The solution set is bounded.

30.
$$\begin{cases} x + y > 12 \\ y < \frac{1}{2}x - 6 \\ 3x + y < 6 \end{cases}$$

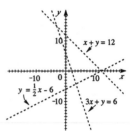

Graphing these inequalities, we see that there are no points that satisfy all three, and hence the solution set is empty.

32.
$$\begin{cases} x^2 - y \geq 0 \\ x + y < 6 \\ x - y < 6 \end{cases}$$

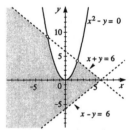

Adding the equations $x + y = 6$ and $x - y = 6$ yields $2x = 12$ $\Leftrightarrow$ $x = 6$. So these equations intersect at the point $(6, 0)$. To find where $x^2 - y = 0$ and $x + y = 6$ intersect, we solve the first for y, giving $y = x^2$, and then substitute into the second equation to get $x + x^2 = 6$ $\Leftrightarrow$ $x^2 + x - 6 = 0$ $\Leftrightarrow$ $(x + 3)(x - 2) = 0$ $\Leftrightarrow$ $x = -3$ or $x = 2$. When $x = -3$, we have $y = 9$, and when $x = 2$, we have $y = 4$, so the points of intersection are $(-3, 9)$ and $(2, 4)$. Substituting for $y = x^2$ into the equation $x - y = 6$ gives $x - x^2 = 6$, which has no solution. Thus the vertices are $(6, 0)$, $(-3, 9)$, and $(2, 4)$ (however, they are not in the solution set). The solution set is not bounded.

34.
$$\begin{cases} y \geq x^3 \\ y \leq 2x + 4 \\ x + y \geq 0 \end{cases}$$

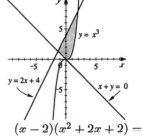

The curves $y = x^3$ and $x + y = 0$ intersect when $x^3 + x = 0$ $\Leftrightarrow$ $x = 0$ $\Rightarrow$ $y = 0$. The lines $x + y = 0$ and $y = 2x + 4$ intersect when $-x = 2x + 4$ $\Leftrightarrow$ $3x = -4$ $\Leftrightarrow$ $x = -\frac{4}{3}$ $\Rightarrow$ $y = \frac{4}{3}$. To find where $y = x^3$ and $y = 2x + 4$ intersect, we substitute for y and get $x^3 = 2x + 4$ $\Leftrightarrow$ $x^3 - 2x - 4 = 0$ $\Leftrightarrow$ $(x - 2)(x^2 + 2x + 2) = 0$ $\Rightarrow$ $x = 2$ (the other factor has no real solution). When $x = 2$ we have $y = 8$. Thus the vertices of the region are $(0, 0)$, $(-\frac{4}{3}, \frac{4}{3})$, and $(2, 8)$. The solution set is bounded.

36. Let $x =$ number of chairs made and $y =$ number of tables made. Then, the following system of inequalities holds:

$$\begin{cases} 3y + 2x \leq 12 \\ y + 2x \leq 8 \\ x \geq 0 \\ y \geq 0 \end{cases}$$. The intersection points are $(0, 4)$, $(0, 8)$, $(6, 0)$,

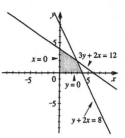

$(4, 0)$, $(0, 0)$, and $(3, 2)$. Since the points $(0, 8)$ and $(6, 0)$ are not in the solution set, the vertices are $(0, 4)$, $(0, 0)$, $(4, 0)$, and $(3, 2)$.

Exercises 10.8

2. $\dfrac{x}{x^2 + 3x - 4} = \dfrac{x}{(x-1)(x+4)} = \dfrac{A}{(x-1)} + \dfrac{B}{(x+4)}$

4. $\dfrac{1}{x^4 - x^3} = \dfrac{1}{x^3(x-1)} = \dfrac{A}{x} + \dfrac{B}{x^2} + \dfrac{C}{x^3} + \dfrac{D}{x-1}$

6. $\dfrac{1}{x^4 - 1} = \dfrac{1}{(x^2-1)(x^2+1)} = \dfrac{1}{(x-1)(x+1)(x^2+1)} = \dfrac{A}{x-1} + \dfrac{B}{x+1} + \dfrac{Cx+D}{x^2+1}$

8. $\dfrac{x^4 + x^2 + 1}{x^2(x^2+4)^2} = \dfrac{A}{x} + \dfrac{B}{x^2} + \dfrac{Cx+D}{x^2+4} + \dfrac{Ex+F}{(x^2+4)^2}$

10. Since $(x^6 - 1)(x^4 - 1) = (x^3 - 1)(x^3 + 1)(x^2 - 1)(x^2 + 1)$

    $= (x-1)(x^2 + x + 1)(x+1)(x^2 - x + 1)(x-1)(x+1)(x^2+1)$

    $= (x-1)^2(x+1)^2(x^2 + x + 1)(x^2 - x + 1)(x^2+1)$, we have

    $$\frac{1}{(x^6-1)(x^4-1)} = \frac{1}{(x-1)^2(x+1)^2(x^2+x+1)(x^2-x+1)(x^2+1)}$$

    $$= \frac{A}{x-1} + \frac{B}{(x-1)^2} + \frac{C}{x+1} + \frac{D}{(x+1)^2} + \frac{Ex+F}{x^2+x+1} + \frac{Gx+H}{x^2-x+1} + \frac{Jx+K}{x^2+1}.$$

12. $\dfrac{x+6}{x(x+3)} = \dfrac{A}{x} + \dfrac{B}{x+3}$. Multiplying by $x(x+3)$ we get

    $x + 6 = A(x+3) + xB \quad \Leftrightarrow \quad x + 6 = Ax + 3A + Bx = (A+B)x + 3A$. Thus

    $\begin{cases} A + B = 1 \\ \quad 3A = 6 \end{cases}$. Now $3A = 6 \quad \Leftrightarrow \quad A = 2$, and $2 + B = 1 \quad \Leftrightarrow \quad B = -1$. The required

    partial fraction decomposition is $\dfrac{x+6}{x(x+3)} = \dfrac{2}{x} - \dfrac{1}{x+3}$.

14. $\dfrac{x-12}{x^2 - 4x} = \dfrac{x-12}{x(x-4)} = \dfrac{A}{x} + \dfrac{B}{x-4}$. Multiplying by $x(x-4)$, we get $x - 12 = A(x-4) + Bx$

    $= Ax - 4A + Bx = (A+B)x - 4A$. Thus we must solve the system $\begin{cases} A + B = 1 \\ -4A = -12 \end{cases}$. This

    gives $-4A = -12 \quad \Leftrightarrow \quad A = 3$, and $3 + B = 1 \quad \Leftrightarrow \quad B = -2$. Thus $\dfrac{x-12}{x^2-4x} = \dfrac{3}{x} - \dfrac{2}{x-4}$.

16. $\dfrac{2x+1}{x^2 + x - 2} = \dfrac{2x+1}{(x+2)(x-1)} = \dfrac{A}{x+2} + \dfrac{B}{x-1}$. Thus, $2x + 1 = A(x-1) + B(x+2)$

    $= (A+B)x + (-A + 2B)$, and so $\begin{cases} A + B = 2 \\ -A + 2B = 1 \end{cases}$. Adding the two equations, we get $3B = 3$

    $\Leftrightarrow \quad B = 1$. Thus $A + 1 = 2 \quad \Leftrightarrow \quad A = 1$. Therefore, $\dfrac{2x+1}{x^2+x-2} = \dfrac{1}{x+2} + \dfrac{1}{x-1}$.

18. $\dfrac{8x-3}{2x^2 - x} = \dfrac{8x-3}{x(2x-1)} = \dfrac{A}{x} + \dfrac{B}{2x-1}$. Hence, $8x - 3 = A(2x-1) + Bx = (2A+B)x + (-A)$.

    $\begin{cases} 2A + B = 8 \\ \quad -A = -3 \end{cases}$. So $-A = -3 \quad \Leftrightarrow \quad A = 3$, and $2(3) + B = 8 \quad \Leftrightarrow \quad B = 2$. Therefore,

$$\frac{8x-3}{2x^2-x} = \frac{3}{x} + \frac{2}{2x-1}.$$

20. $\dfrac{7x-3}{x^3+2x^2-3x} = \dfrac{7x-3}{x(x+3)(x-1)} = \dfrac{A}{x} + \dfrac{B}{x+3} + \dfrac{C}{x-1}.$ Hence,

$7x-3 = A(x+3)(x-1) + Bx(x-1) + Cx(x+3)$
$= A(x^2+2x-3) + B(x^2-x) + C(x^2+3x) = (A+B+C)x^2 + (2A-B+3C)x - 3A.$

Thus $\begin{cases} A+B+C=0 \\ 2A-B+3C=7 \\ -3A=-3 \end{cases}$. So $-3A=-3 \Leftrightarrow A=1$. Substituting, the system reduces to

$\begin{cases} 1+B+C=0 \\ 2-B+3C=7 \end{cases}$ Adding these two equations, we get $3+4C=7 \Leftrightarrow C=1$. Thus

$1+B+1=0 \Leftrightarrow B=-2$. Therefore, $\dfrac{7x-3}{x^3+2x^2-3x} = \dfrac{1}{x} - \dfrac{2}{x+3} + \dfrac{1}{x-1}.$

22. $\dfrac{-3x^2-3x+27}{(x+2)(2x^2+3x-9)} = \dfrac{-3x^2-3x+27}{(x+2)(2x-3)(x+3)} = \dfrac{A}{x+2} + \dfrac{B}{2x-3} + \dfrac{C}{x+3}.$ Thus,

$-3x^2-3x+27 = A(2x-3)(x+3) + B(x+2)(x+3) + C(x+2)(2x-3)$
$= A(2x^2+3x-9) + B(x^2+5x+6) + C(2x^2+x-6)$
$= (2A+B+2C)x^2 + (3A+5B+C)x + (-9A+6B-6C).$

The resulting system has the following matrix representation:

$\begin{bmatrix} 2 & 1 & 2 & -3 \\ 3 & 5 & 1 & -3 \\ -9 & 6 & -6 & 27 \end{bmatrix} \xrightarrow[-\frac{1}{3}R_3]{R_2-R_1 \to R_2} \begin{bmatrix} 2 & 1 & 2 & -3 \\ 1 & 4 & -1 & 0 \\ 3 & -2 & 2 & -9 \end{bmatrix} \xrightarrow{R_1 \leftrightarrow R_2} \begin{bmatrix} 1 & 4 & -1 & 0 \\ 2 & 1 & 2 & -3 \\ 3 & -2 & 2 & -9 \end{bmatrix}$

$\xrightarrow[R_3-3R_1 \to R_3]{R_2-2R_1 \to R_2} \begin{bmatrix} 1 & 4 & -1 & 0 \\ 0 & -7 & 4 & -3 \\ 0 & -14 & 5 & -9 \end{bmatrix} \xrightarrow{R_3-2R_2 \to R_3} \begin{bmatrix} 1 & 4 & -1 & 0 \\ 0 & -7 & 4 & -3 \\ 0 & 0 & -3 & -3 \end{bmatrix}.$

Hence, $-3C=-3 \Leftrightarrow C=1$; $-7B+4=-3 \Leftrightarrow B=1$; and $A+4-1=0 \Leftrightarrow A=-3.$

Therefore, $\dfrac{-3x^2-3x+27}{(x+2)(2x^2+3x-9)} = \dfrac{-3}{x+2} + \dfrac{1}{2x-3} + \dfrac{1}{x+3}.$

24. $\dfrac{3x^2+5x-13}{(3x+2)(x^2-4x+4)} = \dfrac{3x^2+5x-13}{(3x+2)(x-2)^2} = \dfrac{A}{3x+2} + \dfrac{B}{x-2} + \dfrac{C}{(x-2)^2}.$ Thus,

$3x^2+5x-13 = A(x-2)^2 + B(3x+2)(x-2) + C(3x+2)$
$= A(x^2-4x+4) + B(3x^2-4x-4) + C(3x+2)$
$= (A+3B)x^2 + (-4A-4B+3C)x + (4A-4B+2C).$

The resulting system has the following matrix representation:

$\begin{bmatrix} 1 & 3 & 0 & 3 \\ -4 & -4 & 3 & 5 \\ 4 & -4 & 2 & -13 \end{bmatrix} \xrightarrow[R_3-4R_1 \to R_3]{R_2+4R_1 \to R_2} \begin{bmatrix} 1 & 3 & 0 & 3 \\ 0 & 8 & 3 & 17 \\ 0 & -16 & 2 & -25 \end{bmatrix} \xrightarrow{R_3+2R_2 \to R_3}$

$\begin{bmatrix} 1 & 3 & 0 & 3 \\ 0 & 8 & 3 & 17 \\ 0 & 0 & 8 & 9 \end{bmatrix}.$

Hence, $8C = 9 \Leftrightarrow C = \frac{9}{8}$; $8B + \frac{27}{8} = 17 \Leftrightarrow B = \frac{109}{64}$; and $A + \frac{327}{64} = 3 \Leftrightarrow A = -\frac{135}{64}$.

Therefore, $\dfrac{3x^2 + 5x - 13}{(3x + 2)(x - 2)^2} = \dfrac{\frac{-135}{64}}{3x + 2} + \dfrac{\frac{109}{64}}{x - 2} + \dfrac{\frac{9}{8}}{(x - 2)^2}$.

26. $\dfrac{x - 4}{(2x - 5)^2} = \dfrac{A}{2x - 5} + \dfrac{B}{(2x - 5)^2}$. Hence, $x - 4 = A(2x - 5) + B = 2Ax + (-5A + B)$, and so

$\begin{cases} 2A = 1 \\ -5A + B = -4 \end{cases}$. $A = \frac{1}{2}$, and $-5\left(\frac{1}{2}\right) + B = -4 \Leftrightarrow B = -\frac{3}{2}$. Therefore,

$\dfrac{x - 4}{(2x - 5)^2} = \dfrac{1/2}{2x - 5} - \dfrac{3/2}{(2x - 5)^2}$.

28. $\dfrac{x^3 - 2x^2 - 4x + 3}{x^4} = \dfrac{A}{x} + \dfrac{B}{x^2} + \dfrac{C}{x^3} + \dfrac{D}{x^4}$. Hence, $x^3 - 2x^2 - 4x + 3 = Ax^3 + Bx^2 + Cx + D$.

Thus $A = 1$; $B = -2$; $C = -4$; and $D = 3$. Therefore,

$\dfrac{x^3 - 2x^2 - 4x + 3}{x^4} = \dfrac{1}{x} - \dfrac{2}{x^2} - \dfrac{4}{x^3} + \dfrac{3}{x^4}$.

30. $\dfrac{-2x^2 + 5x - 1}{x^4 - 2x^3 + 2x - 1} = \dfrac{-2x^2 + 5x - 1}{(x - 1)(x^3 - x^2 - x + 1)} = \dfrac{-2x^2 + 5x - 1}{(x - 1)^3(x + 1)}$

$= \dfrac{A}{x + 1} + \dfrac{B}{x - 1} + \dfrac{C}{(x - 1)^2} + \dfrac{D}{(x - 1)^3}$. Thus,

$-2x^2 + 5x - 1 = A(x - 1)^3 + B(x + 1)(x - 1)^2 + C(x + 1)(x - 1) + D(x + 1)$

$= A(x^3 - 3x^2 + 3x - 1) + B(x + 1)(x^2 - 2x + 1) + C(x^2 - 1) + D(x + 1)$

$= A(x^3 - 3x^2 + 3x - 1) + B(x^3 - x^2 - x + 1) + C(x^2 - 1) + D(x + 1)$

$= (A + B)x^3 + (-3A - B + C)x^2 + (3A - B + D)x + (-A + B - C + D)$, which leads to the

system:

$$\begin{bmatrix} 1 & 1 & 0 & 0 & 0 \\ -3 & -1 & 1 & 0 & -2 \\ 3 & -1 & 0 & 1 & 5 \\ -1 & 1 & -1 & 1 & -1 \end{bmatrix} \xrightarrow[R_4 + R_1 \to R_4]{R_2 + 3R_1 \to R_2,\ R_3 - 3R_1 \to R_3} \begin{bmatrix} 1 & 1 & 0 & 0 & 0 \\ 0 & 2 & 1 & 0 & -2 \\ 0 & -4 & 0 & 1 & 5 \\ 0 & 2 & -1 & 1 & -1 \end{bmatrix}$$

$$\xrightarrow[R_4 - R_2 \to R_4]{R_3 + 2R_2 \to R_3} \begin{bmatrix} 1 & 1 & 0 & 0 & 0 \\ 0 & 2 & 1 & 0 & -2 \\ 0 & 0 & 2 & 1 & 1 \\ 0 & 0 & -2 & 1 & 1 \end{bmatrix} \xrightarrow{R_4 + R_3 \to R_4} \begin{bmatrix} 1 & 1 & 0 & 0 & 0 \\ 0 & 2 & 1 & 0 & -2 \\ 0 & 0 & 2 & 1 & 1 \\ 0 & 0 & 0 & 2 & 2 \end{bmatrix}.$$

Hence, $2D = 2 \Leftrightarrow D = 1$; $2C + 1 = 1 \Leftrightarrow C = 0$; $2B + 0 = -2 \Leftrightarrow B = -1$; and $A - 1 = 0$

$\Leftrightarrow A = 1$. Therefore, $\dfrac{-2x^2 + 5x - 1}{x^4 - 2x^3 + 2x - 1} = \dfrac{1}{x + 1} - \dfrac{1}{x - 1} + \dfrac{1}{(x - 1)^3}$.

32. $\dfrac{3x^2 + 12x - 20}{x^4 - 8x^2 + 16} = \dfrac{3x^2 + 12x - 20}{(x^2 - 4)^2} = \dfrac{3x^2 + 12x - 20}{(x + 2)^2(x - 2)^2}$

$= \dfrac{A}{x + 2} + \dfrac{B}{(x + 2)^2} + \dfrac{C}{x - 2} + \dfrac{D}{(x - 2)^2}$. Thus,

$3x^2 + 12x - 20 = A(x + 2)(x - 2)^2 + B(x - 2)^2 + C(x + 2)^2(x - 2) + D(x + 2)^2$

$= A(x^3 - 2x^2 - 4x + 8) + B(x^2 - 4x + 4) + C(x^3 + 2x^2 - 4x - 8) + D(x^2 + 4x + 4)$

$$= (A+C)x^3 + (-2A+B+2C+D)x^2 + (-4A-4B-4C+4D)x$$
$$+ (8A+4B-8C+4D), \text{ which leads to the system:}$$

$$\begin{bmatrix} 1 & 0 & 1 & 0 & 0 \\ -2 & 1 & 2 & 1 & 3 \\ -4 & -4 & -4 & 4 & 12 \\ 8 & 4 & -8 & 4 & -20 \end{bmatrix} \xrightarrow[R_4-8R_1 \to R_4]{R_2+2R_1 \to R_2, \ R_3+4R_1 \to R_3}$$

$$\begin{bmatrix} 1 & 0 & 1 & 0 & 0 \\ 0 & 1 & 4 & 1 & 3 \\ 0 & -4 & 0 & 4 & 12 \\ 0 & 4 & -16 & 4 & -20 \end{bmatrix} \xrightarrow[R_4-4R_2 \to R_4]{R_3+4R_2 \to R_3} \begin{bmatrix} 1 & 0 & 1 & 0 & 0 \\ 0 & 1 & 4 & 1 & 3 \\ 0 & 0 & 16 & 8 & 24 \\ 0 & 0 & -32 & 0 & -32 \end{bmatrix}.$$

Hence, $-32C = -32 \Leftrightarrow C = 1$; $16 + 8D = 24 \Leftrightarrow D = 1$; $B + 4 + 1 = 3 \Leftrightarrow B = -2$; and

$A + 1 = 0 \Leftrightarrow A = -1$. Therefore, $\dfrac{3x^2 + 12x - 20}{x^4 - 8x^2 + 16} = -\dfrac{1}{x+2} - \dfrac{2}{(x+2)^2} + \dfrac{1}{x-2} + \dfrac{1}{(x-2)^2}$.

34. $\dfrac{3x^2 - 2x + 8}{x^3 - x^2 + 2x - 2} = \dfrac{3x^2 - 2x + 8}{(x^2 + 2)(x - 1)} = \dfrac{Ax + B}{x^2 + 2} + \dfrac{C}{x - 1}$. Thus,

$3x^2 - 2x + 8 = (Ax + B)(x - 1) + C(x^2 + 2) = (A + C)x^2 + (-A + B)x + (-B + 2C)$,

which leads to the system:

$$\begin{bmatrix} 1 & 0 & 1 & 3 \\ -1 & 1 & 0 & -2 \\ 0 & -1 & 2 & 8 \end{bmatrix} \xrightarrow{R_2+R_1 \to R_2} \begin{bmatrix} 1 & 0 & 1 & 3 \\ 0 & 1 & 1 & 1 \\ 0 & -1 & 2 & 8 \end{bmatrix} \xrightarrow{R_3+R_2 \to R_3} \begin{bmatrix} 1 & 0 & 1 & 3 \\ 0 & 1 & 1 & 1 \\ 0 & 0 & 3 & 9 \end{bmatrix}.$$

Hence, $3C = 9 \Leftrightarrow C = 3$; $B + 3 = 1 \Leftrightarrow B = -2$; and $A + 3 = 3 \Leftrightarrow A = 0$. Therefore,

$$\dfrac{3x^2 - 2x + 8}{x^3 - x^2 + 2x - 2} = -\dfrac{2}{x^2 + 2} + \dfrac{3}{x - 1}.$$

36. $\dfrac{x^2 + x + 1}{2x^4 + 3x^2 + 1} = \dfrac{x^2 + x + 1}{(2x^2 + 1)(x^2 + 1)} = \dfrac{Ax + B}{2x^2 + 1} + \dfrac{Cx + D}{x^2 + 1}$. Thus,

$x^2 + x + 1 = (Ax + B)(x^2 + 1) + (Cx + D)(2x^2 + 1)$

$= Ax^3 + Ax + Bx^2 + B + 2Cx^3 + 2Dx^2 + Cx + D$

$= (A + 2C)x^3 + (B + 2D)x^2 + (A + C)x + (B + D)$, which leads to the system:

$$\begin{bmatrix} 1 & 0 & 2 & 0 & 0 \\ 0 & 1 & 0 & 2 & 1 \\ 1 & 0 & 1 & 0 & 1 \\ 0 & 1 & 0 & 1 & 1 \end{bmatrix} \xrightarrow[R_4-R_2 \to R_4]{R_3-R_1 \to R_3} \begin{bmatrix} 1 & 0 & 2 & 0 & 0 \\ 0 & 1 & 0 & 2 & 1 \\ 0 & 0 & -1 & 0 & 1 \\ 0 & 0 & 0 & -1 & 0 \end{bmatrix}.$$

Hence, $-D = 0 \Leftrightarrow D = 0$; $-C = 1 \Leftrightarrow C = -1$; $B + 0 = 1 \Leftrightarrow B = 1$; and $A - 2 = 0 \Leftrightarrow$

$A = 2$. Therefore, $\dfrac{x^2 + x + 1}{2x^4 + 3x^2 + 1} = \dfrac{2x + 1}{2x^2 + 1} - \dfrac{x}{x^2 + 1}$.

38. $\dfrac{2x^2 - x + 8}{(x^2 + 4)^2} = \dfrac{Ax + B}{x^2 + 4} + \dfrac{Cx + D}{(x^2 + 4)^2}$. Thus, $2x^2 - x + 8 = (Ax + B)(x^2 + 4) + Cx + D$

$= Ax^3 + 4Ax + Bx^2 + 4B + Cx + D = Ax^3 + Bx^2 + (4A + C)x + (4B + D)$, and so $A = 0$;

$B = 2$; $0 + C = -1 \Leftrightarrow C = -1$; and $8 + D = 8 \Leftrightarrow D = 0$. Therefore,

$$\dfrac{2x^2 - x + 8}{(x^2 + 4)^2} = \dfrac{2}{x^2 + 4} - \dfrac{1}{(x^2 + 4)^2}.$$

40. $\dfrac{x^5 - 3x^4 + 3x^3 - 4x^2 + 4x + 12}{(x-2)^2(x^2+2)} = \dfrac{x^5 - 3x^4 + 3x^3 - 4x^2 + 4x + 12}{x^4 - 4x^3 + 6x^2 - 8x + 8}$. Next use long division to

get a proper rational function.

$$
\begin{array}{r}
x \quad +1 \\
x^4 - 4x^3 + 6x^2 - 8x + 8 \overline{\smash{\big)}\ x^5 - 3x^4 + 3x^3 - 4x^2 + 4x + 12} \\
\underline{x^5 - 4x^4 + 6x^3 - 8x^2 + 8x} \\
x^4 - 3x^3 + 4x^2 - 4x + 12 \\
\underline{x^4 - 4x^3 + 6x^2 - 8x \ + 8} \\
x^3 - 2x^2 + 4x \ + 4
\end{array}
$$

Thus $\dfrac{x^5 - 3x^4 + 3x^3 - 4x^2 + 4x + 12}{(x-2)^2(x^2+2)} = x + 1 + \dfrac{x^3 - 2x^2 + 4x + 4}{(x-2)^2(x^2+2)}$. Now,

$\dfrac{x^3 - 2x^2 + 4x + 4}{(x-2)^2(x^2+2)} = \dfrac{A}{x-2} + \dfrac{B}{(x-2)^2} + \dfrac{Cx+D}{x^2+2}$, and so

$x^3 - 2x^2 + 4x + 4 = A(x-2)(x^2+2) + B(x^2+2) + (Cx+D)(x-2)^2$

$\quad = A(x^3 - 2x^2 + 2x - 4) + B(x^2+2) + (Cx+D)(x^2 - 4x + 4)$

$\quad = Ax^3 - 2Ax^2 + 2Ax - 4A + Bx^2 + 2B + Cx^3 - 4Cx^2 + 4Cx + Dx^2 - 4Dx + 4D$

$\quad = (A+C)x^3 + (-2A+B-4C+D)x^2 + (2A+4C-4D)x + (-4A+2B+4D).$

The resulting system has the following matrix representation:

$$
\begin{bmatrix}
1 & 0 & 1 & 0 & 1 \\
-2 & 1 & -4 & 1 & -2 \\
2 & 0 & 4 & -4 & 4 \\
-4 & 2 & 0 & 4 & 4
\end{bmatrix}
\quad
\begin{array}{c} R_2 + 2R_1 \to R_2,\ R_3 - 2R_1 \to R_3 \\ \hline R_4 + 4R_1 \to R_4 \end{array}
\quad
\begin{bmatrix}
1 & 0 & 1 & 0 & 1 \\
0 & 1 & -2 & 1 & 0 \\
0 & 0 & 2 & -4 & 2 \\
0 & 2 & 4 & 4 & 8
\end{bmatrix}
$$

$$
\begin{array}{c} \frac{1}{2}R_3 \\ \hline R_4 - 2R_2 \to R_4 \end{array}
\quad
\begin{bmatrix}
1 & 0 & 1 & 0 & 1 \\
0 & 1 & -2 & 1 & 0 \\
0 & 0 & 1 & -2 & 1 \\
0 & 0 & 8 & 2 & 8
\end{bmatrix}
\quad
\begin{array}{c} R_4 - 8R_3 \to R_3 \\ \hline \end{array}
\quad
\begin{bmatrix}
1 & 0 & 1 & 0 & 1 \\
0 & 1 & -2 & 1 & 0 \\
0 & 0 & 1 & -2 & 1 \\
0 & 0 & 0 & 18 & 0
\end{bmatrix}
$$

Then, $D = 0$; $C = 1$; $B - 2 = 0 \Leftrightarrow B = 2$; and $A + 1 = 1 \Leftrightarrow A = 0$. Therefore,

$\dfrac{x^5 - 3x^4 + 3x^3 - 4x^2 + 4x + 12}{(x-2)^2(x^2+2)} = x + 1 + \dfrac{2}{(x-2)^2} + \dfrac{x}{x^2+2}$.

42. $\dfrac{ax^3 + bx^2}{(x^2+1)^2} = \dfrac{Ax+B}{x^2+1} + \dfrac{Cx+D}{(x^2+1)^2}$. Hence, $ax^3 + bx^2 = (Ax+B)(x^2+1) + Cx + D$

$\quad = Ax^3 + Ax + Bx^2 + B + Cx + D = Ax^3 + Bx^2 + (A+C)x + (B+D)$, and so $A = a$;

$B = b$; $a + C = 0 \Leftrightarrow C = -a$; and $b + D = 0 \Leftrightarrow D = -b$. Therefore, $A = a$, $B = b$, $C = -a$,

and $D = -b$.

44. Combining the terms, we have

$$\dfrac{2}{x-1} + \dfrac{1}{(x-1)^2} + \dfrac{1}{x+1} = \dfrac{2(x^2-1)}{(x-1)^2(x+1)} + \dfrac{1(x+1)}{(x-1)^2(x+1)} + \dfrac{1(x^2-2x+1)}{(x-1)^2(x+1)}$$

$$= \dfrac{2x^2 - 2 + x + 1 + x^2 - 2x + 1}{(x-1)^2(x+1)} = \dfrac{3x^2 - x}{(x-1)^2(x+1)}.$$

Now to find the partial fraction decomposition, we have

$$\frac{3x^2 - x}{(x-1)^2(x+1)} = \frac{A}{x-1} + \frac{B}{(x-1)^2} + \frac{C}{x+1}, \text{ and so}$$

$$3x^2 - x = A(x-1)(x+1) + B(x+1) + C(x-1)^2 = A(x^2 - 1) + B(x+1) + C(x^2 - 2x + 1)$$

$$= Ax^2 - A + Bx + B + Cx^2 - 2Cx + C = (A+C)x^2 + (B-2C)x + (-A+B+C)$$

The resulting system has the following matrix representation:

$$\begin{bmatrix} 1 & 0 & 1 & 3 \\ 0 & 1 & -2 & -1 \\ -1 & 1 & 1 & 0 \end{bmatrix} \xrightarrow{R_3+R_1 \to R_3} \begin{bmatrix} 1 & 0 & 1 & 3 \\ 0 & 1 & -2 & -1 \\ 0 & 1 & 2 & 3 \end{bmatrix} \xrightarrow{R_3-R_2 \to R_3} \begin{bmatrix} 1 & 0 & 1 & 3 \\ 0 & 1 & -2 & -1 \\ 0 & 0 & 4 & 4 \end{bmatrix}$$

$$\xrightarrow{\frac{1}{4}R_3} \begin{bmatrix} 1 & 0 & 1 & 3 \\ 0 & 1 & -2 & -1 \\ 0 & 0 & 1 & 1 \end{bmatrix}.$$

Then, $C = 1$; $B - 2 = -1 \Leftrightarrow B = 1$; and $A + 1 = 3 \Leftrightarrow A = 2$. Therefore we get back the same

expression, $\dfrac{3x^2 - x}{(x-1)^2(x+1)} = \dfrac{2}{x-1} + \dfrac{1}{(x-1)^2} + \dfrac{1}{x+1}$.

Review Exercises for Chapter 10

2. $\begin{cases} y = 2x + 6 \\ y = -x + 3 \end{cases}$ Subtracting the second equation from the first, we

get $0 = 3x + 3$ $\Leftrightarrow$ $x = -1$. So $y = -(-1) + 3 = 4$. Thus the solution is $(-1, 4)$.

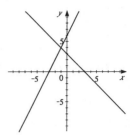

4. $\begin{cases} 6x - 8y = 15 \\ -\frac{3}{2}x + 2y = -4 \end{cases}$ $\Leftrightarrow$ $\begin{cases} 6x - 8y = 15 \\ -6x + 8y = -16 \end{cases}$ Adding gives

$0 = -1$ which is false. Hence, there is no solution. The lines are parallel.

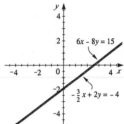

6. $\begin{cases} 2x + 5y = 9 \\ -x + 3y = 1 \\ 7x - 2y = 14 \end{cases}$ Adding the first equation to twice the second

equation gives $11y = 11$ $\Leftrightarrow$ $y = 1$. Substituting back into the second equation, we get $-x + 3(1) = 1$ $\Leftrightarrow$ $x = 4$. Checking point $(4, 1)$ in the third equation gives $7(4) - 2(1) = 26 \neq 14$. Thus there is no solution, and the lines do not intersect at one point.

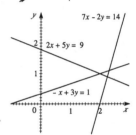

8. $\begin{cases} x^2 + y^2 = 8 \\ y = x + 2 \end{cases}$ Substituting for y in the first equation gives $x^2 + (x + 2)^2 = 8$ $\Leftrightarrow$

$2x^2 + 4x - 4 = 0$ $\Leftrightarrow$ $2(x^2 + 2x - 2) = 0$. Using the quadratic formula, we have $x = \frac{-2 \pm \sqrt{4+8}}{2} = \frac{-2 \pm 2\sqrt{3}}{2} = -1 \pm \sqrt{3}$. If $x = -1 - \sqrt{3}$. then $y = (-1 - \sqrt{3}) + 2 = 1 - \sqrt{3}$, and if $x = -1 + \sqrt{3}$, then $y = (-1 + \sqrt{3}) + 2 = 1 + \sqrt{3}$. Thus, the solutions are $(-1 - \sqrt{3}, 1 - \sqrt{3})$ and $(-1 + \sqrt{3}, 1 + \sqrt{3})$

10. $\begin{cases} x^2 + y^2 = 10 \\ x^2 + 2y^2 - 7y = 0 \end{cases}$ Subtracting the first equation from the second equation gives

$y^2 - 7y = -10$ $\Leftrightarrow$ $y^2 - 7y + 10 = 0$ $\Leftrightarrow$ $(y - 2)(y - 5) = 0$ $\Rightarrow$ $y = 2, y = 5$. If $y = 2$, then $x^2 + 4 = 10$ $\Leftrightarrow$ $x^2 = 6$ $\Rightarrow$ $x = \pm\sqrt{6}$, and if $y = 5$, then $x^2 + 25 = 10$ $\Leftrightarrow$ $x^2 = -15$, which leads to no real solution. Thus the solutions are $(\sqrt{6}, 2)$ and $(-\sqrt{6}, 2)$.

12. $\begin{bmatrix} 1 & -2 & 3 & 1 \\ 1 & -3 & -1 & 0 \\ 2 & 0 & -6 & 6 \end{bmatrix}$ $\xrightarrow[R_3 - 2R_1 \to R_3]{R_2 - R_1 \to R_2}$ $\begin{bmatrix} 1 & -2 & 3 & 1 \\ 0 & -1 & -4 & -1 \\ 0 & 4 & -12 & 4 \end{bmatrix}$ $\xrightarrow{-R_2 \to R_2}$ $\begin{bmatrix} 1 & -2 & 3 & 1 \\ 0 & 1 & 4 & 1 \\ 0 & 4 & -12 & 4 \end{bmatrix}$

$\xrightarrow{R_3 - 4R_2 \to R_3}$ $\begin{bmatrix} 1 & -2 & 3 & 1 \\ 0 & 1 & 4 & 1 \\ 0 & 0 & -28 & 0 \end{bmatrix}$.

Thus, $z = 0$; $y = 1$; and $x - 2(1) + 3(0) = 1 \Leftrightarrow x = 3$, and so the solution is $(3, 1, 0)$.

14.
$$\begin{bmatrix} 1 & 1 & 1 & 1 & 2 \\ 2 & 0 & -3 & 0 & 5 \\ 1 & -2 & 0 & 4 & 9 \\ 1 & 1 & 2 & 3 & 5 \end{bmatrix} \xrightarrow[R_4-R_1 \to R_4]{R_2-2R_1 \to R_2,\ R_3-R_1 \to R_3} \begin{bmatrix} 1 & 1 & 1 & 1 & 2 \\ 0 & -2 & -5 & -2 & 1 \\ 0 & -3 & -1 & 3 & 7 \\ 0 & 0 & 1 & 2 & 3 \end{bmatrix} \xrightarrow{R_3-R_2 \to R_3}$$

$$\begin{bmatrix} 1 & 1 & 1 & 1 & 2 \\ 0 & -2 & -5 & -2 & 1 \\ 0 & -1 & 4 & 5 & 6 \\ 0 & 0 & 1 & 2 & 3 \end{bmatrix} \xrightarrow{R_3 \leftrightarrow R_2} \begin{bmatrix} 1 & 1 & 1 & 1 & 2 \\ 0 & -1 & 4 & 5 & 6 \\ 0 & -2 & -5 & -2 & 1 \\ 0 & 0 & 1 & 2 & 3 \end{bmatrix} \xrightarrow{-R_2}$$

$$\begin{bmatrix} 1 & 1 & 1 & 1 & 2 \\ 0 & 1 & -4 & -5 & -6 \\ 0 & -2 & -5 & -2 & 1 \\ 0 & 0 & 1 & 2 & 3 \end{bmatrix} \xrightarrow{R_3+2R_2 \to R_3} \begin{bmatrix} 1 & 1 & 1 & 1 & 2 \\ 0 & 1 & -4 & -5 & -6 \\ 0 & 0 & -13 & -12 & -11 \\ 0 & 0 & 1 & 2 & 3 \end{bmatrix} \xrightarrow{R_3 \leftrightarrow R_4}$$

$$\begin{bmatrix} 1 & 1 & 1 & 1 & 2 \\ 0 & 1 & -4 & -5 & -6 \\ 0 & 0 & 1 & 2 & 3 \\ 0 & 0 & -13 & -12 & -11 \end{bmatrix} \xrightarrow{R_4+13R_3 \to R_4} \begin{bmatrix} 1 & 1 & 1 & 1 & 2 \\ 0 & 1 & -4 & -5 & -6 \\ 0 & 0 & 1 & 2 & 3 \\ 0 & 0 & 0 & 14 & 28 \end{bmatrix}$$

Therefore, $14w = 28 \Leftrightarrow w = 2$; $z + 4 = 3 \Leftrightarrow z = -1$; $y + 4 - 10 = -6 \Leftrightarrow y = 0$; and $x - 1 + 2 = 2 \Leftrightarrow x = 1$. So, the solution is $(1, 0, -1, 2)$.

16.
$$\begin{bmatrix} 2 & -3 & 4 & 3 \\ 4 & -5 & 9 & 13 \\ 2 & 0 & 7 & 0 \end{bmatrix} \xrightarrow[R_3-R_1 \to R_3]{R_2-2R_1 \to R_2} \begin{bmatrix} 2 & -3 & 4 & 3 \\ 0 & 1 & 1 & 7 \\ 0 & 3 & 3 & -3 \end{bmatrix} \xrightarrow{R_3-3R_2 \to R_3} \begin{bmatrix} 2 & -3 & 4 & 3 \\ 0 & 1 & 1 & 7 \\ 0 & 0 & 0 & -24 \end{bmatrix}$$

Therefore, the system is inconsistent and has no solution.

18.
$$\begin{bmatrix} 1 & 0 & -1 & 1 & 2 \\ 2 & 1 & 0 & -2 & 12 \\ 0 & 3 & 1 & 1 & 4 \\ 1 & 1 & -1 & 0 & 10 \end{bmatrix} \xrightarrow[R_4-R_1 \to R_4]{R_2-2R_1 \to R_2} \begin{bmatrix} 1 & 0 & -1 & 1 & 2 \\ 0 & 1 & 2 & -4 & 8 \\ 0 & 3 & 1 & 1 & 4 \\ 0 & 1 & 0 & -1 & 8 \end{bmatrix} \xrightarrow[R_4-R_2 \to R_4]{R_3-3R_2 \to R_3}$$

$$\begin{bmatrix} 1 & 0 & -1 & 1 & 2 \\ 0 & 1 & 2 & -4 & 8 \\ 0 & 0 & -5 & 13 & -20 \\ 0 & 0 & -2 & 3 & 0 \end{bmatrix} \xrightarrow{5R_4-2R_3 \to R_4} \begin{bmatrix} 1 & 0 & -1 & 1 & 2 \\ 0 & 1 & 2 & -4 & 8 \\ 0 & 0 & -5 & 13 & -20 \\ 0 & 0 & 0 & -11 & 40 \end{bmatrix}$$

Therefore, $-11w = 40 \Leftrightarrow w = -\frac{40}{11}$; $-5z + 13\left(-\frac{40}{11}\right) = -20 \Leftrightarrow z = -\frac{60}{11}$; $y + 2\left(-\frac{60}{11}\right) - 4\left(-\frac{40}{11}\right) = 8 \Leftrightarrow y = \frac{48}{11}$; and $x - \left(-\frac{60}{11}\right) + \left(-\frac{40}{11}\right) = 2 \Leftrightarrow x = \frac{2}{11}$. Hence, the solution is $\left(\frac{2}{11}, \frac{48}{11}, -\frac{60}{11}, -\frac{40}{11}\right)$.

20. Since the parabola $y = ax^2 + bx + c$ passes through the points $(1, 0)$, $(-1, -4)$, and $(2, 11)$, we substitute these points into the equation of the parabola and get the system:

$$\begin{cases} a + b + c = 0 \\ a - b + c = -4 \\ 4a + 2b + c = 11 \end{cases}$$

This has the following matrix representation:

$$\begin{bmatrix} 1 & 1 & 1 & 0 \\ 1 & -1 & 1 & -4 \\ 4 & 2 & 1 & 11 \end{bmatrix} \xrightarrow[R_3-4R_1 \to R_3]{R_2-R_1 \to R_2} \begin{bmatrix} 1 & 1 & 1 & 0 \\ 0 & -2 & 0 & -4 \\ 0 & -2 & -3 & 11 \end{bmatrix} \xrightarrow{R_3-R_2 \to R_3} \begin{bmatrix} 1 & 1 & 1 & 0 \\ 0 & -2 & 0 & -4 \\ 0 & 0 & -3 & 15 \end{bmatrix}$$

Therefore, $-3c = 15 \Leftrightarrow c = -5$; $-2b = -4 \Leftrightarrow b = 2$;   and $a + (2) + (-5) = 0 \Leftrightarrow a = 3$. So, the solution is $(a, b, c) = (3, 2, -5)$, and the equation of the parabola is $y = 3x^2 + 2x - 5$.

In Exercises 22–32,

$$A = \begin{bmatrix} 2 & 0 & -1 \end{bmatrix}$$

$$B = \begin{bmatrix} 1 & 2 & 4 \\ -2 & 1 & 0 \end{bmatrix}$$

$$C = \begin{bmatrix} \frac{1}{2} & 3 \\ 2 & \frac{3}{2} \\ -2 & 1 \end{bmatrix}$$

$$D = \begin{bmatrix} 1 & 4 \\ 0 & -1 \\ 2 & 0 \end{bmatrix}$$

$$E = \begin{bmatrix} 2 & -1 \\ -\frac{1}{2} & 1 \end{bmatrix}$$

$$F = \begin{bmatrix} 4 & 0 & 2 \\ -1 & 1 & 0 \\ 7 & 5 & 0 \end{bmatrix}$$

$$G = \begin{bmatrix} 5 \end{bmatrix}$$

22. $C - D = \begin{bmatrix} \frac{1}{2} & 3 \\ 2 & \frac{3}{2} \\ -2 & 1 \end{bmatrix} - \begin{bmatrix} 1 & 4 \\ 0 & -1 \\ 2 & 0 \end{bmatrix} = \begin{bmatrix} -\frac{1}{2} & -1 \\ 2 & \frac{5}{2} \\ -4 & 1 \end{bmatrix}$

24. $5B - 2C$ cannot be performed because the matrix dimensions (2×3 and 3×2) are not compatible.

26. $A\,G$ cannot be performed because the matrix dimensions (1×3 and 1×1) are not compatible.

28. $C\,B = \begin{bmatrix} \frac{1}{2} & 3 \\ 2 & \frac{3}{2} \\ -2 & 1 \end{bmatrix} \begin{bmatrix} 1 & 2 & 4 \\ -2 & 1 & 0 \end{bmatrix} = \begin{bmatrix} -\frac{11}{2} & 4 & 2 \\ -1 & \frac{11}{2} & 8 \\ -4 & -3 & -8 \end{bmatrix}$

30. $F\,C = \begin{bmatrix} 4 & 0 & 2 \\ -1 & 1 & 0 \\ 7 & 5 & 0 \end{bmatrix} \begin{bmatrix} \frac{1}{2} & 3 \\ 2 & \frac{3}{2} \\ -2 & 1 \end{bmatrix} = \begin{bmatrix} -2 & 14 \\ \frac{3}{2} & -\frac{3}{2} \\ \frac{27}{2} & \frac{57}{2} \end{bmatrix}$

32. $F(2C - D) = \begin{bmatrix} 4 & 0 & 2 \\ -1 & 1 & 0 \\ 7 & 5 & 0 \end{bmatrix} \left(\begin{bmatrix} 1 & 6 \\ 4 & 3 \\ -4 & 2 \end{bmatrix} - \begin{bmatrix} 1 & 4 \\ 0 & -1 \\ 2 & 0 \end{bmatrix} \right) = \begin{bmatrix} 4 & 0 & 2 \\ -1 & 1 & 0 \\ 7 & 5 & 0 \end{bmatrix} \begin{bmatrix} 0 & 2 \\ 4 & 4 \\ -6 & 2 \end{bmatrix}$

$= \begin{bmatrix} -12 & 12 \\ 4 & 2 \\ 20 & 34 \end{bmatrix}$

34. $D = \begin{bmatrix} 2 & 2 \\ 1 & -3 \end{bmatrix}$. Then, $|D| = 2(-3) - 1(2) = -8$, and so $D^{-1} = -\frac{1}{8} \begin{bmatrix} -3 & -2 \\ -1 & 2 \end{bmatrix} = \begin{bmatrix} \frac{3}{8} & \frac{1}{4} \\ \frac{1}{8} & -\frac{1}{4} \end{bmatrix}$.

36. $D = \begin{bmatrix} 2 & 4 & 0 \\ -1 & 1 & 2 \\ 0 & 3 & 2 \end{bmatrix}$. Then, $|D| = 2 \begin{vmatrix} 1 & 2 \\ 3 & 2 \end{vmatrix} - 4 \begin{vmatrix} -1 & 2 \\ 0 & 2 \end{vmatrix} = 2(2 - 6) - 4(-2) = 0$, and so D has no inverse.

38. $D = \begin{bmatrix} 1 & 0 & 0 & 1 \\ 0 & 2 & 0 & 2 \\ 0 & 0 & 3 & 3 \\ 0 & 0 & 0 & 4 \end{bmatrix}$. Thus, $|D| = \begin{vmatrix} 2 & 0 & 2 \\ 0 & 3 & 3 \\ 0 & 0 & 4 \end{vmatrix} = 2 \begin{vmatrix} 3 & 3 \\ 0 & 4 \end{vmatrix} = 24$ and D^{-1} exists.

$$\begin{bmatrix} 1 & 0 & 0 & 1 & 1 & 0 & 0 & 0 \\ 0 & 2 & 0 & 2 & 0 & 1 & 0 & 0 \\ 0 & 0 & 3 & 3 & 0 & 0 & 1 & 0 \\ 0 & 0 & 0 & 4 & 0 & 0 & 0 & 1 \end{bmatrix} \xrightarrow[\frac{1}{4}R_4]{\frac{1}{2}R_2, \frac{1}{3}R_3} \begin{bmatrix} 1 & 0 & 0 & 1 & 1 & 0 & 0 & 0 \\ 0 & 1 & 0 & 1 & 0 & \frac{1}{2} & 0 & 0 \\ 0 & 0 & 1 & 1 & 0 & 0 & \frac{1}{3} & 0 \\ 0 & 0 & 0 & 1 & 0 & 0 & 0 & \frac{1}{4} \end{bmatrix}$$

$$\xrightarrow[R_3-R_4 \to R_3]{R_1-R_4 \to R_1,\, R_2-R_4 \to R_2} \begin{bmatrix} 1 & 0 & 0 & 0 & 1 & 0 & 0 & -\frac{1}{4} \\ 0 & 1 & 0 & 0 & 0 & \frac{1}{2} & 0 & -\frac{1}{4} \\ 0 & 0 & 1 & 0 & 0 & 0 & \frac{1}{3} & -\frac{1}{4} \\ 0 & 0 & 0 & 1 & 0 & 0 & 0 & \frac{1}{4} \end{bmatrix}.$$

Therefore, $D^{-1} = \begin{bmatrix} 1 & 0 & 0 & -\frac{1}{4} \\ 0 & \frac{1}{2} & 0 & -\frac{1}{4} \\ 0 & 0 & \frac{1}{3} & -\frac{1}{4} \\ 0 & 0 & 0 & \frac{1}{4} \end{bmatrix}.$

40. $\begin{bmatrix} 2 & 1 & 5 \\ 1 & 2 & 2 \\ 1 & 0 & 3 \end{bmatrix} \begin{bmatrix} x \\ y \\ z \end{bmatrix} = \begin{bmatrix} \frac{1}{3} \\ \frac{1}{4} \\ \frac{1}{6} \end{bmatrix}.$ Let $A = \begin{bmatrix} 2 & 1 & 5 \\ 1 & 2 & 2 \\ 1 & 0 & 3 \end{bmatrix}.$ Then,

$$\begin{bmatrix} 2 & 1 & 5 & 1 & 0 & 0 \\ 1 & 2 & 2 & 0 & 1 & 0 \\ 1 & 0 & 3 & 0 & 0 & 1 \end{bmatrix} \xrightarrow{R_1 \leftrightarrow R_2} \begin{bmatrix} 1 & 2 & 2 & 0 & 1 & 0 \\ 2 & 1 & 5 & 1 & 0 & 0 \\ 1 & 0 & 3 & 0 & 0 & 1 \end{bmatrix} \xrightarrow[R_3-R_1 \to R_3]{R_2-2R_1 \to R_2}$$

$$\begin{bmatrix} 1 & 2 & 2 & 0 & 1 & 0 \\ 0 & -3 & 1 & 1 & -2 & 0 \\ 0 & -2 & 1 & 0 & -1 & 1 \end{bmatrix} \xrightarrow{R_2-2R_3 \to R_2} \begin{bmatrix} 1 & 2 & 2 & 0 & 1 & 0 \\ 0 & 1 & -1 & 1 & 0 & -2 \\ 0 & -2 & 1 & 0 & -1 & 1 \end{bmatrix} \xrightarrow[R_3 \to R_3+2R_2]{R_1-2R_2 \to R_1}$$

$$\begin{bmatrix} 1 & 0 & 4 & -2 & 1 & 4 \\ 0 & 1 & -1 & 1 & 0 & -2 \\ 0 & 0 & -1 & 2 & -1 & -3 \end{bmatrix} \xrightarrow{-R_3} \begin{bmatrix} 1 & 0 & 4 & -2 & 1 & 4 \\ 0 & 1 & -1 & 1 & 0 & -2 \\ 0 & 0 & 1 & -2 & 1 & 3 \end{bmatrix} \xrightarrow[R_2+R_3 \to R_2]{R_1-4R_3 \to R_1}$$

$$\begin{bmatrix} 1 & 0 & 0 & 6 & -3 & -8 \\ 0 & 1 & 0 & -1 & 1 & 1 \\ 0 & 0 & 1 & -2 & 1 & 3 \end{bmatrix}.$$

Hence, $A^{-1} = \begin{bmatrix} 6 & -3 & -8 \\ -1 & 1 & 1 \\ -2 & 1 & 3 \end{bmatrix}$ and $\begin{bmatrix} x \\ y \\ z \end{bmatrix} = \begin{bmatrix} 6 & -3 & -8 \\ -1 & 1 & 1 \\ -2 & 1 & 3 \end{bmatrix} \begin{bmatrix} \frac{1}{3} \\ \frac{1}{4} \\ \frac{1}{6} \end{bmatrix} = \begin{bmatrix} -\frac{1}{12} \\ \frac{1}{12} \\ \frac{1}{12} \end{bmatrix}$, and so the

solution is $\left(-\frac{1}{12}, \frac{1}{12}, \frac{1}{12}\right)$.

42. $|D| = \begin{vmatrix} 12 & -11 \\ 7 & 9 \end{vmatrix} = 108 + 77 = 185; \quad |D_x| = \begin{vmatrix} 140 & -11 \\ 20 & 9 \end{vmatrix} = 1260 + 220 = 1480; \quad$ and

$|D_y| = \begin{vmatrix} 12 & 140 \\ 7 & 20 \end{vmatrix} = 240 - 980 = -740.$ Therefore, $x = \frac{1480}{185} = 8$ and $y = \frac{-740}{185} = -4$, and so

the solution is $(8, -4)$.

44. $|D| = \begin{vmatrix} 3 & 4 & -1 \\ 1 & 0 & -4 \\ 2 & 1 & 5 \end{vmatrix} = -4 \begin{vmatrix} 1 & -4 \\ 2 & 5 \end{vmatrix} - 1 \begin{vmatrix} 3 & -1 \\ 1 & -4 \end{vmatrix} = -52 + 11 = -41;$

$$|D_x| = \begin{vmatrix} 10 & 4 & -1 \\ 20 & 0 & -4 \\ 30 & 1 & 5 \end{vmatrix} = -4\begin{vmatrix} 20 & -4 \\ 30 & 5 \end{vmatrix} - 1\begin{vmatrix} 10 & -1 \\ 20 & -4 \end{vmatrix} = -880 + 20 = -860;$$

$$|D_y| = \begin{vmatrix} 3 & 10 & -1 \\ 1 & 20 & -4 \\ 2 & 30 & 5 \end{vmatrix} = 3\begin{vmatrix} 20 & -4 \\ 30 & 5 \end{vmatrix} - 1\begin{vmatrix} 10 & -1 \\ 30 & 5 \end{vmatrix} + 2\begin{vmatrix} 10 & -1 \\ 20 & -4 \end{vmatrix} = 660 - 80 - 40 = 540; \text{ and}$$

$$|D_z| = \begin{vmatrix} 3 & 4 & 10 \\ 1 & 0 & 20 \\ 2 & 1 & 30 \end{vmatrix} = -4\begin{vmatrix} 1 & 20 \\ 2 & 30 \end{vmatrix} - 1\begin{vmatrix} 3 & 10 \\ 1 & 20 \end{vmatrix} = 40 - 50 = -10.$$

Therefore, $x = \frac{-860}{-41} = \frac{860}{41}$, $y = -\frac{540}{41}$, and $z = \frac{10}{41}$, and so the solution is $\left(\frac{860}{41}, -\frac{540}{41}, \frac{10}{41}\right)$.

46. $\begin{cases} y - x^2 \geq 4 \\ \quad y < 20 \end{cases}$ The vertices occur where $y = x^2 + 4$ and $y = 2$.

By substitution, $x^2 + 4 = 20 \Leftrightarrow x^2 = 16 \Leftrightarrow x = \pm 4$, and $y = 20$. Thus, the vertices are $(\pm 4, 20)$, and the solution set is bounded.

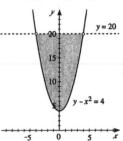

48. $\begin{cases} \quad x \geq 4 \\ x + y \geq 24 \\ \quad x \leq 2y + 12 \end{cases}$

The lines $x + y = 24$ and $x = 2y + 12$ intersect at the point $(20, 4)$. The lines $x = 4$ and $x = 2y + 12$ intersect at the point $(-4, 4)$, however, this vertex does not satisfy the other inequality. The lines $x + y = 24$ and $x = 4$ intersect at the point $(4, 20)$. Hence, the vertices are $(4, 20)$ and $(20, 4)$. The solution set is not bounded.

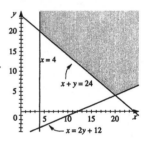

50. $\begin{cases} ax + by + cz = a - b + c \\ bx + by + cz = c \\ cx + cy + cz = c \end{cases}$ $a \neq b, b \neq c, c \neq 0 \Leftrightarrow \begin{cases} ax + by + cz = a - b + c \\ bx + by + cz = c \\ x + y + z = 1 \end{cases}$

Subtracting the second equation from the first gives $(a - b)x = a - b \Leftrightarrow x = 1$. Subtracting the third equation from the second, $(b - c)x + (b - c)y = 0 \Leftrightarrow y = -x = -1$. So, $1 - 1 + z = 1 \Leftrightarrow z = 1$, and the solution is $(1, -1, 1)$.

52. The system will have infinitely many solutions when the determinant of he coefficient matrix is 0.

Then $\begin{vmatrix} k & 1 & 1 \\ 1 & 2 & k \\ -1 & 0 & 3 \end{vmatrix} = -1\begin{vmatrix} 1 & 1 \\ 2 & k \end{vmatrix} + 3\begin{vmatrix} k & 1 \\ 1 & 2 \end{vmatrix} = -1(k - 2) + 3(2k - 1) = 0 \Leftrightarrow$

$5k - 1 = 0 \Leftrightarrow k = \frac{1}{5}$.

54. $\begin{cases} \sqrt{12}\,x - 3\sqrt{2}\,y = 660 \\ 7137x + 3931y = 20{,}000 \end{cases} \Leftrightarrow$

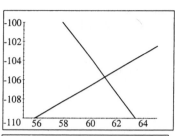

$$\begin{cases} y = \dfrac{\sqrt{12}}{3\sqrt{2}}\,x - \dfrac{660}{3\sqrt{2}} \\ y = -\dfrac{7137}{3931}\,x + \dfrac{20{,}000}{3931} \end{cases}$$

The solution is approximately $(61.04, -105.73)$

56. $\begin{cases} y = 5^x + x \\ y = x^5 + 5 \end{cases}$

The solutions are approximately $(-1.45, -1.35)$, $(1, 6)$, and $(1.51, 12.93)$.

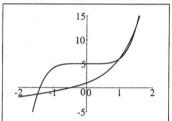

58. $\dfrac{8}{x^3 - 4x} = \dfrac{8}{x(x^2 - 4)} = \dfrac{8}{x(x+2)(x-2)} = \dfrac{A}{x} + \dfrac{B}{x-2} + \dfrac{C}{x+2}$. Then,

$8 = A(x^2 - 4) + Bx(x+2) + Cx(x-2) = x^2(A + B + C) + x(2B - 2C) - 4A$. Thus,

$-4A = 8 \Leftrightarrow A = -2$; $2B - 2C = 0 \Leftrightarrow B = C$; and $-2 + 2B = 0 \Leftrightarrow B = 1$ so $C = 1$.

Therefore, $\dfrac{8}{x^3 - 4x} = -\dfrac{2}{x} + \dfrac{1}{x-2} + \dfrac{1}{x+2}$.

60. $\dfrac{x+6}{x^3 - 2x^2 + 4x - 8} = \dfrac{x+6}{(x^2 + 4)(x - 2)} = \dfrac{Ax + B}{x^2 + 4} + \dfrac{C}{x-2}$. Thus,

$x + 6 = (Ax + B)(x - 2) + C(x^2 + 4) = Ax^2 - 2Ax + Bx - 2B + Cx^2 + 4C$

$= x^2(A + C) + x(-2A + B) + (-2B + 4C)$, and so we get the system

$\begin{cases} A + C = 0 \\ -2A + B = 1 \\ -2B + 4C = 6 \end{cases}$, which has the following matrix representation:

$$\begin{bmatrix} 1 & 0 & 1 & 0 \\ -2 & 1 & 0 & 1 \\ 0 & -2 & 4 & 6 \end{bmatrix} \xrightarrow{R_2 + 2R_1 \to R_2} \begin{bmatrix} 1 & 0 & 1 & 0 \\ 0 & 1 & 2 & 1 \\ 0 & -2 & 4 & 6 \end{bmatrix} \xrightarrow{R_3 + 2R_2 \to R_3} \begin{bmatrix} 1 & 0 & 1 & 0 \\ 0 & 1 & 2 & 1 \\ 0 & 0 & 8 & 8 \end{bmatrix}.$$

Thus, $8C = 8 \Leftrightarrow C = 1$; $B + 2 = 1 \Leftrightarrow B = -1$; and $A + 1 = 0 \Leftrightarrow A = -1$. So,

$\dfrac{x+6}{x^3 - 2x^2 + 4x - 8} = -\dfrac{x+1}{x^2 + 4} + \dfrac{1}{x-2}$.

Focus on Modeling

2.

Vertex	$N = \frac{1}{2}x + \frac{1}{4}y + 40$
$(1,0)$	$\frac{1}{2}(1) + \frac{1}{4}(0) + 40 = 40.5$
$(\frac{1}{2}, \frac{1}{2})$	$\frac{1}{2}(\frac{1}{2}) + \frac{1}{4}(\frac{1}{2}) + 40 = 40.375$ ← minimum value
$(2,2)$	$\frac{1}{2}(2) + \frac{1}{4}(2) + 40 = 41.5$
$(4,0)$	$\frac{1}{2}(4) + \frac{1}{4}(0) + 40 = 42$ ← maximum value

Thus the maximum value is 42, and the minimum value is 40.375.

4.
$$\begin{cases} x \geq 0, y \geq 0 \\ x \leq 10, y \leq 20 \\ x + y \geq 5 \\ x + 2y \leq 18 \end{cases}$$

The objective function is $Q = 70x + 82y$.
From the graph, the vertices are at $(0,9)$, $(0,5)$, $(5,0)$, $(10,0)$, and $(10,4)$.

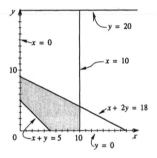

Vertex	$Q = 70x + 82y$
$(0,9)$	$70(0) + 82(9) = 738$
$(0,5)$	$70(0) + 82(5) = 410$
$(5,0)$	$70(5) + 82(0) = 350$ ← minimum value
$(10,0)$	$70(10) + 82(0) = 700$
$(10,4)$	$70(10) + 82(4) = 1028$ ← maximum value

Thus, the maximum value of Q is 1028, and the minimum value is 350.

6. Let c be the number of colonial homes built and r be the number of ranch homes built. Since there are 100 lots available, $c + r \leq 100$. From the capital restriction, we get $30{,}000c + 40{,}000r \leq 3{,}600{,}000$, or $3c + 4r \leq 360$. Thus, we wish to maximize the profit, $P = 4000c + 8000r$, subject to the constraints:
$$\begin{cases} c \geq 0, r \geq 0 \\ c + r \leq 100 \\ 3c + 4r \leq 360. \end{cases}$$

From the graph, the vertices occur at $(0,0)$, $(100,0)$, $(40,60)$, and $(0,90)$.

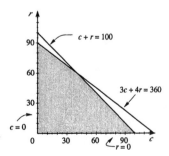

Vertex	$P = 4000c + 8000r$
$(0,0)$	$4000(0) + 8000(0) = 0$
$(100,0)$	$4000(100) + 8000(0) = 400{,}000$
$(40,60)$	$4000(40) + 8000(60) = 640{,}000$
$(0,90)$	$4000(0) + 8000(90) = 720{,}000$ ← maximum value

Therefore, he should build 0 colonial style and 90 ranch style houses for a maximum profit of $720,000. Ten of the lots will be left vacant.

8. Let x be the daily production of standard calculators and y be
the daily production of scientific calculators. Then, the
following inequalities describe the constraints:
$$\begin{cases} x \geq 100, \, y \geq 80 \\ x \leq 200, \, y \leq 170 \\ \quad x + y \geq 200. \end{cases}$$
From the graph, the vertices at $(100, 100)$, $(100, 170)$,
$(200, 170)$, $(200, 80)$, and $(120, 80)$.

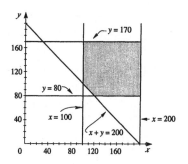

(a) Minimize the objective function (cost): $C = 5x + 7y$

Vertex	$C = 5x + 7y$	
$(100, 100)$	$5(100) + 7(100) = 1200$	
$(100, 170)$	$5(100) + 7(170) = 1690$	
$(200, 170)$	$5(200) + 7(170) = 2190$	
$(200, 80)$	$5(200) + 7(80) = 1560$	
$(120, 80)$	$5(120) + 7(80) = 1160$	← minimum cost

So, to minimize costs, they should produce 120 standard and 80 scientific calculators.

(b) Maximize the objective function (profit): $P = -2x + 5y$

Vertex	$P = -2x + 5y$	
$(100, 100)$	$-2(100) + 5(100) = 300$	
$(100, 170)$	$-2(100) + 5(170) = 650$	← maximum profit
$(200, 170)$	$-2(200) + 5(170) = 450$	
$(200, 80)$	$-2(200) + 5(80) = 0$	
$(120, 80)$	$-2(120) + 5(80) = 160$	

So, to maximize profit, they should produce 100 standard and 170 scientific calculators.

10. Let x be the number of sheets shipped from the east-side store to customer A and y be the number of
sheets shipped from the east-side store to customer B. Then, $50 - x$ sheets must be shipped to
customer A from the west-side store, and $70 - y$ sheets must be shipped to customer B from the
west-side store. Thus we obtain the constraints:
$$\begin{cases} \quad x \geq 0, \, y \geq 0 \\ \quad x \leq 50, \, y \leq 70 \\ \quad x + y \leq 80 \\ 50 - x + 70 - y \leq 45 \end{cases} \quad \Leftrightarrow \quad \begin{cases} x \geq 0, \, y \geq 0 \\ x \leq 50, \, y \leq 70 \\ x + y \leq 80 \\ x + y \geq 75. \end{cases}$$
The objective function is cost,
$C = 0.5x + 0.6y + 0.4(50 - x) + 0.55(70 - y)$
$= 0.1x + 0.05y + 58.5$, which we wish to minimize. From the
graph, the vertices occur at $(5, 70)$, $(10, 70)$, $(50, 30)$, and $(50, 25)$.

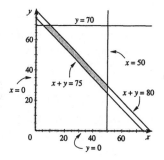

Vertex	$C = 0.1x + 0.05y + 58.5$	
$(5, 70)$	$0.1(5) + 0.05(70) + 58.5 = 62.5$	← minimum cost
$(10, 70)$	$0.1(10) + 0.05(70) + 58.5 = 63$	
$(50, 30)$	$0.1(50) + 0.05(30) + 58.5 = 65$	
$(50, 25)$	$0.1(50) + 0.05(25) + 58.5 = 64.75$	

Therefore, the minimum cost is $62.50 and occurs when $x = 5$ and $y = 70$. So 5 sheets should be shipped from the east-side to customer A, 70 sheets from the east-side store to customer B, 45 sheets from the west-side store to customer A, and 0 sheets from the west-side store to customer B.

12. Let x be the quantity, in ounces, of type I food and y be the quantity of type II food. Then the data can be summarized by the following table:

	type I	type II	required
fat	8 g	12 g	24 g
carbohydrate	12 g	12 g	36 g
protein	2 g	1 g	4 g
cost	$0.20	$0.30	

Also, the total amount of food must be no more than 5 oz. Thus the constraints are:

$$\begin{cases} x \geq 0, y \geq 0 \\ x + y \leq 5 \\ 8x + 12y \geq 24 \\ 12x + 12y \geq 36 \\ 2x + y \geq 4. \end{cases}$$

The objective function is cost, $C = 0.2x + 0.3y$, which we wish to minimize. From the graph, the vertices occur at $(1, 2)$, $(0, 4)$, $(0, 5)$, $(5, 0)$, and $(3, 0)$.

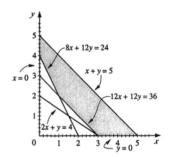

Vertex	$C = 0.2x + 0.3y$
$(1, 2)$	$0.2(1) + 0.3(2) = 0.8$
$(0, 4)$	$0.2(0) + 0.3(4) = 1.2$
$(0, 5)$	$0.2(0) + 0.3(5) = 1.5$
$(5, 0)$	$0.2(5) + 0.3(0) = 1.0$
$(3, 0)$	$0.2(3) + 0.3(0) = 0.6$ ← minimum cost

Hence, the rabbits should be fed 3 ounces of type I food and no type II food, for a minimum cost of $0.60.

14. The only change that needs to be made to the constraints in Exercise 13 is that the 2000 in the last inequality becomes 3000. Then we have

$$\begin{cases} x \geq 0, y \geq 0 \\ 12{,}000 - x - y \geq 0 \\ x \geq 3y \\ 12000 - x - y \leq 3000 \end{cases} \Leftrightarrow \begin{cases} x \geq 0, y \geq 0 \\ x + y \leq 12{,}000 \\ x \geq 3y \\ x + y \geq 9000. \end{cases}$$

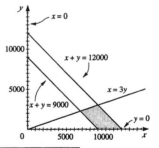

From the graph, the vertices occur at $(6750, 2250)$, $(9000, 0)$, $(12000, 0)$, and $(9000, 3000)$. The objective function is
$Y = 0.07x + 0.08y + 0.12(12000 - x - y)$
$= 1440 - 0.05x - 0.04y$, which we wish to maximize.

Vertex	$Y = 1440 - 0.05x - 0.04y$
$(6750, 2250)$	$1440 - 0.05(6750) - 0.04(2250) = 1012.5$ ← maximum value
$(9000, 0)$	$1440 - 0.05(9000) - 0.04(0) = 990$
$(12000, 0)$	$1440 - 0.05(12000) - 0.04(0) = 840$
$(9000, 3000)$	$1440 - 0.05(9000) - 0.04(3000) = 870$

Hence, she should invest $6750 in municipal bonds, $2250 in bank certificates, and $3000 in high-risk bonds for a maximum yield of $1012.50 which is an increase of $47.50 over her yield in Exercise 13.

16. $\begin{cases} x \geq 0, \ x \geq y \\ x + 2y \leq 12 \\ x + y \leq 10 \end{cases}$

(a)

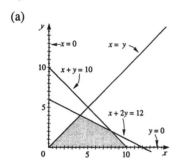

(b)

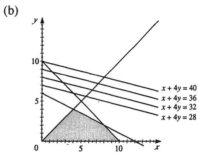

(c)   These lines will first touch the feasible region at the top vertex, $(4, 4)$.

(d)

Vertex	$P = x + 4y$
$(0, 0)$	$(0) + 4(0) = 0$
$(10, 0)$	$(10) + 4(0) = 10$
$(4, 4)$	$(4) + 4(4) = 20$ ← maximum value
$(8, 2)$	$(8) + 4(2) = 16$

So, the maximum value of the objective function occurs at the vertex $(4, 4)$.

Chapter Eleven
Exercises 11.1

2. $x^2 = y$. Then $4p = 1 \iff p = \frac{1}{4}$.
   Focus: $\left(0, \frac{1}{4}\right)$
   Directrix: $y = -\frac{1}{4}$
   Focal diameter: 1

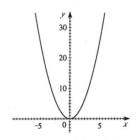

4. $y^2 = 3x$. Then $4p = 3 \iff p = \frac{3}{4}$.
   Focus: $\left(\frac{3}{4}, 0\right)$
   Directrix: $x = -\frac{3}{4}$
   Focal diameter: 3

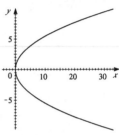

6. $y = -2x^2 \iff x^2 = -\frac{1}{2}y$. Then $4p = -\frac{1}{2} \iff p = -\frac{1}{8}$.
   Focus: $\left(0, -\frac{1}{8}\right)$
   Directrix: $y = \frac{1}{8}$
   Focal diameter: $\frac{1}{2}$

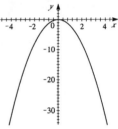

8. $x = \frac{1}{2}y^2 \iff y^2 = 2x$. Then $4p = 2 \iff p = \frac{1}{2}$.
   Focus: $\left(\frac{1}{2}, 0\right)$
   Directrix: $x = -\frac{1}{2}$
   Focal diameter: 2

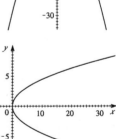

10. $x - 7y^2 = 0 \iff y^2 = \frac{1}{7}x$. Then $4p = \frac{1}{7} \iff p = \frac{1}{28}$.
    Focus: $\left(\frac{1}{28}, 0\right)$
    Directrix: $x = -\frac{1}{28}$
    Focal diameter: $\frac{1}{7}$

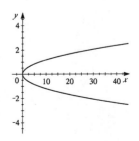

12. $8x^2 + 12y = 0 \quad \Leftrightarrow \quad x^2 = -\frac{3}{2}y$. Then $4p = -\frac{3}{2} \quad \Leftrightarrow \quad p = -\frac{3}{8}$.

Focus: $\left(0, -\frac{3}{8}\right)$

Directrix: $y = \frac{3}{8}$

Focal diameter: $\frac{3}{2}$

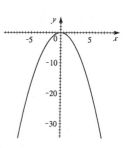

14. Since the focus is $\left(0, -\frac{1}{2}\right)$, $p = -\frac{1}{2} \quad \Leftrightarrow \quad 4p = -2$. So the equation of the parabola is $x^2 = -2y$.

16. Since the focus is $(5, 0)$, $p = 5 \quad \Leftrightarrow \quad 4p = 20$. Hence, the equation of the parabola is $y^2 = 20x$.

18. Since the directrix is $y = 6$, $p = -6 \quad \Leftrightarrow \quad 4p = -24$. Hence, the equation of the parabola is $x^2 = -24y$.

20. Since the directrix is $x = -\frac{1}{8}$, $p = \frac{1}{8} \quad \Leftrightarrow \quad 4p = \frac{1}{2}$. Hence, the equation of the parabola is $y^2 = \frac{1}{2}x$.

22. The directrix has y-intercept 6, and so $p = -6 \quad \Leftrightarrow \quad 4p = -24$. Therefore, the equation of the parabola is $x^2 = -24y$.

24. Since the focal diameter is 8 and the focus is on the negative y-axis, $4p = -8$. So the equation is $x^2 = -8y$.

26. The directrix is $x = -2$, and so $p = 2 \quad \Leftrightarrow \quad 4p = 8$. Since the parabola opens to the left, its equation is $y^2 = 8x$.

28. The focal diameter is $4p = 2(5) = 10$. Since the parabola opens upward, its equation is $x^2 = 10y$.

30. Since the directrix is $x = -p$, we have $p^2 = 16$, so $p = 4$, and the equation is $y^2 = 4px$ or $y^2 = 16x$.

32. The focus is $(0, p)$. Since the line has slope $\frac{1}{2}$, the equation of the line is $y = \frac{1}{2}x + p$. Therefore, the point where the line intersects the parabola has y-coordinate $\frac{1}{2}(2) + p = p + 1$. The parabola's equation is of the form $x^2 = 4py$, so $(2)^2 = 4p(p + 1) \quad \Leftrightarrow \quad p^2 + p - 1 = 0 \quad \Leftrightarrow \quad p = \frac{-1 + \sqrt{5}}{2}$ (since $p > 0$). Hence, the equation of the parabola is $x^2 = 2(\sqrt{5} - 1)y$.

34. The equation of the parabola has the form $x^2 = 4py$. From the diagram, the parabola passes through the point $(10, 1)$, and so $(10)^2 = 4p(1) \quad \Leftrightarrow \quad 4p = 100$ and $p = 25$. Therefore, the receiver is 25 ft from the vertex.

36. The equation of the parabola has the form $x^2 = 4py$. From the diagram, the parabola passes through the point $(100, 3.79)$, and so $(100)^2 = 4p(3.79) \quad \Leftrightarrow \quad 15.16p = 10000$ and $p \approx 659.63$. Therefore, the receiver is about 659.63 inches from the vertex.

38. Many answers are possible: satellite dish TV antennas, sound surveillance equipment, solar collectors for hot water heating or electricity generation, etc.

Exercises 11.2

2. $\frac{x^2}{16} + \frac{y^2}{25} = 1$. This ellipse has $a = 5$, $b = 4$, and so
    $c^2 = 25 - 16 = 9 \iff c = 3$.
    Vertices: $(0, \pm 5)$; foci: $(0, \pm 3)$; eccentricity: $e = \frac{c}{a} = \frac{3}{5} = 0.6$;
    length of the major axis: $2a = 10$; length of the minor axis: $2b = 8$.

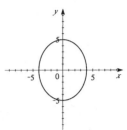

4. $4x^2 + 25y^2 = 100 \iff \frac{x^2}{25} + \frac{y^2}{4} = 1$. This ellipse has $a = 5$,
    $b = 2$, and so $c^2 = 25 - 4 = 21 \iff c = \sqrt{21}$.
    Vertices: $(\pm 5, 0)$; foci: $(\pm \sqrt{21}, 0)$; eccentricity: $e = \frac{c}{a} = \frac{\sqrt{21}}{5}$;
    length of the major axis: $2a = 10$; length of the minor axis: $2b = 4$.

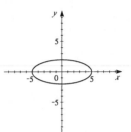

6. $4x^2 + y^2 = 16 \iff \frac{x^2}{4} + \frac{y^2}{16} = 1$. This ellipse has $a = 4$, $b = 2$,
    and so $c^2 = 16 - 4 = 12 \iff c = 2\sqrt{3}$.
    Vertices: $(0, \pm 4)$; foci: $(0, \pm 2\sqrt{3})$; eccentricity:
    $e = \frac{c}{a} = \frac{2\sqrt{3}}{4} = \frac{\sqrt{3}}{2}$; length of the major axis: $2a = 8$; length of
    the minor axis: $2b = 4$.

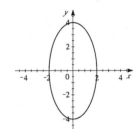

8. $5x^2 + 6y^2 = 30 \iff \frac{x^2}{6} + \frac{y^2}{5} = 1$. This ellipse has $a = \sqrt{6}$,
    $b = \sqrt{5}$, and so $c^2 = 6 - 5 = 1 \iff c = 1$.
    Vertices: $(\pm \sqrt{6}, 0)$; foci: $(\pm 1, 0)$; eccentricity:
    $e = \frac{c}{a} = \frac{1}{\sqrt{6}} = \frac{\sqrt{6}}{6}$: length of the major axis: $2a = 2\sqrt{6}$; length
    of the minor axis: $2b = 2\sqrt{5}$.

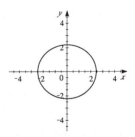

10. $9x^2 + 4y^2 = 1 \iff \frac{x^2}{1/9} + \frac{y^2}{1/4} = 1$. This ellipse has $a = \frac{1}{2}$,
    and so $c^2 = \frac{1}{4} - \frac{1}{9} = \frac{5}{36} \iff c = \frac{\sqrt{5}}{6}$.
    Vertices: $\left(0, \pm \frac{1}{2}\right)$; foci: $\left(0, \pm \frac{\sqrt{5}}{6}\right)$; eccentricity:
    $e = \frac{c}{a} = \frac{\sqrt{5/6}}{1/2} = \frac{\sqrt{5}}{3}$; length of the major axis: $2a = 1$; length
    of the minor axis: $2b = \frac{2}{3}$.

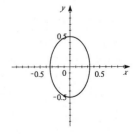

12. $x^2 = 4 - 2y^2$ $\Leftrightarrow$ $x^2 + 2y^2 = 4$ $\Leftrightarrow$ $\dfrac{x^2}{4} + \dfrac{y^2}{2} = 1$. This

ellipse has $a = 2$, $b = \sqrt{2}$, and so $c^2 = 4 - 2 = 2$ $\Leftrightarrow$ $c = \sqrt{2}$.
Vertices: $(\pm 2, 0)$; foci: $(\pm\sqrt{2}, 0)$; eccentricity: $e = \frac{c}{a} = \frac{\sqrt{2}}{2}$;
length of the major axis: $2a = 4$; length of the minor axis:
$2b = 2\sqrt{2}$.

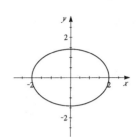

14. $20x^2 + 4y^2 = 5$ $\Leftrightarrow$ $\dfrac{x^2}{1/4} + \dfrac{y^2}{5/4} = 1$. This ellipse has $a = \frac{\sqrt{5}}{2}$,
$b = \frac{1}{2}$, and so $c^2 = \frac{5}{4} - \frac{1}{4} = 1$ $\Leftrightarrow$ $c = 1$.
Vertices: $\left(0, \pm\frac{\sqrt{5}}{2}\right)$; foci: $(0, \pm 1)$; eccentricity:
$e = \frac{c}{a} = \dfrac{1}{\frac{\sqrt{5}}{2}} = \frac{2\sqrt{5}}{5}$; length of the major axis: $2a = \sqrt{5}$;
length of the minor axis: $2b = 1$.

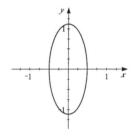

16. This ellipse has a vertical major axis with $a = 4$ and $c = 3$. So $c^2 = a^2 - b^2$ $\Leftrightarrow$ $9 = 16 - b^2$
$\Leftrightarrow$ $b^2 = 7$. Thus the equation is $\dfrac{x^2}{7} + \dfrac{y^2}{4^2} = 1$ $\Leftrightarrow$ $\dfrac{x^2}{7} + \dfrac{y^2}{16} = 1$.

18. This ellipse has a horizontal major axis with $a = 16$, so the equation of the ellipse is of the form
$\dfrac{x^2}{16^2} + \dfrac{y^2}{b^2} = 1$. Substituting the point $(8, 6)$ into the equation, we get $\dfrac{64}{256} + \dfrac{36}{b^2} = 1$ $\Leftrightarrow$
$\dfrac{36}{b^2} = 1 - \dfrac{1}{4}$ $\Leftrightarrow$ $\dfrac{36}{b^2} = \dfrac{3}{4}$ $\Leftrightarrow$ $b^2 = \dfrac{4(36)}{3} = 48$. Thus, the equation of the ellipse is
$\dfrac{x^2}{256} + \dfrac{y^2}{48} = 1$

20. The foci are $(0, \pm 3)$ and the vertices are $(0, \pm 5)$. Thus, $c = 3$ and $a = 5$, and so $c^2 = a^2 - b^2$ $\Leftrightarrow$
$9 = 25 - b^2$ $\Leftrightarrow$ $b^2 = 25 - 9 = 16$. Therefore, the equation of the ellipse is $\dfrac{x^2}{16} + \dfrac{y^2}{25} = 1$.

22. The length of the major axis is $2a = 6$ $\Leftrightarrow$ $a = 3$, the length of the minor axis is $2b = 4$ $\Leftrightarrow$
$b = 2$, and the foci are on the x-axis. Therefore, the equation of the ellipse is $\dfrac{x^2}{9} + \dfrac{y^2}{4} = 1$.

24. The foci are $(\pm 5, 0)$, and the length of the major axis is $2a = 12$ $\Leftrightarrow$ $a = 6$. Thus, $c^2 = a^2 - b^2$
$\Leftrightarrow$ $25 = 36 - b^2$ $\Leftrightarrow$ $b^2 = 36 - 25 = 11$. Since the foci are on the x-axis, the equation is
$\dfrac{x^2}{36} + \dfrac{y^2}{11} = 1$.

26. Since the endpoints of the minor axis are $(0, \pm 3)$, we have $b = 3$. The distance between the foci is
$2c = 8$, so $c = 4$. Thus, $a^2 = b^2 + c^2 = 9 + 16 = 25$, and the equation of the ellipse is
$\dfrac{x^2}{25} + \dfrac{y^2}{9} = 1$.

28. Since the foci are $(0, \pm2)$, we have $c = 2$. The eccentricity is $\dfrac{1}{9} = \dfrac{c}{a}$ $\Leftrightarrow$ $a = 9c = 9(2) = 18$, and so $b^2 = a^2 - c^2 = 18^2 - 2^2 = 320$. Since the foci lie on the y-axis, the equation of the ellipse is $\dfrac{x^2}{320} + \dfrac{y^2}{324} = 1$.

30. Since the length of the major axis is $2a = 4$, we have $a = 2$. The eccentricity is $\dfrac{\sqrt{3}}{2} = \dfrac{c}{a} = \dfrac{c}{2}$, so $c = \sqrt{3}$. Then $b^2 = a^2 - c^2 = 4 - 3 = 1$, and since the foci are on the y-axis, the equation of the ellipse is $x^2 + \dfrac{y^2}{4} = 1$.

32.
$$\begin{cases} \dfrac{x^2}{16} + \dfrac{y^2}{9} = 1 \\[2mm] \dfrac{x^2}{9} + \dfrac{y^2}{16} = 1 \end{cases} \Leftrightarrow \begin{cases} 9x^2 + 16y^2 = 144 \\ 16x^2 + 9y^2 = 144 \end{cases} \Leftrightarrow$$

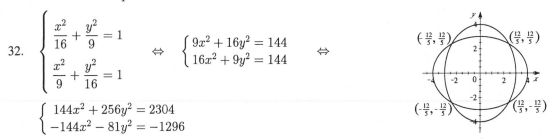

$$\begin{cases} 144x^2 + 256y^2 = 2304 \\ -144x^2 - 81y^2 = -1296 \end{cases}$$

Adding gives $175y^2 = 1008$ $\Rightarrow$ $y = \pm\dfrac{12}{5}$. Substituting for y gives $9x^2 + 16\left(\dfrac{12}{5}\right)^2 = 144$ $\Leftrightarrow$ $9x^2 = 144 - \dfrac{2304}{25} = \dfrac{1296}{25}$ $\Leftrightarrow$ $x = \pm\dfrac{12}{5}$, and so the four points of intersection are $\left(\pm\dfrac{12}{5}, \pm\dfrac{12}{5}\right)$.

34. Using the eccentricity, $e = 0.25 = \dfrac{c}{a}$ $\Leftrightarrow$ $c = 0.25a$. Using the length of the minor axis, $2b = 10{,}000{,}000{,}000$ $\Leftrightarrow$ $b = 5 \times 10^9$. Since $a^2 = c^2 + b^2$, $a^2 = (0.25a)^2 + 25 \times 10^{18}$ $\Leftrightarrow$ $\dfrac{15}{16}a^2 = 25 \times 10^{18}$ $\Leftrightarrow$ $a^2 = \dfrac{80}{3} \times 10^{18}$ $\Leftrightarrow$ $a = \sqrt{\dfrac{80}{3}} \times 10^9 = 4\sqrt{\dfrac{5}{3}} \times 10^9$. Then $c = 0.25\left(4\sqrt{\dfrac{5}{3}} \times 10^9\right) = \sqrt{\dfrac{5}{3}} \times 10^9$. Since the Sun is at one focus of the ellipse, the distance from Pluto to the Sun at perihelion is $a - c = 4\sqrt{\dfrac{5}{3}} \times 10^9 - \sqrt{\dfrac{5}{3}} \times 10^9 = 3\sqrt{\dfrac{5}{3}} \times 10^9 \approx 3.87 \times 10^9$; the distance from Pluto to the Sun at aphelion is $a + c = 4\sqrt{\dfrac{5}{3}} \times 10^9 + \sqrt{\dfrac{5}{3}} \times 10^9 = 5\sqrt{\dfrac{5}{3}} \times 10^9 \approx 6.45 \times 10^9$.

36. Placing the origin at the center of the sheet of plywood and letting the x-axis be the long central axis, we have $2a = 8$, so that $a = 4$, and $2b = 4$, so that $b = 2$. So $c^2 = a^2 - b^2 = 4^2 - 2^2 = 12$ $\Rightarrow$ $c = 2\sqrt{3} \approx 3.46$. So the tacks should be located $2(3.46) = 6.92$ feet apart and the string should be $2a = 8$ feet long.

38. (a) The ellipse $x^2 + 4y^2 = 16$ $\Leftrightarrow$ $\dfrac{x^2}{16} + \dfrac{y^2}{4} = 1$ has $a = 4$ and $b = 2$. Thus, the equation of the ancillary circle is $x^2 + y^2 = 4$.

    (b) If (s, t) is a point on the ancillary circle, then $s^2 + t^2 = 4$ $\Leftrightarrow$ $4s^2 + 4t^2 = 16$ $\Leftrightarrow$ $(2s)^2 + 4(t)^2 = 16$, which implies that $(2s, t)$ is a point on the ellipse.

40. $\dfrac{x^2}{k} + \dfrac{y^2}{4+k} = 1$ is an ellipse for $k > 0$. Then $a^2 = 4 + k$, $b^2 = k$, and so $c^2 = 4 + k - k = 4$ $\Leftrightarrow$ $c = \pm2$. Therefore, all of the ellipses' foci are at $(0, \pm2)$, no matter what the value of k is.

42. (a) $x^2 + ky^2 = 100$ $\Leftrightarrow$ $ky^2 = 100 - x^2$ $\Rightarrow$ $y = \pm\dfrac{1}{k}\sqrt{100 - x^2}$. For the top half, we graph $y = \dfrac{1}{k}\sqrt{100 - x^2}$ for $k = 4, 10, 25,$ and 50.

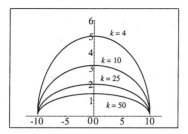

(b) This family of ellipses have common major axes and vertices, and the eccentricity increases as k increases.

44. We start with the flashlight perpendicular to the wall; this shape is a circle. As the angle of elevation increases, the shape of the light changes to an ellipse. When the flashlight is angled so that the outer edge of the light cone is parallel to the wall, the shape of the light is a parabola. Finally, as the angle of elevation increases further, the shape of the light is hyperbolic.

Exercises 11.3

2.   The hyperbola $\dfrac{y^2}{9} - \dfrac{x^2}{16} = 1$ has $a = 3$, $b = 4$, and $c^2 = 9 + 16 = 25$

    $\Rightarrow$ $c = 5$.

Vertices: $(0, \pm 3)$; foci: $(0, \pm 5)$; asymptotes: $y = \pm \frac{3}{4} x$.

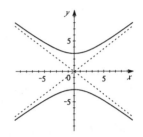

4.   The hyperbola $\dfrac{x^2}{2} - \dfrac{y^2}{1} = 1$ has $a = \sqrt{2}$, $b = 1$, and $c^2 = 2 + 1 = 3$

    $\Rightarrow$ $c = \sqrt{3}$.

Vertices: $(\pm\sqrt{2}, 0)$; foci: $(\pm\sqrt{3}, 0)$; asymptotes: $y = \pm \frac{1}{\sqrt{2}} x$.

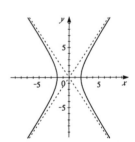

6.   The hyperbola $9x^2 - 4y^2 = 36$ $\Leftrightarrow$ $\dfrac{x^2}{4} - \dfrac{y^2}{9} = 1$ has $a = 2$,

$b = 3$, and $c^2 = 4 + 9 = 13$ $\Rightarrow$ $c = \sqrt{13}$.

Vertices: $(\pm 2, 0)$; foci: $(\pm\sqrt{13}, 0)$; asymptotes: $y = \pm \frac{3}{2} x$.

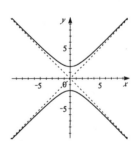

8.   The hyperbola $x^2 - y^2 + 4 = 0$ $\Leftrightarrow$ $y^2 - x^2 = 4$ $\Leftrightarrow$

$\dfrac{y^2}{4} - \dfrac{x^2}{4} = 1$ has $a = 2$, $b = 2$, and $c^2 = 4 + 4 = 8 = 2\sqrt{2}$.

Vertices: $(0, \pm 2)$; foci: $(0, \pm 2\sqrt{2})$; asymptotes: $y = \pm x$.

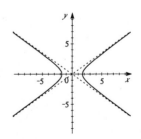

10. The hyperbola $x^2 - 2y^2 = 3$ $\Leftrightarrow$ $\dfrac{x^2}{3} - \dfrac{y^2}{3/2} = 1$ has $a = \sqrt{3}$,

$b = \sqrt{3/2}$, and $c^2 = 3 + \frac{3}{2} = \frac{9}{2}$ $\Rightarrow$ $c = \frac{3\sqrt{2}}{2}$.

Vertices: $(\pm\sqrt{3}, 0)$; foci: $(\pm\sqrt{\frac{3}{2}}, 0)$; asymptotes:

$y = \pm \dfrac{\sqrt{3/2}}{\sqrt{3}} x = \pm \dfrac{\sqrt{2}}{2} x$.

12. The hyperbola $9x^2 - 16y^2 = 1$ $\Leftrightarrow$ $\dfrac{x^2}{1/9} - \dfrac{y^2}{1/16} = 1$ has $a = \frac{1}{3}$,

$b = \frac{1}{4}$, and $c^2 = \frac{1}{9} + \frac{1}{16} = \frac{25}{144}$ $\Rightarrow$ $c = \frac{5}{12}$.

Vertices: $(\pm\frac{1}{3}, 0)$; foci: $(\pm\frac{5}{12}, 0)$; asymptotes:

$y = \pm\dfrac{1/4}{1/3}x = \pm\frac{3}{4}x.$

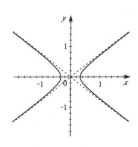

14. From the graph, the foci are $(0, \pm13)$ and the vertices are $(0, \pm12)$, so $c = 13$ and $a = 12$. Then $b^2 = c^2 - a^2 = 169 - 144 = 25$, and since the vertices are on the y-axis, the equation of the

hyperbola is $\dfrac{y^2}{144} - \dfrac{x^2}{25} = 1.$

16. The vertices are $(\pm3, 0)$, so $a = 3$. Since the asymptotes are $y = \pm\frac{1}{2}x = \pm\frac{b}{a}x$, we have $\frac{b}{3} = \frac{1}{2}$

$\Leftrightarrow$ $b = \frac{3}{2}$. Since the vertices are on the x-axis, the equation is $\dfrac{x^2}{3^2} - \dfrac{y^2}{(3/2)^2} = 1$ $\Leftrightarrow$

$\dfrac{x^2}{9} - \dfrac{4y^2}{9} = 1.$

18. The foci are $(0, \pm10)$ and the vertices are $(0, \pm8)$, so $c = 10$ and $a = 8$. Then $b^2 = c^2 - a^2 = 100 - 64 = 36$, and since the vertices are on the y-axis, the equation of the

hyperbola is $\dfrac{y^2}{64} - \dfrac{x^2}{36} = 1.$

20. The foci are $(\pm6, 0)$, and the vertices are $(\pm2, 0)$, so $c = 6$ and $a = 2$. Then $b^2 = c^2 - a^2$

$= 36 - 4 = 32$, and since the vertices are on the x-axis, the equation is $\dfrac{x^2}{4} - \dfrac{y^2}{32} = 1.$

22. The vertices are $(0, \pm6)$, so $a = 6$. The asymptotes are $y = \pm\frac{1}{3}x = \pm\frac{a}{b}x$ $\Leftrightarrow$ $\frac{6}{b} = \frac{1}{3}$ $\Leftrightarrow$

$b = 18$. Since the vertices are on the y-axis, the equation of the hyperbola is $\dfrac{y^2}{36} - \dfrac{x^2}{324} = 1.$

24. The vertices are $(0, \pm6)$, so $a = 6$. Since the vertices are on the y-axis, the hyperbola has an

equation of the form $\dfrac{y^2}{36} - \dfrac{x^2}{b^2} = 1$. Since the hyperbola passes through the point $(-5, 9)$, we have

$\dfrac{81}{36} - \dfrac{25}{b^2} = 1$ $\Leftrightarrow$ $\dfrac{25}{b^2} = \dfrac{45}{36}$ $\Leftrightarrow$ $b^2 = 20$. Thus, the equation is $\dfrac{y^2}{36} - \dfrac{x^2}{20} = 1.$

26. The foci are $(\pm3, 0)$, so $c = 3$. Since the vertices are on the x-axis, the equation of the hyperbola is

of the form $\dfrac{x^2}{a^2} - \dfrac{y^2}{b^2} = 1$. Since the hyperbola passes through the point $(4, 1)$, we have

$\dfrac{16}{a^2} - \dfrac{1}{b^2} = 1$. Using the foci, $c^2 = a^2 + b^2 = 9$ $\Leftrightarrow$ $a^2 = 9 - b^2$, and substituting gives

$\dfrac{16}{9 - b^2} - \dfrac{1}{b^2} = 1$ $\Leftrightarrow$ $16b^2 - (9 - b^2) = b^2(9 - b^2)$ $\Leftrightarrow$ $17b^2 - 9 = 9b^2 - b^4$ $\Leftrightarrow$

$b^4 + 8b^2 - 9 = 0$ $\Leftrightarrow$ $(b^2 + 9)(b^2 - 1) = 0$ $\Leftrightarrow$ $b^2 = 1$ or $b^2 = -9$ (never). Then we have

$a^2 = 9 - b^2 = 8$. Thus, the equation of the hyperbola is $\dfrac{x^2}{8} - y^2 = 1.$

28. The foci are $(0, \pm 1)$, and the length of the transverse axis is 1, so $c = 1$ and $2a = 1 \iff a = \frac{1}{2}$.
Then, $b^2 = c^2 - a^2 = 1 - \frac{1}{4} = \frac{3}{4}$, and since the foci are on the y-axis, the equation is $\dfrac{y^2}{1/4} - \dfrac{x^2}{3/4} = 1$
$\iff 12y^2 - 4x^2 = 3$.

30. The hyperbolas $\dfrac{x^2}{a^2} - \dfrac{y^2}{b^2} = 1$ and $\dfrac{x^2}{a^2} - \dfrac{y^2}{b^2} = -1$ are conjugate to each other.

(a) $x^2 - 4y^2 + 16 = 0 \iff$
$\dfrac{x^2}{16} - \dfrac{y^2}{4} = -1$, and $4y^2 - x^2 + 16 = 0$
$\iff \dfrac{x^2}{16} - \dfrac{y^2}{4} = 1$. So the hyperbolas
are conjugate to each other.

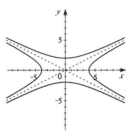

(b) They both have the same asymptotes, $y = \pm \frac{1}{2}x$.

(c) The two general conjugate hyperbolas both have asymptotes $y = \pm \frac{b}{a}x$.

32. (a) The hyperbola $\dfrac{x^2}{9} - \dfrac{y^2}{16} = 1$ has $a = 3$, $b = 4$, so $c^2 = 9 + 16 = 25$, and $c = 5$. Therefore, the
foci are $F_1(5, 0)$ and $F_2(-5, 0)$.

(b) Substituting $P(5, \frac{16}{3})$ into the equation of the hyperbola, we get $\dfrac{25}{9} - \dfrac{256/9}{16} = \dfrac{25}{9} - \dfrac{16}{9} = 1$,
so P lies on the hyperbola.

(c) $d(P, F_1) = \sqrt{(5-5)^2 + (16/3 - 0)^2} = \frac{16}{3}$, and $d(P, F_2) = \sqrt{(-5-5)^2 + (16/3 - 0)^2}$
$= \frac{1}{3}\sqrt{900 + 256} = \frac{34}{3}$.

(d) $d(P, F_2) - d(P, F_1) = \frac{34}{3} - \frac{16}{3} = 6 = 2(3) = 2a$.

34. Since the asymptotes are perpendicular, $a = b$. Also, since the sun is a focus and the closest distance
is 2×10^9, it follows that $c - a = 2 \times 10^9$. Now $c^2 = a^2 + b^2 = 2a^2$, and so $c = \sqrt{2}a$. Thus,
$\sqrt{2}a - a = 2 \times 10^9 \implies a = \dfrac{2 \times 10^9}{\sqrt{2} - 1}$ and $a^2 = b^2 = \dfrac{4 \times 10^{18}}{3 - 2\sqrt{2}} \approx 2.3 \times 10^{19}$. Therefore, the
equation of the hyperbola is $\dfrac{x^2}{2.3 \times 10^{19}} - \dfrac{y^2}{2.3 \times 10^{19}} = 1 \iff x^2 - y^2 = 2.3 \times 10^{19}$.

36. Some possible answer are: as cross-sections of nuclear power plant cooling towers, or as reflectors
for camouflaging the location of secret installations (see Figure 7 on page 560 of the text).

Exercises 11.4

2. The ellipse $\dfrac{(x-3)^2}{16} + (y+3)^2 = 1$ is obtained from the ellipse

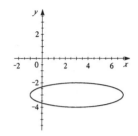

$\dfrac{x^2}{16} + y^2 = 1$ by shifting to the right 3 units and downward 3 units. So $a = 4$, $b = 1$, and $c = \sqrt{16-1} = \sqrt{15}$.

Center: $(3, -3)$; foci: $(3 \pm \sqrt{15}, -3)$; vertices: $(3 \pm 4, -3) = (-1, -3)$ and $(7, -3)$; length of the major axis: $2a = 8$; length of the minor axis: $2b = 2$.

4. The ellipse $\dfrac{(x+2)^2}{4} + y^2 = 1$ is obtained from the ellipse

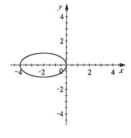

$\dfrac{x^2}{4} + \dfrac{y^2}{1} = 1$ by shifting to the left 2 units. So $a = 2$, $b = 1$, and $c = \sqrt{4-1} = \sqrt{3}$.

Center: $(-2, 0)$; foci: $(-2 \pm \sqrt{3}, 0)$; vertices: $(-2 \pm 2, 0) = (-4, 0)$ and $(0, 0)$; length of the major axis: $2a = 4$; length of the minor axis: $2b = 2$.

6. The parabola $(y+5)^2 = -6x + 12 = -6(x-2)$ is obtained from the parabola $y^2 = -6x$ by shifting to the right 2 units and down 5 units. So $4p = -6 \quad \Leftrightarrow \quad p = -\frac{3}{2}$.

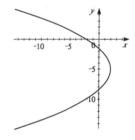

Vertex: $(2, -5)$; focus: $\left(2 - \frac{3}{2}, -5\right) = \left(\frac{1}{2}, -5\right)$; directrix: $x = 2 + \frac{3}{2} = \frac{7}{2}$.

8. The parabola $y^2 = 16x - 8 = 16\left(x - \frac{1}{2}\right)$ is obtained from the parabola $y^2 = 16x$ by shifting to the right $\frac{1}{2}$ unit. So $4p = 16 \quad \Leftrightarrow \quad p = 4$.

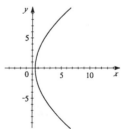

Vertex: $\left(\frac{1}{2}, 0\right)$; focus: $\left(\frac{1}{2} + 4, 0\right) = \left(\frac{9}{2}, 0\right)$; directrix: $x = \frac{1}{2} - 4 = -\frac{7}{2}$.

10. The hyperbola $(x-8)^2 - (y+6)^2 = 1$ is obtained from the hyperbola $x^2 - y^2 = 1$ by shifting to the right 8 units and downward 6 units. So $a = 1$, $b = 1$, and $c = \sqrt{1+1} = \sqrt{2}$.

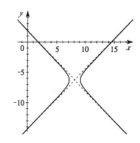

Center: $(8, -6)$; foci: $(8 \pm \sqrt{2}, -6)$; vertices: $(8 \pm 1, -6)$, so the vertices are $(7, -6)$ and $(9, -6)$; asymptotes: $(y + 6) = \pm(x - 8) \quad \Leftrightarrow \quad y = x - 14$ and $y = -x + 2$.

12. The hyperbola $\dfrac{(y-1)^2}{25} - (x+3)^2 = 1$ is obtained from the

hyperbola $\dfrac{y^2}{25} - x^2 = 1$ by shifting to the left 3 units and upward 1

unit. So $a = 5$, $b = 1$, and $c = \sqrt{25+1} = \sqrt{26}$.

Center: $(-3,1)$; foci: $(-3, 1 \pm \sqrt{26})$; vertices: $(-3, 1 \pm 5)$, so the
vertices are $(-3,-4)$ and $(-3,6)$; asymptotes: $(y-1) = \pm 5(x+3)$
$\Leftrightarrow$ $y = 5x + 16$ and $y = -5x - 14$.

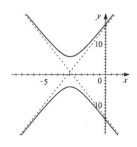

14. This is a parabola that opens to the right with its vertex at $(-6,0)$, so its equation is of the form
$y^2 = 4p(x+6)$, with $p > 0$. Since the distance from the vertex to the directrix is $p = -6 - (-12)$
$= 6$, the equation is $y^2 = 4(6)(x+6)$ $\Leftrightarrow$ $y^2 = 24(x+6)$

16. This is an ellipse with the major axis parallel to the y-axis. From the graph the center is $(2,-3)$,

with $a = 3$ and $b = 2$. Thus, the equation is $\dfrac{(x-2)^2}{4} + \dfrac{(y+3)^2}{9} = 1$.

18. From the graph, the vertices are $(2,0)$ and $(6,0)$. The center is the midpoint between the vertices, so
the center is $\left(\frac{2+6}{2}, \frac{0+0}{2}\right) = (4,0)$. Since a is the distance from the center to a vertex, $a = 2$. Since

the vertices are on the x-axis, the equation is of the form $\dfrac{(x-4)^2}{4} - \dfrac{y^2}{b^2} = 1$. Since the point $(0,4)$

lies on the hyperbola, we have $\dfrac{(0-4)^2}{4} - \dfrac{(4)^2}{b^2} = 1$ $\Leftrightarrow$ $\dfrac{16}{4} - \dfrac{16}{b^2} = 1$ $\Leftrightarrow$ $3 = \dfrac{16}{b^2}$

$\Leftrightarrow$ $b^2 = \frac{16}{3}$. Thus, the equation of the hyperbola is $\dfrac{(x-4)^2}{4} - \dfrac{y^2}{16/3} = 1$ $\Leftrightarrow$

$\dfrac{(x-4)^2}{4} - \dfrac{3y^2}{16} = 1$.

20. $y^2 = 4(x+2y)$ $\Leftrightarrow$ $y^2 - 8y = 4x$ $\Leftrightarrow$
$y^2 - 8y + 16 = 4x + 16$ $\Leftrightarrow$ $(y-4)^2 = 4(x+4)$. This is a
parabola that has $4p = 4$ $\Leftrightarrow$ $p = 1$.

Vertex: $(-4,4)$; focus: $(-4+1, 4) = (-3,4)$; directrix:
$x = -4 - 1 = -5$.

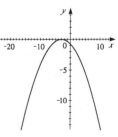

22. $x^2 + 6x + 12y + 9 = 0$ $\Leftrightarrow$ $x^2 + 6x + 9 = -12y$ $\Leftrightarrow$
$(x+3)^2 = -12y$. This is a parabola that has $4p = -12$ $\Leftrightarrow$
$p = -3$.

Vertex: $(-3,0)$; focus: $(-3,-3)$; directrix: $y = 3$.

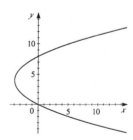

24. $2x^2 + y^2 = 2y + 1$ $\Leftrightarrow$ $2x^2 + (y^2 - 2y + 1) = 1 + 1$ $\Leftrightarrow$

$2x^2 + (y-1)^2 = 2$ $\Leftrightarrow$ $x^2 + \dfrac{(y-1)^2}{2} = 1$. This is an ellipse that

has $a = \sqrt{2}$, $b = 1$, and $c = \sqrt{2-1} = 1$.

Center: $(0,1)$; foci: $(0, 1 \pm 1) = (0,0)$ and $(0,2)$; vertices:
$(0, 1 \pm \sqrt{2})$; length of the major axis: $2a = 2\sqrt{2}$; length of the
minor axis: $2b = 2$.

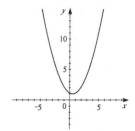

26. $4x^2 - 4x - 8y + 9 = 0$ $\Leftrightarrow$ $4(x^2 - x) - 8y + 9 = 0$ $\Leftrightarrow$
$4(x^2 - x + \frac{1}{4}) = 8y - 9 + 1$ $\Leftrightarrow$ $4(x - \frac{1}{2})^2 = 8(y - 1)$ $\Leftrightarrow$
$(x - \frac{1}{2})^2 = 2(y - 1)$. This is a parabola that has $4p = 2$ $\Leftrightarrow$
$p = \frac{1}{2}$.

Vertex: $(\frac{1}{2}, 1)$; focus: $(\frac{1}{2}, \frac{3}{2})$; directrix: $y = -\frac{1}{2} + 1 = \frac{1}{2}$.

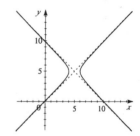

28. $x^2 - y^2 = 10(x - y) + 1$ $\Leftrightarrow$ $x^2 - 10x - y^2 + 10y = 1$ $\Leftrightarrow$
$(x^2 - 10x + 25) - (y^2 - 10y + 25) = 1 + 25 - 25$ $\Leftrightarrow$
$(x - 5)^2 - (y - 5)^2 = 1$. This is a hyperbola that has $a = 1$, $b = 1$,
and $c = \sqrt{1 + 1} = \sqrt{2}$.

Center: $(5,5)$; foci: $(5 \pm \sqrt{2}, 5)$; vertices: $(5 \pm 1, 5) = (4, 5)$ and
$(6,5)$; asymptotes: $y - 5 = \pm(x - 5)$ $\Leftrightarrow$ $y = x$ and
$y = -x + 10$.

30. $x^2 + 4y^2 + 20x - 40y + 300 = 0$ $\Leftrightarrow$ $(x^2 + 20x) + 4(y^2 - 10y) = -300$ $\Leftrightarrow$
$(x^2 + 20x + 100) + 4(y^2 - 10y + 25) = -300 + 100 + 100$ $\Leftrightarrow$
$(x + 10)^2 + 4(y - 5)^2 = -100$. Since $u^2 + v^2 \geq 0$ for all u, $v \in \mathbb{R}$, there is no (x, y) such that
$(x + 10)^2 + 4(y - 5)^2 = -100$. So there is no solution, and the graph is the empty set.

32. The parabola $x^2 + y = 100$ $\Leftrightarrow$ $x^2 = -(y - 100)$ has $4p = -1$ $\Leftrightarrow$ $p = -\frac{1}{4}$. The vertex is
$(0, 100)$ and so the focus is $\left(0, 100 - \frac{1}{4}\right) = \left(0, \frac{399}{4}\right)$. Thus, one vertex of the ellipse is $(0, 100)$, and
one focus is $\left(0, \frac{399}{4}\right)$. Since the second focus of the ellipse is $(0,0)$, the second vertex is $\left(0, -\frac{1}{4}\right)$.
So $2a = 100 + \frac{1}{4} = \frac{401}{4}$ $\Leftrightarrow$ $a = \frac{401}{8}$. Since $2c$ is the distance between the foci of the ellipse,
$2c = \frac{399}{4}$, $c = \frac{399}{8}$, and then $b^2 = a^2 - c^2 = \frac{401^2}{64} - \frac{399^2}{64} = 25$. The center of the ellipse is $\left(0, \frac{399}{8}\right)$

and so its equation is $\dfrac{x^2}{25} + \dfrac{\left(y - \frac{399}{8}\right)^2}{\left(\frac{401}{8}\right)^2} = 1$, which simplifies to $\dfrac{x^2}{25} + \dfrac{(8y - 399)^2}{160{,}801} = 1$.

34. (a) We assume that $(0,1)$ is the focus closer to the vertex $(0,0)$, as shown in the figure in the text.
Then the center of the ellipse will be $(0, a)$ and $1 = a - c$. So $c = a - 1$ and
$(a - 1)^2 = a^2 - b^2$ $\Leftrightarrow$ $a^2 - 2a + 1 = a^2 - b^2$ $\Leftrightarrow$ $b^2 = 2a - 1$. Thus the equation

will be $\dfrac{x^2}{2a - 1} + \dfrac{(y - a)^2}{a^2} = 1$. If we choose $a = 4$, then we get $\dfrac{x^2}{7} + \dfrac{(y - 4)^2}{16} = 1$. If we

choose $a = 2$, then we get $\dfrac{x^2}{3} + \dfrac{(y - 2)^2}{4} = 1$. (Answers will vary, depending on your choice
of $a > 1$.)

(b) Since a vertex is at $(0,0)$ and a focus is at $(0,1)$, we must have $c - a = 1$ $(a > 0)$, and the center of the hyperbola will be at $(0,-a)$. So $c = a + 1$ and $(a+1)^2 = a^2 + b^2$ $\Leftrightarrow$ $a^2 + 2a + 1 = a^2 + b^2$ $\Leftrightarrow$ $b^2 = 2a + 1$. Thus the equation will be $\dfrac{(y+a)^2}{a^2} - \dfrac{x^2}{2a+1} = 1$. If we let $a = 2$, then the equation is $\dfrac{(y+2)^2}{4} - \dfrac{x^2}{3} = 1$. If we let $a = 5$, then the equation is $\dfrac{(y+5)^2}{25} - \dfrac{x^2}{11} = 1$. (Answers will vary, depending on your choice of a.)

(c) Since the vertex is at $(0,0)$ and the focus is at $(0,1)$, we must have $p = 1$. So $(x-0)^2 = 4(1)(y-0)$ $\Leftrightarrow$ $x^2 = 4y$, and there are no other possible parabolas.

(d) (Answers will vary, depending on your choice of a in parts (a) and (b).)

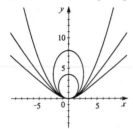

(e) The ellipses will be inside the parabola and the hyperbolas will be outside the parabola.

Exercises 11.5

2. $(x,\ y) = (-2,\ 1)$, $\phi = 30°$. Then, $X = x\cos\phi + y\sin\phi = -2\cdot\frac{\sqrt{3}}{2} + 1\cdot\frac{1}{2} = \frac{1}{2}(1 - 2\sqrt{3})$, and
$Y = -x\sin\phi + y\cos\phi = 2\cdot\frac{1}{2} + 1\cdot\frac{\sqrt{3}}{2} = \frac{1}{2}(2 + \sqrt{3})$. Therefore, the XY-coordinates of the
given point are $(X,\ Y) = \left(\frac{1}{2}[1 - 2\sqrt{3}],\ \frac{1}{2}[2 + \sqrt{3}]\right)$.

4. $(x,\ y) = (2,\ 0)$, $\phi = 15°$. Then, $X = x\cos\phi + y\sin\phi = 2\cos 15° + 0\sin 15° \approx 1.9319$, and
$Y = -x\sin\phi + y\cos\phi = -2\sin 15° + 0\cos 15° \approx -0.5176$. Therefore, the XY-coordinates of
the given point are approximately $(X,\ Y) = (1.9319,\ -0.5176)$.

6. $(x,\ y) = (\sqrt{2},\ 4\sqrt{2})$, $\phi = 45°$. Then, $X = x\cos\phi + y\sin\phi = \sqrt{2}\cdot\frac{1}{\sqrt{2}} + 4\sqrt{2}\cdot\frac{1}{\sqrt{2}} = 5$, and
$Y = -x\sin\phi + y\cos\phi = -\sqrt{2}\cdot\frac{1}{\sqrt{2}} + 4\sqrt{2}\cdot\frac{1}{\sqrt{2}} = 3$. Therefore, the XY-coordinates of the
given point are $(X,\ Y) = (5,\ 3)$.

8. $x^2 - y^2 = 2y$, $\phi = \cos^{-1}(\frac{3}{5})$. So $\cos\phi = \frac{3}{5}$ and $\sin\phi = \frac{4}{5}$. Then,
$(X\cos\phi - Y\sin\phi)^2 - (X\sin\phi + Y\cos\phi)^2 = 2(X\sin\phi + Y\cos\phi)$ $\Leftrightarrow$
$\left(\dfrac{3X}{5} - \dfrac{4Y}{5}\right)^2 - \left(\dfrac{4X}{5} + \dfrac{3Y}{5}\right)^2 = 2\left(\dfrac{4X}{5} + \dfrac{3Y}{5}\right)$ $\Leftrightarrow$
$\dfrac{9X^2}{25} - \dfrac{24XY}{25} + \dfrac{16Y^2}{25} - \dfrac{16X^2}{25} - \dfrac{24XY}{25} - \dfrac{9Y^2}{25} = \dfrac{8X}{5} + \dfrac{6Y}{5}$ $\Leftrightarrow$
$\dfrac{-7X^2}{25} - \dfrac{48XY}{25} + \dfrac{7Y^2}{25} - \dfrac{8X}{5} - \dfrac{6Y}{5} = 0$ $\Leftrightarrow$ $7Y^2 - 48XY - 7X^2 - 40X - 30Y = 0$

10. $xy = x + y$, $\phi = \frac{\pi}{4}$. Therefore, $x = X\cos\frac{\pi}{4} - Y\sin\frac{\pi}{4} = \frac{1}{\sqrt{2}}X - \frac{1}{\sqrt{2}}Y = \frac{1}{\sqrt{2}}(X - Y)$, and
$y = X\sin\frac{\pi}{4} + Y\cos\frac{\pi}{4} = \frac{1}{\sqrt{2}}X + \frac{1}{\sqrt{2}}Y = \frac{1}{\sqrt{2}}(X + Y)$. Substituting into the equation gives:
$\left[\frac{1}{\sqrt{2}}(X - Y)\right]\left[\frac{1}{\sqrt{2}}(X + Y)\right] = \frac{1}{\sqrt{2}}(X - Y) + \frac{1}{\sqrt{2}}(X + Y)$ $\Leftrightarrow$ $\frac{1}{2}(X^2 - Y^2) = \frac{2}{\sqrt{2}}X$ $\Leftrightarrow$
$X^2 - Y^2 = 2\sqrt{2}X$ $\Leftrightarrow$ $\dfrac{(X - \sqrt{2})^2}{2} - \dfrac{Y^2}{2} = 1$. This is a hyperbola.

12. (a) $xy + 4 = 0$ $\Leftrightarrow$ $0x^2 + xy + 0y^2 + 4 = 0$. So $A = 0$, $B = 1$, $C = 0$, and so the
    discriminant is $B^2 - 4AC = 1^2 - 4(0)(0) = 1$. Since the discriminant is positive the equation
    represents a hyperbola.

    (b) $\cot 2\phi = \frac{A-C}{B} = 0$ $\Rightarrow$ $2\phi = 90°$ $\Leftrightarrow$ $\phi = 45°$. Therefore, $x = \dfrac{X}{\sqrt{2}} - \dfrac{Y}{\sqrt{2}}$ and
    $y = \dfrac{X}{\sqrt{2}} + \dfrac{Y}{\sqrt{2}}$. After substitution, the original equation becomes
    $\left(\dfrac{X}{\sqrt{2}} - \dfrac{Y}{\sqrt{2}}\right)\left(\dfrac{X}{\sqrt{2}} + \dfrac{Y}{\sqrt{2}}\right) + 4 = 0$ $\Leftrightarrow$ $\dfrac{(X - Y)(X + Y)}{2} = -4$ $\Leftrightarrow$
    $\dfrac{Y^2}{8} - \dfrac{X^2}{8} = 1$. This is a hyperbola with $a = 2\sqrt{2}$, $b = 2\sqrt{2}$, and $c = 4$. Hence, the vertices
    are at $V(0,\ \pm 2\sqrt{2})$ and the foci are at $F(0,\ \pm 4)$.

(c)

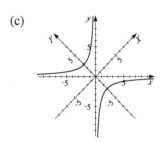

14. (a) $13x^2 + 6\sqrt{3}xy + 7y^2 = 16$. Then, $A = 13$, $B = 6\sqrt{3}$, $C = 7$, and so the discriminant is $B^2 - 4AC = (6\sqrt{3})^2 - 4(13)(7) = -256$. Since the discriminant is negative the equation represents an ellipse.

(b) $\cot 2\phi = \dfrac{A-C}{B} = \dfrac{13-7}{6\sqrt{3}} = \dfrac{1}{\sqrt{2}}$ $\Rightarrow$ $2\phi = 60°$ $\Leftrightarrow$ $\phi = 30°$. Therefore, $x = \dfrac{\sqrt{3}X}{2} - \dfrac{Y}{2}$

and $y = \dfrac{X}{2} + \dfrac{\sqrt{3}Y}{2}$. After substitution, the original equation becomes

$$13\left(\frac{\sqrt{3}X}{2} - \frac{Y}{2}\right)^2 + 6\sqrt{3}\left(\frac{\sqrt{3}X}{2} - \frac{Y}{2}\right)\left(\frac{X}{2} + \frac{\sqrt{3}Y}{2}\right) + 7\left(\frac{X}{2} + \frac{\sqrt{3}Y}{2}\right)^2 = 16 \quad \Leftrightarrow$$

$$\tfrac{13}{4}(3X^2 - 2\sqrt{3}XY + Y^2) + \tfrac{3\sqrt{3}}{2}(\sqrt{3}X^2 + 2XY - \sqrt{3}Y^2)$$
$$+ \tfrac{7}{4}(X^2 + 2\sqrt{3}XY + 3Y^2) = 16 \quad \Leftrightarrow$$

$$X^2\left(\tfrac{39}{4} + \tfrac{9}{2} + \tfrac{7}{4}\right) + XY\left(-\tfrac{13\sqrt{3}}{2} + \tfrac{6\sqrt{3}}{2} + \tfrac{7\sqrt{3}}{2}\right) + Y^2\left(\tfrac{13}{4} - \tfrac{9}{2} + \tfrac{21}{4}\right) = 16 \quad \Leftrightarrow$$

$16X^2 + 4Y^2 = 16$ $\Leftrightarrow$ $X^2 + \dfrac{Y^2}{4} = 1$. This is an ellipse that has $a = 2$, $b = 1$, and

$c = \sqrt{4 - 1} = \sqrt{3}$. Thus, the vertices are at $V(0, \pm 2)$ and the foci are at $F(0, \pm\sqrt{3})$.

(c)

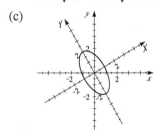

16. (a) $21x^2 + 10\sqrt{3}xy + 31y^2 = 144$. Then, $A = 21$, $B = 10\sqrt{3}$, $C = 31$, and so the discriminant is $B^2 - 4AC = (10\sqrt{3})^2 - 4(21)(31) = -2304$. Since the discriminant is negative the equation represents an ellipse.

(b) $\cot 2\phi = \dfrac{A-C}{B} = \dfrac{21-31}{10\sqrt{3}} = -\dfrac{1}{\sqrt{3}}$ $\Rightarrow$ $2\phi = 120°$ $\Leftrightarrow$ $\phi = 60°$. Therefore,

$x = \dfrac{X}{2} - \dfrac{\sqrt{3}Y}{2}$ and $y = \dfrac{\sqrt{3}X}{2} + \dfrac{Y}{2}$. After substitution, the original equation becomes

$$21\left(\frac{X}{2} - \frac{\sqrt{3}Y}{2}\right)^2 + 10\sqrt{3}\left(\frac{X}{2} - \frac{\sqrt{3}Y}{2}\right)\left(\frac{\sqrt{3}X}{2} + \frac{Y}{2}\right) + 31\left(\frac{\sqrt{3}X}{2} + \frac{Y}{2}\right)^2 = 144$$

$$\Leftrightarrow \quad \tfrac{21}{4}(X^2 - 2\sqrt{3}XY + 3Y^2) + \tfrac{5\sqrt{3}}{2}(\sqrt{3}X^2 - 2XY - \sqrt{3}Y^2)$$

$$+ \tfrac{31}{4}(3X^2 + 2\sqrt{3}XY + Y^2) = 144 \quad \Leftrightarrow$$

$$X^2\left(\tfrac{21}{4} + \tfrac{15}{2} + \tfrac{93}{4}\right) + XY\left(-\tfrac{21\sqrt{3}}{2} - \tfrac{10\sqrt{3}}{2} + \tfrac{31\sqrt{3}}{2}\right) + Y^2\left(\tfrac{63}{4} - \tfrac{15}{2} + \tfrac{31}{4}\right) = 144 \quad \Leftrightarrow$$

$36X^2 + 16Y^2 = 144 \quad \Leftrightarrow \quad \dfrac{X^2}{4} + \dfrac{Y^2}{9} = 1.$ This is an ellipse that has $a = 3, b = 2$, and

$c = \sqrt{9 - 4} = \sqrt{5}.$

(c)

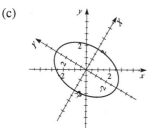

18. (a) $25x^2 - 120xy + 144y^2 - 156x - 65y = 0.$ Then, $A = 25, B = -120, C = 144$, and so the discriminant is $B^2 - 4AC = (-120)^2 - 4(25)(144) = 0.$ Since the discriminant is zero the equation represents a parabola.

(b) $\cot 2\phi = \dfrac{A-C}{B} = \dfrac{25-144}{-120} = \dfrac{-119}{-120} \quad \Rightarrow \quad \cos 2\phi = \dfrac{119}{169}.$ Therefore, $\cos\phi = \sqrt{\dfrac{1+(^{119}/_{169})}{2}} = \dfrac{12}{13}$

and $\sin\phi = \sqrt{\dfrac{1-(^{119}/_{169})}{2}} = \dfrac{5}{13}.$ Hence, $x = \dfrac{12X}{13} - \dfrac{5Y}{13}$ and $y = \dfrac{5X}{13} + \dfrac{12Y}{13}.$ Substituting

gives:

$$25\left(\dfrac{12X}{13} - \dfrac{5Y}{13}\right)^2 - 120\left(\dfrac{12X}{13} - \dfrac{5Y}{13}\right)\left(\dfrac{5X}{13} + \dfrac{12Y}{13}\right) + 144\left(\dfrac{5X}{13} + \dfrac{12Y}{13}\right)^2$$

$$- 156\left(\dfrac{12X}{13} - \dfrac{5Y}{13}\right) - 65\left(\dfrac{5X}{13} + \dfrac{12Y}{13}\right) = 0 \quad \Leftrightarrow$$

$$\dfrac{X^2}{169}(25 \cdot 12^2 - 120 \cdot 12 \cdot 5 + 144 \cdot 5^2) + \dfrac{Y^2}{169}(25 \cdot 5^2 - 120(-5)(12) + 144 \cdot 12^2)$$

$$- \dfrac{X}{13}(156 \cdot 12 + 65 \cdot 5) + \dfrac{Y}{13}(156 \cdot 5 - 65 \cdot 12) = 0 \quad \Leftrightarrow$$

$169Y^2 - 169X = 0 \quad \Leftrightarrow \quad X = Y^2.$ This is a parabola that has $4p = 1.$

(c)

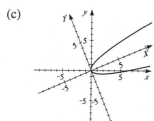

Since $\cos 2\phi = \dfrac{119}{169}$, we have $2\phi = \cos^{-1}\left(\dfrac{119}{169}\right) \approx 45.2°$
and so $\phi \approx 23°.$

20. (a) $153x^2 + 192xy + 97y^2 = 225.$ Then, $A = 153, B = 192, C = 97$, and so the discriminant is $B^2 - 4AC = (192)^2 - 4(153)(97) = -22500.$ Since the discriminant is negative the equation represents an ellipse.

(b) $\cot 2\phi = \dfrac{A-C}{B} = \dfrac{153-97}{192} = \dfrac{56}{192} \quad \Rightarrow \quad \cos 2\phi = \dfrac{56}{200}.$ Therefore, $\cos\phi = \sqrt{\dfrac{1+(^{56}/_{200})}{2}} = \dfrac{16}{20} = \dfrac{4}{5}$

and $\sin\phi = \sqrt{\dfrac{1-(^{56}/_{200})}{2}} = \dfrac{12}{20} = \dfrac{3}{5}.$ Substituting gives:

$$153\left(\frac{4X}{5} - \frac{3Y}{5}\right)^2 + 192\left(\frac{4X}{5} - \frac{3Y}{5}\right)\left(\frac{3X}{5} + \frac{4Y}{5}\right) + 97\left(\frac{3X}{5} + \frac{4Y}{5}\right)^2 = 225 \quad \Leftrightarrow$$

$$\tfrac{153}{25}(16X^2 - 24XY + 9Y^2) + \tfrac{192}{25}(12X^2 + 7XY - 12Y^2) +$$

$$\tfrac{97}{25}(9X^2 + 24XY + 16Y^2) = 225 \quad \Leftrightarrow$$

$$X^2(2448 + 2304 + 873) + XY(-3672 + 1344 + 2328) + Y^2(1377 - 2304 + 1552) = 5625$$

$$\Leftrightarrow \quad 5625X^2 + 625Y^2 = 5625 \quad \Leftrightarrow \quad X^2 + \frac{Y^2}{9} = 1. \text{ This is an ellipse that has } a = 3,$$

$b = 1$, and $c = \sqrt{9 - 1} = 2\sqrt{2}$.

(c)

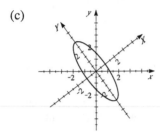

22. (a) $9x^2 - 24xy + 16y^2 = 100(x - y - 1)$. Then, $A = 9$, $B = -24$, $C = 16$, and so the discriminant is $B^2 - 4AC = (-24)^2 - 4(9)(16) = 0$. Since the discriminant is zero the equation represents a parabola.

(b) $\cot 2\phi = \frac{A-C}{B} = \frac{9-16}{-24} = \frac{7}{24} \quad \Rightarrow \quad \cos 2\phi = \frac{7}{25}$. So, $\cos \phi = \sqrt{\frac{1+(7/25)}{2}} = \frac{4}{5}$ and

$\sin \phi = \sqrt{\frac{1-(7/25)}{2}} = \frac{3}{5}$, and so $x = \frac{4X}{5} - \frac{3Y}{5}$, $y = \frac{3X}{5} + \frac{4Y}{5}$. By substitution,

$$9\left(\frac{4X}{5} - \frac{3Y}{5}\right)^2 - 24\left(\frac{4X}{5} - \frac{3Y}{5}\right)\left(\frac{3X}{5} + \frac{4Y}{5}\right) + 16\left(\frac{3X}{5} + \frac{4Y}{5}\right)^2$$

$$= 100\left(\frac{4X}{5} - \frac{3Y}{5} - \frac{3X}{5} - \frac{4Y}{5} - 1\right) \quad \Leftrightarrow$$

$$\tfrac{9}{25}(16X^2 - 24XY + 9Y^2) - \tfrac{24}{25}(12X^2 + 7XY - 12Y^2) +$$

$$\tfrac{16}{25}(9X^2 + 24XY + 16Y^2) = 100(\tfrac{X}{5} - \tfrac{7Y}{5} - 1) \quad \Leftrightarrow$$

$$144X^2 - 216XY + 81Y^2 - 288X^2 - 168XY + 288Y^2 + 144X^2 +$$

$$384XY + 256Y^2 = 500X - 3500Y - 2500 \quad \Leftrightarrow$$

$625Y^2 = 500X - 3500Y - 2500 \quad \Leftrightarrow \quad 5Y^2 + 28Y = 4X - 20 \quad \Leftrightarrow$

$5(Y^2 + \frac{28}{5}Y + \frac{196}{25}) = 4X - 20 + \frac{196}{5} = 4X + \frac{96}{5} \quad \Leftrightarrow \quad (Y + \frac{14}{5})^2 = \frac{4}{5}(X + \frac{25}{4})$. This is a

parabola that has $4p = \frac{4}{5}$ and $V(-\frac{25}{4}, -\frac{14}{5})$.

(c)

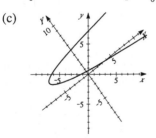

Since $\cos 2\phi = \frac{7}{25}$, we have $2\phi = \cos^{-1}\left(\frac{7}{25}\right) \approx 73.74°$ and so $\phi \approx 37°$.

24. (a) $(7x + 24y)^2 = 49x^2 + 336xy + 576y^2 = 600x - 175y + 25$. So $A = 49$, $B = 336$, $C = 576$, and so the discriminant is $B^2 - 4AC = (336)^2 - 4(49)(576) = 0$. Since the discriminant is zero the equation represents a parabola.

(b) $\cot 2\phi = \frac{A-C}{B} = \frac{49-576}{336} = \frac{-527}{336} \Rightarrow \cos 2\phi = \frac{-527}{625}$. Therefore, $\cos\phi = \sqrt{\frac{1-(527/625)}{2}} = \frac{7}{25}$

and $\sin\phi = \sqrt{\frac{1+(527/625)}{2}} = \frac{24}{25}$. Substituting $x = \dfrac{7X}{25} - \dfrac{24Y}{25}$ and $y = \dfrac{24X}{25} + \dfrac{7Y}{25}$ gives:

$$49\left(\frac{7X}{25} - \frac{24Y}{25}\right)^2 + 336\left(\frac{7X}{25} - \frac{24Y}{25}\right)\left(\frac{24X}{25} + \frac{7Y}{25}\right) + 576\left(\frac{24X}{25} + \frac{7Y}{25}\right)^2$$

$$= 600\left(\frac{7X}{25} - \frac{24Y}{25}\right) - 175\left(\frac{24X}{25} + \frac{7Y}{25}\right) + 25 \quad \Leftrightarrow$$

$\frac{49}{625}(49X^2 - 336XY + 576Y^2) + \frac{336}{625}(168X^2 - 527XY - 168Y^2)$

$\qquad + \frac{576}{625}(576X^2 + 336XY + 49Y^2) = 168X - 576Y - 168X - 49Y + 25 \quad \Leftrightarrow$

$X^2(2401 + 56{,}448 + 331{,}776) + XY(-16{,}464 - 177{,}072 + 193{,}536)$

$\qquad + Y^2(28{,}224 - 56{,}448 + 28{,}224) = -625^2 Y + 15{,}625 \quad \Leftrightarrow$

$390{,}625X^2 + 390{,}625Y = 15{,}625 \quad \Leftrightarrow \quad 25X^2 + 25Y = 1 \quad \Leftrightarrow$

$X^2 = -Y + \frac{1}{25} = -(Y - \frac{1}{25})$. This is a parabola that has $4p = -1$ and vertex $(0, \frac{1}{25})$.

(c)

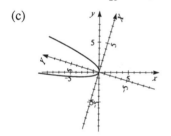

Since $\cos 2\phi = \frac{-527}{625}$, we have $2\phi = \cos^{-1}\left(\frac{-527}{625}\right) \approx 147.48°$ and so $\phi \approx 74°$.

26. (a) $2\sqrt{2}(x + y)^2 = 7x + 9y \quad \Leftrightarrow \quad 2\sqrt{2}x^2 + 4\sqrt{2}xy + 2\sqrt{2}y^2 = 7x + 9y$. Therefore, $A = 2\sqrt{2}$, $B = 4\sqrt{2}$, $C = 2\sqrt{2}$, and so $\cot 2\phi = \frac{A-C}{B} = 0 \quad \Rightarrow \quad 2\phi = 90° \quad \Rightarrow \quad \phi = 45°$. Thus $x = \frac{X-Y}{\sqrt{2}}$, $y = \frac{X+Y}{\sqrt{2}} \quad \Rightarrow \quad x + y = \sqrt{2}X$. Thus the equation becomes

$2\sqrt{2}(\sqrt{2}X)^2 = \dfrac{16X + 2Y}{\sqrt{2}} \quad \Leftrightarrow \quad 8X^2 = 16X + 2Y \quad \Leftrightarrow \quad 4(X^2 + 2X + 1) = Y + 4$

$\Leftrightarrow \quad 4(X + 1)^2 = Y + 4$. This is a parabola.

(b) $4p = \frac{1}{4}$ so $p = \frac{1}{16}$. Thus in XY-coordinates the vertex is $V(-1, -4)$ and the focus is $F(-1, -\frac{63}{16})$. In xy-coordinates, $V\left(\frac{3}{\sqrt{2}}, \frac{-5}{\sqrt{2}}\right)$ and $F\left(\frac{47}{16\sqrt{2}}, \frac{-79}{16\sqrt{2}}\right)$.

(c) The directrix is $Y = -\frac{65}{16}$. Thus $\frac{-x+y}{\sqrt{2}} = -\frac{65}{16}$ or $y = x - \frac{65\sqrt{2}}{16}$.

28. $\sqrt{x} + \sqrt{y} = 1$. Squaring both sides gives $x + 2\sqrt{xy} + y = 1 \quad \Leftrightarrow \quad 2\sqrt{xy} = 1 - x - y$, and squaring both sides again gives: $4xy = (1 - x - y)^2 = 1 - x - y - x + x^2 + xy - y + xy + y^2$

$\Leftrightarrow \quad 4xy = x^2 + y^2 + 2xy - 2x - 2y + 1 \quad \Leftrightarrow \quad x^2 + y^2 - 2xy - 2x - 2y + 1 = 0$. Then,

$A = 1$, $B = -2$, and $C = 1$, and so $\cot 2\phi = \frac{A-C}{B} = 0 \Rightarrow 2\phi = 90° \quad \Leftrightarrow \quad \phi = 45°$. Therefore,

$x = \dfrac{X}{\sqrt{2}} - \dfrac{Y}{\sqrt{2}}$ and $y = \dfrac{X}{\sqrt{2}} + \dfrac{Y}{\sqrt{2}}$, and substituting gives $\left(\dfrac{X}{\sqrt{2}} - \dfrac{Y}{\sqrt{2}}\right)^2 - 2\left(\dfrac{X}{\sqrt{2}} - \dfrac{Y}{\sqrt{2}}\right)$

$$\left(\frac{X}{\sqrt{2}}+\frac{Y}{\sqrt{2}}\right)+\left(\frac{X}{\sqrt{2}}+\frac{Y}{\sqrt{2}}\right)^2-2\left(\frac{X}{\sqrt{2}}-\frac{Y}{\sqrt{2}}\right)-2\left(\frac{X}{\sqrt{2}}+\frac{Y}{\sqrt{2}}\right)+1=0 \quad\Leftrightarrow$$

$$\tfrac{1}{2}(X^2-2XY+Y^2)-(X^2-Y^2)+\tfrac{1}{2}(X^2+2XY+Y^2)-2\sqrt{2}X+1=0 \quad\Leftrightarrow$$

$$X^2\left(\tfrac{1}{2}-1+\tfrac{1}{2}\right)+XY(-1+1)+Y^2\left(\tfrac{1}{2}+1+\tfrac{1}{2}\right)-2\sqrt{2}X+1=0 \quad\Leftrightarrow\quad 2Y^2=2\sqrt{2}X-1$$

$$\Leftrightarrow\quad Y^2=\sqrt{2}X-\tfrac{1}{2}=\sqrt{2}\left(X-\tfrac{1}{2\sqrt{2}}\right). \text{ This is a parabola that has } 4p=\sqrt{2} \text{ and vertex}$$

$V(\frac{1}{2\sqrt{2}},0)$. However, in the original equation we must have $x\geq 0$ and $y\geq 0$, so we get only the part of the parabola that lies in the first quadrant.

30.   Using $A'=A\cos^2\phi+B\sin\phi\cos\phi+C\sin^2\phi$ and $C'=A\sin^2\phi-B\sin\phi\cos\phi+C\cos^2\phi$, we have $A'+C'=A\cos^2\phi+B\sin\phi\cos\phi+C\sin^2\phi+A\sin^2\phi-B\sin\phi\cos\phi+C\cos^2\phi$
$=A(\sin^2\phi+\cos^2\phi)+C(\sin^2\phi+\cos^2\phi)=A+C$. Since $F'=F$, F is also invariant under rotation.

Exercises 11.6

Solutions to Exercises $2 - 6$ will vary. Some possible solutions are given.

2. $(2, \frac{3\pi}{4})$ also has polar coordinates $(2, \frac{11\pi}{4})$ or $(-2, \frac{7\pi}{4})$.

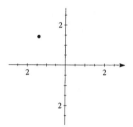

4. $(-2, -\frac{\pi}{3})$ also has polar coordinates $(2, \frac{2\pi}{3})$ or $(-2, \frac{5\pi}{3})$.

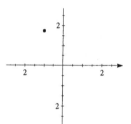

6. $(3, 1)$ also has polar coordinates $(3, 1 + 2\pi)$ or $(-3, 1 + \pi)$.

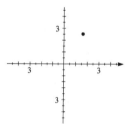

8. $(r, \theta) = (6, \frac{2\pi}{3})$. So $x = r \cos \theta = 6 \cos \frac{2\pi}{3} = -6 \cdot \frac{1}{2} = -3$ and $y = r \sin \theta = 6 \sin \frac{2\pi}{3} = 6 \cdot \frac{\sqrt{3}}{2}$
    $= 3\sqrt{3}$. Thus, the rectangular coordinates are $(-3, 3\sqrt{3})$.

10. $(r, \theta) = (-1, \frac{5\pi}{2})$. So $x = r \cos \theta = -1 \cos \frac{5\pi}{2} = -1 \cdot 0 = 0$ and $y = r \sin \theta = -1 \sin \frac{5\pi}{2}$
    $= -1 \cdot 1 = -1$. Thus, the rectangular coordinates are $(0, -1)$.

12. $(r, \theta) = (0, 13\pi)$. So $(x, y) = (0, 0)$ because $r = 0$.

14. $(x, y) = (3\sqrt{3}, -3)$. Since $r^2 = x^2 + y^2$, we have $r^2 = (3\sqrt{3})^2 + (-3)^2 = 36$, so $r = 6$. Now
    $\tan \theta = \frac{y}{x} = \frac{-3}{3\sqrt{3}} = -\frac{1}{\sqrt{3}}$, so, since the point is in the fourth quadrant, $\theta = \frac{11\pi}{6}$. Thus, the polar
    coordinates are $(6, \frac{11\pi}{6})$.

16. $(x, y) = (-\sqrt{6}, -\sqrt{2})$. Since $r^2 = x^2 + y^2$, we have $r^2 = (-\sqrt{6})^2 + (-\sqrt{2})^2 = 8$, so $r = 2\sqrt{2}$.
    Now $\tan \theta = \frac{y}{x} = \frac{-\sqrt{2}}{-\sqrt{6}} = \frac{1}{\sqrt{3}}$, so, since the point is in the third quadrant, $\theta = \frac{7\pi}{6}$. Thus, the polar
    coordinates are $(2\sqrt{2}, \frac{7\pi}{6})$.

18. $(x, y) = (1, -2)$. Since $r^2 = x^2 + y^2$, we have $r^2 = 1^2 + (-2)^2 = 2$, so $r = \sqrt{5}$. Now, $\tan\theta = \dfrac{y}{x}$
   $= \dfrac{-2}{1} = -2$, and since the point is in the fourth quadrant, $\theta = 2\pi + \tan^{-1}(-2)$ (since we need
   $0 \le \theta < 2\pi$). Thus, the polar coordinates are $\left(\sqrt{5},\, 2\pi + \tan^{-1}(-2)\right)$.

20. $x^2 + y^2 = 9$. By substitution, $(r\cos\theta)^2 + (r\sin\theta)^2 = 9 \quad\Leftrightarrow\quad r^2(\cos^2\theta + \sin^2\theta) = 9 \quad\Leftrightarrow$
   $r^2 = 9 \quad\Leftrightarrow\quad r = 3$.

22. $y = 5$. By substitution, $r\sin\theta = 5 \quad\Leftrightarrow\quad r = \dfrac{5}{\sin\theta} = 5\csc\theta$.

24. $x^2 - y^2 = 1$. By substitution, $(r\cos\theta)^2 - (r\sin\theta)^2 = 1 \quad\Leftrightarrow\quad r^2(\cos^2\theta - \sin^2\theta) = 1 \quad\Leftrightarrow$
   $r^2\cos 2\theta = 1 \quad\Leftrightarrow\quad r^2 = \dfrac{1}{\cos 2\theta} = \sec 2\theta$.

26. $\theta = \pi \quad\Rightarrow\quad \tan\theta = 0 \quad\Rightarrow\quad \dfrac{y}{x} = 0 \quad\Rightarrow\quad y = 0$.

28. $r = 6\cos\theta \quad\Leftrightarrow\quad r^2 = 6r\cos\theta$. By substitution, $x^2 + y^2 = 6x \quad\Leftrightarrow\quad (x^2 - 6x + 9) + y^2 = 9$
   $\Leftrightarrow \quad (x - 3)^2 + y^2 = 9$.

30. $r^2 = \sin 2\theta = 2\sin\theta\cos\theta \quad\Leftrightarrow\quad r^4 = 2r^2\sin\theta\cos\theta = 2(r\cos\theta)(r\sin\theta)$. By substitution,
   $(x^2 + y^2)^2 = 2xy \quad\Leftrightarrow\quad x^4 + 2x^2y^2 + y^4 - 2xy = 0$.

32. $r = \dfrac{1}{1 + \sin\theta} \quad\Leftrightarrow\quad r(1 + \sin\theta) = 1 \quad\Leftrightarrow\quad r + r\sin\theta = 1$. Thus $r = 1 - r\sin\theta$, and squaring
   both sides gives $r^2 = (1 - r\sin\theta)^2 \quad\Leftrightarrow\quad x^2 + y^2 = (1 - y)^2 = 1 - 2y + y^2 \quad\Leftrightarrow$
   $x^2 + 2y - 1 = 0$.

34. $r = \dfrac{4}{1 + 2\sin\theta} \quad\Leftrightarrow\quad r(1 + 2\sin\theta) = 4 \quad\Leftrightarrow\quad r + 2r\sin\theta = 4$. Thus $r = 4 - 2r\sin\theta$.
   Squaring both sides, we get $r^2 = (4 - 2r\sin\theta)^2$. Substituting we get $x^2 + y^2 = (4 - 2y)^2 \quad\Leftrightarrow$
   $x^2 + y^2 = 16 - 16y + 4y^2 \quad\Leftrightarrow\quad x^2 - 3y^2 + 16y - 16 = 0$.

36. $r = 2 - \cos\theta \quad\Leftrightarrow\quad r^2 = 2r - r\cos\theta \quad\Leftrightarrow\quad r^2 + r\cos\theta = 2r \quad\Leftrightarrow\quad (r^2 + r\cos\theta)^2 = (2r)^2$
   $\Leftrightarrow\quad (r^2 + r\cos\theta)^2 = 4r^2 \quad\Rightarrow\quad (x^2 + y^2 - x)^2 = 4(x^2 + y^2)$

38. $\cos 2\theta = 1$ means that $2\theta = 0 \quad\Rightarrow\quad \theta = 0 \quad\Rightarrow\quad \tan\theta = 0 \quad\Rightarrow\quad \dfrac{y}{x} = 0 \quad\Rightarrow\quad y = 0$

40. $r = -1$. Circle.   42. $\theta = \frac{5\pi}{6}$. Line.

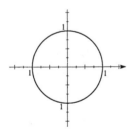

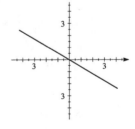

44. $r = \cos\theta$. Circle.

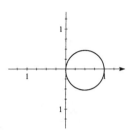

46. $r = 2\sin\theta + 2\cos\theta \quad \Leftrightarrow$
    $r^2 = 2r\sin\theta + 2r\cos\theta \quad \Leftrightarrow$
    $x^2 + y^2 = 2x + 2y \quad \Leftrightarrow$
    $(x-1)^2 + (y-1)^2 = 2$. Circle.

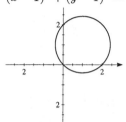

48. $r = 1 + \sin\theta$. Cardioid.

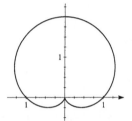

50. $r = \cos\theta - 1$. Cardioid.

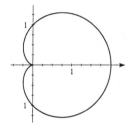

52. $r\theta = 1, \theta > 0$

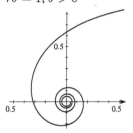

54. $r = 2\cos 3\theta$

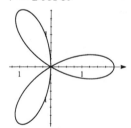

56. $r^2 = 4\sin 2\theta$

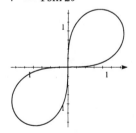

58. $r = 1 - 2\cos\theta$

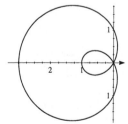

60. $r = \sin\theta \tan\theta$

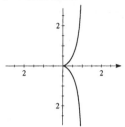

62. $r = \sin\left(\frac{8\theta}{5}\right)$; Domain: $[0, 10\pi]$

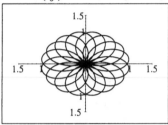

64. $r = \sqrt{1 - 0.8\sin^2 2\theta}$; Domain: $[0, 2\pi]$

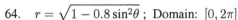

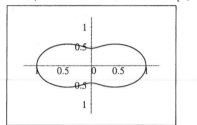

66. $r = 1 + c\sin 2\theta$

As c increases the "dimple" gets more
pronounced until it becomes an inner loop.
The "bump" also grows as c increases.

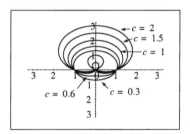

68.   The graph of $r = \dfrac{1}{\sqrt{\theta}}$ is I, since as θ increase, r decreases ($\theta > 0$). So this is a spiral into the origin.

70.   The graph of $r = 1 + 3\cos(3\theta)$ is II, since when $\theta = 0$, $r = 1 + 3 = 4$ and when $\theta = \pi$,
       $r = 1 - 3 = -2$, so there should be two intercepts on the positive-axis.

72. $r = a\cos\theta + b\sin\theta \quad\Leftrightarrow\quad r^2 = ar\cos\theta + br\sin\theta \quad\Leftrightarrow\quad x^2 + y^2 = ax + by \quad\Leftrightarrow$
       $x^2 - ax + y^2 - by = 0 \quad\Leftrightarrow\quad x^2 - ax + \frac{a^2}{4} + y^2 - by + \frac{b^2}{4} = \frac{a^2}{4} + \frac{b^2}{4} \quad\Leftrightarrow$
       $\left(x - \frac{a}{2}\right)^2 + \left(y - \frac{b}{2}\right)^2 = \frac{a^2+b^2}{4}$. Thus (in rectangular coordinates) the center is $\left(\frac{a}{2}, \frac{b}{2}\right)$ and the radius is
       $\frac{\sqrt{a^2+b^2}}{2}$.

74.   The circle $r = 2$ (in polar coordinates) has rectangular coordinate equation $x^2 + y^2 = 4$. The polar
       coordinate form is simpler.

       The graph of the equation $r = \sin 2\theta$ is a four leaf rose. Multiply both sides by r^2 we get
       $r^3 = r^2\, 2\cos\theta\sin\theta = 2(r\cos\theta)(r\sin\theta)$ which is $(x^2 + y^2)^{\frac{3}{2}} = 2xy$ in rectangular form. The polar
       form is definitely simpler.

Exercises 11.7

2. Substituting $e = \frac{4}{3}$ and $d = 3$ into the general equation of a conic with vertical directrix, we get

$$r = \frac{\frac{4}{3} \cdot 3}{1 - \frac{4}{3} \cos \theta} \quad \Leftrightarrow \quad r = \frac{12}{3 - 4 \cos \theta}.$$

4. Substituting $e = \frac{1}{2}$ and $d = 4$ into the general equation of a conic with horizontal directrix, we get

$$r = \frac{\frac{1}{2} \cdot 4}{1 - \frac{1}{2} \sin \theta} \quad \Leftrightarrow \quad r = \frac{4}{2 - \sin \theta}.$$

6. $r = 2 \csc \theta \quad \Leftrightarrow \quad r \sin \theta = 2 \quad \Leftrightarrow \quad y = 2.$ So $d = 2$ and $e = 0.6$ gives $r = \dfrac{0.6 \cdot 2}{1 + 0.6 \sin \theta} \quad \Leftrightarrow$

$$r = \frac{1.2}{1 + 0.6 \sin \theta}.$$

8. Since the vertex is at $(2, 0)$ we have $d(P, F) = 2$. Now, since $\dfrac{d(P, F)}{d(P, \ell)} = e$ we get $\dfrac{2}{d(P, \ell)} = 0.4$

$\Leftrightarrow \quad d(P, \ell) = \frac{2}{0.4} = 5.$ The directrix is $x = 7$, so substituting $e = 0.4$ and $d = 7$ we get

$$r = \frac{0.4 \cdot 7}{1 + 0.4 \cos \theta} \quad \Leftrightarrow \quad r = \frac{2.8}{1 + 0.4 \cos \theta}.$$

10. (a) $r = \dfrac{8}{3 + 3 \cos \theta} \quad \Leftrightarrow \quad r = \dfrac{\frac{8}{3}}{1 + \cos \theta} \quad \Rightarrow \quad e = 1$, thus the conic is a parabola.

(b) Substituting $\theta = 0$, we have $r = \dfrac{8}{3 + 3 \cos 0} = \frac{8}{6} = \frac{4}{3}.$

Thus the vertex is $\left(\frac{4}{3}, 0 \right)$.

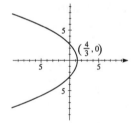

12. (a) $r = \dfrac{10}{3 - 2 \sin \theta} \quad \Leftrightarrow \quad r = \dfrac{\frac{10}{3}}{1 - \frac{2}{3} \sin \theta} \quad \Rightarrow \quad e = \frac{2}{3}$, thus the conic is an ellipse.

(b) The vertices occur where $\theta = \frac{\pi}{2}$ and $\theta = \frac{3\pi}{2}$.

Now $\theta = \frac{\pi}{2} \quad \Rightarrow \quad r = \dfrac{10}{3 - 2 \sin \frac{\pi}{2}} = \frac{10}{1} = 10,$

and $\theta = \frac{3\pi}{2} \quad \Rightarrow \quad r = \dfrac{10}{3 - 2 \sin \frac{3\pi}{2}} = \frac{10}{5} = 2.$

Thus the vertices are $\left(10, \frac{\pi}{2} \right)$ and $\left(2, \frac{3\pi}{2} \right)$.

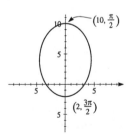

14. (a) $r = \dfrac{5}{2 - 3 \sin \theta} \quad \Leftrightarrow \quad r = \dfrac{\frac{5}{2}}{1 - \frac{3}{2} \sin \theta} \quad \Rightarrow \quad e = \frac{3}{2}$, thus the conic is a hyperbola.

(b)   The vertices occur where $\theta = \frac{\pi}{2}$ and $\theta = \frac{3\pi}{2}$.

Now $\theta = \frac{\pi}{2}$ $\Rightarrow$ $r = \dfrac{5}{2 - 3\sin\frac{\pi}{2}} = \dfrac{5}{-1} = -5,$

and $\theta = \frac{3\pi}{2}$ $\Rightarrow$ $r = \dfrac{5}{2 - 3\sin\frac{3\pi}{2}} = \dfrac{5}{5} = 1.$

Thus the vertices are $\left(-5,\ \frac{\pi}{2}\right)$ and $\left(1,\ \frac{3\pi}{2}\right)$.

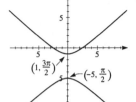

16. (a) $r = \dfrac{8}{3 + \cos\theta}$ $\Leftrightarrow$ $r = \dfrac{\frac{8}{3}}{1 + \frac{1}{3}\cos\theta}$ $\Rightarrow$ $e = \frac{1}{3}$, thus the conic is an ellipse.

(b)   The vertices occur where $\theta = 0$ and $\theta = \pi$.

Now $\theta = 0$ $\Rightarrow$ $r = \dfrac{8}{3 + \cos 0} = \frac{8}{4} = 2,$

and $\theta = \pi$ $\Rightarrow$ $r = \dfrac{8}{3 + \cos\pi} = \frac{8}{2} = 4.$

Thus the vertices are $(2,\ 0)$ and $(4,\ \pi)$.

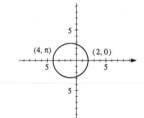

18. $r = \dfrac{5}{2 + 2\sin\theta}$ $\Leftrightarrow$ $r = \dfrac{\frac{5}{2}}{1 + \sin\theta}$. Thus
$d = \frac{5}{2}$ and the directrix is $y = \frac{5}{2}$ $\Leftrightarrow$
$r = \frac{5}{2}\csc\theta$. The equation of the conic
obtained by rotating this parabola about its
focus through an angle of $\frac{\pi}{6}$ is
$$r = \dfrac{5}{2 + 2\sin\left(\theta - \frac{\pi}{6}\right)}.$$

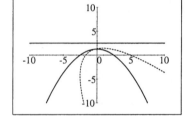

20. (a)   Shown are the graphs of the conics
$r = \dfrac{d}{1 + \sin\theta}$ where $d = \frac{1}{2}, d = 2$, and
$d = 10$. As d increases the conics get
flatter while the vertex moves further
from the focus at the origin.

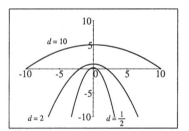

(b)   Shown are the graphs of the conics
$r = \dfrac{e}{1 + e\sin\theta}$ where $e = \frac{1}{2}, e = 1$, and
$d = 2$. As e changes the conic changes
from an ellipse to a parabola, and finally
to a hyperbola. The vertex gets closer to
the directrix (shown as a dashed line in
the figure).

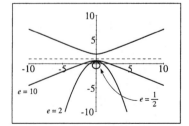

22. (a)   Using the form of the equation from Exercise 21, the perihelion distance occurs when $\theta = \pi$
and the aphelion distance occurs when $\theta = 0$. Using the form from Exercise 21 and since the

focus is at the origin, the perihelion distance is $\dfrac{a(1-e^2)}{1+e} = \dfrac{a(1-e)(1+e)}{1+e} = a(1-e)$ and the aphelion distance is $\dfrac{a(1-e^2)}{1-e} = \dfrac{a(1-e)(1+e)}{1-e} = a(1+e)$.

(b) Given $e = 0.017$ and $2a = 2.99 \times 10^8$ we have $a = 1.495 \times 10^8$. Thus the perihelion distance is $1.495 \times 10^8[1 - (0.017)] \approx 1.468 \times 10^8$ km and the aphelion distance is $1.495 \times 10^8[1 + 0.017] \approx 1.520 \times 10^8$ km.

24. Since the focus is at the origin, the distance from the focus to any point on the conic is the absolute value of the r-coordinate of that point, which we can obtain from the polar equation.

Exercises 11.8

2. (a) $x = 6t - 4, y = 3t, t \geq 0$

    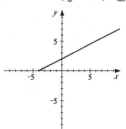

    (b) Since $y = 3t$, $t = \dfrac{y}{3}$ and so

    $$x = 6\left(\frac{y}{3}\right) - 4 = 2y - 4 \quad \Leftrightarrow$$
    $$2y = x + 4, y \geq 0.$$

4. (a) $x = 2t + 1, y = (t + \frac{1}{2})^2$

    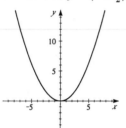

    (b) Since $y = (t + \frac{1}{2})^2$,
    $4y = 4(t + \frac{1}{2})^2 = (2t + 1)^2$, and since
    $x = 2t + 1$, we have
    $$x^2 = (2t + 1)^2 = 4y \quad \Leftrightarrow \quad y = \tfrac{1}{4}x^2.$$

6. (a) $x = t^2, y = t^4 + 1$

    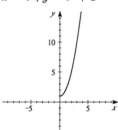

    (b) Since $x = t^2$, we have $x^2 = t^4$ and so
    $y = x^2 + 1, x \geq 0.$

8. (a) $x = t + 1, y = \dfrac{t}{t + 1}$

    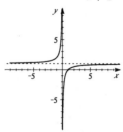

    (b) Since $x = t + 1$, we have $t = x - 1$ and
    so $y = \dfrac{x - 1}{x}.$

10. (a) $x = |t|, y = |1 - |t||$

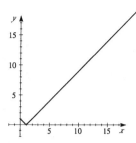

(b) Since $x = |t|$, we have $y = |1 - x|$,
     where $x \geq 0$.

12. (a) $x = 2 \cos t,\ y = 3 \sin t,\ 0 \leq t \leq 2\pi$

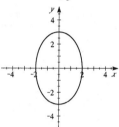

(b) We have $\cos t = \dfrac{x}{2}$ and $\sin t = \dfrac{y}{3}$, so
$$\left(\frac{x}{2}\right)^2 + \left(\frac{y}{3}\right)^2 = \cos^2 t + \sin^2 t = 1$$
$$\Leftrightarrow \quad \frac{x^2}{4} + \frac{y^2}{9} = 1.$$

14. (a) $x = \sin^2 t,\ y = \cos t$

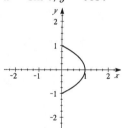

(b) Since $y = \cos t$, we have $y^2 = \cos^2 t$ and
     so $x + y^2 = \sin^2 t + \cos^2 t = 1$ or
     $x = 1 - y^2$, where $x \geq 0$.

16. (a) $x = \cos 2t,\ y = \sin 2t$

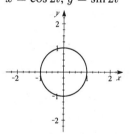

(b) $x^2 = \cos^2 2t$ and $y^2 = \sin^2 2t$. Then,
     $x^2 + y^2 = \cos^2 2t + \sin^2 2t = 1$ $\Leftrightarrow$
     $x^2 + y^2 = 1$.

18. (a) $x = \cot t,\ y = \csc t,\ 0 < t < \pi$ so $y \geq 1$.

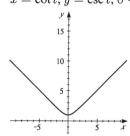

(b) $x^2 = \cot^2 t,\ y^2 = \csc^2 t$, and so
     $x^2 + 1 = \cot^2 t + 1 = \csc^2 t = y^2$.
     Therefore, $y^2 = x^2 + 1$, with $y \geq 1$.
     This is the top half of the hyperbola
     $y^2 - x^2 = 1$.

20. (a) $x = e^{2t}, y = e^t, t \geq 0.$ (b) $y^2 = e^{2t}$ so $x = y^2$, with $y \geq 1$.

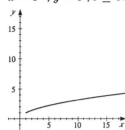

22. (a) $x = \cos^3 t, y = \sin^3 t, 0 \leq t \leq 2\pi$ (b) $x^{2/3} = \cos^2 t$ and $y^{2/3} = \sin^2 t$, and so $x^{2/3} + y^{2/3} = 1$.

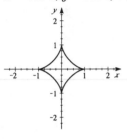

24. Since the line passes through the point $(-10, -20)$ and has slope -2, parametric equations for the line are $x = -10 + t, y = -20 - 2t$.

26. Since the line passes through the points $(0, 0)$ and $(12, 7)$, its slope is $\frac{7-0}{12-0} = \frac{7}{12}$. Thus, parametric equations for the line are $x = t, y = \frac{7}{12}t$.

28. Since $\cos^2 t + \sin^2 t = 1$, we have $\dfrac{a^2 \cos^2 t}{a^2} + \dfrac{b^2 \sin^2 t}{b^2} = 1$. If we let $x = a \cos t$ and $y = b \sin t$, then $\dfrac{x^2}{a^2} + \dfrac{y^2}{b^2} = 1$. Hence, parametric equations for the ellipse are $x = a \cos t, y = b \sin t$.

30. Substituting the given values for x and y into the equation we derived in Exercise 29, we get $\dfrac{(b\sqrt{t+1})^2}{b^2} - \dfrac{(a\sqrt{t})^2}{a^2} = (t+1) - t = 1$. Thus the points on this curve satisfy the hyperbola equation. However, this hyperbola is only the part of $\dfrac{y^2}{b^2} - \dfrac{x^2}{a^2} = 1$ for which $x \geq 0$ and $y \geq 0$.

32. $x = \sin t, y = \sin 2t$ 34. $x = \cot t, y = \sin^2 t, 0 < t < \pi$

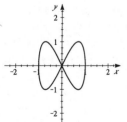   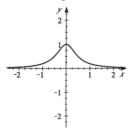

36. $v_0 = 2048$ ft/s and $\alpha = 30°$.

    (a)   The bullet will hit the ground when $y = 0$. Since $y = (v_0 \sin \alpha)t - 16t^2$, we have
$$0 = (2048 \cdot \sin 30°)\, t - 16t^2 \quad \Leftrightarrow \quad 0 = 1024t - 16t^2 \quad \Leftrightarrow \quad 16t\,(t - 64) = 0 \quad \Leftrightarrow$$
$t = 0$ or $t = 64$. Hence, the bullet will hit the ground after 64 seconds.

    (b)   After 64 seconds, the bullet will hit the ground at $x = (2048 \cdot \cos 30°) \cdot 64 = 65{,}536\sqrt{3}$
$\approx 113{,}511.7$ ft ≈ 21.5 miles.

    (c)   The maximum height attained by the bullet is the maximum value of the y parameter. Since
$y = 1024t - 16t^2 = -16(t^2 - 64t) = -16(t^2 - 64t + 1024) + 16{,}384$
$= -16(t - 32)^2 + 16{,}384$, y is maximized when $t = 32$, and therefore the maximum height is
16,384 ft ≈ 3.1 miles.

38. $x = 2 \sin t,\ y = \cos 4t$ 40. $x = \sin 4t,\ y = \cos 3t$

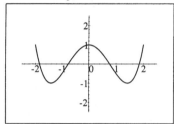   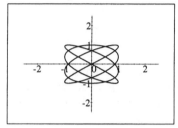

42. $x = 2 \cos t + \cos 2t,\ y = 2 \sin t - \sin 2t$

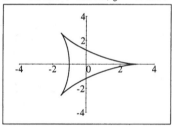

44.   (a) $r = \sin \theta + 2 \cos \theta \quad \Rightarrow$ (b)
                 $x = (\sin \theta + 2 \cos \theta)\cos \theta$
                 $y = (\sin \theta + 2 \cos \theta)\sin \theta$

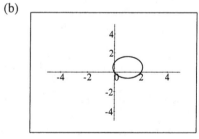

46.   (a) $r = 2^{\sin \theta} \quad \Rightarrow$ (b)
                 $x = 2^{\sin \theta} \cdot \cos \theta$
                 $y = 2^{\sin \theta} \cdot \sin \theta$

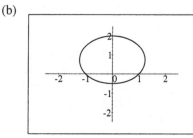

48.   This is IV, since when $t = 0$ and $t = \pi$ the curve passes through $(0, 0)$. Thus this curve must pass
      through the $(0, 0)$ twice.

50.   This is I, since this curve will not pass through the point $(0, 0)$.

52.   From the figure on the right, we see that $x = |OT| - |PQ|$
      $= a\theta - b\sin\theta$ and $y = |TC| - |CQ| = a - b\cos\theta$. When
      $a = 1$ and $b = 2$, the parametric equations become
      $x = \theta - 2\sin\theta$ and $y = 1 - 2\cos\theta$, which is graphed below.

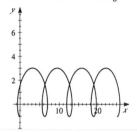
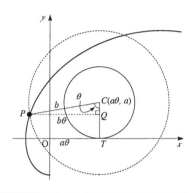

54.   The coordinates of C are $([a + b]\cos\theta,\ [a + b]\sin\theta)$.
      Let ϕ be the $\angle OCP$ as shown in the first figure.
      Then the arcs traced out by rolling the circle along the
      outside are equal, that is, $b\phi = a\theta \quad \Leftrightarrow \quad \phi = \dfrac{a}{b}\theta$.
      P is displaced from C by amounts equal to the legs
      of the right triangle CPT where CP is the
      hypotenuse. Since $\triangle OCQ$ is a right triangle, it
      follows that $\angle OCQ = \frac{\pi}{2} - \theta$. Thus

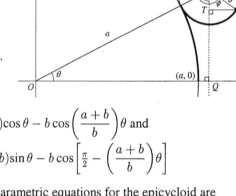

$$\alpha = \phi - \left(\tfrac{\pi}{2} - \theta\right) = \frac{a}{b}\theta - \tfrac{\pi}{2} + \theta = \left(\frac{a+b}{b}\right)\theta - \tfrac{\pi}{2}.$$

So, $x = (a + b)\cos\theta + b\sin\left[\left(\dfrac{a+b}{b}\right)\theta - \dfrac{\pi}{2}\right]$

$= (a+b)\cos\theta - b\sin\left[\dfrac{\pi}{2} - \left(\dfrac{a+b}{b}\right)\theta\right] = (a+b)\cos\theta - b\cos\left(\dfrac{a+b}{b}\right)\theta$ and

$y = (a+b)\sin\theta - b\cos\left[\left(\dfrac{a+b}{b}\right)\theta - \dfrac{\pi}{2}\right] = (a+b)\sin\theta - b\cos\left[\dfrac{\pi}{2} - \left(\dfrac{a+b}{b}\right)\theta\right]$

$= (a+b)\sin\theta - b\sin\left(\dfrac{a+b}{b}\right)\theta.$ Therefore, the parametric equations for the epicycloid are

$x = (a + b)\cos\theta - b\cos\left(\dfrac{a+b}{b}\right)\theta$ and $y = (a + b)\sin\theta - b\sin\left(\dfrac{a+b}{b}\right)\theta.$

56.   Since the string is taut, the line segment TP is tangent to the circle. In
      the figure on the right, since OQ and QT are perpendicular and OT
      and TP are perpendicular, the angles formed by their intersections are
      equal, that is, $\theta = \angle PTQ$. Now the coordinates of T are
      $(a\cos\theta,\ a\sin\theta)$. Since $|TP|$ is the length of the string that has been
      unwound from the circle, it must also have arc length $a\theta$, so $|TP| = a\theta$.
      Thus the x displacement from T to P is $a\theta \cdot \sin\theta$ while the y
      displacement from T to P is $a\theta \cdot \cos\theta$. So the coordinates of P are:

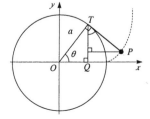

$x = a\cos\theta + a\theta \cdot \sin\theta = a(\cos\theta + \theta\sin\theta)$ and $y = a\sin\theta - a\theta \cdot \cos\theta = a(\sin\theta - \theta\cos\theta)$.

58. (a) It takes 2π units of time. The parametric equations of the particle that moves twice as fast around the circle are $x = \sin 2t$, $y = \cos 2t$.

(b) We make a table of selected values:

From this table we see that the particle travels counterclockwise.

t	$x = \sin t$	$y = \cos t$
0	0	1
$\frac{\pi}{2}$	1	0
π	0	-1
$\frac{3\pi}{2}$	-1	0
2π	0	1

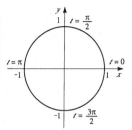

If we want the particle to travel in a clockwise direction, then we want the table to look like the table to the right.

Thus the parametric equations are:

$x = -\sin t \quad y = \cos t.$

t	x	y
0	0	1
$\frac{\pi}{2}$	-1	0
π	0	-1
$\frac{3\pi}{2}$	1	0
2π	0	1

Review Exercises for Chapter 11

2. $2x - y^2 = 0 \quad \Leftrightarrow \quad y^2 = 2x$. This is a parabola that has $4p = 2$
    $\Leftrightarrow \quad p = \frac{1}{2}$.

    Vertex: $(0,0)$; focus: $\left(\frac{1}{2}, 0\right)$; directrix: $x = -\frac{1}{2}$.

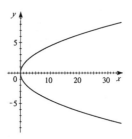

4. $2x^2 + 6x + 5y + 10 = 0 \quad \Leftrightarrow \quad 2\left(x^2 + 3x + \frac{9}{4}\right) + 5y + 10 = \frac{9}{2}$
    $\Leftrightarrow \quad 2\left(x + \frac{3}{2}\right)^2 = -5y - \frac{11}{2} \quad \Leftrightarrow \quad 2\left(x + \frac{3}{2}\right)^2 = -5\left(y + \frac{11}{10}\right)$
    $\Leftrightarrow \quad \left(x + \frac{3}{2}\right)^2 = -\frac{5}{2}\left(y + \frac{11}{10}\right)$. This is a parabola that has $4p = -\frac{5}{2}$
    $\Leftrightarrow \quad p = -\frac{5}{8}$.

    Vertex: $\left(-\frac{3}{2}, -\frac{11}{10}\right)$; focus: $\left(-\frac{3}{2}, -\frac{11}{10} - \frac{5}{8}\right) = \left(-\frac{3}{2}, -\frac{44+25}{40}\right)$
    $= \left(-\frac{3}{2}, -\frac{69}{20}\right)$; directrix: $y = -\frac{11}{10} + \frac{5}{8} = \frac{-44+25}{40} = -\frac{19}{40}$.

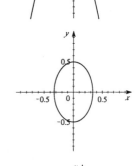

6. $9x^2 + 4y^2 = 1 \quad \Leftrightarrow \quad \dfrac{x^2}{1/9} + \dfrac{y^2}{1/4} = 1$. This is an ellipse with

    $a = \frac{1}{2}, b = \frac{1}{3}$, and $c = \sqrt{\frac{1}{4} - \frac{1}{9}} = \frac{1}{6}\sqrt{5}$.

    Center: $(0,0)$; vertices: $\left(0, \pm\frac{1}{2}\right)$; foci: $\left(0, \pm\frac{1}{6}\sqrt{5}\right)$; length of the
    major axis: $2a = 1$; length of the minor axis: $2b = \frac{2}{3}$.

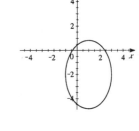

8. $2x^2 + y^2 = 2 + 4(x - y) \quad \Leftrightarrow \quad 2x^2 - 4x + y^2 + 4y = 2 \quad \Leftrightarrow$
    $2(x^2 - 2x + 1) + (y^2 + 4y + 4) = 2 + 2 + 4 \quad \Leftrightarrow$
    $2(x - 1)^2 + (y + 2)^2 = 8 \quad \Leftrightarrow \quad \dfrac{(x - 1)^2}{4} + \dfrac{(y + 2)^2}{8} = 1$. This is
    an ellipse with $a = 2\sqrt{2}, b = 2$, and $c = \sqrt{8 - 4} = 2$.
    Center: $(1, -2)$; vertices: $(1, -2 \pm 2\sqrt{2})$; foci: $(1, -2 \pm 2)$, so the
    foci are $(1, 0)$ and $(1, -4)$; length of the major axis: $2a = 4\sqrt{2}$;
    length of the minor axis: $2b = 4$.

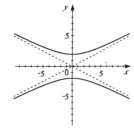

10. $x^2 - 4y^2 + 16 = 0 \quad \Leftrightarrow \quad 4y^2 - x^2 = 16 \quad \Leftrightarrow \quad \dfrac{y^2}{4} - \dfrac{x^2}{16} = 1$.
    This is a hyperbola that has $a = 2$, $b = 4$, and $c = \sqrt{4 + 16} = 2\sqrt{5}$.
    Center: $(0,0)$; vertices: $(0, \pm 2)$; foci: $(0, \pm 2\sqrt{5})$; asymptotes:
    $y = \pm\frac{2}{4}x \quad \Leftrightarrow \quad y = \pm\frac{1}{2}x$.

12. $y^2 = x^2 + 6y$ $\Leftrightarrow$ $(y^2 - 6y + 9) - x^2 = 9$ $\Leftrightarrow$

$(y - 3)^2 - x^2 = 9$ $\Leftrightarrow$ $\dfrac{(y - 3)^2}{9} - \dfrac{x^2}{9} = 1$. This is a hyperbola

that has $a = 3$, $b = 3$, and $c = \sqrt{9 + 9} = 3\sqrt{2}$.

Center: $(0, 3)$; vertices: $(0, 3 \pm 3)$, so the vertices are $(0, 6)$ and
$(0, 0)$; foci: $(0, 3 \pm 3\sqrt{2})$; asymptotes: $y - 3 = \pm x$ $\Leftrightarrow$
$y = x + 3$ and $y = -x + 3$.

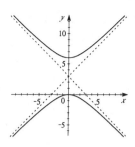

14. This is an ellipse with the center at $(0, 0)$, $a = 12$, and $b = 5$. The equation is then $\dfrac{x^2}{12^2} + \dfrac{y^2}{5^2} = 1$

$\Leftrightarrow$ $\dfrac{x^2}{144} + \dfrac{y^2}{25} = 1$.

16. This is a parabola that opens to the left with its vertex at $(4, 4)$, so its equation is of the form
$(y - 4)^2 = 4p(x - 4)$ with $p < 0$. Since $(0, 0)$ is a point on this hyperbola, we must have
$(0 - 4)^2 = 4p(0 - 4)$ $\Leftrightarrow$ $16 = -16p$ $\Leftrightarrow$ $p = -1$. Thus the equation is
$(y - 4)^2 = -4(x - 4)$.

18. From the graph, the center is at $(1, 0)$, and the vertices are at $(0, 0)$ and $(2, 0)$. Since a is the
distance form the center to a vertex, $a = 1$. From the graph, the slope of one of the asymptotes is
$\dfrac{b}{a} = 1$ $\Leftrightarrow$ $b = 1$. Thus the equation of the hyperbola is $(x - 1)^2 - y^2 = 1$.

20. $\dfrac{x^2}{12} + \dfrac{y^2}{144} = \dfrac{y}{12}$ $\Leftrightarrow$ $12x^2 + y^2 - 12y = 0$ $\Leftrightarrow$

$12x^2 + (y^2 - 12y + 36) = 36$ $\Leftrightarrow$ $\dfrac{x^2}{3} + \dfrac{(y - 6)^2}{36} = 1$. This is an

ellipse that has $a = 6$, $b = \sqrt{3}$, and $c = \sqrt{36 - 3} = \sqrt{33}$.

Vertices: $(0, 6 \pm 6)$, so the vertices are $(0, 0)$ and $(0, 12)$; foci:
$(0, 6 \pm \sqrt{33})$.

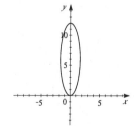

22. $x^2 + 6x = 9y^2$ $\Leftrightarrow$ $(x^2 + 6x + 9) - 9y^2 = 9$ $\Leftrightarrow$

$\dfrac{(x + 3)^2}{9} - y^2 = 1$. This is a hyperbola that has $a = 3$, $b = 1$, and

$c = \sqrt{9 + 1} = \sqrt{10}$.

Vertices: $(-3 \pm 3, 0)$, so the vertices are $(-6, 0)$ and $(0, 0)$; foci:
$(-3 \pm \sqrt{10}, 0)$.

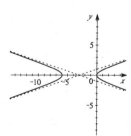

24. $3x^2 - 6(x + y) = 10$ $\Leftrightarrow$ $3x^2 - 6x = 6y + 10$ $\Leftrightarrow$
$3(x^2 - 2x + 1) = 6y + 10 + 3$ $\Leftrightarrow$ $3(x - 1)^2 = 6y + 13$ $\Leftrightarrow$
$3(x - 1)^2 = 6\left(y + \frac{13}{6}\right)$ $\Leftrightarrow$ $(x - 1)^2 = 2\left(y + \frac{13}{6}\right)$. This is a
parabola that has $4p = 2$ $\Leftrightarrow$ $p = \frac{1}{2}$.

Vertex: $\left(1, -\frac{13}{6}\right)$; focus: $\left(1, -\frac{13}{6} + \frac{1}{2}\right) = \left(1, -\frac{10}{6}\right) = \left(1, -\frac{5}{3}\right)$.

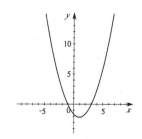

26. $2x^2 + 4 = 4x + y^2 \quad \Leftrightarrow \quad y^2 - 2x^2 + 4x = 4 \quad \Leftrightarrow$
    $y^2 - 2(x^2 - 2x + 1) = 4 - 2 \quad \Leftrightarrow \quad y^2 - 2(x - 1)^2 = 2 \quad \Leftrightarrow$
    $\dfrac{y^2}{2} - (x - 1)^2 = 1.$ This is a hyperbola that has $a = \sqrt{2}$, $b = 1$, and
    $c = \sqrt{2 + 1} = \sqrt{3}.$

    Vertices: $(1, \pm\sqrt{2})$; foci: $(1, \pm\sqrt{3})$.

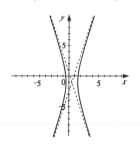

28. $36x^2 - 4y^2 - 36x - 8y = 31 \quad \Leftrightarrow \quad 36(x^2 - x) - 4(y^2 + 2y) = 31$
    $\Leftrightarrow \quad 36\left(x^2 - x + \tfrac{1}{4}\right) - 4(y^2 + 2y + 1) = 31 + 9 - 4 \quad \Leftrightarrow$
    $36\left(x - \tfrac{1}{2}\right)^2 - 4(y + 1)^2 = 36 \quad \Leftrightarrow \quad \left(x - \tfrac{1}{2}\right)^2 - \dfrac{(y + 1)^2}{9} = 1.$

    This is a hyperbola that has $a = 1$, $b = 3$, and $c = \sqrt{1 + 9} = \sqrt{10}.$

    Vertices: $\left(\tfrac{1}{2} \pm 1, -1\right)$, so the vertices are $\left(-\tfrac{1}{2}, -1\right)$ and $\left(\tfrac{3}{2}, -1\right)$;
    foci: $\left(\tfrac{1}{2} \pm \sqrt{10}, -1\right).$

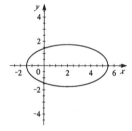

30. $x^2 + 4y^2 = 4x + 8 \quad \Leftrightarrow \quad (x^2 - 4x + 4) + 4y^2 = 8 + 4 \quad \Leftrightarrow$
    $(x - 2)^2 + 4y^2 = 12 \quad \Leftrightarrow \quad \dfrac{(x - 2)^2}{12} + \dfrac{y^2}{3} = 1.$ This is an ellipse
    that has $a = 2\sqrt{3}$, $b = \sqrt{3}$, and $c = \sqrt{12 - 3} = 3.$

    Vertices: $(2 \pm 2\sqrt{3}, 0)$; foci: $(2 \pm 3, 0)$, so the foci are $(-1, 0)$ and
    $(5, 0).$

32. The ellipse has center $C(0, 4)$, foci $F_1(0, 0)$ and $F_2(0, 8)$, and major axis of length 10. Then
    $2c = 8 - 0 \quad \Leftrightarrow \quad c = 4.$ Also, since the length of the major axis is 10, $2a = 10 \quad \Leftrightarrow \quad a = 5.$
    Therefore, $b^2 = a^2 - c^2 = 25 - 16 = 9.$ Since the foci are on the y-axis, the vertices are on the y-
    axis, and the equation of the ellipse is $\dfrac{x^2}{9} + \dfrac{(y - 4)^2}{25} = 1.$

34. The hyperbola has center $C(2, 4)$, foci $F_1(2, 7)$ and $F_2(2, 1)$, and vertices $V_1(2, 6)$ and $V_2(2, 2)$.
    Thus, $2a = 6 - 2 = 4 \quad \Leftrightarrow \quad a = 2.$ Also, $2c = 7 - 1 = 6 \quad \Leftrightarrow \quad c = 3.$ So $b^2 = 9 - 4 = 5.$
    Since the hyperbola has center $C(2, 4)$, its equation is $\dfrac{(y - 4)^2}{4} - \dfrac{(x - 2)^2}{5} = 1.$

36. The parabola has vertex $V(5, 5)$ and directrix the y-axis. Therefore, $-p = 0 - 5 \quad \Leftrightarrow \quad p = 5$
    $\Leftrightarrow \quad 4p = 20.$ Since the parabola opens to the right, its equation is $(y - 5)^2 = 20(x - 5).$

38. The parabola has vertex $V(-1, 0)$, horizontal axis of symmetry, and crosses the y-axis where $y = 2$.
    Since the parabola has a horizontal axis of symmetry and $V(-1, 0)$, its equation is of the form
    $y^2 = 4p(x + 1).$ Also, since the parabola crosses the y-axis where $y = 2$, it passes through the point
    $(0, 2)$. Substituting this point gives $(2)^2 = 4p(0 + 1) \quad \Leftrightarrow \quad 4p = 4.$ Therefore, the equation of the
    parabola is $y^2 = 4(x + 1).$

40. Since the height of the satellite *above the earth* varies between 140 and 440, the length of the major axis is
$2a = 140 + 2(3960) + 440 = 8500 \quad \Leftrightarrow \quad a = 4250.$
Since the center of the earth is at one focus, we have
$a - c = (earth\ radius) + 140 = 3960 + 140 = 4100$
$\Leftrightarrow \quad c = a - 4100 = 4250 - 4100 = 150.$ Thus the center of the ellipse is $(-150, 0).$ So
$b^2 = a^2 - c^2 = 4250^2 - 150^2$
$= 18{,}062{,}500 - 22500 = 18{,}040{,}000.$ Hence the equation is $\dfrac{(x + 150)^2}{18{,}062{,}500} + \dfrac{y^2}{18{,}040{,}000} = 1.$

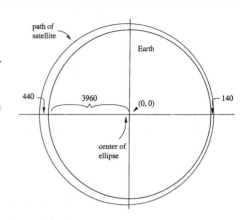

42. We sketch the LORAN station on the y-axis and place the x-axis halfway between them as suggested in the exercise. This gives us the
general form $\dfrac{y^2}{a^2} - \dfrac{x^2}{b^2} = 1.$ Since the ship is 80 miles closer to A than to B we have $2a = 80 \quad \Leftrightarrow \quad a = 40.$ Since the foci are $(0, \pm 150),$ we have $c = 150.$ Thus $b^2 = c^2 - a^2 = 150^2 - 40^2 = 20900.$ So this places the ship on the hyperbola given by the equation
$\dfrac{y^2}{1600} - \dfrac{x^2}{20900} = 1.$ When $x = 40,$ we get $\dfrac{y^2}{1600} - \dfrac{1600}{20900} = 1 \quad \Leftrightarrow$
$\dfrac{y^2}{1600} = \dfrac{225}{209} \quad \Leftrightarrow \quad y = 41.5.$ (Note that $y > 0,$ since A is on the positive y-axis.) Thus the ship's position is $(40, 41.5).$

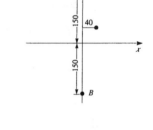

44. (a) The graphs of $y = kx^2$ for $k = \frac{1}{2},$ 1, 2, and 4 are shown in the figure.

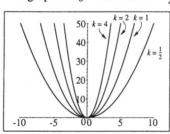

   (b) $y = kx^2 \quad \Leftrightarrow \quad x^2 = \frac{1}{k}y = 4\left(\frac{1}{4k}\right)y.$ Thus the foci are $\left(0, \frac{1}{4k}\right).$

   (c) As k increases, the focus gets closer to the vertex.

46. (a) $5x^2 - 6xy + 5y^2 - 8x + 8y - 8 = 0.$ Then $A = 5, B = -6,$ and $C = 5,$ so the discriminant is $(-6)^2 - 4(5)(5) = 64.$ Since the discriminant is negative the equation represents an ellipse.

   (b) $\cot 2\phi = \frac{A-C}{B} = 0 \quad \Rightarrow \quad 2\phi = 90° \quad \Leftrightarrow \quad \phi = 45°.$ Therefore, $x = \frac{X}{\sqrt{2}} - \frac{Y}{\sqrt{2}}$ and
   $y = \frac{X}{\sqrt{2}} + \frac{Y}{\sqrt{2}}.$ Substituting into the original equation gives:
   $$5\left(\frac{X}{\sqrt{2}} - \frac{Y}{\sqrt{2}}\right)^2 - 6\left(\frac{X}{\sqrt{2}} - \frac{Y}{\sqrt{2}}\right)\left(\frac{X}{\sqrt{2}} + \frac{Y}{\sqrt{2}}\right) + 5\left(\frac{X}{\sqrt{2}} + \frac{Y}{\sqrt{2}}\right)^2$$
   $$- 8\left(\frac{X}{\sqrt{2}} - \frac{Y}{\sqrt{2}}\right) + 8\left(\frac{X}{\sqrt{2}} + \frac{Y}{\sqrt{2}}\right) - 8 = 0 \quad \Leftrightarrow$$

$$\tfrac{5}{2}(X^2 - 2XY + Y^2) - 3(X^2 - Y^2) + \tfrac{5}{2}(X^2 + 2XY + Y^2)$$

$$-\tfrac{8X}{\sqrt{2}} + \tfrac{8Y}{\sqrt{2}} + \tfrac{8X}{\sqrt{2}} + \tfrac{8Y}{\sqrt{2}} - 8 = 0$$

$\Leftrightarrow \quad 5X^2 - 3X^2 + 3Y^2 + 5Y^2 + \tfrac{16Y}{\sqrt{2}} - 8 = 0$

(c)

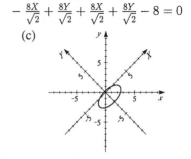

$\Leftrightarrow \quad 2X^2 + 8\left(Y^2 + \tfrac{2Y}{\sqrt{2}} + \tfrac{1}{2}\right) = 8 + 4 \quad \Leftrightarrow$

$\tfrac{X^2}{6} + \tfrac{(Y+1)^2}{3/2} = 1$. This ellipse has $a = \sqrt{6}$, $b = \sqrt{3/2}$,

and $c = \sqrt{6 - \tfrac{3}{2}} = \tfrac{3\sqrt{2}}{2}$. Therefore, the vertices are

$V(\pm\sqrt{6}, -1)$ and the foci are $F(\pm\tfrac{3\sqrt{2}}{2}, -1)$.

48.   (a) $9x^2 + 24xy + 16y^2 = 25$. Then $A = 9$, $B = 24$, and $C = 16$, so the discriminant is
$24^2 - 4(9)(16) = 0$. Since the discriminant is zero the equation represents a parabola.

    (b) $\cot 2\phi = \tfrac{A-C}{B} = \tfrac{9-16}{24} = \tfrac{-7}{24} \Rightarrow \cos 2\phi = \tfrac{-7}{25}$, so $\cos\phi = \sqrt{\tfrac{1-(7/25)}{2}} = \tfrac{3}{5}$,

$\sin\phi = \sqrt{\tfrac{1+(7/25)}{2}} = \tfrac{4}{5}$, so $x = \tfrac{3}{5}X - \tfrac{4}{5}Y$ and $y = \tfrac{4}{5}X + \tfrac{3}{5}Y$. Thus $9x^2 + 24xy + 16y^2 = 25$

$\Leftrightarrow \quad 9\left(\tfrac{3}{5}X - \tfrac{4}{5}Y\right)^2 + 24\left(\tfrac{3}{5}X - \tfrac{4}{5}Y\right)\left(\tfrac{4}{5}X + \tfrac{3}{5}Y\right) + 16\left(\tfrac{4}{5}X + \tfrac{3}{5}Y\right)^2 = 25 \quad \Leftrightarrow$

$25X^2 = 25 \quad \Leftrightarrow \quad X^2 = 1 \quad \Leftrightarrow \quad X = \pm 1$. Thus the graph is a degenerate conic that

consists of two lines. Converting back to xy-coordinates, we see that $X = \tfrac{3}{5}x + \tfrac{4}{5}y$, so $\tfrac{3}{5}$

$x + \tfrac{4}{5}y = \pm 1 \quad \Leftrightarrow \quad 3x + 4y = \pm 5$.

    (c)

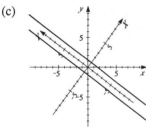

50.   (a)

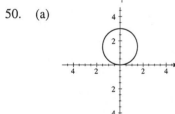

    (b) $r = 3\sin\theta \quad \Leftrightarrow \quad r^2 = 3r\sin\theta$ which
gives $x^2 + y^2 = 3y \quad \Leftrightarrow$
$x^2 + (y^2 - 3y + \tfrac{9}{4}) = \tfrac{9}{4} \quad \Leftrightarrow$
$x^2 + (y - \tfrac{3}{2})^2 = \tfrac{9}{4}$.

52.   (a)

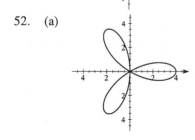

    (b) $r = 4\cos 3\theta$
$= 4(\cos 2\theta \cos\theta - \sin 2\theta \sin\theta)$
$= 4[\cos\theta(\cos^2\theta - \sin^2\theta) - 2\sin^2\theta \cos\theta]$
$\Leftrightarrow \quad r = 4[\cos^3\theta - 3\sin^2\theta \cos\theta] \quad \Leftrightarrow$
$r^4 = 4r^3[\cos^3\theta - 3\sin^2\theta \cos\theta]$, which
gives $(x^2 + y^2)^2 = 4x^3 - 12xy^2$.

54. (a)

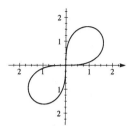

(b) $r^2 = 4\sin 2\theta = 8\sin\theta\cos\theta \quad \Leftrightarrow$
$r^4 = 8r^2\sin\theta\cos\theta$ which gives
$(x^2 + y^2)^2 = 8xy.$

56. (a)

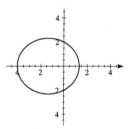

(b) $r = \dfrac{4}{2 + \cos\theta} \quad \Leftrightarrow \quad 2r + r\cos\theta = 4$
which gives $2\sqrt{x^2 + y^2} + x = 4 \quad \Leftrightarrow$
$2\sqrt{x^2 + y^2} = 4 - x.$ Squaring both
sides gives $4(x^2 + y^2) = (4 - x)^2$
$= 16 - 8x + x^2 \quad \Leftrightarrow$
$3x^2 + 8x + 4y^2 = 16 \quad \Leftrightarrow$
$3(x + \frac{4}{3})^2 + 4y^2 = 16 + \frac{16}{3} \quad \Leftrightarrow$
$\dfrac{(x + \frac{4}{3})^2}{\frac{64}{9}} + \dfrac{y^2}{\frac{16}{9}} = 1.$

58. Domain of θ shown is $[0,\ 8\pi]$

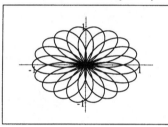

60. Domain of θ shown is $[-6\pi,\ 6\pi]$

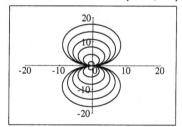

62. (a) $r = \dfrac{2}{1 + 2\sin\theta} \quad \Rightarrow \quad e = 2.$ Therefore,
this is a hyperbola.

(b)

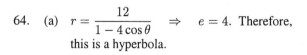

$(-2, \frac{3\pi}{2})$ $(\frac{2}{3}, \frac{\pi}{2})$

64. (a) $r = \dfrac{12}{1 - 4\cos\theta} \quad \Rightarrow \quad e = 4.$ Therefore,
this is a hyperbola.

(b)

$(-4, 0)$ $(\frac{12}{5}, \pi)$

66. $x = t^2 - 1, y = t^2 + 1 \quad \Leftrightarrow \quad t^2 = y - 1.$
Substituting for t^2 gives $x = (y - 1) - 1$
$\Leftrightarrow \quad y = x + 2$ where $x \geq -1$ and $y \geq 1.$

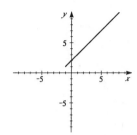

68. $x = \dfrac{1}{t} + 2 \quad \Leftrightarrow \quad \dfrac{1}{t} = x - 2, y = \dfrac{2}{t^2}$
Substituting for $\frac{1}{t}$ gives $y = 2(x - 2)^2.$ Since
t is restricted by $0 < t \leq 2$, we have $\frac{1}{t} \geq \frac{1}{2}$, so
$x \geq \frac{5}{2}$ and $y \geq \frac{1}{2}.$ The rectangular coordinate
equation is $y = 2(x - 2)^2, x \geq \frac{5}{2}.$

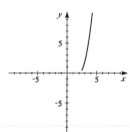

70. $x = \sin(t + \cos 2t), y = \cos(t + \sin 3t)$

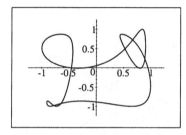

72. The coordinates of Q are $x = \cos \theta$ and $y = \sin \theta.$ The coordinates of R are $x = 1$ and $y = \tan \theta.$
Hence, the midpoint P is $\left(\dfrac{1 + \cos \theta}{2}, \dfrac{\sin \theta + \tan \theta}{2} \right)$, so the parametric equations for the curve are
$x = \dfrac{1 + \cos \theta}{2}$ and $y = \dfrac{\sin \theta + \tan \theta}{2}.$

Focus on Modeling

2. Applying the given values we get $x = (v_0 \cos\theta)t = 15t$ and
$y = 4 + (v_0 \sin\theta)t - \frac{1}{2}gt^2 = 4 + 25.98t - 16t^2$ as the parametric equations for the path of the
baseball. The baseball will hit the ground when $y = 0 = 4 + 25.98t - 16t^2$. Using the quadratic

formula: $t = \dfrac{-25.98 \pm \sqrt{(25.98)^2 + 4(-16)(4)}}{-32} \approx 1.77$ seconds (since t must be positive). So the

baseball travels $x = 15 \cdot 1.77 = 26.5$ ft, before hitting the ground after 1.77 s.

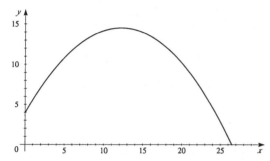

4. The missile hits the ground when $t = \dfrac{2v_0 \sin\theta}{g}$ so the missile travels

$x = (v_0 \cos\theta)\dfrac{2v_0 \sin\theta}{g} = \dfrac{v_0^2}{g}\sin 2\theta$ meters. Substituting $v_0 = 330$ m/s, $x = 10$ km and

$g = 9.8$ m/s^2, we get $10000 = \frac{330^2}{9.8}\sin 2\theta \Rightarrow \sin 2\theta = 0.8999$. So $2\theta = 64.15°$ $\Leftrightarrow$
$\theta = 32.08°$ or $2\theta = 115.85°$ $\Leftrightarrow$ $\theta = 57.93°$. The missile fired at $32.08°$ will hit the target in
35.7 seconds while the missile fired at $57.93°$ reaches the target in 57.1 seconds.

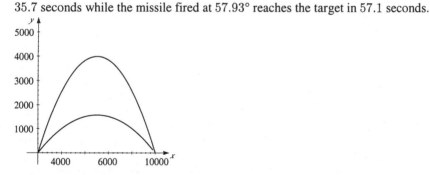

6. Since the horizontal component of the projectile's velocity has been reduced by w, the parametric
equations become: $x = (v_0 \cos\theta - w)t$, $y = (v_0 \sin\theta)t - \frac{1}{2}gt^2$.

Chapter Twelve

Exercises 12.1

2. $a_n = 2n + 3$. Then $a_1 = 2(1) + 3 = 5$; $a_2 = 2(2) + 3 = 7$; $a_3 = 2(3) + 3 = 9$; $a_4 = 2(4) + 3 = 11$; and $a_{1000} = 2(1000) + 3 = 2003$.

4. $a_n = n^2 + 1$. Then $a_1 = (1)^2 + 1 = 2$; $a_2 = (2)^2 + 1 = 5$; $a_3 = (3)^2 + 1 = 10$; $a_4 = (4)^2 + 1 = 17$; and $a_{1000} = (1000)^2 + 1 = 1,000,001$.

6. $a_n = \dfrac{1}{n^2}$. Then $a_1 = \dfrac{1}{(1)^2} = 1$; $a_2 = \dfrac{1}{(2)^2} = \frac{1}{4}$; $a_3 = \dfrac{1}{(3)^2} = \frac{1}{9}$; $a_4 = \dfrac{1}{(4)^2} = \frac{1}{16}$; and
    $a_{1000} = \dfrac{1}{(1000)^2} = \frac{1}{1000000}$.

8. $a_n = \dfrac{(-1)^{n+1} n}{n + 1}$. Then $a_1 = \dfrac{(-1)^2 \cdot 1}{1 + 1} = \frac{1}{2}$; $a_2 = \dfrac{(-1)^3 \cdot 2}{2 + 1} = -\frac{2}{3}$; $a_3 = \dfrac{(-1)^4 \cdot 3}{3 + 1} = \frac{3}{4}$;
    $a_4 = \dfrac{(-1)^5 \cdot 4}{4 + 1} = -\frac{4}{5}$; and $a_{1000} = \dfrac{(-1)^{1001} \cdot 1000}{1001} = -\frac{1000}{1001}$.

10. $a_n = 3$. Then $a_1 = 3$; $a_2 = 3$; $a_3 = 3$; $a_4 = 3$; and $a_{1000} = 3$.

12. $a_n = \dfrac{a_{n-1}}{2}$ and $a_1 = -8$. Then $a_2 = \frac{-8}{2} = -4$; $a_3 = \frac{-4}{2} = -2$; $a_4 = \frac{-2}{2} = -1$; and
    $a_5 = \frac{-1}{2} = -\frac{1}{2}$.

14. $a_n = \dfrac{1}{1 + a_{n-1}}$ and $a_1 = 1$. Then $a_2 = \dfrac{1}{1 + (1)} = \frac{1}{2}$; $a_3 = \dfrac{1}{1 + \left(\frac{1}{2}\right)} = \frac{2}{3}$; $a_4 = \dfrac{1}{1 + \left(\frac{2}{3}\right)} = \frac{3}{5}$; and
    $a_5 = \dfrac{1}{1 + \left(\frac{3}{5}\right)} = \frac{5}{8}$.

16. $a_n = a_{n-1} + a_{n-2} + a_{n-3}$ and $a_1 = 1$; $a_2 = 1$; and $a_3 = 1$. Then $a_4 = 1 + 1 + 1 = 3$ and
    $a_5 = 3 + 1 + 1 = 5$.

18. $-\frac{1}{3}, \frac{1}{9}, -\frac{1}{27}, \frac{1}{81}, \ldots$. The denominators are all powers of 3, and the terms alternate in sign. Thus
    $a_1 = \dfrac{(-1)^1}{3^1}, a_2 = \dfrac{(-1)^2}{3^2}, a_3 = \dfrac{(-1)^3}{3^3}, a_4 = \dfrac{(-1)^4}{3^4}, \ldots$. So $a_n = \dfrac{(-1)^n}{3^n}$.

20. $5, -25, 125, -625, \ldots$. These terms are powers of 5, and the terms alternate in sign. So
    $a_1 = (-1)^2 \cdot 5^1, a_2 = (-1)^3 \cdot 5^2, a_3 = (-1)^4 \cdot 5^3, a_4 = (-1)^5 \cdot 5^4, \ldots$. Thus $a_n = (-1)^{n+1} \cdot 5^n$.

22. $\frac{3}{4}, \frac{4}{5}, \frac{5}{6}, \frac{6}{7}, \ldots$. Both the numerator and the denominator increase by 1, so $a_1 = \frac{1+2}{1+3}, a_2 = \frac{2+2}{2+3}$,
    $a_3 = \frac{3+2}{3+3}, a_4 = \frac{4+2}{4+3}, \ldots$. Thus $a_n = \dfrac{n + 2}{n + 3}$.

24. $1, \frac{1}{2}, 3, \frac{1}{4}, 5, \frac{1}{6}, \ldots$. So $a_1 = 1, a_2 = 2^{-1}, a_3 = 3^1, a_4 = 4^{-1}, \ldots$. Thus $a_n = n^{(-1)^{n+1}}$.

26. $a_1 = 1^2, a_2 = 2^2, a_3 = 3^2, a_4 = 4^2, \ldots$. Therefore, $a_n = n^2$. So $S_1 = 1^2 = 1$; $S_2 = 1 + 2^2 = 5$;
    $S_3 = 5 + 3^2 = 5 + 9 = 14$; $S_4 = 14 + 4^2 = 14 + 16 = 30$; $S_5 = 30 + 5^2 = 30 + 25 = 55$; and
    $S_6 = 55 + 6^2 = 55 + 36 = 91$.

28. $a_1 = -1, a_2 = 1, a_3 = -1, a_4 = 1, \ldots$. Therefore, $a_n = (-1)^n$. So $S_1 = -1$; $S_2 = -1 + 1 = 0$;
    $S_3 = 0 - 1 = -1$; $S_4 = -1 + 1 = 0$; $S_5 = 0 - 1 = -1$; and $S_6 = -1 + 1 = 0$.

30. $a_n = \dfrac{1}{n+1} - \dfrac{1}{n+2}$. So $S_1 = \frac{1}{2} - \frac{1}{3}$; $S_2 = \left(\frac{1}{2} - \frac{1}{3}\right) + \left(\frac{1}{3} - \frac{1}{4}\right) = \frac{1}{2} + \left(-\frac{1}{3} + \frac{1}{3}\right) - \frac{1}{4} = \frac{1}{2} - \frac{1}{4}$;

$S_3 = \left(\frac{1}{2} - \frac{1}{3}\right) + \left(\frac{1}{3} - \frac{1}{4}\right) + \left(\frac{1}{4} - \frac{1}{5}\right) = \frac{1}{2} + \left(-\frac{1}{3} + \frac{1}{3}\right) + \left(-\frac{1}{4} + \frac{1}{4}\right) - \frac{1}{5} = \frac{1}{2} - \frac{1}{5}$; and

$S_4 = \left(\frac{1}{2} - \frac{1}{3}\right) + \left(\frac{1}{3} - \frac{1}{4}\right) + \left(\frac{1}{4} - \frac{1}{5}\right) + \left(\frac{1}{5} - \frac{1}{6}\right)$

$\qquad = \frac{1}{2} + \left(-\frac{1}{3} + \frac{1}{3}\right) + \left(-\frac{1}{4} + \frac{1}{4}\right) + \left(-\frac{1}{5} + \frac{1}{5}\right) - \frac{1}{6} = \frac{1}{2} - \frac{1}{6}$. Therefore,

$S_n = \left(\frac{1}{2} - \frac{1}{3}\right) + \left(\frac{1}{3} - \frac{1}{4}\right) + \cdots + \left(\dfrac{1}{n+1} - \dfrac{1}{n+2}\right)$

$\qquad = \frac{1}{2} + \left(-\frac{1}{3} + \frac{1}{3}\right) + \cdots + \left(-\dfrac{1}{n+1} + \dfrac{1}{n+1}\right) - \dfrac{1}{n+2} = \dfrac{1}{2} - \dfrac{1}{n+2}$.

32. $a_n = \log\left(\dfrac{k}{k+1}\right) = [\log k - \log(k+1)]$. So $S_1 = \log 1 - \log 2 = -\log 2$,

$S_2 = (-\log 2) + (\log 2 - \log 3) = -\log 3$;

$S_3 = -\log 2 + (\log 2 - \log 3) + (\log 3 - \log 4) = (-\log 2 + \log 2) + (-\log 3 + \log 3) - \log 4$

$\qquad = -\log 4$; and

$S_4 = -\log 2 + (\log 2 - \log 3) + (\log 3 - \log 4) + (\log 4 - \log 5)$

$\qquad = (-\log 2 + \log 2) + (-\log 3 + \log 3) + (-\log 4 + \log 4) - \log 5 = -\log 5$.

Therefore, $S_n = -\log(n+1)$.

34. $\displaystyle\sum_{k=1}^{4} k^2 = 1 + 2^2 + 3^2 + 4^2 = 1 + 4 + 9 + 16 = 30$

36. $\displaystyle\sum_{j=1}^{100} (-1)^j = (-1)^1 + (-1)^2 + (-1)^3 + (-1)^4 + \cdots + (-1)^{99} + (-1)^{100}$

$\qquad = -1 + 1 - 1 + 1 - 1 + \cdots - 1 + 1 = 0$

38. $\displaystyle\sum_{i=4}^{12} 10 = 10 + 10 + 10 + 10 + 10 + 10 + 10 + 10 + 10 = 90$

40. $\displaystyle\sum_{i=1}^{3} i\, 2^i = 1 \cdot 2^1 + 2 \cdot 2^2 + 3 \cdot 2^3 = 2 + 8 + 24 = 34$

42. $\displaystyle\sum_{i=0}^{4} \dfrac{2i-1}{2i+1} = \dfrac{2 \cdot 0 - 1}{2 \cdot 0 + 1} + \dfrac{2 \cdot 1 - 1}{2 \cdot 1 + 1} + \dfrac{2 \cdot 2 - 1}{2 \cdot 2 + 1} + \dfrac{2 \cdot 3 - 1}{2 \cdot 3 + 1} + \dfrac{2 \cdot 4 - 1}{2 \cdot 4 + 1} = -1 + \dfrac{1}{3} + \dfrac{3}{5} + \dfrac{5}{7} + \dfrac{7}{9}$

44. $\displaystyle\sum_{k=6}^{9} k(k+3) = 6 \cdot 9 + 7 \cdot 10 + 8 \cdot 11 + 9 \cdot 12 = 54 + 70 + 88 + 108$

46. $\displaystyle\sum_{j=1}^{n} (-1)^{j+1} x^j = (-1)^2 x + (-1)^3 x^2 + (-1)^4 x^3 + \cdots + (-1)^{n+1} x^n$

$\qquad = x - x^2 + x^3 - \cdots + (-1)^{n+1} x^n$

48. $2 + 4 + 6 + \cdots + 20 = \displaystyle\sum_{k=1}^{10} 2k$

50. $\dfrac{1}{2\ln 2} - \dfrac{1}{3\ln 3} + \dfrac{1}{4\ln 4} - \dfrac{1}{5\ln 5} + \cdots + \dfrac{1}{100\ln 100} = \displaystyle\sum_{k=2}^{100} \dfrac{(-1)^k}{k\ln k}$

52. $\dfrac{\sqrt{1}}{1^2} + \dfrac{\sqrt{2}}{2^2} + \dfrac{\sqrt{3}}{3^2} + \cdots + \dfrac{\sqrt{n}}{n^2} = \displaystyle\sum_{k=1}^{n} \dfrac{\sqrt{k}}{k^2}$

54. $1 - 2x + 3x^2 - 4x^3 + 5x^4 + \cdots - 100x^{99} = \displaystyle\sum_{k=1}^{100} (-1)^{k+1} \cdot k \cdot x^{k-1}$

56. Let F_n be the number of pairs of rabbits in the nth month. Clearly $F_1 = F_2 = 1$. In the nth month each pair that is two or more months old (that is, F_{n-2} pairs) will add a pair of offspring to the F_{n-1} pairs already present. Thus $F_n = F_{n-1} + F_{n-2}$. So F_n is the Fibonacci sequence.

58. $a_{n+1} = \begin{cases} \dfrac{a_n}{2} & \text{if } a_n \text{ is an even number} \\ 3a_n + 1 & \text{if } a_n \text{ is an odd number} \end{cases}$

With $a_1 = 11$, we have $a_2 = 34$; $a_3 = 17$; $a_4 = 52$; $a_5 = 26$; $a_6 = 13$; $a_7 = 40$; $a_8 = 20$; $a_9 = 10$; $a_{10} = 5$; $a_{11} = 16$; $a_{12} = 8$; $a_{13} = 4$; $a_{14} = 2$; $a_{15} = 1$; $a_{16} = 4$; $a_{17} = 2$; $a_{18} = 1$; ... (with 4, 2, 1 repeating). So $a_{3n+1} = 4$; $a_{3n+2} = 2$; and $a_{3n} = 1$, for $n \geq 5$.

With $a_1 = 25$, we have $a_2 = 76$; $a_3 = 38$; $a_4 = 19$; $a_5 = 58$; $a_6 = 29$; $a_7 = 88$; $a_8 = 44$; $a_9 = 22$; $a_{10} = 11$; $a_{11} = 34$; $a_{12} = 17$; $a_{13} = 52$; $a_{14} = 26$; $a_{15} = 13$; $a_{16} = 40$; $a_{17} = 20$; $a_{18} = 10$; $a_{19} = 5$; $a_{20} = 16$; $a_{21} = 8$; $a_{22} = 4$; $a_{23} = 2$; $a_{24} = 1$; $a_{25} = 4$; $a_{26} = 2$; $a_{27} = 1$; ... (with 4, 2, 1 repeating). So $a_{3n+1} = 4$; $a_{3n+2} = 2$; and $a_{3n} = 1$, for $n \geq 8$

Conjecture: The sequence will always return to the numbers 4, 2, 1 repeating.

Exercises 12.2

2. Since $a_2 - a_1 = 6 - 3 = 3$ and $a_4 - a_3 = 13 - 9 = 4$, the terms of the sequence do not have a common difference. This sequence is not arithmetic.

4. $a_4 - a_3 = a_3 - a_2 = a_2 - a_1 = 2$. This sequence is arithmetic with the common difference 2.

6. $a_4 - a_3 = \ln 16 - \ln 8 = \ln \frac{16}{8} = \ln 2$; $a_3 - a_2 = \ln 8 - \ln 4 = \ln \frac{8}{4} = \ln 2$;
    $a_2 - a_1 = \ln 4 - \ln 2 = \ln \frac{4}{2} = \ln 2$. This sequence is arithmetic with the common difference $\ln 2$.

8. $1, 5, 9, 13, \ldots$. Then $d = a_2 - a_1 = 5 - 1 = 4$; $a_5 = a_4 + 4 = 13 + 4 = 17$; $a_n = 1 + 4(n - 1)$;
    $a_{100} = 1 + 4(99) = 397$.

10. $11, 8, 5, 2, \ldots$. Then $d = a_2 - a_1 = 8 - 11 = -3$; $a_5 = a_4 - 3 = 2 - 3 = -1$;
    $a_n = 11 - 3(n - 1)$; and $a_{100} = 11 - 3(99) = -286$.

12. $\frac{7}{6}, \frac{5}{3}, \frac{13}{6}, \frac{8}{3}, \ldots$. Then $d = a_2 - a_1 = \frac{10}{6} - \frac{7}{6} = \frac{1}{2}$; $a_5 = a_4 + \frac{1}{2} = \frac{8}{3} + \frac{1}{2} = \frac{19}{6}$; $a_n = \frac{7}{6} + \frac{1}{2}(n - 1)$;
    $a_{100} = \frac{7}{6} + \frac{1}{2}(99) = \frac{7 + 297}{6} = \frac{152}{3}$.

14. $15, 12.3, 9.6, 6.9, \ldots$. Then $d = a_2 - a_1 = 12.3 - 15 = -2.7$; $a_5 = a_4 - 2.7 = 6.9 - 2.7 = 4.2$;
    $a_n = 15 - 2.7(n - 1)$; and $a_{100} = 15 - 2.7(99) = -252.3$.

16. $-t, -t + 3, -t + 6, -t + 9, \ldots$. Then $d = a_2 - a_1 = (-t + 3) - (-t) = 3$;
    $a_5 = a_4 + 3 = -t + 9 + 3 = -t + 12$; $a_n = -t + 3(n - 1)$; and $a_{100} = -t + 3(99) = -t + 297$.

18. $a_{12} = 32$, $a_5 = 18$, and $a_n = a + d(n - 1)$. Then $a_5 = a + 4d = 18$ $\Leftrightarrow$ $a = 18 - 4d$.
    Substituting for a, we have $a_{12} = a + 11d = 32$ $\Leftrightarrow$ $(18 - 4d) + 11d = 32$ $\Leftrightarrow$ $7d = 14$
    $\Leftrightarrow$ $d = 2$. Then we have $a = 18 - 4 \cdot 2 = 10$, and hence, the 20th term is
    $a_{20} = 10 + 19(2) = 48$.

20. $a_{20} = 101$, and $d = 3$. Note that $a_{20} = a + 19d = a + 19(3) = a + 57$. Since $a_{20} = 101$ we have
    $a + 57 = a_{20} = 101$ $\Leftrightarrow$ $a = 44$. Hence the nth term is $a_n = 44 + 3(n - 1) = 41 + 3n$.

22. If 11,937 is a term of an arithmetic sequence with $a_1 = 1$ and common difference 4, then
    $11937 = 1 + 4(n - 1)$ for some integer n. Solving for n, we have
    $11937 = 1 + 4(n - 1) = -3 + 4n$ $\Leftrightarrow$ $11940 = 4n$ $\Leftrightarrow$ $n = 2985$. Thus 11,937 is the
    2985th term of this sequence.

24. $a = 3$, $d = 2$, $n = 12$. Then $S_{12} = \frac{12}{2}[2a + (12 - 1)d] = \frac{12}{2}[2 \cdot 3 + 11 \cdot 2] = 168$.

26. $a = 100$, $d = -5$, $n = 8$. Then $S_8 = \frac{8}{2}[2a + (8 - 1)d] = \frac{8}{2}[2 \cdot 100 - 7 \cdot 5] = 660$.

28. $a_2 = 8$, $a_5 = 9.5$, $n = 15$. Thus $a_2 = a + d = 8$ and $a_5 = a + 4d = 9.5$. Subtracting the first
    equation from the second gives $3d = 1.5$ $\Leftrightarrow$ $d = 0.5$. Substituting for d in the first equation
    gives $a + 0.5 = 8$ $\Leftrightarrow$ $a = 7.5$. Thus $S_{15} = \frac{15}{2}[2 \cdot 7.5 + 14 \cdot 0.5] = 165$.

30. $-3 + \left(-\frac{3}{2}\right) + 0 + \frac{3}{2} + 3 + \cdots + 30$ is a partial sum of an arithmetic sequence, where $a = -3$ and
    $d = \left(-\frac{3}{2}\right) - (-3) = \frac{3}{2}$. The last term is $30 = a_n = -3 + \frac{3}{2}(n - 1)$, so $22 = n - 1$ $\Leftrightarrow$
    $n = 23$. So, the partial sum is $S_{23} = \frac{23}{2}(-3 + 30) = \frac{621}{2} = 310.5$.

32. $-10 + (-9.9) + (-9.8) + \cdots + (-0.1)$ is a partial sum of an arithmetic sequence, where $a = -10$
    and $d = 0.1$. The last term is $-0.1 = a_n = -10 + 0.1(n - 1)$, so $99 = n - 1$ $\Leftrightarrow$ $n = 100$.
    So, the partial sum is $S_{100} = \frac{100}{2}(-10 - 0.1) = -505$.

34. $\displaystyle\sum_{n=0}^{20}(1-2n)$ is a partial sum of an arithmetic sequence, where $a = 1 - 2 \cdot 0 = 1$, $d = -2$, and the last term is $a_{21} = 1 - 2 \cdot 20 = -39$. So, the partial sum is $S_{21} = \frac{21}{2}(1 - 39) = -399$.

36. The number of poles in a layer can be viewed as an arithmetic sequence, where $a_1 = 25$ and the common difference is -1. The number of poles in the first 12 layers is
$S_{12} = \frac{12}{2}[2(25) + 11(-1)] = 6 \cdot 39 = 234$.

38. The number of cars that can park in a row can be viewed as an arithmetic sequence, where $a_1 = 20$ and the common difference is 2. Thus the number of cars that can park in the 21 rows is
$S_{21} = \frac{21}{2}[2(20) + 20(2)] = 10.5 \cdot 80 = 840$.

40. We have an arithmetic sequence with $a = 5$ and $d = 2$. We seek n such that
$2700 = S_n = \frac{n}{2}[2a + (n-1)d]$. Solving for n, we have $2700 = \frac{n}{2}[10 + 2(n-1)]$ $\Leftrightarrow$
$5400 = 10n + 2n^2 - 2n$ $\Leftrightarrow$ $n^2 + 4n - 2700 = 0$ $\Leftrightarrow$ $(n-50)(n+54) = 0$ $\Leftrightarrow$
$n = 50$ or $n = -54$. Since n is a positive integer, 50 terms of the sequence must be added to get 2700.

42. The number of gifts on the 12th day is $1 + 2 + 3 + 4 + \cdots + 12$. Since $a_2 - a_1 = a_3 - a_2$
$= a_4 - a_3 = \cdots = 1$, the number of gifts on the 12th day is the partial sum of an arithmetic sequence with $a = 1$ and $d = 1$. So the sum is $S_{12} = 12\left(\frac{1+12}{2}\right) = 6 \cdot 13 = 78$.

44. $P = 10^{1/10} \cdot 10^{2/10} \cdot 10^{3/10} \cdot \cdots \cdot 10^{19/10} = 10^{(1+2+3+\ldots+19)/10}$. Now, $1 + 2 + 3 + \cdots + 19$ is an arithmetic series with $a = 1$, $d = 1$, and $n = 19$. Thus,
$1 + 2 + 3 + \cdots + 19 = S_{19} = 19\frac{(1+19)}{2} = 190$, and so $P = 10^{190/10} = 10^{19}$.

46. The two original numbers are 3 and 5. Thus, the reciprocals are $\frac{1}{3}$ and $\frac{1}{5}$, and their average is
$\frac{1}{2}\left(\frac{1}{3} + \frac{1}{5}\right) = \frac{1}{2}\left(\frac{5}{15} + \frac{3}{15}\right) = \frac{4}{15}$. Therefore, the harmonic mean is $\frac{15}{4}$.

Exercises 12.3

2. $\dfrac{a_2}{a_1} = \dfrac{6}{2} = 3$; $\dfrac{a_4}{a_3} = \dfrac{36}{18} = 2$. Since these ratios are not the same, this is not a geometric sequence.

4. $\dfrac{a_2}{a_1} = \dfrac{-9}{27} = -\dfrac{1}{3}$; $\dfrac{a_3}{a_2} = \dfrac{3}{-9} = -\dfrac{1}{3}$; $\dfrac{a_4}{a_3} = -\dfrac{1}{3}$. Since these ratios are the same, the sequence is geometric with the common ratio $-\dfrac{1}{3}$.

6. $\dfrac{a_2}{a_1} = \dfrac{e^4}{e^2} = e^2$; $\dfrac{a_3}{a_2} = \dfrac{e^6}{e^4} = e^2$; $\dfrac{a_4}{a_3} = \dfrac{e^8}{e^6} = e^2$. Since these ratios are the same, the sequence is geometric with the common ratio e^2.

8. $7, \dfrac{14}{3}, \dfrac{28}{9}, \dfrac{56}{27}, \ldots$. Then $r = \dfrac{a_2}{a_1} = \dfrac{\frac{14}{3}}{7} = \dfrac{2}{3}$; $a_5 = a_4 \cdot \dfrac{2}{3} = \dfrac{56}{27} \cdot \dfrac{2}{3} = \dfrac{112}{81}$; and $a_n = 7\left(\dfrac{2}{3}\right)^{n-1}$.

10. $1, \sqrt{2}, 2, 2\sqrt{2}, \ldots$. Then $r = \dfrac{a_2}{a_1} = \dfrac{\sqrt{2}}{1} = \sqrt{2}$; $a_5 = a_4 \cdot \sqrt{2} = 2\sqrt{2} \cdot \sqrt{2} = 4$; and $a_n = \left(\sqrt{2}\right)^{n-1}$.

12. $-8, -2, -\dfrac{1}{2}, -\dfrac{1}{8}, \ldots$. Then $r = \dfrac{a_2}{a_1} = \dfrac{-2}{-8} = \dfrac{1}{4}$; $a_5 = a_4 \cdot \dfrac{1}{4} = -\dfrac{1}{8} \cdot \dfrac{1}{4} = -\dfrac{1}{32}$; and $a_n = -8\left(\dfrac{1}{4}\right)^{n-1}$.

14. $t, \dfrac{t^2}{2}, \dfrac{t^3}{4}, \dfrac{t^4}{8}, \ldots$. Then $r = \dfrac{a_2}{a_1} = \dfrac{\frac{t^2}{2}}{t} = \dfrac{t}{2}$; $a_5 = a_4 \cdot \dfrac{t}{2} = \dfrac{t^4}{8} \cdot \dfrac{t}{2} = \dfrac{t^5}{16}$; and $a_n = t\left(\dfrac{t}{2}\right)^{n-1}$.

16. $5, 5^{c+1}, 5^{2c+1}, 5^{3c+1}, \ldots$. Then $r = \dfrac{a_2}{a_1} = \dfrac{5^{c+1}}{5} = 5^c$; $a_5 = a_4 \cdot 5^c = 5^{3c+1} \cdot 5^c = 5^{4c+1}$; and $a_n = 5(5^c)^{n-1} = 5 \cdot 5^{cn-c} = 5^{cn-c+1}$.

18. $a_1 = 3$, $a_3 = \dfrac{4}{3}$. Thus $r^2 = \dfrac{\frac{4}{3}}{3} = \dfrac{4}{9}$ $\Leftrightarrow$ $r = \pm\dfrac{2}{3}$. If $r = \dfrac{2}{3}$, then $a_5 = 3\left(\dfrac{2}{3}\right)^4 = \dfrac{16}{27}$, and if $r = -\dfrac{2}{3}$, then $a_5 = 3\left(-\dfrac{2}{3}\right)^4 = \dfrac{16}{27}$. Therefore, $a_5 = \dfrac{16}{27}$.

20. $r = \dfrac{3}{2}$, $a_5 = 1$. Then $1 = a_5 = a \cdot r^4 = a\left(\dfrac{3}{2}\right)^4$ $\Leftrightarrow$ $1 = a\left(\dfrac{3}{2}\right)^4$ $\Leftrightarrow$ $a = \left(\dfrac{2}{3}\right)^4 = \dfrac{16}{81}$. Therefore, $a_1 = \dfrac{16}{81}$, $a_2 = \dfrac{16}{81}\left(\dfrac{3}{2}\right) = \dfrac{8}{27}$, and $a_3 = \dfrac{8}{27}\left(\dfrac{3}{2}\right) = \dfrac{4}{9}$.

22. $a_2 = 10$, $a_5 = 1250$. Thus, $\dfrac{1250}{10} = \dfrac{a_5}{a_2} = \dfrac{ar^4}{ar} = r^3$ $\Leftrightarrow$ $r = 5$. Then $a_1 = \dfrac{a_2}{r} = \dfrac{10}{5} = 2$, so $a_n = 2 \cdot 5^{n-1}$. We seek n such that $a_n = 31{,}250$ $\Leftrightarrow$ $2 \cdot 5^{n-1} = 31{,}250$ $\Leftrightarrow$ $5^{n-1} = 15{,}625$ $\Leftrightarrow$ $n - 1 = \log_5 15{,}625 = 6$ $\Leftrightarrow$ $n = 7$. Therefore, $31{,}250$ is the 7th term of the sequence.

24. $a = \dfrac{2}{3}$, $r = \dfrac{1}{3}$, $n = 4$. Then $S_4 = \left(\dfrac{2}{3}\right)\dfrac{1 - \left(\frac{1}{3}\right)^4}{1 - \frac{1}{3}} = \left(\dfrac{2}{3}\right)\dfrac{\frac{80}{81}}{\frac{2}{3}} = \dfrac{80}{81}$.

26. $a_2 = 0.12$, $a_5 = 0.00096$, $n = 4$. So, $r^3 = \dfrac{a_5}{a_2} = \dfrac{0.00096}{0.12} = 0.008$ $\Leftrightarrow$ $r = 0.2$, and thus $a_1 = \dfrac{a_2}{r} = \dfrac{0.12}{0.2} = 0.6$. Therefore, $S_4 = (0.6)\dfrac{1 - (0.2)^4}{1 - 0.2} = 0.7488$.

28. $1 - \frac{1}{2} + \frac{1}{4} - \frac{1}{8} + \cdots - \frac{1}{512}$ is a partial sum of a geometric sequence, where $a = 1$ and

$r = \dfrac{a_2}{a_1} = \dfrac{-\frac{1}{2}}{1} = -\frac{1}{2}$. The last term is a_n, where $\frac{-1}{512} = a_n = 1\left(-\frac{1}{2}\right)^{n-1}$, so $n = 10$. So, the partial

sum is $S_{10} = (1)\dfrac{1 - \left(-\frac{1}{2}\right)^{10}}{1 - \left(-\frac{1}{2}\right)} = \frac{341}{512}$.

30. $\displaystyle\sum_{j=0}^{5} 7\left(\frac{3}{2}\right)^j$ is a partial sum of a geometric sequence, where $a = 7$, $r = \frac{3}{2}$, and $n = 6$. So, the partial

sum is $S_6 = (7)\dfrac{1 - \left(\frac{3}{2}\right)^6}{1 - \frac{3}{2}} = (7)\dfrac{1 - \left(\frac{729}{64}\right)}{-\frac{1}{2}} = -14\left(1 - \frac{729}{64}\right) = \frac{4655}{32}$.

32. $a = 5000$, $r = 1.08$. After 1 hour, there are $5000 \cdot 1.08 = 5400$; after 2 hours, $5400 \cdot 1.08 = 5832$; after 3 hours, $5832 \cdot 1.08 = 6298.56$; after 4 hours, $6298.56 \cdot 1.08 = 6802.4448$; and after 5 hours, $6802.4448 \cdot 1.08 \approx 7347$ bacteria. After n hours, the number of bacteria is $a_n = 5000 \cdot (1.08)^n$.

34. We have a geometric sequence with $a = 1$ and $r = 2$. Then $S_n = (1)\dfrac{1 - 2^n}{1 - 2} = 2^n - 1$. At the end of 30 days, she will have $S_{30} = 2^{30} - 1 = 1{,}073{,}741{,}823$ cents $= \$10{,}737{,}418.23$. To become a billionaire, we want $2^n - 1 = 10^{11}$ or approximately $2^n = 10^{11}$. So $\log 2^n = \log 10^{11}$ $\Leftrightarrow$ $n = \frac{11}{\log 2} \approx 36.5$. Thus it will take 37 days.

36. Let $a_1 = 1$ be the man with 7 wives. Also, let $a_2 = 7$ (the wives), $a_3 = 7a_2 = 7^2$ (the sacks), $a_4 = 7a_3 = 7^3$ (the cats), and $a_5 = 7a_4 = 7^4$ (the kits). The total is $a_1 + a_2 + a_3 + a_4 + a_5 = 1 + 7 + 7^2 + 7^3 + 7^4$, which is a partial sum of a geometric sequence with $a = 1$ and $r = 7$. Thus, the number in the party is $S_5 = 1 \cdot \dfrac{1 - 7^5}{1 - 7} = 2801$.

38. $1 - \frac{1}{2} + \frac{1}{4} - \frac{1}{8} + \cdots$ is an infinite geometric series with $a = 1$ and $r = -\frac{1}{2}$. Therefore, the sum of the series is $S = \dfrac{1}{1 - \left(-\frac{1}{2}\right)} = \dfrac{1}{\frac{3}{2}} = \frac{2}{3}$.

40. $\frac{2}{5} + \frac{4}{25} + \frac{8}{125} + \cdots$ is an infinite geometric series with $a = \frac{2}{5}$ and $r = \frac{2}{5}$. Therefore, the sum of the series is $S = \dfrac{\frac{2}{5}}{1 - \frac{2}{5}} = \dfrac{\frac{2}{5}}{\frac{3}{5}} = \frac{2}{3}$.

42. $3 - \frac{3}{2} + \frac{3}{4} - \frac{3}{8} + \cdots$ is an infinite geometric series with $a = 3$ and $r = -\frac{1}{2}$. Therefore, the sum of the series is $S = \dfrac{3}{1 - \left(-\frac{1}{2}\right)} = 2$.

44. $\frac{1}{\sqrt{2}} + \frac{1}{2} + \frac{1}{2\sqrt{2}} + \frac{1}{4} + \cdots$ is an infinite geometric series with $a = \frac{1}{\sqrt{2}}$ and $r = \frac{1}{\sqrt{2}}$. Therefore, the sum of the series is $S = \dfrac{\frac{1}{\sqrt{2}}}{1 - \frac{1}{\sqrt{2}}} = \frac{1}{\sqrt{2}-1} = \sqrt{2} + 1$.

46. $0.2535353\ldots = 0.2 + \frac{53}{1000} + \frac{53}{100{,}000} + \frac{53}{10{,}000{,}000} + \cdots$ is an infinite geometric series

(after the first term) with $a = \frac{53}{1000}$ and $r = \frac{1}{100}$. Thus $0.05353\ldots = \dfrac{\frac{53}{1000}}{1 - \frac{1}{100}} = \frac{53}{1000} \cdot \frac{100}{99} = \frac{53}{990}$,

and so $0.2535353\ldots = \frac{2}{10} + \frac{53}{990} = \frac{2 \cdot 99 + 53}{990} = \frac{251}{990}$.

48. $2.11252525\ldots = 2.11 + \frac{25}{10,000} + \frac{25}{1,000,000} + \frac{25}{100,000,000} + \cdots$ is an infinite geometric series

(after the first term) with $a = \frac{25}{10,000}$ and $r = \frac{1}{100}$. Thus $0.00252525\ldots = \frac{\frac{25}{10,000}}{1 - \frac{1}{100}} = \frac{25}{9900}$, and so

$2.11252525\ldots = \frac{211}{100} + \frac{25}{9900} = \frac{211 \cdot 99 + 25}{9900} = \frac{20,914}{9900} = \frac{10,457}{4950}$.

50. $0.123123123\ldots = \frac{123}{1000} + \frac{123}{1,000,000} + \frac{123}{1,000,000,000} + \cdots$ is an infinite geometric series with $a = \frac{123}{1000}$

and $r = \frac{1}{1000}$. Thus $0.123123123\ldots = \frac{\frac{123}{1000}}{1 - \frac{1}{1000}} = \frac{123}{999}$.

52. The time required for the ball to stop bouncing is $t = 1 + \frac{1}{\sqrt{2}} + \left(\frac{1}{\sqrt{2}}\right)^2 + \cdots$ which is an infinite

geometric series with $a = 1$ and $r = \frac{1}{\sqrt{2}}$. The sum of this series is $t = \frac{1}{1 - \frac{1}{\sqrt{2}}} = \frac{\sqrt{2}}{\sqrt{2} - 1}$

$= \frac{\sqrt{2}}{\sqrt{2} - 1} \cdot \frac{\sqrt{2} + 1}{\sqrt{2} + 1} = \frac{2 + \sqrt{2}}{2 - 1} = 2 + \sqrt{2}$. Thus the time required for the ball to stop is

$2 + \sqrt{2} \approx 3.41$ s.

54. Let A_n be the area of the disks of paper placed at the nth stage. Then $A_1 = \pi R^2$,

$A_2 = 2 \cdot \pi \left(\frac{1}{2}R\right)^2 = \frac{\pi}{2}R^2$, $A_3 = 4 \cdot \pi \left(\frac{1}{4}R\right)^2 = \frac{\pi}{4}R^2$, $\ldots$. We see from this pattern that the total

area is $A = \pi R^2 + \frac{1}{2}\pi R^2 + \frac{1}{4}\pi R^2 + \cdots$. Thus, the total area, A, is an infinite geometric series with

$a_1 = \pi R^2$ and $r = \frac{1}{2}$. So, $A = \frac{\pi R^2}{1 - \frac{1}{2}} = 2\pi R^2$.

56. Since we have 5 terms, let us denote $a_1 = 5$ and $a_5 = 80$. Also, $\frac{a_5}{a_1} = r^4$ because the sequence is

geometric, and so $r^4 = \frac{80}{5} = 16 \quad \Leftrightarrow \quad r = \pm 2$. If $r = 2$, the three geometric means are $a_2 = 10$,

$a_3 = 20$, and $a_4 = 40$. (If $r = -2$, the three geometric means are $a_2 = -10$, $a_3 = 20$, and

$a_4 = -40$, but these are not between 5 and 80.)

58. (a) $5, -3, 5, -3, \ldots$. Now $a_2 - a_1 = -3 - 5 = -8$, but $a_3 - a_2 = 5 - (-3) = 8$, and $\frac{a_2}{a_1} = \frac{-3}{5}$,

but $\frac{a_3}{a_2} = \frac{5}{-3}$. Thus, the sequence is neither arithmetic nor geometric.

(b) $\frac{1}{3}, 1, \frac{5}{3}, \frac{7}{3}, \ldots$. Now $a_2 - a_1 = 1 - \frac{1}{3} = \frac{2}{3}$; $a_3 - a_2 = \frac{5}{3} - 1 = \frac{2}{3}$; and $a_4 - a_3 = \frac{7}{3} - \frac{5}{3} = \frac{2}{3}$.

Therefore, the sequence is arithmetic with $d = \frac{2}{3}$ and $a_5 = \frac{7}{3} + \frac{2}{3} = 3$.

(c) $\sqrt{3}, 3, 3\sqrt{3}, 9, \ldots$. Now $\frac{a_2}{a_1} = \frac{3}{\sqrt{3}} = \sqrt{3}$; $\frac{a_3}{a_2} = \frac{3\sqrt{3}}{3} = \sqrt{3}$; and $\frac{a_4}{a_3} = \frac{9}{3\sqrt{3}} = \sqrt{3}$.

Therefore, the sequence is geometric with $r = \sqrt{3}$ and $a_5 = 9\sqrt{3}$.

(d) $1, -1, 1, -1, \ldots$. Now $\frac{a_2}{a_1} = \frac{-1}{1} = -1$; $\frac{a_3}{a_2} = \frac{1}{-1} = -1$; and $\frac{a_4}{a_3} = \frac{-1}{1} = -1$. Therefore, the

sequence is geometric with $r = -1$ and $a_5 = (-1)(-1) = 1$.

(e) $2, -1, \frac{1}{2}, 2, \ldots$. Now $a_2 - a_1 = -1 - 2 = -3$, but $a_3 - a_2 = \frac{1}{2} + 1 = \frac{3}{2}$, and so the

sequence is not arithmetic. Also, $\frac{a_2}{a_1} = \frac{-1}{2}$, but $\frac{a_4}{a_3} = \frac{2}{\frac{1}{2}} = 4$, and so the sequence is not

geometric. Thus, the sequence is neither arithmetic nor geometric.

(f) $x - 1, x, x + 1, x + 2, \ldots$. Now $a_2 - a_1 = x - (x - 1) = 1$; $a_3 - a_2 = (x + 1) - x = 1$;

and $a_4 - a_3 = (x + 2) - (x + 1) = 1$. Therefore, the sequence is arithmetic with $d = 1$ and

$a_5 = (x + 2) + 1 = x + 3$.

(g) $-3, -\frac{3}{2}, 0, \frac{3}{2}, \ldots$. Now $a_2 - a_1 = -\frac{3}{2} - (-3) = \frac{3}{2}$; $a_3 - a_2 = 0 - (-\frac{3}{2}) = \frac{3}{2}$; and
     $a_4 - a_3 = \frac{3}{2} - 0 = \frac{3}{2}$. Therefore, the sequence is arithmetic with $d = \frac{3}{2}$, and $a_5 = \frac{3}{2} + \frac{3}{2} = 3$.

(h) $\sqrt{5}, \sqrt[3]{5}, \sqrt[6]{5}, 1, \ldots$. Now $a_2 - a_1 = \sqrt[3]{5} - \sqrt{5}$, but $a_3 - a_2 = \sqrt[6]{5} - \sqrt[3]{5}$. Thus the
     sequence is not arithmetic. However, $\dfrac{a_2}{a_1} = \dfrac{\sqrt[3]{5}}{\sqrt{5}} = \dfrac{5^{1/3}}{5^{1/2}} = 5^{-1/6}$, $\dfrac{a_3}{a_2} = \dfrac{\sqrt[6]{5}}{\sqrt[3]{5}} = \dfrac{5^{1/6}}{5^{1/3}} = 5^{-1/6}$,
     and $\dfrac{a_4}{a_3} = \dfrac{1}{\sqrt[6]{5}} = \dfrac{1}{5^{1/6}} = 5^{-1/6}$. Therefore, the sequence is geometric with $r = 5^{-1/6}$ and
     $a_5 = 1 \cdot 5^{-1/6} = \dfrac{1}{\sqrt[6]{5}}$.

60. $a_1, a_2, a_3, \ldots$ is a geometric sequence with common ratio r. Thus $a_2 = a_1 r$, $a_3 = a_1 \cdot r^2, \ldots$,
     $a_n = a_1 \cdot r^{n-1}$. Hence $\log a_2 = \log(a_1 r) = \log a_1 + \log r$, $\log a_3 = \log(a_1 \cdot r^2) = \log a_1 + \log(r^2)$
     $= \log a_1 + 2 \log r, \ldots$, $\log a_n = \log(a_1 \cdot r^{n-1}) = \log a_1 + \log(r^{n-1}) = \log a_1 + (n-1) \log r$, and
     so $\log a_1, \log a_2, \log a_3, \ldots$ is an arithmetic sequence with common difference $\log r$.

Exercises 12.4

2. $R = 500$, $n = 24$, $i = \frac{0.08}{12} \approx 0.0066667$. So $A_f = R\frac{(1+i)^n - 1}{i} = 500\frac{(1.0066667)^{24} - 1}{0.0066667}$
   $= \$12{,}966.59$.

4. $R = 500$, $n = 20$, $i = \frac{0.06}{2} = 0.03$. So $A_f = R\frac{(1+i)^n - 1}{i} = 500\frac{(1.03)^{20} - 1}{0.03} = \$13{,}435.19$.

6. $A_f = 5000$, $n = 4 \cdot 2 = 8$, $i = \frac{0.10}{4} = 0.025$. So $R = \frac{iA_f}{(1+i)^n - 1} = \frac{(0.025)(5000)}{(1.025)^8 - 1} = \$572.34$.

8. $R = 1000$, $n = 20$, $i = \frac{0.09}{2} = 0.045$. So $A_p = R\frac{1 - (1+i)^{-n}}{i} = 1000\frac{1 - (1.045)^{-20}}{0.045}$
   $= \$13{,}007.94$.

10. $A_p = 50{,}000$, $n = 10(2) = 20$, $i = \frac{0.08}{2} = 0.04$. So $R = \frac{iA_p}{1 - (1+i)^{-n}} = \frac{(0.04)(50{,}000)}{1 - (1.04)^{-20}}$
    $= \$3679.09$.

12. $A_p = 80{,}000$, $i = \frac{0.09}{12} = 0.0075$. Over a 30 year period, $n = 30(12) = 360$, and the monthly
    payment is $R = \frac{iA_p}{1 - (1+i)^{-n}} = \frac{(0.0075)(80{,}000)}{1 - (1.0075)^{-360}} = \$643.70$. Over a 15 year period,
    $n = 15 \cdot 12 = 180$, and so the monthly payment is $R = \frac{80{,}000 \cdot 0.0075}{1 - (1.0075)^{-180}} = \$811.41$.

14. $R = 650$, $n = 12(30) = 360$, $i = \frac{0.09}{12} = 0.0075$. So $A_p = R\frac{1 - (1+i)^{-n}}{i}$
    $= 650\frac{1 - (1.0075)^{-360}}{0.0075} = \$80{,}783.21$. Therefore, the couple can afford a loan of \$80,783.21.

16. $R = 220$, $n = 12(3) = 36$, $i = \frac{0.08}{12} \approx 0.00667$. The amount borrowed is $A_p = R\frac{1 - (1+i)^{-n}}{i}$
    $= 220\frac{1 - (1.00667)^{-36}}{0.00667} = \$7{,}020.60$. So she purchased the car for
    $\$7{,}020.60 + \$2000 = \$9020.60$.

18. $A_p = \$12{,}500$, $R = \$420$, $n = 36$. We want to solve for the
    interest rate using the equation $R = \frac{iA_P}{1 - (1+i)^{-n}}$. Let x be
    the interest rate, then $i = \frac{x}{12}$. So we can express R as a
    function of x as follows: $R(x) = \dfrac{\frac{x}{12} \cdot 12{,}500}{1 - \left(1 + \frac{x}{12}\right)^{-36}}$. We

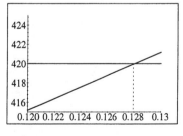

graph $R(x)$ and $y = 420$ in the rectangle $[0.12, 0.13]$ by $[415, 425]$. The x-coordinate of the
intersection is about 0.1280, which corresponds to an interest rate of 12.80%.

20. $A_p = \$2000 - \$200 = \$1800$, $R = \$88$, $n = 24$. We want
to solve for the interest rate using the equation
$R = \dfrac{iA_P}{1 - (1+i)^{-n}}$. Let x be the interest rate, then $i = \dfrac{x}{12}$.
So we can express R as a function of x as follows:
$$R(x) = \frac{\dfrac{x}{12} \cdot 1800}{1 - \left(1 + \dfrac{x}{12}\right)^{-24}}.$$

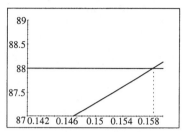

We graph $R(x)$ and $y = 88$ in the viewing rectangle $[0.14, 0.16]$ by $[87, 89]$. The x-coordinate of
the intersection is about 0.1584, which corresponds to an interest rate of 15.84%.

22. (a) The present value of the kth payment is $PV = R(1+i)^{-k} = \dfrac{R}{(1+i)^k}$. The present value of
an annuity is the sum of the present values of each of the payments of R dollars, as the time line
below shows.

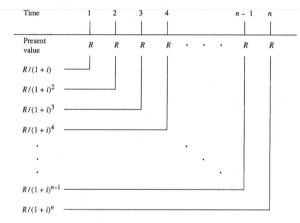

(b) $A_p = \dfrac{R}{1+i} + \dfrac{R}{(1+i)^2} + \dfrac{R}{(1+i)^3} + \cdots + \dfrac{R}{(1+i)^n}$

$= \dfrac{R}{1+i} + \left(\dfrac{R}{1+i}\right)\left(\dfrac{1}{1+i}\right) + \left(\dfrac{R}{1+i}\right)\left(\dfrac{1}{1+i}\right)^2 + \cdots + \left(\dfrac{R}{1+i}\right)\left(\dfrac{1}{1+i}\right)^{n-1}$. This is a

geometric series with $a = \dfrac{R}{1+i}$ and $r = \dfrac{1}{1+i}$. Since $S_n = a\dfrac{1-r^n}{1-r}$, we have

$$A_p = \left(\frac{R}{1+i}\right)\frac{1 - \left[\frac{1}{(1+i)}\right]^n}{1 - \left(\frac{1}{1+i}\right)} = R\frac{1 - (1+i)^{-n}}{(1+i)\left[1 - \left(\frac{1}{1+i}\right)\right]} = R\frac{1 - (1+i)^{-n}}{(1+i) - 1} = R\frac{1 - (1+i)^{-n}}{i}.$$

Exercises 12.5

2. Let $P(n)$ denote the statement $1 + 4 + 7 + 10 + \cdots + (3n - 2) = \dfrac{n(3n-1)}{2}$.

    Step 1 $P(1)$ is the statement that $1 = \dfrac{1[3(1)-1]}{2} = \dfrac{1 \cdot 2}{2}$, which is true.

    Step 2 Assume that $P(k)$ is true; that is. $1 + 4 + 7 + \cdots + (3k-2) = \dfrac{k(3k-1)}{2}$. We want to use

    this to show that $P(k+1)$ is true. Now,

    $1 + 4 + 7 + 10 + \cdots + (3k - 2) + [3(k+1) - 2] =$

    $\dfrac{k(3k-1)}{2} + 3k + 1 =$ induction hypothesis

    $\dfrac{k(3k-1)}{2} + \dfrac{6k+2}{2} = \dfrac{3k^2 - k + 6k + 2}{2} =$

    $\dfrac{3k^2 + 5k + 2}{2} = \dfrac{(k+1)(3k+2)}{2} = \dfrac{(k+1)[3(k+1)-1]}{2}$.

    Thus, $P(k+1)$ follows from $P(k)$. So by the Principle of Mathematical Induction, $P(n)$ is
    true for all n.

4. Let $P(n)$ denote the statement $1^2 + 2^2 + 3^2 + \cdots + n^2 = \dfrac{n(n+1)(2n+1)}{6}$.

    Step 1 $P(1)$ is the statement that $1^2 = \dfrac{1 \cdot 2 \cdot 3}{6}$, which is true.

    Step 2 Assume that $P(k)$ is true; that is, $1^2 + 2^2 + 3^2 + \cdots + k^2 = \dfrac{k(k+1)(2k+1)}{6}$. We want to

    use this to show that $P(k+1)$ is true. Now,

    $1^2 + 2^2 + 3^2 + \cdots + k^2 + (k+1)^2 =$

    $\dfrac{k(k+1)(2k+1)}{6} + (k+1)^2 =$ induction hypothesis

    $(k+1)\left[\dfrac{k(2k+1) + 6(k+1)}{6}\right] =$

    $(k+1)\left[\dfrac{2k^2 + k + 6k + 6}{6}\right] =$

    $(k+1)\left[\dfrac{2k^2 + 7k + 6}{6}\right] =$

    $\dfrac{(k+1)(k+2)(2k+3)}{6} = \dfrac{(k+1)[(k+1)+1][2(k+1)+1]]}{6}$.

    Thus $P(k+1)$ follows from $P(k)$. So by the Principle of Mathematical Induction, $P(n)$ is
    true for all n.

6. Let $P(n)$ denote the statement $1 \cdot 3 + 2 \cdot 4 + 3 \cdot 5 + \cdots + n(n+2) = \dfrac{n(n+1)(2n+7)}{6}$.

    Step 1 $P(1)$ is the statement that $1 \cdot 3 = \dfrac{1 \cdot 2 \cdot 9}{6}$, which is true.

<u>Step 2</u> Assume that $P(k)$ is true; that is, $1 \cdot 3 + 2 \cdot 4 + 3 \cdot 5 + \cdots + k(k+2) = \dfrac{k(k+1)(2k+7)}{6}$.

We want to use this to show that $P(k+1)$ is true. Now,

$$1 \cdot 3 + 2 \cdot 4 + 3 \cdot 5 + \cdots + k(k+2) + (k+1)[(k+1) + 2] =$$

$$\frac{k(k+1)(2k+7)}{6} + (k+1)(k+3) = \qquad \text{induction hypothesis}$$

$$(k+1)\left[\frac{k(2k+7)}{6} + \frac{6(k+3)}{6}\right] =$$

$$(k+1)\left(\frac{2k^2 + 7k + 6k + 18}{6}\right) =$$

$$\frac{(k+1)[(k+1) + 1][2(k+1) + 7]}{6}.$$

Thus $P(k+1)$ follows from $P(k)$. So by the Principle of Mathematical Induction, $P(n)$ is true for all n.

8. Let $P(n)$ denote the statement $1^3 + 3^3 + 5^3 + \cdots + (2n-1)^3 = n^2(2n^2 - 1)$.

    <u>Step 1</u> $P(1)$ is the statement that $1^3 = 1^2(2 \cdot 1^2 - 1)$, which is clearly true.

    <u>Step 2</u> Assume that $P(k)$ is true; that is, $1^3 + 3^3 + 5^3 + \cdots + (2k-1)^3 = k^2(2k^2 - 1)$. We want to use this to show that $P(k+1)$ is true. Now,

    $$1^3 + 3^3 + 5^3 + \cdots + (2k-1)^3 + (2k+1)^3 =$$

    $$k^2(2k^2 - 1) + (2k+1)^3 = \qquad \text{induction hypothesis}$$

    $$2k^4 - k^2 + 8k^3 + 12k^2 + 6k + 1 =$$

    $$2k^4 + 8k^3 + 11k^2 + 6k + 1 =$$

    $$(k^2 + 2k + 1)(2k^2 + 4k + 1) = (k+1)^2[2(k+1)^2 - 1].$$

    Thus $P(k+1)$ follows from $P(k)$. So by the Principle of Mathematical Induction, $P(n)$ is true for all n.

10. Let $P(n)$ denote the statement $\dfrac{1}{1 \cdot 2} + \dfrac{1}{2 \cdot 3} + \dfrac{1}{3 \cdot 4} + \cdots + \dfrac{1}{n(n+1)} = \dfrac{n}{n+1}$.

    <u>Step 1</u> $P(1)$ is the statement that $\dfrac{1}{1 \cdot 2} = \dfrac{1}{2}$, which is clearly true.

    <u>Step 2</u> Assume that $P(k)$ is true; that is $\dfrac{1}{1 \cdot 2} + \dfrac{1}{2 \cdot 3} + \dfrac{1}{3 \cdot 4} + \cdots + \dfrac{1}{k(k+1)} = \dfrac{k}{k+1}$. We want to use this to show that $P(k+1)$ is true. Now,

    $$\frac{1}{1 \cdot 2} + \frac{1}{2 \cdot 3} + \cdots + \frac{1}{k(k+1)} + \frac{1}{(k+1)(k+2)} =$$

    $$\frac{k}{k+1} + \frac{1}{(k+1)(k+2)} = \qquad \text{induction hypothesis}$$

    $$\frac{k(k+2) + 1}{(k+1)(k+2)} = \frac{k^2 + 2k + 1}{(k+1)(k+2)} =$$

    $$\frac{(k+1)^2}{(k+1)(k+2)} = \frac{k+1}{k+2} = \frac{k+1}{(k+1) + 1}.$$

    Thus $P(k+1)$ follows from $P(k)$. So by the Principle of Mathematical Induction, $P(n)$ is true for all n.

12. Let $P(n)$ denote the statement $1 + 2 + 2^2 + \cdots + 2^{n-1} = 2^n - 1$.

Step 1 $P(1)$ is the statement that $1 = 2^1 - 1$, which is clearly true.

Step 2 Assume that $P(k)$ is true; that is, $1 + 2 + 2^2 + \cdots + 2^{k-1} = 2^k - 1$. We want to use this to show that $P(k+1)$ is true. Now,
$$1 + 2 + 2^2 + \cdots + 2^{k-1} + 2^k =$$
$$2^k - 1 + 2^k = \qquad \text{induction hypothesis}$$
$$2 \cdot 2^k - 1 = 2^{k+1} - 1.$$
Thus $P(k+1)$ follows from $P(k)$. So by the Principle of Mathematical Induction, $P(n)$ is true for all n.

14. Let $P(n)$ denote the statement that $5^n - 1$ is divisible by 4.

Step 1 $P(1)$ is the statement that $5^1 - 1 = 4$ is divisible by 4, which is clearly true.

Step 2 Assume that $P(k)$ is true; that is, $5^k - 1$ is divisible by 4. We want to use this to show that $P(k+1)$ is true. Now, $5^{(k+1)} - 1 = 5 \cdot 5^k - 1 = 5 \cdot 5^k - 5 + 4 = 5(5^k - 1) + 4$ which is divisible by 4 since $5(5^k - 1)$ is divisible by 4 by the induction hypothesis. Thus $P(k+1)$ follows from $P(k)$. So by the Principle of Mathematical Induction, $P(n)$ is true for all n.

16. Let $P(n)$ denote the statement that $n^3 - n + 3$ is divisible by 3.

Step 1 $P(1)$ is the statement that $1^3 - 1 + 3 = 3$ is divisible by 3, which is true.

Step 2 Assume that $P(k)$ is true; that is, $k^3 - k + 3$ is divisible by 3. We want to use this to show that $P(k+1)$ is true. Now,
$(k+1)^3 - (k+1) + 3 = k^3 + 3k^2 + 3k + 1 - k - 1 + 3 = k^3 - k + 3 + 3k^2 + 3k$
$= (k^3 - k + 3) + 3(k^2 + k)$, which is divisible by 3, since $k^3 - k + 3$ is divisible by 3 by the induction hypothesis, and $3(k^2 + k)$ is divisible by 3. Thus $P(k+1)$ follows from $P(k)$. So by the Principle of Mathematical Induction, $P(n)$ is true for all n.

18. Let $P(n)$ denote the statement that $3^{2n} - 1$ is divisible by 8.

Step 1 $P(1)$ is the statement that $3^2 - 1 = 8$ is divisible by 8, which is clearly true.

Step 2 Assume that $P(k)$ is true; that is, $3^{2k} - 1$ is divisible by 8. We want to use this to show that $P(k+1)$ is true. Now, $3^{2(k+1)} - 1 = 9 \cdot 3^{2k} - 1 = 9 \cdot 3^{2k} - 9 + 8 = 9(3^{2k} - 1) + 8$, which is divisible by 8, since $3^{2k} - 1$ is divisible by 8 by the induction hypothesis. Thus $P(k+1)$ follows from $P(k)$. So by the Principle of Mathematical Induction, $P(n)$ is true for all n.

20. Let $P(n)$ denote the statement $(n+1)^2 < 2n^2$, for all $n \geq 3$.

Step 1 $P(3)$ is the statement that $(3+1)^2 < 2 \cdot 3^2$ or $16 < 18$, which is true.

Step 2 Assume that $P(k)$ is true; that is, $(k+1)^2 < 2k^2$, $k \geq 3$. We want to use this to show that $P(k+1)$ is true. Now,
$$(k+2)^2 =$$
$$k^2 + 4k + 4 =$$
$$(k^2 + 2k + 1) + (2k + 3) =$$
$$(k+1)^2 + (2k+1) < 2k^2 + (2k+3) \qquad \text{induction hypothesis}$$
$$< 2k^2 + (2k+3) + (2k-1) \qquad \text{because } 2k-1 > 0 \text{ for } k \geq 3$$
$$= 2k^2 + 4k + 2 = 2(k+1)^2.$$
Thus $P(k+1)$ follows from $P(k)$. So by the Principle of Mathematical Induction, $P(n)$ is true for all $n \geq 3$.

22. Let $P(n)$ denote the statement $100n \leq n^2$, for all $n \geq 100$.

Step 1 $P(100)$ is the statement that $100(100) \leq (100)^2$, which is true.

Step 2 Assume that $P(k)$ is true; that is, $100k \leq k^2$. We want to use this to show that $P(k+1)$ is true. Now,
$$100(k+1) =$$
$$100k + 100 \leq k^2 + 100 \qquad\qquad \text{induction hypothesis}$$
$$\leq k^2 + 2k + 1 = (k+1)^2. \qquad\qquad \text{because } 2k + 1 \geq 100 \text{ for } k \geq 100$$
Thus $P(k+1)$ follows from $P(k)$. So by the Principle of Mathematical Induction, $P(n)$ is true for all $n \geq 100$.

24. $a_{n+1} = 3a_n - 8$ and $a_1 = 4$. Then $a_2 = 3 \cdot 4 - 8 = 4$, $a_3 = 3 \cdot 4 - 8 = 4$, $a_4 = 3 \cdot 4 - 8 = 4, \ldots$, and the conjecture is that $a_n = 4$. Let $P(n)$ denote the statement that $a_n = 4$.

Step 1 $P(1)$ is the statement that $a_1 = 4$, which is true.

Step 2 Assume that $P(k)$ is true; that is, $a_k = 4$. We want to use this to show that $P(k+1)$ is true. Now, $a_{k+1} = 3 \cdot a_k - 8 = 3 \cdot 4 - 8 = 4$, by the induction hypothesis. This is exactly $P(k+1)$, so by the Principle of Mathematical Induction, $P(n)$ is true for all n.

26. Let $P(n)$ be the statement that $x + y$ is a factor of $x^{2n-1} + y^{2n-1}$.

Step 1 $P(1)$ is the statement that $x + y$ is a factor of $x^1 + y^1$, which is clearly true.

Step 2 Assume that $P(k)$ is true; that is, $x + y$ is a factor of $x^{2k-1} + y^{2k-1}$. We want to use this to show that $P(k+1)$ is true. Now, $x^{2(k+1)-1} + y^{2(k+1)-1} = x^{2k+1} + y^{2k+1}$
$$= x^{2k+1} - x^{2k-1}y^2 + x^{2k-1}y^2 + y^{2k+1} = x^{2k-1}(x^2 - y^2) + (x^{2k-1} + y^{2k-1})y^2, \text{ for which}$$
$x + y$ is a factor. This is because $x + y$ is a factor of $x^2 - y^2 = (x+y)(x-y)$ and $(x+y)$ is a factor of $x^{2k-1} + y^{2k-1}$ by our induction hypothesis. Thus $P(k+1)$ follows from $P(k)$. So by the Principle of Mathematical Induction, $P(n)$ is true for all n.

28. Let $P(n)$ denote the statement that $F_1 + F_2 + F_3 + \cdots + F_n = F_{n+2} - 1$.

Step 1 $P(1)$ is the statement that $F_1 = F_3 - 1$. But $F_1 = 1 = 2 - 1 = F_3 - 1$, which is true.

Step 2 Assume that $P(k)$ is true; that is, $F_1 + F_2 + F_3 + \cdots + F_k = F_{k+2} - 1$. We want to use this to show that $P(k+1)$ is true. Now, $F_{(k+1)+2} - 1 = F_{k+3} - 1 = F_{k+2} + F_{k+1} - 1$
$$= (F_{k+2} - 1) + F_{k+1} = F_1 + F_2 + F_3 + \cdots + F_k + F_{k+1} \text{ by the induction hypothesis. Thus}$$
$P(k+1)$ follows from $P(k)$. So by the Principle of Mathematical Induction, $P(n)$ is true for all n.

30. Let $a_1 = a_2 = 2$ and $a_{n+2} = a_{n+1} \cdot a_n$, for $n \geq 1$. Let $P(n)$ denote the statement that $a_m = 2^{F_m}$, for $m = 1, \ldots, n$. (Notice that this is a slightly different statement, $P(n)$ is a statement that involves all the previous cases, not only n.)

Step 1 $P(1)$ is the statement that $a_1 = 2^{F_1}$, which is true since $a_1 = 2$ and $2^{F_1} = 2^1 = 2$.

Step 2 Assume that $P(k)$ is true; that is, $a_m = 2^{F_m}$, for $m = 1, \ldots, k$. We want to use this to show that $P(k+1)$ is true; that is, $a_{m+1} = 2^{F_{m+1}}$, for $m = 1, \ldots, k+1$. Now,
$$a_{k+1} =$$
$$a_k \cdot a_{k-1} = \qquad\qquad \text{by the definition of } a_{k+1}$$
$$2^{F_k} \cdot 2^{F_{k-1}} = \qquad\qquad \text{induction hypothesis}$$
$$2^{F_k + F_{k-1}} = 2^{F_{k+1}}. \qquad\qquad \text{definition of } F_{k+1}$$

Therefore, $a_m = 2^{F_m}$, for $m = 1, 2, \ldots, k, k+1$, which is exactly $P(k+1)$. So by the Principle of Mathematical Induction, $P(n)$ is true for all n.

32. Let $a_1 = 1$ and $a_{n+1} = \dfrac{1}{1 + a_n}$, for $n \geq 1$. Let $P(n)$ be the statement that $a_n = \dfrac{F_n}{F_{n+1}}$, for all $n \geq 1$.

Step 1 $P(1)$ is the statement that $a_1 = \dfrac{F_1}{F_2}$, which is true since $a_1 = 1$ and $\dfrac{F_1}{F_2} = \dfrac{1}{1} = 1$.

Step 2 Assume that $P(k)$ is true; that is, $a_k = \dfrac{F_k}{F_{k+1}}$. We want to use this to show that $P(k+1)$ is true. Now,

$$a_{k+1} =$$
$$\dfrac{1}{1 + a_k} = \qquad\qquad \text{by the definition of } a_{k+1}$$
$$\dfrac{1}{1 + \frac{F_k}{F_{k+1}}} = \qquad\qquad \text{induction hypothesis}$$
$$\dfrac{F_{k+1}}{F_k + F_{k+1}} = \dfrac{F_{k+1}}{F_{k+2}}. \qquad\qquad \text{definition of } F_{k+2}$$

Thus $P(k+1)$ follows from $P(k)$. So by the Principle of Mathematical Induction, $P(n)$ is true for all $n \geq 100$.

34. Since $100 \cdot 10 = 10^3$, $100 \cdot 11 < 11^3$, $100 \cdot 12 < 12^3, \ldots$ our conjecture is that $100n \leq n^3$, for all natural numbers $n \geq 10$. Let $P(n)$ denote the statement that $100n \leq n^3$, for $n \geq 10$.

Step 1 $P(10)$ is the statement that $100 \cdot 10 = 1{,}000 \leq 10^3 = 1{,}000$, which is true.

Step 2 Assume that $P(k)$ is true; that is, $100k \leq k^3$. We want to use this to show that $P(k+1)$ is true. Now,

$$100(k+1) =$$
$$100k + 100 \leq k^2 + 100 \qquad\qquad \text{induction hypothesis}$$
$$\leq k^3 + k^2 \qquad\qquad \text{because } k \geq 10$$
$$\leq k^3 + 3k^2 + 3k + 1 = (k+1)^3.$$

Thus $P(k+1)$ follows from $P(k)$. So by the Principle of Mathematical Induction, $P(n)$ is true for all $n \geq 10$.

36. The induction step fails when $k = 2$, that is, $P(2)$ does not follow from $P(1)$. If there are only two cats, Midnight and Sparky, and we remove Sparky, then only Midnight remains. So at this point, we still only know that Midnight is black. Now removing Midnight and putting Sparky back leaves Sparky alone. So the induction hypothesis does not allow us to conclude that Sparky is black.

Exercises 12.6

2. $(2x+1)^4 = (2x)^4 + 4(2x)^3 + 6(2x)^2 + 4 \cdot 2x + 1 = 16x^4 + 32x^3 + 24x^2 + 8x + 1$

4. $(x-y)^5 = x^5 - 5x^4y + 10x^3y^2 - 10x^2y^3 + 5xy^4 - y^5$

6. $\left(\sqrt{a} + \sqrt{b}\right)^6 = a^3 + 6a^2\sqrt{a}\sqrt{b} + 15a^2b + 20a\sqrt{ab}\sqrt{b} + 15ab^2 + 6\sqrt{a}b^2\sqrt{b} + b^3$
    $= a^3 + 6a^2\sqrt{ab} + 15a^2b + 20ab\sqrt{ab} + 15ab^2 + 6b^2\sqrt{ab} + b^3$

8. $\left(1 + \sqrt{2}\right)^6 = 1^6 + 6 \cdot 1^5 \cdot \sqrt{2} + 15 \cdot 1^4 \cdot 2 + 20 \cdot 1^3 \cdot 2\sqrt{2} + 15 \cdot 1^2 \cdot 4 + 6 \cdot 1 \cdot 4\sqrt{2} + 2^3$
    $= 1 + 6\sqrt{2} + 30 + 40\sqrt{2} + 60 + 24\sqrt{2} + 8 = 99 + 70\sqrt{2}$

10. $(1 + x^3)^3 = 1^3 + 3 \cdot 1^2 \cdot x^3 + 3 \cdot 1(x^3)^2 + (x^3)^3 = 1 + 3x^3 + 3x^6 + x^9$

12. $\left(2 + \dfrac{x}{2}\right)^5 = (2)^5 + 5(2)^4\dfrac{x}{2} + 10(2)^3\left(\dfrac{x}{2}\right)^2 + 10(2)^2\left(\dfrac{x}{2}\right)^3 + 5(2)\left(\dfrac{x}{2}\right)^4 + \left(\dfrac{x}{2}\right)^5$
    $= 32 + 40x + 20x^2 + 5x^3 + \dfrac{5}{8}x^4 + \dfrac{x^5}{32}$

14. $\dbinom{8}{3} = \dfrac{8!}{3!\,5!} = \dfrac{8 \cdot 7 \cdot 6 \cdot 5!}{3 \cdot 2 \cdot 1 \cdot 5!} = 8 \cdot 7 = 56$

16. $\dbinom{10}{5} = \dfrac{10!}{5!\,5!} = \dfrac{10 \cdot 9 \cdot 8 \cdot 7 \cdot 6 \cdot 5!}{5 \cdot 4 \cdot 3 \cdot 2 \cdot 1 \cdot 5!} = 3 \cdot 2 \cdot 7 \cdot 6 = 252$

18. $\dbinom{5}{2}\dbinom{5}{3} = \dfrac{5!}{2!\,3!} \cdot \dfrac{5!}{3!\,2!} = \dfrac{5 \cdot 4 \cdot 3!}{2 \cdot 1 \cdot 3!} \cdot \dfrac{5 \cdot 4 \cdot 3!}{3! \cdot 2 \cdot 1} = 10 \cdot 10 = 100$

20. $\dbinom{5}{0} - \dbinom{5}{1} + \dbinom{5}{2} - \dbinom{5}{3} + \dbinom{5}{4} - \dbinom{5}{5} = 1 - \dfrac{5!}{1!\,4!} + \dfrac{5!}{2!\,3!} - \dfrac{5!}{3!\,2!} + \dfrac{5!}{4!\,1!} - 1 = 0.$
Notice that the 1st and 6th terms cancel, as do the 2nd and 5th terms and the 3rd and 4th terms.

22. $(1-x)^5 = \dbinom{5}{0}(1)^5 - \dbinom{5}{1}(1)^4x + \dbinom{5}{2}(1)^3x^2 - \dbinom{5}{3}(1)^2x^3 + \dbinom{5}{4}(1)x^4 - \dbinom{5}{5}x^5$
    $= 1 - 5x + 10x^2 - 10x^3 + 5x^4 - x^5$

24. $(2A + B^2)^4 = \dbinom{4}{0}(2A)^4 + \dbinom{4}{1}(2A)^3(B^2) + \dbinom{4}{2}(2A)^2(B^2)^2 + \dbinom{4}{3}(2A)(B^2)^3$
    $+ \binom{4}{4}(B^2)^4 = 16A^4 + 32A^3B^2 + 24A^2B^4 + 8AB^6 + B^8$

26. The first four terms in the expansion of $\left(x^{1/2} + 1\right)^{30}$ are $\dbinom{30}{0}\left(x^{1/2}\right)^{30} = x^{15}$,
    $\dbinom{30}{1}\left(x^{1/2}\right)^{29}(1) = 30x^{29/2}$, $\dbinom{30}{2}\left(x^{1/2}\right)^{28}(1)^2 = 435x^{14}$, and $\dbinom{30}{3}\left(x^{1/2}\right)^{27}(1)^3 = 4060x^{27/2}$.

28. The first three terms in the expansion of $\left(x + \dfrac{1}{x}\right)^{40}$ are $\dbinom{40}{0}x^{40} = x^{40}$, $\dbinom{40}{1}x^{39}\left(\dfrac{1}{x}\right) = 40x^{38}$,
    and $\binom{40}{2}x^{38}\left(\frac{1}{x}\right)^2 = 780x^{36}$.

30. The fifth term in the expansion of $(ab - 1)^{20}$ is $\dbinom{20}{4}(ab)^{16}(-1)^4 = 4845a^{16}b^{16}$.

32. The 28th term in the expansion of $(A - B)^{30}$ is $\dbinom{30}{27}A^3(-B)^{27} = -4060A^3B^{27}$.

34. The 2nd term in the expansion of $\left(x^2 - \dfrac{1}{x}\right)^{25}$ is $\dbinom{25}{1}(x^2)^{24}\left(-\dfrac{1}{x}\right) = -25x^{47}$.

36. The rth term in the expansion of $\left(\sqrt{2} + y\right)^{12}$ is $\dbinom{12}{r}\left(\sqrt{2}\right)^r y^{12-r}$. The term that contains y^3

    occurs when $12 - r = 3 \iff r = 9$. Therefore, the term is $\binom{12}{9}\left(\sqrt{2}\right)^9 y^3 = 3520\sqrt{2}\,y^3$.

38. The rth term is $\dbinom{8}{r}(8x)^r\left(\dfrac{1}{2x}\right)^{8-r} = \dbinom{8}{r}\dfrac{8^r}{2^{8-r}}\cdot\dfrac{x^r}{x^{8-r}} = \dbinom{8}{r}\dfrac{8^r}{2^{8-r}}\cdot x^{2r-8}$. So the term that
    does not contain x occurs when $2r - 8 = 0 \iff r = 4$. Thus, the term is
    $\dbinom{8}{4}(8x)^4\left(\dfrac{1}{2x}\right)^4 = 17{,}920$.

40. $(x-1)^5 + 5(x-1)^4 + 10(x-1)^3 + 10(x-1)^2 + 5(x-1) + 1 = [(x-1) + 1]^5 = x^5$.

42. $x^8 + 4x^6y + 6x^4y^2 + 4x^2y^3 + y^4 = \dbinom{4}{0}(x^2)^4 + \dbinom{4}{1}(x^2)^3y + \dbinom{4}{2}(x^2)^2y^2 + \dbinom{4}{3}x^2y^3$

    $+ \dbinom{4}{4}y^4 = (x^2 + y)^4$.

44. $\dfrac{(x+h)^4 - x^4}{h} = \dfrac{\dbinom{4}{0}x^4 + \dbinom{4}{1}x^3h + \dbinom{4}{2}x^2h^2 + \dbinom{4}{3}xh^3 + \dbinom{4}{4}h^4 - x^4}{h}$

    $= \dfrac{x^4 + 4x^3h + 6x^2h^2 + 4xh^3 + h^4 - x^4}{h} = \dfrac{4x^3h + 6x^2h^2 + 4xh^3 + h^4}{h}$

    $= \dfrac{h(4x^3 + 6x^2h + 4xh^2 + h^3)}{h} = 4x^3 + 6x^2h + 4xh^2 + h^3$.

46. $\dbinom{n}{0} = \dfrac{n!}{0!\,n!} = \dfrac{n!}{1\cdot n!} = 1$. $\dbinom{n}{n} = \dfrac{n!}{n!\,0!} = \dfrac{n!}{n!\cdot 1} = 1$. Therefore, $\dbinom{n}{0} = \dbinom{n}{n}$.

48. $\dbinom{n}{r} = \dfrac{n!}{r!\,(n-r)!} = \dfrac{n!}{(n-r)!\,r!} = \dbinom{n}{n-r}$, for $0 \le r \le n$.

50. Let $P(n)$ be the proposition that $\dbinom{n}{r}$ is an integer for the number n, $0 \le r \le n$.

    Step 1 Suppose $n = 0$. If $0 \le r \le n$, then $r = 0$, and so $\dbinom{n}{r} = \dbinom{0}{0} = 1$, which is obviously an

         integer. Therefore, $P(0)$ is true.

    Step 2 Suppose that $P(k)$ is true. We want to use this to show that $P(k+1)$ must also be true; that

         is, $\dbinom{k+1}{r}$ is an integer for $0 \le r \le k+1$. But we know that

         $\dbinom{k+1}{r} = \dbinom{k}{r-1} + \dbinom{k}{r}$ by the key property of binomial coefficients (see Exercise

49). Furthermore, $\binom{k}{r-1}$ and $\binom{k}{r}$ are both integers by the induction hypothesis. Since the sum of two integers is always an integer, $\binom{k+1}{r}$ must be an integer. Thus, $P(k+1)$ is true if $P(k)$ is true. So by the Principal of Mathematical induction, $\binom{n}{r}$ is an integer for all $n \geq 0, \ 0 \leq r \leq n$.

52.
$$1 + 1 = 2$$
$$1 + 2 + 1 = 4$$
$$1 + 3 + 3 + 1 = 8$$
$$1 + 4 + 6 + 4 + 1 = 16$$
$$1 + 5 + 10 + 10 + 5 + 1 = 32.$$

Conjecture: The sum is 2^n.

Proof:

$$2^n = (1+1)^n = \binom{n}{0}1^0 \cdot 1^n + \binom{n}{1}1^1 \cdot 1^{n-1} + \binom{n}{2}1^2 \cdot 1^{n-2} + \cdots + \binom{n}{n}1^n \cdot 1^0$$
$$= \binom{n}{0} + \binom{n}{1} + \binom{n}{2} + \cdots + \binom{n}{n}.$$

Review Exercises for Chapter 12

2. $a_n = (-1)^n \dfrac{2^n}{n}$. Then $a_1 = (-1)^1 \dfrac{2^1}{1} = -2$; $a_2 = (-1)^2 \dfrac{2^2}{2} = 2$; $a_3 = (-1)^3 \dfrac{2^3}{3} = -\dfrac{8}{3}$;

     $a_4 = (-1)^4 \dfrac{2^4}{4} = 4$, and $a_{10} = (-1)^{10} \dfrac{2^{10}}{10} = \dfrac{1024}{10} = \dfrac{512}{5}$.

4. $a_n = \dfrac{n(n+1)}{2}$. Then $a_1 = \dfrac{1(1+1)}{2} = 1$; $a_2 = \dfrac{2(2+1)}{2} = 3$; $a_3 = \dfrac{3(3+1)}{2} = 6$;

     $a_4 = \dfrac{4(4+1)}{2} = 10$; and $a_{10} = \dfrac{10(10+1)}{2} = 55$.

6. $a_n = \dbinom{n+1}{2}$. Then $a_1 = \dbinom{1+1}{2} = 1$; $a_2 = \dbinom{2+1}{2} = \dfrac{3!}{2!\,1!} = 3$; $a_3 = \dbinom{3+1}{2}$

     $= \dfrac{4!}{2!\,2!} = 6$; $a_4 = \dbinom{4+1}{2} = \dfrac{5!}{2!\,3!} = 10$; and $a_{10} = \dbinom{10+1}{2} = \dfrac{11!}{2!\,9!} = 55$.

8. $a_n = \dfrac{a_{n-1}}{n}$ and $a_1 = 1$. Then $a_2 = \dfrac{a_1}{2} = \dfrac{1}{2}$; $a_3 = \dfrac{a_2}{3} = \dfrac{1}{6}$; $a_4 = \dfrac{a_3}{4} = \dfrac{1}{24}$; $a_5 = \dfrac{a_4}{5} = \dfrac{1}{120}$;

     $a_6 = \dfrac{a_5}{6} = \dfrac{1}{720}$; and $a_7 = \dfrac{a_6}{7} = \dfrac{1}{5040}$.

10. $a_n = \sqrt{3a_{n-1}}$ and $a_1 = \sqrt{3} = 3^{1/2}$. Then $a_2 = \sqrt{3a_1} = \sqrt{3\sqrt{3}} = (3 \cdot 3^{1/2})^{1/2} = 3^{3/4}$;

     $a_3 = \sqrt{3a_2} = \sqrt{3 \cdot 3^{3/4}} = 3^{1/2} \cdot 3^{3/8} = 3^{7/8}$; $a_4 = \sqrt{3a_3} = \sqrt{3 \cdot 3^{7/8}} = 3^{1/2} \cdot 3^{7/16} = 3^{15/16}$;

     $a_5 = \sqrt{3a_4} = \sqrt{3 \cdot 3^{15/16}} = 3^{1/2} \cdot 3^{15/32} = 3^{31/32}$;

     $a_6 = \sqrt{3a_5} = \sqrt{3 \cdot 3^{31/32}} = 3^{1/2} \cdot 3^{31/64} = 3^{63/64}$;

     $a_7 = \sqrt{3a_6} = \sqrt{3 \cdot 3^{63/64}} = 3^{1/2} \cdot 3^{63/128} = 3^{127/128}$.

12. $1, -\dfrac{3}{2}, 2, -\dfrac{5}{2}, \dots$. Since $-\dfrac{3}{2} - 1 \neq 2 + \dfrac{3}{2}$, and $\dfrac{-\frac{3}{2}}{1} \neq \dfrac{2}{-\frac{3}{2}}$, the series is neither arithmetic nor geometric.

14. $\sqrt{2}, 2, 2\sqrt{2}, 4, \dots$. Since $\dfrac{2}{\sqrt{2}} = \dfrac{2\sqrt{2}}{2} = \dfrac{4}{2\sqrt{2}} = \sqrt{2}$, this is a geometric sequence with $a_1 = \sqrt{2}$ and $r = \sqrt{2}$. Then $a_5 = a_4 \cdot r = 4 \cdot \sqrt{2} = 4\sqrt{2}$.

16. $t^3, t^2, t, 1, \dots$. Since $\dfrac{t^2}{t^3} = \dfrac{t}{t^2} = \dfrac{1}{t}$, this is a geometric sequence with $a_1 = t^3$ and $r = \dfrac{1}{t}$. Then $a_5 = a_4 \cdot r = 1 \cdot \frac{1}{t} = \frac{1}{t}$.

18. $a, 1, \dfrac{1}{a}, \dfrac{1}{a^2}, \dots$. Since $\dfrac{1}{a} = \dfrac{\frac{1}{a}}{1}$ and $\dfrac{\frac{1}{a^2}}{\frac{1}{a}} = \dfrac{1}{a}$, this is a geometric sequence with $a_1 = a$ and $r = \dfrac{1}{a}$.

     Then $a_5 = a_4 \cdot r = \dfrac{1}{a^2} \cdot \dfrac{1}{a} = \dfrac{1}{a^3}$.

20.   The sequence $2, 2+2i, 4i, -4+4i, -8, \dots$ is geometric (where $i^2 = -1$), since

     $\dfrac{a_2}{a_1} = \dfrac{2+2i}{2} = 1+i$; $\dfrac{a_3}{a_2} = \dfrac{4i}{2+2i} = \dfrac{4i}{2+2i} \cdot \dfrac{2-2i}{2-2i} = \dfrac{8+8i}{8} = 1+i$;

$$\frac{a_4}{a_3} = \frac{-4+4i}{4i} = -\frac{1}{i} + 1 = -\frac{1}{i} \cdot \frac{i}{i} + 1 = \frac{-i}{i^2} + 1 = 1 + i;$$

$$\frac{a_5}{a_4} = \frac{-8}{-4+4i} = \frac{-8}{-4+4i} \cdot \frac{-4-4i}{-4-4i} = \frac{32+32i}{32} = 1 + i. \text{ Thus the common ratio is } i+1, \text{ and}$$

the first term is 2. So the nth term is $a_n = a_1 r^{n-1} = 2(1+i)^{n-1}$.

22. $a_{20} = 96$ and $d = 5$. Then $96 = a_{20} = a + 19 \cdot 5 = a + 95 \quad \Leftrightarrow \quad a = 96 - 95 = 1$. Therefore, $a_n = 1 + 5(n-1)$.

24. $a_2 = 10$ and $a_5 = \dfrac{1250}{27}$. Then $r^3 = \dfrac{a_5}{a_2} = \dfrac{\frac{1250}{27}}{10} = \dfrac{125}{27} \quad \Leftrightarrow \quad r = \dfrac{5}{3}$ and $a = a_1 = \dfrac{a_2}{r}$

$= \dfrac{10}{\frac{5}{3}} = 6$. Therefore, $a_n = ar^{n-1} = 6\left(\dfrac{5}{3}\right)^{n-1}$.

26. Let a_n denote the number of ancestors a person has n generations back. Then $a_1 = 2$, $a_2 = 4$, $a_3 = 8, \dots$. Since $\dfrac{4}{2} = \dfrac{8}{4} = 2$, etc...., this is a geometric sequence with $r = 2$. Therefore, $a_{15} = 2 \cdot 2^{14} = 2^{15} = 32{,}768$.

28. Let d be the common difference in the arithmetic sequence $a_1, a_2, a_3, \dots$, so that $a_n = a_1 + (n-1)d$, $n = 1, 2, 3, \dots$, and let e be the common difference for $b_1, b_2, b_3, \dots$, so that $b_n = b_1 + (n-1)e$. Then $a_n + b_n = [a_1 + (n-1)a] + [b_1 + (n-1)e]$ $= (a_1 + b_1) + (n-1)(d+e)$, $n = 1, 2, 3, \dots$. Thus $a_1 + b_1$, $a_2 + b_2$, $\dots$ is an arithmetic sequence with first term $a_1 + b_1$ and common difference $d + e$.

30. (a) Yes. If the common difference is d, then $a_n = a_1 + (n-1)d$. So $a_n + 2 = a_1 + 2 + (n-1)d$, and thus the sequence $a_1 + 2$, $a_2 + 2$, $a_3 + 2$, $\dots$ is an arithmetic sequence with the same common difference, but with the first term $a_1 + 2$.

     (b) Yes. If the common ratio is r, then $a_n = a_1 \cdot r^{n-1}$. So $5a_n = (5a_1) \cdot r^{n-1}$, and the sequence $5a_1$, $5a_2$, $5a_3$, $\dots$ is also geometric, with common ratio r, but with the first term $5a_1$.

32. (a) $2, x, y, 17, \dots$ is arithmetic. Therefore, $15 = 17 - 2 = a_4 - a_1 = a + 3d - a = 3d$. So $d = 5$, and hence, $x = a + d = 2 + 5 = 7$ and $y = a + 2d = 2 + 2 \cdot 5 = 12$.

     (b) $2, x, y, 17, \dots$ is geometric. Therefore, $\dfrac{17}{2} = \dfrac{a_4}{a_1} = \dfrac{ar^3}{a} = r^3 \quad \Leftrightarrow \quad r = \sqrt[3]{\dfrac{17}{2}}$. So $x = a_2 = ar = 2\sqrt[3]{\dfrac{17}{2}} = 2\left(\dfrac{17}{2}\right)^{1/3}$ and $y = a_3 = ar^2 = 2\left(\dfrac{17}{2}\right)^{2/3}$.

34. $\displaystyle\sum_{i=1}^{4} \frac{2i}{2i-1} = \frac{2 \cdot 1}{2 \cdot 1 - 1} + \frac{2 \cdot 2}{2 \cdot 2 - 1} + \frac{2 \cdot 3}{2 \cdot 3 - 1} + \frac{2 \cdot 4}{2 \cdot 4 - 1} = 2 + \frac{4}{3} + \frac{6}{5} + \frac{8}{7}$

$= \dfrac{210 + 140 + 126 + 120}{105} = \dfrac{596}{105}$

36. $\displaystyle\sum_{m=1}^{5} 3^{m-2} = 3^{-1} + 3^0 + 3^1 + 3^2 + 3^3 = \frac{1}{3} + 1 + 3 + 9 + 27 = \frac{121}{3}$

38. $\displaystyle\sum_{j=2}^{100} \frac{1}{j-1} = \frac{1}{1} + \frac{1}{2} + \frac{1}{3} + \frac{1}{4} + \frac{1}{5} + \cdots + \frac{1}{98} + \frac{1}{99}$

40. $\displaystyle\sum_{n=1}^{10} n^2 2^n = 1^2 \cdot 2^1 + 2^2 \cdot 2^2 + 3^2 \cdot 2^3 + \cdots + 9^2 \cdot 2^9 + 10^2 \cdot 2^{10}$

42. $1^2 + 2^2 + 3^3 + \cdots + 100^2 = \displaystyle\sum_{k=1}^{100} k^2$

44. $\dfrac{1}{1 \cdot 2} + \dfrac{1}{2 \cdot 3} + \dfrac{1}{3 \cdot 4} + \cdots + \dfrac{1}{999 \cdot 1000} = \displaystyle\sum_{k=1}^{999} \dfrac{1}{k(k+1)}$

46. $3 + 3.7 + 4.4 + \cdots + 10$ is an arithmetic series with $a = 3$ and $d = 0.7$. Then
$10 = a_n = 3 + 0.7(n-1) \quad \Leftrightarrow \quad 0.7(n-1) = 7 \quad \Leftrightarrow \quad n = 11$. So the sum of the series is
$S_{11} = \dfrac{11}{2}(3 + 10) = \dfrac{143}{2} = 71.5$

48. $\frac{1}{3} + \frac{2}{3} + 1 + \frac{4}{3} + \cdots + 33$ is an arithmetic series with $a = \frac{1}{3}$ and $d = \frac{1}{3}$. Then
$a_n = 33 = \frac{1}{3} + \frac{1}{3}(n-1) \quad \Leftrightarrow \quad n = 99$. So the sum is $S_{99} = \frac{99}{2}\left(\frac{2}{3} + \frac{99-1}{3}\right) = \frac{99}{2} \cdot \frac{100}{3} = 1650$.

50. $\displaystyle\sum_{k=0}^{8} 7 \cdot 5^{k/2}$ is a geometric series with $a = 7$, $r = 5^{1/2}$, and $n = 9$. Thus, the sum of the series is
$S_9 = 7 \cdot \dfrac{1 - 5^{9/2}}{1 - 5} = \dfrac{7}{4}(5^{9/2} - 1) = \dfrac{7}{4}(625\sqrt{5} - 1)$.

52. We have a geometric series with $S_3 = 52$ and $r = 3$. Then $52 = S_3 = a + 3a + 9a = 13a \quad \Leftrightarrow$
$a = 4$, and so the first term is 4.

54. $R = 1000$, $i = 0.08$, and $n = 16$. Thus, $A = 1000\dfrac{1.08^{16} - 1}{1.08 - 1} = 12{,}500[1.08^{16} - 1] = \$30{,}324.28$.

56. $A = 60{,}000$ and $i = \dfrac{0.09}{12} = 0.0075$.

(a) If the period is 30 years, $n = 360$ and $R = \dfrac{60{,}000 \cdot 0.0075}{1 - 1.0075^{-360}} = \$482.77$.

(b) If the period is 15 years, $n = 180$ and $R = \dfrac{60{,}000 \cdot 0.0075}{1 - 1.0075^{-180}} = \$608.56$.

58. $0.1 + 0.01 + 0.001 + 0.0001 + \cdots$ is an infinite geometric series with $a = 0.1$ and $r = 0.1$.
Therefore, the sum is $S = \frac{0.1}{1 - 0.1} = \frac{1}{9}$.

60. $a + ab^2 + ab^4 + ab^6 + \cdots$ is an infinite geometric series with first term a and common ratio b^2.
Thus, the sum is $S = \dfrac{a}{1 - b^2}$.

62. Let $P(n)$ denote the statement that $\dfrac{1}{1 \cdot 3} + \dfrac{1}{3 \cdot 5} + \dfrac{1}{5 \cdot 7} + \cdots + \dfrac{1}{(2n-1)(2n+1)} = \dfrac{n}{2n+1}$.

<u>Step 1</u> $P(1)$ is the statement that $\dfrac{1}{1 \cdot 3} = \dfrac{1}{2 \cdot 1 + 1}$, which is true.

<u>Step 2</u> Assume that $P(k)$ is true; that is, $\dfrac{1}{1 \cdot 3} + \dfrac{1}{3 \cdot 5} + \dfrac{1}{5 \cdot 7} + \cdots + \dfrac{1}{(2k-1)(2k+1)} = \dfrac{k}{2k+1}$.
We want to use this to show that $P(k+1)$ is true. Now,

$$\frac{1}{1\cdot 3}+\frac{1}{3\cdot 5}+\frac{1}{5\cdot 7}+\cdots +\frac{1}{(2k-1)(2k+1)}+\frac{1}{(2k+1)(2k+3)}=$$

$$\frac{k}{2k+1}+\frac{1}{(2k+1)(2k+3)}=\quad\text{induction hypothesis}$$

$$\frac{k(2k+3)+1}{(2k+1)(2k+3)}=\frac{2k^2+3k+1}{(2k+1)(2k+3)}=$$

$$\frac{(k+1)(2k+1)}{(2k+1)(2k+3)}=\frac{k+1}{2k+3}=\frac{k+1}{2(k+1)+1}.$$

Thus $P(k+1)$ follows from $P(k)$. So by the Principle of Mathematical Induction, $P(n)$ is true for all n.

64. Let $P(n)$ denote the statement that 7^n-1 is divisible by 6.

Step 1 $P(1)$ is the statement that $7^1-1=6$ is divisible by 6, which is clearly true.

Step 2 Assume that $P(k)$ is true; that is, 7^k-1 is divisible by 6. We want to use this to show that $P(k+1)$ is true. Now $7^{k+1}-1=7\cdot 7^k-1=7\cdot 7^k-7+6=7(7^k-1)+6$, which is divisible by 6. This is because 7^k-1 is divisible by 6 by the induction hypothesis, and clearly 6 is divisible by 6. Thus $P(k+1)$ follows from $P(k)$. So by the Principle of Mathematical Induction, $P(n)$ is true for all n.

66. Let $P(n)$ denote the statement that F_{4n} is divisible by 3.

Step 1 Show that $P(1)$ is true, but $P(1)$ is true since $F_4=3$ is divisible by 3.

Step 2 Assume that $P(k)$ is true; that is, F_{4k} is divisible by 3. We want to use this to show that $P(k+1)$ is true. Now, $F_{4(k+1)}=F_{4k+4}=F_{4k+2}+F_{4k+3}$
$=(F_{4k}+F_{4k+1})+(F_{4k+1}+F_{4k+2})=F_{4k}+F_{4k+1}+F_{4k+1}+(F_{4k}+F_{4k+1})$
$=2\cdot F_{4k}+3\cdot F_{4k+1}$, which is divisible by 3 because F_{4k} is divisible by 3 by our induction hypothesis, and $3\cdot F_{4k+1}$ is clearly divisible by 3. Thus, $P(k+1)$ follows from $P(k)$. So by the Principle of Mathematical Induction, $P(n)$ is true for all n.

68. $\dbinom{5}{2}\dbinom{5}{3}=\dfrac{5!}{2!3!}\cdot \dfrac{5!}{3!2!}=\dfrac{5\cdot 4}{2}\cdot \dfrac{5\cdot 4}{2}=10\cdot 10=100$

70. $\displaystyle\sum_{k=0}^{5}\dbinom{5}{k}=\dbinom{5}{0}+\dbinom{5}{1}+\dbinom{5}{2}+\dbinom{5}{3}+\dbinom{5}{4}+\dbinom{5}{5}=2\left(\dfrac{5!}{0!\,5!}+\dfrac{5!}{1!\,4!}+\dfrac{5!}{2!\,3!}\right)$
$=2(1+5+10)=32$

72. $(1-x^2)^6=\dbinom{6}{0}1^6-\dbinom{6}{1}1^5x^2+\dbinom{6}{2}1^4x^4-\dbinom{6}{3}1^3x^6+\dbinom{6}{4}1^2x^8-\dbinom{6}{5}x^{10}+\dbinom{6}{6}x^{12}$
$=1-6x^2+15x^4-20x^6+15x^8-6x^{10}+x^{12}$

74. The 20th term is $\dbinom{22}{19}a^3b^{19}=1540a^3b^{19}$.

76. The rth term in the expansion of $(A+3B)^{10}$ is $\dbinom{10}{r}A^r(3B)^{10-r}$. The term that contains A^6 occurs when $r=6$. Thus, the term is $\dbinom{10}{6}A^6(3B)^4=210A^681B^4=17{,}010A^6B^4$.

Focus on Problem Solving

2. Each small square in the rectangle is F_k by F_k, and the rectangle is F_n by $(F_n + F_{n-1})$, which is just F_n by F_{n+1}. Thus the sum of the areas of the smaller squares must equal the area of the rectangle, so $F_1^2 + F_2^2 + \cdots + F_n^2 = F_n \cdot F_{n+1}$.

4. (a) Let $P_n = \left(1 - \frac{1}{2}\right)\left(1 - \frac{1}{3}\right) \cdots \left(1 - \frac{1}{n}\right)$. Then $P_2 = \frac{1}{2}$, $P_3 = \frac{1}{2} \cdot \frac{2}{3} = \frac{1}{3}$, $P_4 = \frac{1}{2} \cdot \frac{2}{3} \cdot \frac{3}{4} = \frac{1}{4}$. We could prove by mathematical induction that $P_n = \frac{1}{n}$. Or, simply by cancellation, we can see that $P_{200} = \frac{1}{2} \cdot \frac{2}{3} \cdot \frac{3}{4} \cdot \ldots \cdot \frac{198}{199} \cdot \frac{199}{200} = \frac{1}{200}$.

   (b) Let $S_n = \left(1 - \frac{1}{4}\right)\left(1 - \frac{1}{9}\right)\left(1 - \frac{1}{16}\right) \cdots \left(1 - \frac{1}{n^2}\right)$. Then $S_2 = \frac{3}{4}$; $S_3 = \frac{3}{4} \cdot \frac{8}{9} = \frac{4}{6}$;
   $S_4 = \frac{3}{4} \cdot \frac{8}{9} \cdot \frac{15}{16} = \frac{5}{8}$; $S_5 = \frac{3}{4} \cdot \frac{8}{9} \cdot \frac{15}{16} \cdot \frac{24}{25} = \frac{6}{10}$; and $S_6 = \frac{3}{4} \cdot \frac{8}{9} \cdot \frac{15}{16} \cdot \frac{24}{25} \cdot \frac{35}{36} = \frac{7}{12}$. The numerators are increasing by 1 while the denominator are increasing by 2, so our guess is that $S_n = \dfrac{n+1}{2n}$. We now prove by Mathematical Induction.

   Let $P(n)$ be the statement that $S_n = \left(1 - \frac{1}{4}\right)\left(1 - \frac{1}{9}\right)\left(1 - \frac{1}{16}\right) \cdots \left(1 - \frac{1}{n^2}\right) = \dfrac{n+1}{2n}$

   <u>Step 1</u> $P(2)$ is the statement that $1 - \dfrac{1}{2^2} = \dfrac{2+1}{2 \cdot 2}$ which is true.

   <u>Step 2</u> Suppose $P(k)$ is true. Then

   $$S_{k+1} =$$
   $$S_k \cdot \left(1 - \frac{1}{(k+1)^2}\right) =$$
   $$\frac{k+1}{2k}\left(1 - \frac{1}{(k+1)^2}\right) = \qquad \text{inductive hypothesis}$$
   $$\frac{k+1}{2k} \cdot \frac{k^2 + 2k}{(k+1)^2} = \frac{k+2}{2(k+1)} = \frac{(k+1)+1}{2(k+1)}$$

   Thus $P(k+1)$ follows from $P(k)$. So by the Principle of Mathematical Induction, $P(n)$ is true for all n.

6. (a) 16

   (b) 2^{n-1} (one would think)

   (c) No, we get 31 instead of 32.

$n = 5$ $\qquad\qquad$ $n = 6$

(d)   We construct the difference table as in Problem 6.

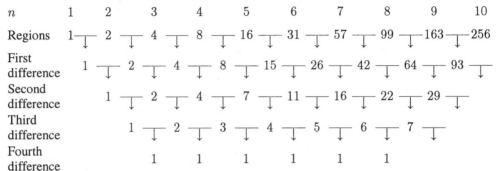

n	1	2	3	4	5	6	7	8	9	10
Regions	1	2	4	8	16	31	57	99	163	256
First difference	1	2	4	8	15	26	42	64	93	
Second difference	1	2	4	7	11	16	22	29		
Third difference	1	2	3	4	5	6	7			
Fourth difference	1	1	1	1	1	1				

From the difference table, we see that for $n = 7, 8, 9$, and 10 points, we get 57, 99, 163, and 256 regions, respectively.

8.   Let N be the number of people who have shaken hands an odd number of times. Let $P(n)$ be the statement: If n handshakes have taken place, then N is even.

Step 1 Then $P(1)$ is true ($N = 2$).

Step 2 Suppose that $P(k)$ is true; that is, N is even after k handshakes. Consider handshake number $k + 1$ between two people, A and B. We consider three cases:

Case 1: If A and B have both shaken hands with an odd number of people, then N is decreased by 2 after handshake $k + 1$. So N is still even.

Case 2: If A and B have both shaken hands with an even number of people, then N is increased by 2. So N is still even.

Case 3: If A has shaken hands with an odd number of people and B with an even number, or vice versa, then N remains the same. So N is still even.

In all cases N remains even, so $P(k + 1)$ follows from $P(k)$. Thus by the Principle of Mathematical Induction, $P(n)$ is true for all n.

Alternate Solution (by James Merryfield, 9th grade, Long Beach Polytechnic High School).

The sum of the number of handshakes of all persons is an even number (because each handshake counts twice, once for each person). The sum of the number of handshakes of those persons who have shaken hands an even number of times is clearly an even number (because it is the sum of even numbers). It follows that the sum of the number of handshakes of those persons who have shaken hands an odd number of times is an even number (because it is the difference of two even numbers). But if a sum of odd numbers is even, there must be an even number of terms in the sum. So it follows that the number of people who have shaken hands an odd number of times is an even number.

10. (a) $\binom{p}{k} = \dfrac{p!}{k!(p-k)!}$. Since p is prime and $1 \le k < p$, p is a factor of the numerator but not a factor of the denominator. Thus $\binom{p}{k}$ is divisible by p, for $1 \le k < p$.

(b)   For each fixed prime p we use induction on n.

Let $P(n)$ be the statement that $n^p - n$ divisible by p.

Step 1 $P(1)$ is the statement $1^p - 1$ is divisible by p, which is true.

Step 2 Suppose $P(k)$ is true. Then

$$(k+1)^p - (k+1) = k^p + \binom{p}{1}k^{p-1} + \binom{p}{2}k^{p-2} + \cdots + \binom{p}{p-1}k + 1 - k - 1$$
$$= (k^p - k) + \left[\binom{p}{1}k^{p-1} + \binom{p}{2}k^{p-2} + \cdots + \binom{p}{p-1}k\right].$$

By the induction hypothesis, $k^p - k$ is divisible by p, and by part (a), each of the individual terms in the second bracket is divisible by p. This shows that $(k+1)^p - (k+1)$ is divisible by p. Thus $P(k+1)$ follows from $P(k)$. So by the Principle of Mathematic Induction, $P(n)$ is true for all $n \geq 1$.

Chapter Thirteen
Exercises 13.1

2. By the Fundamental Counting Principle, the possible number of 3-letter words is
$$\left(\begin{smallmatrix}\text{number of ways to}\\\text{choose the 1}^{\text{st}}\text{ letter}\end{smallmatrix}\right) \cdot \left(\begin{smallmatrix}\text{number of ways to}\\\text{choose the 2}^{\text{nd}}\text{ letter}\end{smallmatrix}\right) \cdot \left(\begin{smallmatrix}\text{number of ways to}\\\text{choose the 3}^{\text{rd}}\text{ letter}\end{smallmatrix}\right).$$

(a) Since repetitions are allowed, we have 26 choices for each letter. Thus, there are $26 \cdot 26 \cdot 26 = 17{,}576$ words.

(b) Since repetitions are *not* allowed, we have 26 choices for the 1st letter, 25 choices for the 2nd letter, and 24 choices for the 3rd letter. Thus there are $26 \cdot 25 \cdot 24 = 15{,}600$ words.

4. (a) By the Fundamental Counting Principle, the possible number of ways 8 horses can complete a race, assuming no ties in any position, is
$$\left(\begin{smallmatrix}\text{number of ways to}\\\text{choose the 1}^{\text{st}}\text{ finisher}\end{smallmatrix}\right) \cdot \left(\begin{smallmatrix}\text{number of ways to}\\\text{choose the 2}^{\text{nd}}\text{ finisher}\end{smallmatrix}\right) \cdot \cdots \cdot \left(\begin{smallmatrix}\text{number of ways to}\\\text{choose the 8}^{\text{th}}\text{ finisher}\end{smallmatrix}\right)$$
$$= 8 \cdot 7 \cdot 6 \cdot 5 \cdot 4 \cdot 3 \cdot 2 \cdot 1 = 8! = 40{,}320.$$

(b) By the Fundamental Counting Principle, the possible number of ways the first, second, and third place can be decided, assuming no ties, is
$$\left(\begin{smallmatrix}\text{number of ways to}\\\text{choose the 1}^{\text{st}}\text{ finisher}\end{smallmatrix}\right) \cdot \left(\begin{smallmatrix}\text{number of ways to}\\\text{choose the 2}^{\text{nd}}\text{ finisher}\end{smallmatrix}\right) \cdot \left(\begin{smallmatrix}\text{number of ways to}\\\text{choose the 3}^{\text{th}}\text{ finisher}\end{smallmatrix}\right) = 8 \cdot 7 \cdot 6 = 336.$$

6. The number of possible seven-digit phone numbers is
$$\left(\begin{smallmatrix}\text{number of ways to}\\\text{choose the 1}^{\text{st}}\text{ digit}\end{smallmatrix}\right) \cdot \left(\begin{smallmatrix}\text{number of ways to}\\\text{choose the 2}^{\text{nd}}\text{ digit}\end{smallmatrix}\right) \cdot \cdots \cdot \left(\begin{smallmatrix}\text{number of ways to}\\\text{choose the 7}^{\text{th}}\text{ digit}\end{smallmatrix}\right).$$

Since the first digit cannot be a 0 or a 1, there are only 8 digits to choose from, while there are 10 digits to choose from for the other six digits in the phone number. Thus the number of possible seven-digit phone numbers is $8 \cdot 10 \cdot 10 \cdot 10 \cdot 10 \cdot 10 \cdot 10 = 8{,}000{,}000.$

8. By the Fundamental Counting Principle, the number of ways of seating 5 people in a row of 5 seats is $5 \cdot 4 \cdot 3 \cdot 2 \cdot 1 = 5! = 120.$

10. By the Fundamental Counting Principle, the number of ways of arranging 5 mathematics books is $5 \cdot 4 \cdot 3 \cdot 2 \cdot 1 = 5! = 120.$

12. The number of different boy-girl combinations of 4 children is
$$\left(\begin{smallmatrix}\text{number of ways to}\\\text{choose a boy or a}\\\text{girl for the 1}^{\text{st}}\text{ child}\end{smallmatrix}\right) \cdot \left(\begin{smallmatrix}\text{number of ways to}\\\text{choose a boy or a}\\\text{girl for the 2}^{\text{nd}}\text{ child}\end{smallmatrix}\right) \cdot \cdots \cdot \left(\begin{smallmatrix}\text{number of ways to}\\\text{choose a boy or a}\\\text{girl for the 4}^{\text{th}}\text{ child}\end{smallmatrix}\right) = 2^4 = 16.$$

14. Since each die has six different faces, the number of different outcomes when rolling a red and a white die is $6 \cdot 6 = 36.$

16. (a) Since there are 13 spades and 13 hearts, the number of ways for which the first card is a spade and the second is a heart is $(13)(13) = 169.$

(b) Since the card is not replaced, the number of ways for which the first card is a spade and the second is a spade is $(13)(12) = 156.$

18. The number of possible ID numbers consisting of one letter followed by 3 digits is $(26)(10)(10)(10) = 26{,}000.$

20. The number of possible pairs of a pitcher and a catcher is $\left(\begin{smallmatrix}\text{number of ways to}\\\text{choose a pitcher}\end{smallmatrix}\right) \cdot \left(\begin{smallmatrix}\text{number of ways to}\\\text{choose a catcher}\end{smallmatrix}\right)$
$= (7)(3) = 21.$

22. Since successive numbers cannot be the same, the number of possible choices for the second number in the combination is only 59. The third number in the combination cannot be the same as the second in the combination, but it can be the same as the first number, so the number of possible choices for the third number in the combination is also 59. So the number of possible combinations consisting of a number in the clockwise direction, a number in the counterclockwise direction, and then a number in the clockwise direction is $(60)(59)(59) = 208{,}860.$

24. The possible number of different cars is

$\left(\begin{smallmatrix}\text{number of}\\\text{models}\end{smallmatrix}\right) \cdot \left(\begin{smallmatrix}\text{number}\\\text{of colors}\end{smallmatrix}\right) \cdot \left(\begin{smallmatrix}\text{number of}\\\text{types of stereos}\end{smallmatrix}\right) \cdot \left(\begin{smallmatrix}\text{air cond.}\\\text{or none}\end{smallmatrix}\right) \cdot \left(\begin{smallmatrix}\text{sunroof}\\\text{or none}\end{smallmatrix}\right) = (5)(4)(3)(2)(2) = 240.$

26. The possible number of three initial monograms is

$\left(\begin{smallmatrix}\text{number of ways to}\\\text{chose the 1}^{\text{st}}\text{ initial}\end{smallmatrix}\right) \cdot \left(\begin{smallmatrix}\text{number of ways to}\\\text{chose the 2}^{\text{nd}}\text{ initial}\end{smallmatrix}\right) \cdot \left(\begin{smallmatrix}\text{number of ways to}\\\text{chose the 3}^{\text{rd}}\text{ initial}\end{smallmatrix}\right) = (26)(26)(26) = 17{,}576.$

28. (a) The number of different plates consisting of 1 letter followed by 5 digits is $(26)(10^5) = 2{,}600{,}000 = 2.6$ million. Since this is less than the 17 million registered cars, there are not enough different plates to go around.

    (b) The system with two letters followed by 4 digits gives $(26^2)(10^4) = 6{,}760{,}000 < 17$ million which is not enough. The system consisting of 3 letters followed by 3 digits gives $(26^3)(10^3) = 17{,}576{,}000 > 17$ million. Thus the fewest number of letters that will provide enough different plates is 3.

30. The number of ways that a president, a vice-president and a secretary can be chosen is
$\left(\begin{smallmatrix}\text{number of ways to choose a}\\\text{female from the 20 females}\end{smallmatrix}\right) \cdot \left(\begin{smallmatrix}\text{number of ways to choose a}\\\text{male from the 30 males}\end{smallmatrix}\right) \cdot \left(\begin{smallmatrix}\text{number of ways to choose the}\\\text{sect. from the remaining 48 students}\end{smallmatrix}\right)$
$= (20)(30)(48) = 28{,}800.$

32. We have seven choices for the first digit and 10 choices for each of the other 8 digits. Thus, the number of Social Security numbers is $7 \cdot 10^8 = 700{,}000{,}000.$

34. Since the fourth letter must be the same as the second letter and the fifth letter must be the same as the first letter, the possible number of 5-letter palindromes is $(26)(26)(26)(1)(1) = 17{,}576.$

36. (a) The number of possible different 3-character code words with a letter as the first entry is $26 \cdot 36 \cdot 36 = 33{,}696.$

    (b) The number of possible different 3-character code words in which zero is not the first entry is $35 \cdot 36 \cdot 36 = 45{,}360.$

38. Since the two algebra books must be next to each other, we first consider them as one object. So we now have four objects to arrange and there are 4! ways to arrange these four objects. Now there are 2 ways to arrange the two algebra books. Thus the number of ways that 5 mathematics books may be placed on a shelf if the two algebra books are to be next to each other is $2 \cdot 4! = 48.$

40. (a) Since the numbers to be formed are less than 700, the first digit must be either 2, 4, or 5. Thus there are 3 possible ways to choose the first digit. The remaining 2 digits can be 2, 4, 5, or 7. Therefore the number of 3-digit numbers that can be formed using the digits 2, 4, 5, and 7 if the numbers are less than 700 is $(3)(4)(4) = 48.$

(b) Since the numbers to be formed must be even, the last digit must be either 2 or 4. The first 2 digits can be 2, 4, 5, or 7. Therefore the number of even 3-digit numbers that can be formed using the digits 2, 4, 5, and 7 is $(4)(4)(2) = 32$.

(c) Since the numbers to be formed must be divisible by 5, the last digit must be 5. The first 2 digits can be 2, 4, 5, or 7. Therefore the number of 3-digit numbers divisible by 5 that can be formed using the digits 2, 4, 5, and 7 is $(4)(4)(1) = 16$.

42. Since there are 26 letters, the possible number of combinations of the first and the last initials is $(26)(26) = 676$. Since $677 > 676$, there must be at least 2 people that have the same first and last initials in any group of 677 people.

Exercises 13.2

2. $P(9,2) = \dfrac{9!}{(9-2)!} = \dfrac{9!}{7!} = 9 \cdot 8 = 72$

4. $P(10,5) = \dfrac{10!}{(10-5)!} = \dfrac{10!}{5!} = 30{,}240$

6. $P(99,3) = \ = \dfrac{99!}{(99-3)!} = \dfrac{99!}{96!} = 941{,}094$

8. Since the order of finish is important, we want the number of permutations of 8 objects (the contestants) taken three at a time, which is $P(8,3) = \dfrac{8!}{(8-3)!} = \dfrac{8!}{5!} = 8 \cdot 7 \cdot 6 = 336.$

10. The number of ways of ordering 6 distinct objects (the 6 people) is $P(6,6) = 6! = 720.$

12. Since the word *permutations* is used in this exercise, we are looking for the number of ways to arrange these 4 letters without repeats. Thus, the number of ways is $P(4,4) = 4! = 24.$

14. The number of ways of ordering 8 pieces in order (without repeats) is $P(8,8) = 8! = 40{,}320.$

16. The number of ways of ordering three of the five distinct flags is $P(5,3) = 60.$

18. In selecting these officers, order is important and repeats are not allowed, so the number of ways of choosing 4 officers from 30 students $= P(30,4) = 657{,}720.$

20. We start by first placing Jack in the middle seat, and then we place the remaining 4 students in the remaining 4 seats. Thus the number of a these arrangements is
$$\left(\begin{smallmatrix} \text{number of ways} \\ \text{to seat Jack} \end{smallmatrix} \right) \cdot \left(\begin{smallmatrix} \text{number of ways to seat} \\ \text{the remaining 4 students} \end{smallmatrix} \right) = 1 \cdot P(4,4) = 1!\,4! = 24.$$

22. Here we have 9 letters, of which 3 are A's, 3 are B's, and 3 are C's. Thus the number of distinguishable permutations is $\dfrac{9!}{3!\,3!\,3!} = \dfrac{9 \cdot 8 \cdot 7 \cdot 6 \cdot 5 \cdot 4 \cdot 3!}{3 \cdot 2 \cdot 1 \cdot 3 \cdot 2 \cdot 1 \cdot 3!} = 1680.$

24. Here we have 8 letters, of which 1 is an A, 1 is a B, 1 is a C, 3 are D's, and 2 are E's. Thus the number of distinguishable permutations is $\dfrac{8!}{1!\,1!\,1!\,3!\,2!} = 3360.$

26. Here we have 14 objects (the 14 balls) of which 5 are red balls, 2 are white balls, and 7 are blue balls. So the number of distinguishable permutations is $\dfrac{14!}{5!\,2!\,7!} = 72{,}072.$

28. The word ELEEMOSYNARY has 12 letters of which 3 are E's, 2 are Y's, and the remaining letters are distinct. So we wish to find the number of distinguishable permutations of 12 objects (the 12 letters) from like groups of size 3, 2, and seven of size 1. We get
$$\dfrac{12!}{3!\,2!\,1!\,1!\,1!\,1!\,1!\,1!\,1!} = 39{,}916{,}800.$$

30. This is the number of distinguishable permutations of 7 objects (the students) from like groups of size 3 (the ones who stay in the 3-person room), size 2 (the ones who stay in the 2-person room), size 1 (the one who stays in the 1-person room), and size 1 (the one who sleeps in the car). This number is $\dfrac{7!}{3!\,2!\,1!\,1!} = 420.$

32. The number of distinguishable permutations of 13 objects (the total number of blocks he must travel) which can be partitioned into like groups of size 8 (the east blocks) and of size 5 (the north blocks) is $\dfrac{13!}{8!\,5!} = 1{,}287$.

34. $C(9,2) = \dfrac{9!}{2!\,(9-2)!} = \dfrac{9!}{2!\,7!} = \dfrac{9 \cdot 8}{2 \cdot 1} = 36$

36. $C(10,5) = \dfrac{10!}{5!\,(10-5)!} = \dfrac{10!}{5!\,5!} = \dfrac{10 \cdot 9 \cdot 8 \cdot 7 \cdot 6}{5 \cdot 4 \cdot 3 \cdot 2 \cdot 1} = 252$

38. $C(99,3) = \dfrac{99!}{3!\,96!} = \dfrac{99 \cdot 98 \cdot 97}{3 \cdot 2 \cdot 1} = 156{,}849$

40. In this exercise, we assume that the pizza toppings cannot be repeated, so we are interested in the number of ways to select a subset of 3 toppings from a set of 12 toppings. The number of ways this can occur is $C(12,3) = \dfrac{12!}{3!\,9!} = \dfrac{12 \cdot 11 \cdot 10}{3 \cdot 2 \cdot 1} = 220$.

42. Here we are interested in the number of ways of choosing 3 objects (the 3 members of the committee) from a set of 25 objects (the 25 members). The number of combinations of 25 objects taken 3 at a time is $C(25,3) = \dfrac{25!}{3!\,22!} = 2300$.

44. Since order is not important in a 7-card hand, the number of combinations of 52 objects (the 52 cards) taken 7 at a time is $C(52,7) = \dfrac{52!}{7!\,45!} = 133{,}784{,}560$.

46. In this exercise, we assume that the pizza toppings cannot be repeated, so we are interested in the number of ways to select a subset of 3 toppings from a set of 16 toppings. The number of ways this can occur is $C(16,3) = \dfrac{16!}{3!\,13!} = 560$.

48. The order the skirts are selected is not important and no skirt is repeated. So the number of combinations of 8 skirts taken 5 at a time is $C(8,5) = \dfrac{8!}{5!\,3!} = 56$.

50. Since Jack must go on the field trip, we first pick Jack to go on the field trip, and then select the six other students from the remaining 29 students. Since $C(29,6) = \dfrac{29!}{6!\,23!} = 475{,}020$, there are 475,020 ways to select the students to go on the field trip with Jack.

52. Since the order in which the numbers are selected is not important, the number of combinations of 49 numbers taken 6 at a time is $C(49,6) = \dfrac{49!}{6!\,43!} = 13{,}983{,}816$.

54. (a) The number of ways of choosing 5 students from the 20 students is $C(20,5) = \dfrac{20!}{5!\,15!}$ $= 15{,}504$.

    (b) The number of ways of choosing 5 students for the committee from the 12 females is $C(12,5) = \dfrac{12!}{5!\,7!} = 792$.

    (c) We use the Fundamental Counting Principle to count the number of possible committees with 3 females and 2 males. Thus, we get

$$\begin{pmatrix} \text{number of ways to choose the} \\ \text{3 females from the 12 females} \end{pmatrix} \cdot \begin{pmatrix} \text{number of ways to choose the} \\ \text{2 males from the 8 males} \end{pmatrix} = C(12,3) \cdot C(8,2) = (220)(28) = 6160.$$

56. We may choose any subset of the 8 available brochures. There are $2^8 = 256$ ways to do this.

58. We consider a set of 20 objects (the shoppers in the mall) and a subset that corresponds to those shoppers that enter the store. Since a set of 20 objects has $2^{20} = 1,048,576$ subsets, there are 1,048,576 outcomes to their decisions.

60. The number of ways the committee can be chosen is

$$\begin{pmatrix} \text{number of ways to} \\ \text{choose 2 of 6 freshmen} \end{pmatrix} \cdot \begin{pmatrix} \text{number of ways to} \\ \text{choose 3 of 8 sophomores} \end{pmatrix} \cdot \begin{pmatrix} \text{number of ways to} \\ \text{choose 4 of 12 juniors} \end{pmatrix} \cdot \begin{pmatrix} \text{number of ways to} \\ \text{choose 5 of 10 seniors} \end{pmatrix}$$

$$= C(6,2) \cdot C(8,3) \cdot C(12,4) \cdot C(10,5) = 15 \cdot 56 \cdot 495 \cdot 252 = 104,781,600.$$

62. We choose 3 forwards from the forwards, 2 defense players from the defense men, and the goalie from the two goalies. Thus the number of ways to pick the 6 starting players is

$$\begin{pmatrix} \text{number of ways to} \\ \text{pick 3 of 12 forwards} \end{pmatrix} \cdot \begin{pmatrix} \text{number of ways to} \\ \text{pick 2 of 6 defenders} \end{pmatrix} \cdot \begin{pmatrix} \text{number of ways to} \\ \text{pick 1 of 2 goalies} \end{pmatrix} = C(12,3) \cdot C(6,2) \cdot C(2,1)$$

$$= (220)(15)(2) = 6600.$$

64. When two objects are chosen from ten objects, it determines a unique set of eight objects, those not chosen. So choosing two objects from ten objects is the same a choosing eight objects from ten objects. In general, every subset of r objects chosen from a set of n objects determines a corresponding set of $(n-r)$ objects, namely, those not chosen. Therefore, the total number of combinations for each type are equal.

66. (a) $(x+y)^5 = (x+y)(x+y)(x+y)(x+y)(x+y)$

$$= (x+y)(x+y)(x+y)(xx + xy + yx + yy)$$

$$= (x+y)(x+y)(xxx + xxy + xyx + xyy + yxx + yxy + yyx + yyy)$$

$$= (x+y)(xxxx + xxxy + xxyx + xxyy + xyxx + xyxy + xyyx + xyyy + yxxx$$
$$\qquad + yxxy + yxyx + yxyy + yyxx + yyxy + yyyx + yyyy)$$

$$= xxxxx + xxxxy + xxxyx + xxxyy + xxyxx + xxyxy + xxyyx + xxyyy$$
$$\qquad + xyxxx + xyxxy + xyxyx + xyxyy + xyyxx + xyyyx + xyyyx + xyyyy$$
$$\qquad + yxxxx + yxxxy + yxxyx + yxxyy + yxyxx + yxyxy + yxyyx + yxyyy$$
$$\qquad + yyxxx + yyxxy + yyxyx + yyxyy + yyyxx + yyyxy + yyyyx + yyyyy$$

(b)   There are ten terms that contain two x's and three y's. They are

$$xxyyy + xyxyy + xyyxy + xyyyx + yxxyy + yxyxy + yxyyx + yyxxy + yyxyx + yyyxx$$

(c)   To count the number of terms with two x's, we must count the number of ways to pick two of the five positions to contain an x. This number is $C(5,2)$.

(d)   In the Binomial Theorem, the coefficient $\begin{pmatrix} n \\ r \end{pmatrix}$ is the number of ways of picking r positions in a term with n factors to contain an x. By definition, this is $C(n,r)$.

Exercises 13.3

2. Let H stand for heads, T for tails; the numbers $1, 2, \ldots, 6$ are the faces of the die.

(a) $S = \{H1, H2, H3, H4, H5, H6, T1, T2, T3, T4, T5, T6\}$.

(b) Let E be the event of getting heads and rolling an even number. So $E = \{H2, H4, H6\}$, and
$$P(E) = \frac{n(E)}{n(S)} = \frac{3}{12} = \frac{1}{4}.$$

(c) Let F be the event of getting heads and rolling a number greater than 4. So $F = \{H5, H6\}$,
and $P(F) = \frac{n(F)}{n(S)} = \frac{2}{12} = \frac{1}{6}.$

(d) Let G be the event of getting tails and rolling an odd number. So $G = \{T1, T3, T5\}$, and
$$P(G) = \frac{n(G)}{n(S)} = \frac{3}{12} = \frac{1}{4}.$$

4. (a) Let E be the event of rolling a two or a three. Then $P(E) = \frac{n(E)}{n(S)} = \frac{2}{6} = \frac{1}{3}.$

(b) Let F be the event of rolling an odd number. So $F = \{1, 3, 5\}$, and $P(F) = \frac{n(F)}{n(S)} = \frac{3}{6} = \frac{1}{2}.$

(c) Let G be the event of rolling a number divisible by 3. So $G = \{3, 6\}$, and $P(G) = \frac{n(G)}{n(S)} = \frac{1}{3}.$

6. (a) Let E be the event of choosing a heart. Since there are 13 hearts, $P(E) = \frac{n(E)}{n(S)} = \frac{13}{52} = \frac{1}{4}.$

(b) Let F be the event of choosing a heart or a spade. Since there are 13 hearts and 13 spades,
$$P(E) = \frac{n(E)}{n(S)} = \frac{26}{52} = \frac{1}{2}.$$

(c) Let G be the event of choosing a heart, a diamond or a spade. Since there are 13 cards in each
suit, $P(G) = \frac{n(G)}{n(S)} = \frac{39}{52} = \frac{3}{4}.$

8. (a) Let E be the event of selecting a white or a yellow ball. Since there are 2 white balls and 1
yellow ball, $P(E') = 1 - P(E) = 1 - \frac{n(E)}{n(S)} = 1 - \frac{3}{8} = \frac{5}{8}.$

(b) Let F be the event of selecting a red, a white or a yellow ball. Since all the types of balls are in
the jar, $P(E) = 1.$

(c) Let G be the event of selecting a white ball. Since there are 2 white balls, $P(E') = 1 - P(E)$
$$= 1 - \frac{n(E)}{n(S)} = 1 - \frac{2}{8} = \frac{6}{8} = \frac{3}{4}.$$

10. The spinner has 9 equal sized regions numbered 1 through 9.

(a) Let E be the event that the spinner stops at an even number. Since there are 4 even numbers,
$$P(E) = \frac{4}{9}.$$

(b) Let F be the event that the spinner stops at an odd number or a number greater than 3. Since the only number not greater than 3 and not odd is 2, $P(E) = 1 - P(E') = 1 - \dfrac{n(E')}{n(S)}$

$= 1 - \frac{1}{9} = \frac{8}{9}$.

12. Let E be the event of dealing 5 hearts. Since there are 13 hearts, $P(E) = \dfrac{C(13,5)}{C(52,5)}$

$= \frac{1287}{2,598,960} \approx .0005$.

14. Let E be the event of dealing 5 face cards. Since there are 3 face cards for each suit and 4 suits, $P(E) = \dfrac{C(12,5)}{C(52,5)} = \frac{792}{2,598,960} \approx .0003$.

16. (a) $S = \{(1,1),(1,2),(1,3),(1,4),(1,5),(1,6),(2,1),(2,2),(2,3),(2,4),(2,5),(2,6),$
    $(3,1),(3,2),(3,3),(3,4),(3,5),(3,6),(4,1),(4,2),(4,3),(4,4),(4,5),(4,6),$
    $(5,1),(5,2),(5,3),(5,4),(5,5),(5,6),(6,1),(6,2),(6,3),(6,4),(6,5),(6,6)\}$.

    (b) Let E be the event of getting a sum of 7. Then $E = \{(1,6),(2,5),(3,4),(4,3),(5,2),(6,1)\}$, and $P(E) = \frac{6}{36} = \frac{1}{6}$.

    (c) Let F be the event of getting a sum of 9. Then $F = \{(3,6),(4,5),(5,4),(6,3)\}$, and $P(F) = \frac{4}{36} = \frac{1}{9}$.

    (d) Let E be the event that the two dice show the same number. Then $P(E) = \frac{6}{36} = \frac{1}{6}$.

    (e) Let E be the event that the two dice show different numbers. Then E' is the event that the two dice show the same number. Thus, $P(E) = 1 - P(E') = 1 - \frac{1}{6} = \frac{5}{6}$.

    (f) Let E be the event of getting a sum of 9 or higher. Then $P(E) = \frac{10}{36} = \frac{5}{18}$.

18. Let E be the event that a 13-card bridge hand consists of all cards from the same suit. Since there are exactly 4 such hands (one for each suit), $P(E) = \dfrac{4}{C(52,13)} \approx 6.29908 \times 10^{-12}$.

20. (a) Let E be the event that the toddler arranges the word "FRENCH". Since the letters are distinct, there are $P(6,6)$ ways of arranging the blocks of which only one spells the word "FRENCH". Thus $P(E) = \dfrac{1}{P(6,6)} = \frac{1}{720} \approx .0013889$.

    (b) Let E be the event that the toddler arranges the letters in alphabetical order. Since there are $P(6,6)$ ways of arranging the blocks of which only one is in alphabetical order, $P(E) = \dfrac{1}{P(6,6)} = \frac{1}{720} \approx .0013889$.

22. Let E be the event that no women are chosen. The number of ways that no women are chosen is the same as the number of ways that only men are chosen, which is $C(11,6)$. Thus $P(E) = \dfrac{C(11,6)}{C(30,6)} \approx 7.78073 \times 10^{-4}$.

24. Let E be the event that the batch will be discarded. Thus, E is the event that at least one defective bulb is found. It is easier to find E', the event that no defective bulbs are found. Since there are 10 bulbs in the batch of which 8 are non-defective, $P(E') = \dfrac{C(8,3)}{C(10,3)}$. Thus $P(E) = 1 - P(E')$

$= 1 - \dfrac{C(8,3)}{C(10,3)} \approx 1 - 0.4667 = .5333$.

26. Let E be the event that the monkey will arrange the 6 blocks to spell "HAMLET". Then $P(E) = \frac{1}{6!} = \frac{1}{720} \approx .00139$.

28. Let E be the event that you predict the correct order for the horses to finish the race. Since there are eight horses, there are $P(8,8) = 8!$ ways that the horses could finish, with only one being the correct order. Thus, $P(E) = \dfrac{1}{P(8,8)} = \frac{1}{40,320} \approx 2.48 \times 10^{-5}$.

30.

		Parent 2	
		t	t
	T	T t	T t
Parent 1	t	t t	t t

   (a) Let E be the event that the offspring will be tall. Since only offspring with genotype Tt will be tall, $P(E) = \frac{2}{4} = \frac{1}{2}$.

   (b) E' is the event that the offspring will not be tall (thus, the offspring is short). So $P(E') = 1 - P(E) = 1 - \frac{1}{2} = \frac{1}{2}$.

32. (a) NO, the events are not mutually exclusive since a student can be female and wear glasses.

   (b) NO, the events are not mutually exclusive since a student can be male and have long hair.

34. (a) NO, the events are not mutually exclusive since 4 is greater than 3 and also less than 5. So $P(E \cup F) = P(E) + P(F) - P(E \cap F) = \frac{3}{6} + \frac{4}{6} - \frac{1}{6} = 1$.

   (b) YES, the events are mutually exclusive since there are only 2 numbers less than 3, namely 1 and 2, but they are not divisible by 3. So $P(E \cup F) = P(E) + P(F) = \frac{2}{6} + \frac{2}{6} = \frac{2}{3}$.

36. (a) NO, events E and F are not mutually exclusive since a king can be a club. So $P(E \cup F) = P(E) + P(F) - P(E \cap F) = \frac{13}{52} + \frac{4}{52} - \frac{1}{52} = \frac{4}{13}$.

   (b) NO, events E and F are not mutually exclusive since an ace can be a spade. So $P(E \cup F) = P(E) + P(F) - P(E \cap F) = \frac{4}{52} + \frac{13}{52} - \frac{1}{52} = \frac{4}{13}$.

38. (a) Let E be the event that the spinner stops on blue. Since only 4 of the regions are blue, $P(E) = \frac{4}{16} = \frac{1}{4}$.

   (b) Let F be the event that the spinner stops on an odd number. Since 8 of the regions are odd-numbered, $P(F) = \frac{8}{16} = \frac{1}{2}$.

   (c) Since none of the odd-numbered regions are blue, $P(E \cup F) = P(E) + P(F) = \frac{1}{4} + \frac{1}{2} = \frac{3}{4}$.

40. Let E be the event of arranging the letters to spell "HAMLET" and F be the event of arranging them to spell "THELMA". There are $P(6,6)$ different ways of arranging these letters and only one way to spell each of these words. So $P(E \cup F) = P(E) + P(F) = \dfrac{1}{P(6,6)} + \dfrac{1}{P(6,6)} = \frac{2}{6!} = \frac{1}{360}$.

42. Let E be the event that a player has exactly 5 winning numbers and F be the event that a player has all 6 winning numbers. These events are mutually exclusive. For a players to have exactly 5 winning numbers means that the player has 5 of the 6 winning numbers and 1 number that was not selected in the lottery. So $n(E) = C(6,5) \cdot C(43,1)$. Thus,

$$P(\text{at least 5 winning numbers}) = P(E \cup F) = P(E) + P(F) = \frac{C(6,5) \cdot C(43,1)}{C(49,6)} + \frac{1}{C(49,6)}$$

$$\approx .00001852.$$

44. (a) YES, because the first flip does not influence the outcome of the second flip.

 (b) The probability of showing heads on both tosses is $P(E \cap F) = P(E) \cdot P(F) = \left(\frac{1}{2}\right)\left(\frac{1}{2}\right) = \frac{1}{4}.$

46. (a) YES. What happens on spinner A does not influence what happens on spinner B.

 (b) The probability that A stops on red and B stops on yellow is
 $P(E \cap F) = P(E) \cdot P(F) = \left(\frac{2}{4}\right)\left(\frac{2}{8}\right) = \frac{1}{8}.$

48. Let E be the event of getting a 1 on the first toss, and let F be the event of getting a 1 on the second toss. Since the events are independent, $P(E \cap F) = P(E) \cdot P(F) = \frac{1}{6} \cdot \frac{1}{6} = \frac{1}{36}.$

50. Since the card is replaced, the selection of the first card does not influence the selection of the second card, so the events are independent.

 (a) Let E be the event of getting an ace on the first draw and F be the event of getting an ace on the second draw. Then $P(E \cap F) = P(E) \cdot P(F) = \left(\frac{4}{52}\right)\left(\frac{4}{52}\right) = \frac{1}{169}.$

 (b) Let E be the event of getting an ace on the first draw and F be the event of getting a spade on the second draw. Then $P(E \cap F) = P(E) \cdot P(F) = \left(\frac{4}{52}\right)\left(\frac{13}{52}\right) = \frac{1}{52}.$

52. The number of ways to arrange the letters E, O, K, M, N, and Y is $P(6,6) = 720$. So the probability that the monkey can arrange the letters correctly (if he is merely arranging the blocks randomly) is $\frac{1}{720}$. Also, since the monkey is arranging the blocks randomly, each arrangement is independent of every other arrangement. Hence, the probability that the monkey will be able to spell the word correctly three consecutive times is $\left(\frac{1}{720}\right)^3 = \frac{1}{373,248,000} \approx 2.679 \times 10^{-9}.$

54. The number of ways a set of six numbers can be selected from a group of 49 numbers is $C(49,6)$. Since the games are independent, the probability of winning the lottery two times in a row is
 $$\left(\frac{1}{C(49,6)}\right)^2 \approx 5.11386 \times 10^{-15}.$$

56. (a) The probability that the first wheel has a bar is $\frac{1}{11}$, and is the same for the second and third wheels. The events are independent, and so the probability of getting 3 bars is
 $\frac{1}{11} \cdot \frac{1}{11} \cdot \frac{1}{11} = \frac{1}{1331}.$

 (b) The probability of getting a number on the first wheel is $\frac{10}{11}$, the probability of getting the same number on the second wheel is $\frac{1}{11}$, and the probability of getting the same number on the third wheel is $\frac{1}{11}$. Thus, the probability of getting the same number on each wheel is
 $\frac{10}{11} \cdot \frac{1}{11} \cdot \frac{1}{11} = \frac{10}{1331}.$

 (c) We use the complement, NO BARS, to determine the probability of at least one bar. The probability that the first wheel does not have a bar is $\frac{10}{11}$, and is the same for the second and third wheels. Since the events are independent, the probability of getting NO BARS is
 $\frac{10}{11} \cdot \frac{10}{11} \cdot \frac{10}{11} = \frac{10^3}{11^3} = \frac{1000}{1331}$, and so $P(\text{at least one BAR}) = 1 - \frac{1000}{1331} = \frac{331}{1331}.$

58. Let E be the event that at least two have a birthday in the same month, so that E' is the event that no two have a birthday in the same month. So

$P(E') = \dfrac{\text{number of ways to assign 6 distinct birth months}}{\text{number of ways to assign 6 birth months}} = \dfrac{P(12,6)}{12^6} = \dfrac{12 \cdot 11 \cdot 10 \cdot 9 \cdot 8 \cdot 7}{12^6} = \dfrac{385}{1728}$. Thus $P(E) = 1 - P(E') = 1 - \dfrac{385}{1728} = \dfrac{1343}{1728}$.

60. Since most families in the U.S. have three or less children, we construct a table in which we calculate the probability that a randomly selected child is the oldest son or daughter.

Number of children in the family	Sample Space	Probability that the child is the oldest son or daughter
1	(b) (g)	$\left.\begin{array}{l} .5 \cdot 1 = .5 \\ .5 \cdot 1 = .5 \end{array}\right\} = 1$
2	(b, b) (b, g) (g, b) (g, g)	$\left.\begin{array}{l} .25 \cdot .5 = .125 \\ .25 \cdot 1 = .25 \\ .25 \cdot 1 = .25 \\ .25 \cdot .5 = .125 \end{array}\right\} = .75$
3	(b, b, b) (b, b, g) (b, g, b) (g, b, b) (b, g, g) (g, b, g) (g, g, b) (g, g, g)	$\left.\begin{array}{l} .125 \cdot .333 = .041625 \\ .125 \cdot .667 = .08325 \\ .125 \cdot .667 = .08325 \\ .125 \cdot .667 = .08325 \\ .125 \cdot .667 = .08325 \\ .125 \cdot .667 = .08325 \\ .125 \cdot .667 = .08325 \\ .125 \cdot .333 = .041625 \end{array}\right\} = .58275$

As the table shows, for families of this size, the relevant probability is always greater than .5.

Exercises 13.4

2. The probability that Jane gets \$10 is $\frac{1}{6}$, and the probability that she loses \$1 is $\frac{5}{6}$. Thus $E = (10)\left(\frac{1}{6}\right) + (-1)\left(\frac{5}{6}\right) \approx 0.833$, and so her expectation is \$0.833.

4. The expected value of this game is $E = (3)\left(\frac{1}{2}\right) + (2)\left(\frac{1}{2}\right) = \frac{5}{2} = 2.5$. So Tim's expected winnings are \$2.50 per game.

6. The probability that Albert gets two tails is $\left(\frac{1}{2}\right)^2 = \frac{1}{4}$, the probability that Albert gets one tail and one head is $C(2,1)\left(\frac{1}{2}\right)^2 = \frac{1}{2}$, and the probability that Albert gets two heads is $\left(\frac{1}{2}\right)^2 = \frac{1}{4}$. If Albert gets two heads, he will receive \$4, if he get one head and one tail, he will get \$2 − \$1 = \$1, and if he get two tails, he will lose \$2. Thus the expected value of this game is $E = (4)\left(\frac{1}{4}\right) + (1)\left(\frac{1}{2}\right) + (-2)\left(\frac{1}{4}\right) = 1$. So Albert's expected winnings are \$1 per game.

8. Since there are 4 aces, 12 face cards and only one 8 of clubs, the expected value of this game is $E = (104)\left(\frac{4}{52}\right) + (26)\left(\frac{12}{52}\right) + (13)\left(\frac{1}{52}\right) = \$14.25$.

10. The probability of choosing 2 white balls (that is, no black balls) is $\frac{8}{10} \cdot \frac{7}{9} = \frac{56}{90}$, and the probability of not choosing 2 white balls (at least one black) is $\left(1 - \frac{56}{90}\right) = \frac{34}{90}$. Therefore, the expected value of this game is $E = (5)\left(\frac{56}{90}\right) + (0)\left(\frac{34}{90}\right) \approx 3.111$. Thus, John's expected winnings are \$3.11 per game.

12. (a) We have $P(\text{winning the first prize}) = \dfrac{1}{2 \times 10^6}$. After the first prize winner is selected, then $P(\text{winning the second prize}) = \frac{1}{2\times10^6-1}$. Similarly, $P(\text{winning the third prize}) = \dfrac{1}{2 \times 10^6 - 2}$. So, the expected value of this game is
$$E = (10^6)\left(\frac{1}{2 \times 10^6}\right) + (10^5)\left(\frac{1}{2 \times 10^6 - 1}\right) + (10^4)\left(\frac{1}{2 \times 10^6 - 2}\right) = \$0.555.$$

    (b) Since we expect to win \$0.555 on the average per game, if we pay \$1.00, then our net outcome is a loss of \$0.445 per game. Hence, it is not worth playing because on the average you will lose \$0.445 per game.

14. Since the safe has a six digit combination, there are 10^6 possible combinations to the safe, of which only one is correct. The expected value of this game is
$$E = (10^6 - 1)\left(\frac{1}{10^6}\right) + (-1)\left(\frac{10^6 - 1}{10^6}\right) = 0.$$

16. Since the wheels of the slot machine are independent, the probability that you get three watermelons is $\left(\frac{1}{11}\right)^3$. So the expected value of this game is $E = (4.75)\left(\frac{1}{11^3}\right) + (-0.25)\left(1 - \frac{1}{11^3}\right) \approx -\$0.246$.

18. Let x be the fair price to pay to play this game. Then if you win, you gain $1 - x$, and if you lose, your loss will be $-x$. So $E = 0 \iff (1 - x)\left(\frac{2}{8}\right) + (-x)\left(\frac{6}{8}\right) = 0 \iff 1 - 4x = 0 \iff x = \frac{1}{4} = 0.25$. Thus, a fair price to play this game is \$0.25.

20. If you win, you win \$1 million minus the price of the stamp. If you lose, you lose only the price of the stamp (currently 33¢). So the expected value of this game is
$$(999{,}999.67) \cdot \frac{1}{20 \times 10^6} + (-0.33) \cdot \frac{20 \times 10^6 - 1}{20 \times 10^6} \approx -0.28.$$ Thus you expect to lose 28¢ on each entry, and so it's not worth it.

Review Exercises for Chapter 13

2. (a) The number of 3-digit numbers that can be formed using the digits 1-6 if a digit can be used any number of times is $(6)(6)(6) = 216$.

    (b) The number of 3-digit numbers that can be formed using the digits 1-6 if a digit can be used only once is $(6)(5)(4) = 120$.

4. Since the order in which the people are chosen is not important and a person cannot be bumped more than once (no repetitions), the number of ways that 7 passengers can be bumped is $C(120, 7) \approx 5.9488 \times 10^{10}$.

6. There 2 ways to answer each of the 10 true-false questions and 4 ways to answer each of the 5 multiple choice questions. So the number of ways that this test can be completed is $(2^{10})(4^5) = 1{,}048{,}576$.

8. Since the order of the scoops of ice cream is not important and the scoops cannot be repeated, the number of ways to have a banana split is $C(15, 4) = 1365$.

10. Since there are $n!$ ways to arrange a group of size n and $5! = 120$, there are 5 students in this class.

12. The number ways to form a license plate consisting of 2 letters followed by 3 numbers is $(26)(26)(10)(10)(10) = 676{,}000$. Since there are fewer possible license plates than 700,000, there must be fewer than 700,000 licensed cars in the Yukon.

14. Each topping corresponds to a subset of a set with n elements. Since a set with n elements has 2^n subsets and $2^{11} = 2048$, there are 11 toppings that the pizza parlor offers.

16. Since the nucleotides can be repeated, the number of possible words of length n is 4^n. Since $4^2 = 16 < 20$ and $4^3 = 64$, the minimum length of word needed is 3.

18. (a) <u>Solution 1</u> Since the left most digit of a three digit number cannot be zero, there are 9 choices for this first digit and 10 choices for the next two digits. Thus, the number of ways to form a three digit number is $(9)(10)(10) = 900$.
    <u>Solution 2</u> Since there are 999 numbers between 1 and 999, of which the numbers between 1 and 99 do not have three digits, there are $999 - 99 = 900$ three digit numbers.

    (b) There are 1001 numbers from 0-1000. From part (a), there are 900 three digit numbers. Therefore the probability that the number chosen is a three digit number is $P(E) = \frac{900}{1001} \approx 0.899$.

20. Since MISSISSIPPI has 4 I's, 4 S's, 2 P's, and 1 M, the number of distinguishable anagrams of the word MISSISSIPPI is $\dfrac{11!}{4!\,4!\,2!\,1!} = 34{,}650$.

22. (a) The probability that the ball is red is $\frac{10}{15} = \frac{2}{3}$.

    (b) The probability that the ball is even numbered is $\frac{8}{15}$.

    (c) The probability that the ball is white and an odd number is $\frac{2}{15}$.

    (d) The probability that the ball is red or odd numbered is
    $P(\text{red}) + P(\text{odd}) - P(\text{red} \cap \text{odd}) = \frac{10}{15} + \frac{7}{15} - \frac{5}{15} = \frac{12}{15} = \frac{4}{5}$.

24. Since rolling a die and selecting a card is independent, the
$P(\text{both show a six}) = P(\text{die shows a six}) \cdot P(\text{card is a six}) = \frac{1}{6} \cdot \frac{4}{52} = \frac{1}{78}$.

26. (a) Since these events are independent, the probability of getting the ace of spades, a six, and a head is $\frac{1}{52} \cdot \frac{1}{6} \cdot \frac{1}{2} = \frac{1}{624}$.

    (b) The probability of getting a spade, a six, and a head is $\frac{13}{52} \cdot \frac{1}{6} \cdot \frac{1}{2} = \frac{1}{48}$.

    (c) The probability of getting a face card, a number greater than 3, and a head is $\frac{12}{52} \cdot \frac{3}{6} \cdot \frac{1}{2} = \frac{3}{52}$.

28. (a) Since there are four kings in a standard deck, $P(\text{4 kings}) = \dfrac{C(4, 4)}{C(52, 4)} = \dfrac{1}{\frac{52 \cdot 51 \cdot 50 \cdot 49}{4 \cdot 3 \cdot 2 \cdot 1}} = \dfrac{1}{270725}$.

    (b) Since there are 13 spades in a standard deck, $P(\text{4 spades}) = \dfrac{C(13, 4)}{C(52, 4)} = \dfrac{\frac{13 \cdot 12 \cdot 11 \cdot 10}{4 \cdot 3 \cdot 2 \cdot 1}}{\frac{52 \cdot 51 \cdot 50 \cdot 49}{4 \cdot 3 \cdot 2 \cdot 1}} = \dfrac{11}{4165}$.

    (c) Since there are 26 red cards and 26 black cards,
$$P(\text{all same color}) = \frac{2 \cdot C(26, 4)}{C(52, 4)} = \frac{2 \cdot \frac{26 \cdot 25 \cdot 24 \cdot 23}{4 \cdot 3 \cdot 2 \cdot 1}}{\frac{52 \cdot 51 \cdot 50 \cdot 49}{4 \cdot 3 \cdot 2 \cdot 1}} = \frac{92}{833}.$$

30. She knows the first digit and must arrange the other four digits. Since only one of the $P(4, 4) = 24$ arrangements is correct, the probability that she guesses correctly is $\frac{1}{24}$.

32. Using the same logic as in Exercise 29 (a), the probability that all three dice show the same number is $1 \cdot \frac{1}{6} \cdot \frac{1}{6} = \frac{1}{36}$, while the probability they are not all the same is $1 - \frac{1}{36} = \frac{35}{36}$. Thus, the expected value of this game is $E = (5)\left(\frac{1}{36}\right) + (-1)\left(\frac{35}{36}\right) = -\frac{30}{36} = -0.83$. So John's expected winnings per game are $-\$0.83$, that is, he expects to lose \$0.83 per game.

34. The number of different pizzas is the number of subsets of the set of 12 toppings, that is, $2^{12} = 4096$. The number of pizzas with anchovies is the number of ways of choosing anchovies and then choosing a subset of the 11 remaining toppings, that is, $(1) \cdot 2^{11} = 2048$. Thus, $P(\text{getting anchovies}) = \frac{2048}{4096} = \frac{1}{2}$. (Note: A probability of $\frac{1}{2}$ makes intuitive sense, for each pizza combination *without anchovies* there is a corresponding one *with anchovies*, so half will have anchovies and half will not.)

36. <u>Solution 1</u> First choose the two forwards, then choose the 3 defense players from the remaining 7 players. Thus the number of ways of choosing a starting line up is $C(9, 2) \cdot C(7, 3) = 1260$.
<u>Solution 2</u> First choose the 3 defensive players, then choose the 2 forwards from the remaining 6 players. Thus the number of ways of choosing a starting line up is $C(9, 3) \cdot C(6, 2) = 1260$.

38. (a) Order is important, and repeats are possible. Thus there are 10 choices for each digit. So the number of different Zip+4 codes is $10 \cdot 10 \cdots \cdot 10 = 10^9$.

    (b) If a Zip+4 code is to be a palindrome, the first 5 digits can be chosen arbitrarily. But once chosen, the last 4 digits are determined. Since there are 10 ways to choose each of the first 5 digits, there are 10^5 palindromes.

    (c) By parts (a) and (b), the probability that a randomly chosen Zip+4 code is a palindrome is $\frac{10^5}{10^9} = 10^{-4}$.

40. <u>Solution 1</u> We choose the 5 states first and then one of the two senators from each state. Thus the number of committees is $C(50, 5) \cdot 2^5 = 67{,}800{,}320$.
<u>Solution 2</u> We choose one of 100 senators, then choose one of the remaining 98 senators (deleting the chosen senator and the other senator form that state), then choose one of the remaining 96

senators, continuing this way until the 5 senators are chosen. Finally, we need to divide by the number of ways to arrange the 5 senators. Thus the number of committees is

$$\frac{100 \cdot 98 \cdot 96 \cdot 94 \cdot 92}{5!} = 67{,}800{,}320.$$

Focus on Modeling

2. (a) You should find that you get a combination consisting of a "head" and a "tail" about 50% of the time.

   (b) The possible gender combinations are $\{BB, BG, GB, GG\}$. Thus, the probability of having one child of each sex is $\frac{2}{4} = \frac{1}{2}$.

4. (a) If you simulate 80 World Series with coin tosses, you should expect the series to end in 4 games about 10 times, in 5 games about 20 times, in 6 games about 25 times, and in 7 games about 25 times.

   (b) We first calculate the number of ways that the series can end with team A winning. (Note that a team must win the final game plus three of the preceding games to win the series.) To win in 4 games, team A must win 4 games right off the bat, and there is only 1 way this can happen. To win in 5 games, team A must win the final game plus 3 of the first 4 games, so this can happen in $C(4, 3) = 4$ ways. To win in 6 games, team A must win the final game plus 3 of the first 5 games, so this can happen in $C(5, 3) = \frac{5 \cdot 4}{2 \cdot 1} = 10$ ways. To win in 7 games, team A must win the final game plus 3 of the first 6 games, so this can happen in $C(6, 3) = \frac{6 \cdot 5 \cdot 4}{3 \cdot 2 \cdot 1} = 20$ ways. By symmetry, it is also true for team B that they can win in 4 games just 1 way, in 5 games 4 ways, in 6 games 10 ways, and in 7 games 20 ways. The probability that any particular team wins a given game is $\frac{1}{2}$; this fact, together with the assumption that the games are independent allows us to calculate the probabilities in the following table.

Series	Number of ways	Probability
4 games	2	$2 \cdot \left(\frac{1}{2} \cdot \frac{1}{2} \cdot \frac{1}{2} \cdot \frac{1}{2}\right) = \frac{1}{8}$
5 games	8	$8 \cdot \left(\frac{1}{2} \cdot \frac{1}{2} \cdot \frac{1}{2} \cdot \frac{1}{2} \cdot \frac{1}{2}\right) = \frac{1}{4}$
6 games	20	$20 \cdot \left(\frac{1}{2} \cdot \frac{1}{2} \cdot \frac{1}{2} \cdot \frac{1}{2} \cdot \frac{1}{2} \cdot \frac{1}{2}\right) = \frac{5}{16}$
7 games	40	$40 \cdot \left(\frac{1}{2} \cdot \frac{1}{2} \cdot \frac{1}{2} \cdot \frac{1}{2} \cdot \frac{1}{2} \cdot \frac{1}{2} \cdot \frac{1}{2}\right) = \frac{5}{16}$

   (c) The expected value is $\frac{1}{8} \cdot 4 + \frac{1}{4} \cdot 5 + \frac{5}{16} \cdot 6 + \frac{5}{16} \cdot 7 = 5\frac{13}{16} \approx 5.8$. Thus, on the average, we expect a World Series to end in about 5.8 games.

6. (a) We can use the following TI-82 program to model this experiment. It is a minor modification of the one given in Problem 5.

   ```
   PROGRAM: PROB6
   :0 → P
   :For(N,1,1000)
   :rand → X:rand → Y
   :P+((X+Y)<1) → P
   :End
   :Disp "PROBABILITY IS APPROX"
   :Disp P/1000
   ```

   You should find that the probability is very close to $\frac{1}{2}$.

   (b) Following the hint, the points in the square for which $x + y < 1$ are the ones that lie below the line $x + y = 1$. This triangle has area $\frac{1}{2}$ (it takes up half the square), so the probability that $x + y < 1$ is $\frac{1}{2}$.